ENGINEERING SOCIETIES MONOGRAPHS

Harrison W. Craver, *Consulting Editor*

THEORY

OF

PLATES AND SHELLS

THEORY

OF

PLATES AND SHELLS

BY

S. TIMOSHENKO

Professor of Theoretical and Applied Mechanics
Stanford University

McGRAW-HILL BOOK COMPANY, Inc.

NEW YORK AND LONDON

1940

ENGINEERING SOCIETIES MONOGRAPHS

Bakhmeteff: *Hydraulics of Open Channels*
Bleich: *Buckling Strength of Metal Structures*
Nadai: *Theory of Flow and Fracture of Solids*
Rich: *Hydraulic Transients*
Timoshenko: *Theory of Elastic Stability*
Timoshenko: *Theory of Plates and Shells*
Timoshenko and Goodier: *Theory of Elasticity*

THEORY OF PLATES AND SHELLS

XIII

PREFACE

In the author's book "Theory of Elasticity" the deformation of bodies all three dimensions of which are of the same order of magnitude was considered. The present book discusses only those problems in which one dimension of a body (the thickness of a plate or shell) can be considered as small in comparison with the other dimensions.

There are many engineering structures in which plates and shells are used extensively. Notable examples include the steel plates of ship hulls submitted to the action of water pressure, concrete and reinforced concrete slabs under the action of lateral loading, domes and thin-walled tanks and containers of various shapes submitted to the action of internal or external pressure. A variety of problems concerning the bending of circular plates or of conical and spherical shells is encountered in the design of boilers, locomotive engines and steam turbines. Particularly at the present time thin-walled structures are finding a wide application in the modern development of airplane structures.

In all cases in which one dimension of a body is small in comparison with the others, the problem of finding stresses and deflections can be simplified and various approximate methods of analysis have been developed. This book is occupied principally with the discussion of such methods.

The book is written principally for engineers engaged in the design of thin walled structures. With specific applications in view, discussion of the general theory of plates is limited to a minimum, most of the space being devoted to the investigation of particular problems. The treatment of these problems is not limited to the development of a general solution, but in many cases complete numerical calculations are carried out and presented in the form of tables containing the values of the deflections and stresses for various proportions of plates and for various load conditions.

The preliminary knowledge of mathematics and strength of materials that is taken for granted is that usually covered by our schools of engineering. Where additional mathematical equipment is necessary, it is given in the book with appropriate explanations. To simplify the reading of the book, the portions which, although of practical importance, are such that they can be omitted during a first reading are put in small type. The reader may return to the study of such topics after finishing the more essential portions.

Numerous references to papers treating problems on bending of plates and shells are given in the book. These references may be of interest to engineers who wish to study some special problems in more detail. They give also a picture of the modern development of the theory of plates and shells and may be of use to graduate students who are planning to take their work in this field.

In writing this volume the author made free use of his earlier Russian text dealing with plates and shells.[1] The numerical tables for laterally loaded plates were taken, in many cases, from the books by J. G. Boobnov[2] and by B. G. Galerkin.[3] In the preparation of the chapters on thin shells, the author consulted often the recent work on this subject by W. Flügge.[4]

In the preparation of the manuscript, the author was helped by his former pupils, Dr. Stewart Way, Dr. Miklós Hetényi, and Dr. Elmer Bergman, and he takes this opportunity to thank them for the reading of portions of the manuscript and for various valuable suggestions which they have made. He also expresses thanks to Mr. Walter Vincenti, his present student at Stanford, for help in the final preparation of the manuscript, for the preparation of the figures and for the reading of proofs. The author wishes here also to express appreciation to the University of Michigan and to Stanford University for financial assistance in the preparation of tables, diagrams and figures.

S. Timoshenko.

Stanford University,
    August, 1940.

[1] "Theory of Elasticity," vol. 2, 1916, St. Petersburg
[2] "Theory of Structure of Ships," 1914, St. Petersburg.
[3] "Elastic Thin Plates," 1933, Moscow.
[4] "Statik und Dynamik der Schalen," 1934, Berlin.

CONTENTS

vii

NOTATIONS

x, y, z Rectangular coordinates

r, θ Polar coordinates

r_x, r_y Radii of curvature of the middle surface of a plate in xz- and yz-planes, respectively

h Thickness of a plate or a shell

q Intensity of a continuously distributed load

p Pressure

γ Weight per unit volume

$\sigma_x, \sigma_y, \sigma_z$ Normal components of stress parallel to x-, y- and z-axes

σ_n Normal component of stress parallel to n-direction

σ_r, σ_θ Radial and tangential normal stresses in polar coordinates

τ Shearing stress

$\tau_{xy}, \tau_{xz}, \tau_{yz}$ Shearing stress components in rectangular coordinates

u, v, w Components of displacements

ϵ Unit elongation

$\epsilon_x, \epsilon_y, \epsilon_z$ Unit elongations in x-, y- and z-directions

$\epsilon_r, \epsilon_\theta$ Radial and tangential unit elongations in polar coordinates

$\epsilon_\phi, \epsilon_\theta$ Unit elongations of a shell in meridional direction and in the direction of parallel circle, respectively

$\gamma_{xy}, \gamma_{xz}, \gamma_{yz}$ Shearing strain components in rectangular coordinates

$\gamma_{r\theta}$ Shearing strain in polar coordinates

E Modulus of elasticity in tension and compression

G Modulus of elasticity in shear

ν Poisson's ratio

V Strain energy

D Flexural rigidity of a plate

M_x, M_y Bending moments per unit length of sections of a plate perpendicular to x- and y-axes, respectively

M_{xy} Twisting moment per unit length of section of a plate perpendicular to x-axis

M_n, M_{nt} Bending and twisting moments per unit length of a section of a plate perpendicular to n-direction

Q_x, Q_y Shearing forces parallel to z-axis per unit length of sections of a plate perpendicular to x- and y-axes, respectively

Q_n Shearing force parallel to z-axis per unit length of section of a plate perpendicular to n-direction

N_x, N_y Normal forces per unit length of sections of a plate perpendicular to x- and y-directions, respectively

N_{xy} Shearing force in direction of y-axis per unit length of section of a plate perpendicular to x-axis

r_1, r_2 Radii of curvature of a shell in the form of a surface of revolution in meridional plane and in the normal plane perpendicular to meridian, respectively

χ_ϕ, χ_θ Changes of curvature of a shell in meridional plane and in the plane perpendicular to meridian, respectively

$\chi_{\theta\phi}$ Twist of a shell

$N_\phi, N_\theta, N_{\phi\theta}.$ Membrane forces per unit length of principal normal sections of a shell

M_θ, M_ϕ Bending moments in a shell per unit length of meridional section and a section perpendicular to meridian, respectively

χ_x, χ_ϕ Changes of curvature of a cylindrical shell in axial plane and in a plane perpendicular to the axis, respectively

$N_\phi, N_x, N_{x\phi}$ Membrane forces per unit length of axial section and a section perpendicular to the axis of a cylindrical shell

M_ϕ, M_x Bending moments per unit length of axial section and a section perpendicular to the axis of a cylindrical shell, respectively

$M_{x\phi}$ Twisting moment per unit length of an axial section of a cylindrical shell

O_ϕ, Q_x Shearing forces parallel to z-axis per unit length of an axial section and a section perpendicular to the axis of a cylindrical shell, respectively

THEORY OF PLATES AND SHELLS

CHAPTER I

BENDING OF LONG RECTANGULAR PLATES TO A CYLINDRICAL SURFACE

1. Differential Equation for Cylindrical Bending of Plates.— We shall begin the theory of bending of plates with the simple problem of the bending of a long rectangular plate that is subjected to a transverse load that does not vary along the length of the plate. The deflected surface of a portion of such a plate at a considerable distance from the ends[1] can be assumed cylindrical, with the axis of the cylinder parallel to the length of the plate. We can therefore restrict ourselves

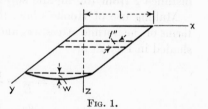

FIG. 1.

to the investigation of the bending of an elemental strip cut from the plate by two planes perpendicular to the length of the plate and a unit distance (say 1 in.) apart. The deflection of this strip is given by a differential equation which is similar to the deflection equation of a bent beam.

To obtain the equation for the deflection, we consider a plate of uniform thickness, equal to h, and take the xy-plane as the middle plane of the plate before loading, $i.e.$, as the plane midway between the faces of the plate. Let the y-axis coincide with one of the longitudinal edges of the plate and let the positive direction of the z-axis be downward, as shown in Fig. 1. Then if the width of the plate is denoted by l, the elemental strip may be considered

---

[1] The relation between the length and the width of a plate in order that the maximum stress may approximate that in an infinitely long plate is discussed later; see pp. 130 and 136.

1

as a bar of rectangular cross section which has a length of l and a depth of h. In calculating the bending stresses in such a bar we assume, as in the ordinary theory of beams, that cross sections of the bar remain plane during bending so that they undergo only a rotation with respect to their neutral axes. If no normal forces are applied to the end sections of the bar, the neutral surface of the bar coincides with the middle surface of the plate, and the unit elongation of a fiber parallel to the x-axis is proportional to its distance z from the middle surface. The curvature of the deflection curve can be taken equal to $-d^2w/dx^2$, where w, the deflection of the bar in the z-direction, is assumed to be small compared with the length of the bar l. The unit elongation ϵ_x of a fiber at a distance z from the middle surface (Fig. 2) is then $-z\, d^2w/dx^2$.

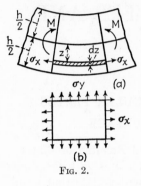

Fig. 2.

Making use of Hooke's law, the unit elongations ϵ_x and ϵ_y in terms of the normal stresses σ_x and σ_y acting on the element shown shaded in Fig. 2a are

$$\left.\begin{aligned}\epsilon_x &= \frac{\sigma_x}{E} - \frac{\nu\sigma_y}{E}; \\ \epsilon_y &= \frac{\sigma_y}{E} - \frac{\nu\sigma_x}{E} = 0,\end{aligned}\right\} \tag{1}$$

where E is the modulus of elasticity of the material and ν is Poisson's ratio. The lateral strain in the y-direction must be zero in order to maintain continuity in the plate during bending, from which it follows from the second of equations (1) that $\sigma_y = \nu\sigma_x$. Substituting this value in the first of equations (1), we obtain

$$\epsilon_x = \frac{(1 - \nu^2)\sigma_x}{E}$$

and

$$\sigma_x = \frac{E\epsilon_x}{1 - \nu^2} = -\frac{Ez}{1 - \nu^2}\frac{d^2w}{dx^2}. \tag{2}$$

If the plate is submitted to the action of tensile or compressive forces acting in the x-direction and uniformly distributed along the longitudinal sides of the plate, the corresponding direct stress must be added to the stress (2) due to bending.

Having the expression for bending stress σ_x, we obtain by integration the bending moment in the elemental strip:

$$M = \int_{-\frac{h}{2}}^{\frac{h}{2}} \sigma_x z \, dz = -\int_{-\frac{h}{2}}^{\frac{h}{2}} \frac{Ez^2}{1-\nu^2} \frac{d^2w}{dx^2} dz = -\frac{Eh^3}{12(1-\nu^2)} \frac{d^2w}{dx^2}.$$

Introducing the notation

$$\frac{Eh^3}{12(1-\nu^2)} = D, \tag{3}$$

we represent the equation for the deflection curve of the elemental strip in the following form:

$$D\frac{d^2w}{dx^2} = -M, \tag{4}$$

in which the quantity D, taking the place of the quantity EI in the case of beams, is called *the flexural rigidity* of a plate. It is seen that the calculation of deflections of the plate reduces to the integration of Eq. (4) which has the same form as the differential equation for deflection of beams. If there is only a lateral load acting on the plate, and the edges are free to approach each other as deflection occurs, the expression for the bending moment M can be readily derived, and the deflection curve will be obtained by integrating Eq. (4). In practice the problem is more complicated, since the plate is usually attached to the boundary, and its edges are not free to move. Such a method of support sets up tensile reactions along the edges as soon as deflection takes place. These reactions depend on the magnitude of deflection and affect the magnitude of bending moment M entering in Eq. (4). The problem reduces to the investigation of bending of an elemental strip submitted to the action of lateral load and of an axial force the magnitude of which depends on the deflection of the strip.[1] In the following we consider this problem for

[1] In such a form the problem was first discussed by I. G. Boobnov; see the English translation of his work in *Trans. Inst. Naval Arch.*, vol. 44, p. 15, 1902, and his "Theory of Structure of Ships," vol. 2, p. 545, St. Petersburg, 1914. See also the paper by Stewart Way presented at the National Meeting of Applied Mechanics, A.S.M.E., New Haven, June, 1932; from this are taken the curves used in Arts. 2 and 3.

a particular case of uniform load acting on the plate and for various conditions along the edges.

2. Cylindrical Bending of Uniformly Loaded Rectangular Plates with Simply Supported Edges.—Let us consider a uniformly loaded long rectangular plate the longitudinal edges of which are free to rotate but cannot move toward each other during bending. An elemental strip cut out from this plate, as shown in Fig. 1, is in the condition of a uniformly loaded bar submitted to the action of an axial force S (Fig. 3), the magnitude of which is such as to prevent the ends of the bar from moving

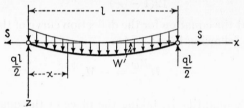

Fig. 3.

along the x-axis. Denoting by q the intensity of the uniform load, the bending moment at any cross section of the strip is

$$M = \frac{ql}{2}x - \frac{qx^2}{2} - Sw.$$

Substituting in Eq. (4), we obtain

$$\frac{d^2w}{dx^2} - \frac{Sw}{D} = -\frac{qlx}{2D} + \frac{qx^2}{2D}. \qquad (a)$$

Introducing the notation

$$\frac{S}{D}\frac{l^2}{4} = u^2, \qquad (5)$$

the general solution of Eq. (a) can be written in the following form:

$$w = C_1 \sinh \frac{2ux}{l} + C_2 \cosh \frac{2ux}{l} + \frac{ql^3x}{8u^2D} - \frac{ql^2x^2}{8u^2D} - \frac{ql^4}{16u^4D}. \qquad (b)$$

The constants of integration C_1 and C_2 will be determined from the conditions at the ends. Since the deflections of the strip at the ends are zero, we have

$$w = 0 \quad \text{for} \quad x = 0 \quad \text{and for} \quad x = l. \qquad (c)$$

Substituting for w its expression (b), we obtain from these two conditions:

$$C_1 = \frac{ql^4}{16u^4D} \frac{1 - \cosh 2u}{\sinh 2u}, \qquad C_2 = \frac{ql^4}{16u^4D};$$

and the expression (b) for deflection w becomes

$$w = \frac{ql^4}{16u^4D}\left(\frac{1 - \cosh 2u}{\sinh 2u} \sinh \frac{2ux}{l} + \cosh \frac{2ux}{l} - 1\right)$$
$$+ \frac{ql^3x}{8u^2D} - \frac{ql^2x^2}{8u^2D}.$$

Substituting

$$\cosh 2u = \cosh^2 u + \sinh^2 u, \qquad \sinh 2u = 2 \sinh u \cosh u,$$
$$\cosh^2 u = 1 + \sinh^2 u,$$

we can represent this expression in a simpler form:

$$w = \frac{ql^4}{16u^4D}\left(\frac{- \sinh u \sinh \dfrac{2ux}{l} + \cosh u \cosh \dfrac{2ux}{l}}{\cosh u} - 1\right)$$
$$+ \frac{ql^2x}{8u^2D}(l - x)$$

or

$$w = \frac{ql^4}{16u^4D}\left[\frac{\cosh u\left(1 - \dfrac{2x}{l}\right)}{\cosh u} - 1\right] + \frac{ql^2x}{8u^2D}(l - x). \qquad (6)$$

Thus, deflections of the elemental strip depend upon the quantity u, which, as we see from Eq. (5), is a function of the axial force S. This force, so far, is unknown and can be determined from the condition that the ends of the strip (Fig. 3) do not move along the x-axis. Hence the extension of the strip produced by the forces S is equal to the difference between the length of the arc along the deflection curve and the chord length l. This difference for small deflections can be represented by the formula[1]

$$\lambda = \frac{1}{2}\int_0^l \left(\frac{dw}{dx}\right)^2 dx. \qquad (7)$$

[1] See author's "Strength of Materials," vol. 1, p. 38, 1930.

In calculating the extension of the strip produced by the forces S, we assume that lateral strain of the strip in the y-direction is prevented and use Eq. (2). Then

$$\lambda = \frac{S(1 - \nu^2)l}{hE} = \frac{1}{2}\int_0^l \left(\frac{dw}{dx}\right)^2 dx. \qquad (d)$$

Substituting expression (6) for w and performing the integration, we obtain the following equation for calculating S:

$$\frac{S(1 - \nu^2)l}{hE} = \frac{q^2l^7}{D^2}\left(\frac{5}{256}\frac{\tanh u}{u^7} + \frac{1}{256}\frac{\tanh^2 u}{u^6} - \frac{5}{256u^6} + \frac{1}{384u^4}\right);$$

or substituting $S = 4u^2D/l^2$, from Eq. (5), and the expression for D, from Eq. (3), we finally obtain the equation

$$\frac{E^2h^8}{(1 - \nu^2)^2q^2l^8} = \frac{135}{16}\frac{\tanh u}{u^9} + \frac{27}{16}\frac{\tanh^2 u}{u^8} - \frac{135}{16u^8} + \frac{9}{8u^6}. \qquad (8)$$

For a given material, a given ratio h/l, and a given load q the left side of this equation can be readily calculated, and the value of u satisfying the equation can be found by trial-and-error method. To simplify this solution, the curves shown in Fig. 4 can be used. The abscissas of these curves represent the values of u; and the ordinates, the quantities $\log_{10}(10^4\sqrt{U_0})$, where U_0 denotes the numerical value of the right side of Eq. (8). $\sqrt{U_0}$ is used because it is more easily calculated from the plate constants and load; and the factor 10^4 is introduced to make the logarithms positive. In each particular case we begin with calculation of the square root of the left side of Eq. (8), equal to $\dfrac{Eh^4}{(1 - \nu^2)ql^4}$, which gives us $\sqrt{U_0}$. The quantity $\log_{10}(10^4\sqrt{U_0})$ then gives the ordinate which must be taken in Fig. 4, and the corresponding value of u can be readily obtained from the curve. Having u, the value of the axial force S is obtained from Eq. (5).

In calculating stresses we observe that the total stress at any cross section of the strip consists of a bending stress proportional to the bending moment and a tensile stress of magnitude S/h which is constant along the length of the strip. The maximum stress occurs at the middle of the strip where the bending

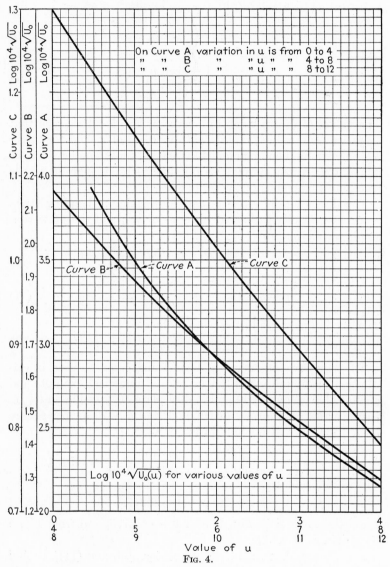

On Curve A variation in u is from 0 to 4
„   „   B   „   „ u „   „   4 to 8
„   „   C   „   „ u „   „   8 to 12

Value of u

FIG. 4.

moment is a maximum. From the differential equation (4) the maximum bending moment is

$$M_{\text{max.}} = -D\left(\frac{d^2w}{dx^2}\right)_{x=\frac{l}{2}}.$$

Substituting expression (6) for w, we obtain

$$M_{\text{max.}} = \frac{ql^2}{8}\psi_0(u), \tag{9}$$

where

$$\psi_0 = \frac{1 - \text{sech } u}{\dfrac{u^2}{2}}. \tag{e}$$

The values of ψ_0 are given by curves in Fig. 5. It is seen that these values diminish rapidly with increase of u, and for larger u the maximum bending moment is several times smaller than the moment $ql^2/8$ which would be obtained if there were no tensile reactions at the ends of the strip.

The direct tensile stress σ_1 and the maximum bending stress σ_2 are now readily expressed in terms of u, q and the plate constants as follows:

$$\sigma_1 = \frac{S}{h} = \frac{4u^2 D}{hl^2} = \frac{Eu^2}{3(1-\nu^2)}\left(\frac{h}{l}\right)^2; \tag{10}$$

$$\sigma_2 = \frac{6}{h^2}M_{\text{max.}} = \frac{3}{4}q\left(\frac{l}{h}\right)^2\psi_0. \tag{11}$$

The maximum stress in the plate is then

$$\sigma_{\text{max.}} = \sigma_1 + \sigma_2.$$

To show how the curves in Figs. 4 and 5 can be used in calculating maximum stress, let us take a numerical example and assume that a long rectangular steel plate 50 in. wide and $\frac{1}{2}$ in. thick carries a uniformly distributed load $q = 20$ lb. per square inch. We start with computation of $\sqrt{U_0}$:

$$\sqrt{U_0} = \frac{E}{(1-\nu^2)q}\left(\frac{h}{l}\right)^4 = \frac{30\cdot10^6}{(1-0.3^2)20}\frac{1}{10^8} = 0.01648.$$

Then, from tables,

$$\log_{10}(10^4\sqrt{U_0}) = 2.217.$$

From the curve A in Fig. 4 we find $u = 3.795$, and from Fig. 5 we obtain $\psi_0 = 0.1329$.

Now, computing stresses by using Eqs. (10) and (11), we find

$$\sigma_1 = \frac{30\cdot10^6\cdot3.795^2}{3(1-0.3^2)}\frac{1}{10^4} = 15{,}830 \text{ lb. per square inch,}$$

$$\sigma_2 = \tfrac{3}{4}\cdot20\cdot10^4\cdot0.1329 = 19{,}930 \text{ lb. per square inch,}$$

$$\sigma_{\text{max.}} = \sigma_1 + \sigma_2 = 35{,}760 \text{ lb. per square inch.}$$

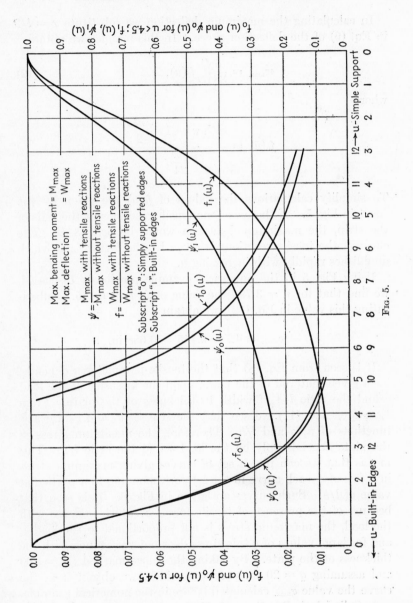

Fig. 5.

In calculating the maximum deflection we substitute $x = l/2$ in Eq. (6) of the deflection curve. In this manner we obtain

$$w_{\text{max.}} = \frac{5ql^4}{384D} f_0(u), \tag{12}$$

where

$$f_0(u) = \frac{\text{sech } u - 1 + \dfrac{u^2}{2}}{\dfrac{5u^4}{24}}.$$

To simplify calculations the values of $f_0(u)$ are given by the curve in Fig. 5. If there were no tensile reactions at the ends of the strip, the maximum deflection would be $5ql^4/384D$. The effect of the tensile reactions is given by the factor $f_0(u)$ which diminishes rapidly with increasing u.

Using Fig. 5 in the numerical example previously discussed, we find that for $u = 3.795$ the value of $f_0(u)$ is 0.145. Substituting this value in Eq. (12), we obtain

$$w_{\text{max.}} = 4.74 \cdot 0.145 = 0.688 \text{ in.}$$

It is seen from Eq. (8) that the tensile parameter u depends, for a given material of the plate, upon the intensity of the load q and the ratio l/h of width to thickness of the plate. From Eqs. (10) and (11) we see that the stresses σ_1 and σ_2 are also functions of u, q and l/h. Therefore, the maximum stress in the plate depends only on the load q and the ratio l/h. This means that we can plot a set of curves giving maximum stress in terms of q, each curve in the set corresponding to a particular value of l/h. Such curves are given in Fig. 6. It is seen that because of the presence of tensile forces S, which increase with the load, the maximum stress is not proportional to the load q; and for large values of q this stress does not vary much with the thickness of the plate. By taking the curve marked $l/h = 100$ and assuming $q = 20$ lb. per square inch, we obtain from the curve the value $\sigma_{\text{max.}}$ calculated before in the numerical example.

3. Cylindrical Bending of Uniformly Loaded Rectangular Plates with Built-in Edges.—We assume that the longitudinal edges of the plate are fixed in such a manner that they cannot rotate. Taking an elemental strip of unit width in the same manner as before (Fig. 1), and denoting by M_0 the bending moment per unit length acting on the longitudinal edges of the

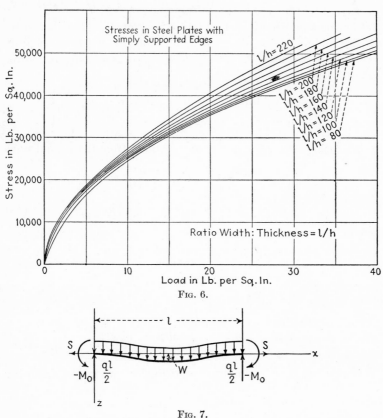

Fig. 6.

Fig. 7.

plate, the forces acting on the strip will be as shown in **Fig. 7.** The bending moment at any cross section of the strip is

$$M = \frac{ql}{2}x - \frac{qx^2}{2} - Sw + M_0.$$

Substituting this expression in Eq. (4) we obtain

$$\frac{d^2w}{dx^2} - \frac{S}{D}w = -\frac{qlx}{2D} + \frac{qx^2}{2D} - \frac{M_0}{D}. \tag{a}$$

The general solution of this equation, using notation (5), will be represented in the following form:

$$w = C_1 \sinh \frac{2ux}{l} + C_2 \cosh \frac{2ux}{l} + \frac{ql^3x}{8u^2D} - \frac{ql^2x^2}{8u^2D}$$
$$- \frac{ql^4}{16u^4D} + \frac{M_0l^2}{4u^2D}. \quad (b)$$

Observing that the deflection curve is symmetrical with respect to the middle of the strip, we determine the constants of integration C_1, C_2 and the moment M_0 from the following three conditions:

$$\left. \begin{array}{llll} \dfrac{dw}{dx} = 0 & \text{for} & x = 0 & \text{and for} & x = \dfrac{l}{2} \\[2mm] w = 0 & \text{for} & x = 0. & \end{array} \right\} \quad (c)$$

Substituting expression (b) for w, we obtain from these conditions

$$C_1 = -\frac{ql^4}{16u^3D}, \qquad C_2 = \frac{ql^4}{16u^3D} \coth u$$
$$M_0 = \frac{ql^2}{4u^2} - \frac{ql^2}{4u} \coth u = -\frac{ql^2}{12}\psi_1(u) \quad (13)$$

where

$$\psi_1(u) = \frac{3(u - \tanh u)}{u^2 \tanh u}.$$

The deflection w is therefore given by the expression

$$w = -\frac{ql^4}{16u^3D} \sinh \frac{2ux}{l} + \frac{ql^4}{16u^3D} \coth u \cosh \frac{2ux}{l}$$
$$+ \frac{ql^3x}{8u^2D} - \frac{ql^2x^2}{8u^2D} - \frac{ql^4}{16u^3D} \coth u.$$

This can be further simplified and finally put in the following form:

$$w = \frac{ql^4}{16u^3D \tanh u} \left\{ \frac{\cosh\left[u\left(1 - \frac{2x}{l}\right)\right]}{\cosh u} - 1 \right\} + \frac{ql^2(l - x)x}{8u^2D}. \quad (14)$$

For calculating the parameter u we proceed as in the previous article and use Eq. (d) of that article. Substituting in it expression (14) for w and performing the integration, we obtain

$$\frac{S(1 - \nu^2)l}{hE} = \frac{q^2l^7}{D^2}\left(-\frac{3}{256u^5 \tanh u} - \frac{1}{256u^4 \sinh^2 u}\right.$$
$$\left. + \frac{1}{64u^6} + \frac{1}{384u^4}\right).$$

Substituting S from Eq. (5) and expression (3) for D, the equation for calculating u finally becomes

$$\frac{E^2h^8}{(1 - \nu^2)^2 q^2 l^8} = \left(-\frac{81}{16u^7 \tanh u} - \frac{27}{16u^6 \sinh^2 u} + \frac{27}{4u^8} + \frac{9}{8u^6}\right).$$

(15)

To simplify the solution of this equation we use the curve in Fig. 8, in which the parameter u is taken as abscissa and the ordinates are equal to $\log_{10} (10^4 \sqrt{U_1})$, where U_1 denotes the right side of Eq. (15). For any given plate we begin with calculation of the square root of the left side of Eq. (15), equal to $Eh^4/(1 - \nu^2)ql^4$, which gives us $\sqrt{U_1}$. The quantity $\log_{10} (10^4 \sqrt{U_1})$ then gives the ordinate of the curve in Fig. 8, and the corresponding abscissa gives us the required value of u.

Having u, we can begin with calculation of maximum stress in the plate. The total stress at any point of a cross section of the strip consists of the constant tensile stress σ_1 and bending stress. The maximum bending stress σ_2 will act at the built-in edges where the bending moment is the largest. Using Eq. (10) to calculate σ_1 and Eq. (13) to calculate the bending moment M_0, we obtain

$$\sigma_1 = \frac{Eu^2}{3(1 - \nu^2)}\left(\frac{h}{l}\right)^2,$$

(16)

$$\sigma_2 = -\frac{6M_0}{h^2} = \frac{q}{2}\left(\frac{l}{h}\right)^2 \psi_1(u),$$

(17)

$$\sigma_{\text{max.}} = \sigma_1 + \sigma_2.$$

To simplify the calculation of bending stress σ_2, the values of the function $\psi_1(u)$ are given by a curve in Fig. 5.

The maximum deflection is at the middle of the strip and is obtained by substituting $x = l/2$ in Eq. (14), from which

$$w_{\text{max.}} = \frac{ql^4}{384D} f_1(u),$$

(18)

where

$$f_1(u) = \frac{24}{u^4}\left(\frac{u^2}{2} + \frac{u}{\sinh u} - \frac{u}{\tanh u}\right).$$

To simplify the calculation of deflections, the function $f_1(u)$ is also given by a curve in Fig. 5.

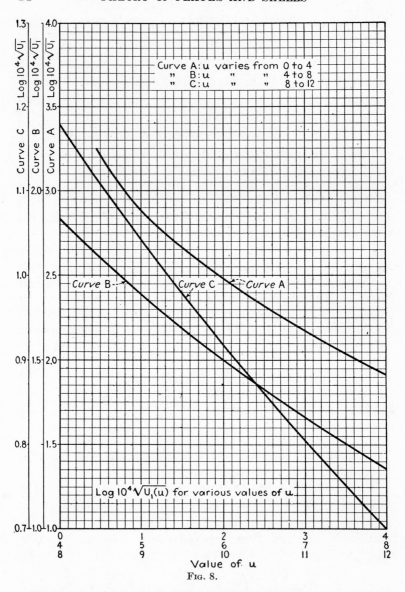

Fɪɢ. 8.

We illustrate the use of curves in Figs. 5 and 8 by a numerical example.   A long rectangular steel plate has the dimensions $l = 50$ in., $h = \frac{1}{2}$ in. and $q = 10$ lb. per square inch.   In such a case

$$\sqrt{U_1} = \frac{E}{(1 - \nu^2)q}\left(\frac{h}{l}\right)^4 = \frac{30 \cdot 10^6}{(1 - 0.3^2)10 \cdot 10^4} = 0.032966,$$
$$\log 10^4\sqrt{U_1} = 2.5181.$$

From Fig. 8 we now find $u = 1.894$; and from Fig. 5, $\psi_1 = 0.8212$. Substituting these values in Eqs. (16) and (17), we find

$$\sigma_1 = \frac{30 \cdot 10^6 \cdot 1.894^2}{3(1 - 0.3^2)10^4} = 3,940 \text{ lb. per square inch,}$$

$$\sigma_2 = \tfrac{1}{2} \cdot 10 \cdot 10^4 \cdot 0.8212 = 41,060 \text{ lb. per square inch,}$$

$$\sigma_{\text{max.}} = \sigma_1 + \sigma_2 = 45,000 \text{ lb. per square inch.}$$

Comparing these stress values with the maximum stress obtained for the plate of the same size, but for a doubled load, on the

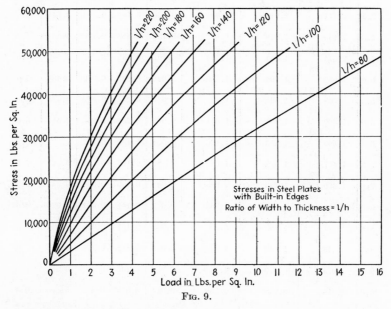

Fig. 9.

assumption of simply supported edges (see page 8), it can be concluded that, owing to clamping of the edges, the direct tensile stress decreases considerably, whereas the maximum bending stress increases several times so that finally the maximum total stress in the case of clamped edges becomes larger than in the case of simply supported edges.

Proceeding as in the previous article it can be shown that the maximum stress in a plate depends only on the load q and the

THEORY OF PLATES AND SHELLS

TABLE 1

u	$\log 10^4\sqrt{U_0}$	$\log 10^4\sqrt{U_1}$	$\log 10^4\sqrt{U_2}$	$f_0(u)$	$f_1(u)$	$\psi_0(u)$	$\psi_1(u)$	u
0	∞	∞	∞	1.000	1.000	1.000	1.000	0
0.5	3.889	3.217	3.801	0.908	0.976	0.905	0.984	0.5
	406	331	425					
1.0	3.483	2.886	3.376	0.711	0.909	0.704	0.939	1.0
	310	223	336					
1.5	3.173	2.663	3.040	0.532	0.817	0.511	0.876	1.5
	262	182	292					
2.0	2.911	2.481	2.748	0.380	0.715	0.367	0.806	2.0
	227	161	257					
2.5	2.684	2.320	2.491	0.281	0.617	0.268	0.736	2.5
	198	146	228					
3.0	2.486	2.174	2.263	0.213	0.529	0.200	0.672	3.0
	175	134	202					
3.5	2.311	2.040	2.061	0.166	0.453	0.153	0.614	3.5
	156	124	180					
4.0	2.155	1.916	1.881	0.132	0.388	0.120	0.563	4.0
	141	115	163					
4.5	2.014	1.801	1.718	0.107	0.335	0.097	0.519	4.5
	128	107	148					
5.0	1.886	1.694	1.570	0.088	0.291	0.079	0.480	5.0
	118	100	135					
5.5	1.768	1.594	1.435	0.074	0.254	0.066	0.446	5.5
	108	93	124					
6.0	1.660	1.501	1.311	0.063	0.223	0.055	0.417	6.0
	100	88	115					
6.5	1.560	1.413	1.196	0.054	0.197	0.047	0.391	6.5
	93	82	107					
7.0	1.467	1.331	1.089	0.047	0.175	0.041	0.367	7.0
	87	78	100					
7.5	1.380	1.253	0.989	0.041	0.156	0.036	0.347	7.5
	82	74	94					
8.0	1.298	1.179	0.895	0.036	0.141	0.031	0.328	8.0
	77	70	89					
8.5	1.221	1.109	0.806	0.032	0.127	0.028	0.311	8.5
	73	67	83					
9.0	1.148	1.042	0.723	0.029	0.115	0.025	0.296	9.0
	69	63	80					
9.5	1.079	0.979	0.643	0.026	0.105	0.022	0.283	9.5
	65	61	75					
10.0	1.014	0.918	0.568	0.024	0.096	0.020	0.270	10.0
	63	58	72					
10.5	0.951	0.860	0.496	0.021	0.088	0.018	0.259	10.5
	59	55	69					
11.0	0.892	0.805	0.427	0.020	0.081	0.017	0.248	11.0
	57	54	65					
11.5	0.835	0.751	0.362	0.018	0.075	0.015	0.238	11.5
	55	51	63					
12.0	0.780	0.700	0.299	0.016	0.069	0.014	0.229	12.0

ratio l/h, and we can plot a set of curves giving maximum stress in terms of q, each curve in the set corresponding to a particular value of l/h. Such curves are given in Fig. 9. It is seen that for small values of the intensity of the load q, when the effect of the axial force on the deflections of the strip is small, the maximum stress increases approximately in the same ratio as q increases. But for larger values of q the relation between the load and the maximum stress becomes non-linear.

In conclusion we give in Table 1 the numerical values of all functions that were given in Figs. 4, 5 and 8. This table can be used instead of curves in calculating maximum stress and maximum deflections of long uniformly loaded rectangular plates.

4. Cylindrical Bending of Uniformly Loaded Rectangular Plates with Elastically Built-in Edges.—Let us assume that when bending occurs, the longitudinal edges of the plate rotate through an angle proportional to the bending moment at the edges. In such a case the forces acting on an elemental strip will again be of such kind as shown in Fig. 7, and we shall obtain expression (b) of the previous article for deflections w. However, the conditions at the edges, from which the constants of integration and the moment M_0 are determined, are different; viz., the slope of the deflection curve at the ends of the strip is no longer zero but is proportional to the magnitude of the moment M_0, and we have

$$\left(\frac{dw}{dx}\right)_{x=0} = -\beta M_0, \qquad (a)$$

where β is a factor depending on the rigidity of restraint along the edges. If this restraint is very flexible, the quantity β is large, and the conditions at the edges approach those of simply supported edges. If the restraint is very rigid, the quantity β becomes small, and the edge conditions approach those of absolutely built-in edges. The remaining two end conditions are the same as we had in the previous article. Thus we have

$$\left(\frac{dw}{dx}\right)_{x=0} = -\beta M_0, \qquad \left(\frac{dw}{dx}\right)_{x=\frac{l}{2}} = 0, \qquad (b)$$

$$(w)_{x=0} = 0.$$

Using these conditions, we shall find both the constants of integration and the magnitude of M_0 in the expression (b) of the previous article. Owing to flexibility of the boundary, the end moments M_0 will be smaller than those given by Eq. (13) for absolutely built-in edges, and the final result can be put in the following form:

$$M_0 = -\gamma\frac{ql^2}{12}\psi_1(u), \tag{19}$$

where γ is a numerical factor smaller than unity and given by the formula

$$\gamma = \frac{\tanh u}{\frac{2\beta}{l}Du + \tanh u}.$$

It is seen that the magnitude of the moments M_0 at the edges depends upon the magnitude of the coefficient β defining the rigidity of the restraint.   When β is very small, the coefficient γ approaches unity, and the moment M_0 approaches the value (13) calculated for absolutely built-in edges.   When β is very large, the coefficient γ and the moment M_0 become small, and the edge conditions approach those of simply supported edges.

The deflection curve in the case under consideration can be represented in the following form:

$$w = \frac{ql^4}{16u^4D}\frac{\tanh u - \gamma(\tanh u - u)}{\tanh u}\left\{\frac{\cosh\left[u\left(1 - \frac{2x}{l}\right)\right]}{\cosh u} - 1\right\}$$
$$+ \frac{ql^2}{8u^2D}x(l - x). \tag{20}$$

For $\gamma = 1$ this expression reduces to expression (14) for deflections of a plate with absolutely built-in edges.   For $\gamma = 0$ we obtain expression (6) for a plate with simply supported edges.

In calculating the tensile parameter u we proceed as in the previous cases and determine the tensile force S from the condition that the extension of the elemental strip is equal to the difference between the length of the arc along the deflection curve and the chord length l.   Hence

$$\frac{S(1 - \nu^2)l}{hE} = \frac{1}{2}\int_0^l\left(\frac{dw}{dx}\right)^2dx.$$

Substituting expression (20) in this equation and performing the integration, we obtain

$$\frac{E^2 h^8}{(1 - \nu^2)^2 q^2 l^8} = (1 - \gamma)U_0 + \gamma U_1 - \gamma(1 - \gamma)U_2, \quad (21)$$

where U_0 and U_1 denote the right-hand sides of Eqs. (8) and (15), respectively, and

$$U_2 = \frac{27}{16} \frac{(u - \tanh u)^2}{u^9 \tanh^2 u}(u \tanh^2 u - u + \tanh u).$$

The values of $\log_{10} (10^4 \sqrt{U_2})$ are given in Table 1. By using this table, Eq. (21) can be readily solved by trial-and-error method. For any particular plate we first calculate the left side of the equation and, by using the curves in Figs. 4 and 8 determine the values of the parameter u (1) for simply supported edges and (2) for absolutely built-in edges. Naturally u for elastically built-in edges must have a value intermediate between these two. Assuming one such value for u, we calculate U_0, U_1 and U_2 by using Table 1 and determine the value of the right side of Eq. (21). Generally this value will be different from the value of the left side calculated previously, and a new trial calculation with a new assumed value for u must be made. Two such trial calculations will usually be sufficient to determine by interpolation the value of u satisfying Eq. (21). As soon as the parameter u is determined, we calculate the bending moments M_0 at the ends from Eq. (19). We can also calculate the moment at the middle of the strip and find the maximum stress. This stress will occur at the ends or at the middle depending on the rigidity of constraint at the edges.

5. The Effect on Stresses and Deflections of Small Displacements of Longitudinal Edges in the Plane of the Plate.—It was assumed in the previous discussion that during bending the longitudinal edges of the plate have no displacement in the plane of the plate. On the basis of this assumption the tensile force S was calculated in each particular case. Let us assume now that the plate edges undergo a displacement toward each other specified by Δ. Owing to this displacement the extension of the elemental strip will be diminished by the same amount, and the equation for calculating the tensile force S becomes

$$\frac{Sl(1 - \nu^2)}{hE} = \frac{1}{2}\int_0^l \left(\frac{dw}{dx}\right)^2 dx - \Delta. \qquad (a)$$

At the same time Eqs. (6), (14), and (20) for the deflection curve hold true regardless of the magnitude of the tensile force S. They may be differentiated and substituted under the integral sign in Eq. (a). After evaluating this integral and substituting $S = 4u^2D/l^2$, we obtain for simply supported edges

$$\frac{E^2h^8}{q^2(1 - \nu^2)^2l^8} \frac{u^2 + \dfrac{3l\Delta}{h^2}}{u^2} = U_0 \tag{22}$$

and for built-in edges

$$\frac{E^2h^8}{q^2(1 - \nu^2)^2l^8} \frac{u^2 + \dfrac{3l\Delta}{h^2}}{u^2} = U_1. \tag{23}$$

If Δ is made zero, Eqs. (22) and (23) reduce to Eqs. (8) and (15) obtained previously for immovable edges.

The simplest case is obtained by placing compression bars between the longitudinal sides of the boundary to prevent free motion of one edge of the plate toward the other during bending. Tensile forces S in the plate produce contraction of these bars which results in a displacement Δ proportional to S.[1] If k is the factor of proportionality depending on elasticity and cross-sectional area of the bars, we obtain

$$S = k\Delta,$$

or, substituting, $S = 4u^2D/l^2$, we obtain

$$\Delta = \frac{1}{k} \frac{Eu^2h^3}{3l^2(1 - \nu^2)}$$

and

$$\frac{u^2 + \dfrac{3l\Delta}{h^2}}{u^2} = 1 + \frac{Eh}{kl(1 - \nu^2)}.$$

Thus the second factor on the left side of Eqs. (22) and (23) is a constant that can be readily calculated if the dimensions and the elastic properties of the structure are known. Having the magnitude of this factor, the solution of Eqs. (22) and (23) can be accomplished in exactly the same manner as was done before for the cases of immovable edges.

[1] The edge support is assumed to be such that Δ is uniform along the edges

In the general case the second factor on the left side of Eqs.
(22) and (23) may depend on the magnitude of the load acting
on the structure, and the determination of the parameter u can
be accomplished only by trial-and-error method. This procedure will now be illustrated by an example that we encounter
in analyzing stresses in the hull of a ship. The bottom plates in
the hull of a ship are subjected to a uniformly distributed water
pressure and also to forces in the plane of the plates due to
bending of the hull as a beam. Let b be the width of the ship
at a cross section mn (Fig. 10)
and l be the fore-and-aft distance
between the frames in the bottom. When a vessel is resting on
two waves, as shown in Fig. 11,
bending of the hull is produced,
and the normal distance l between
the frames at the bottom will be

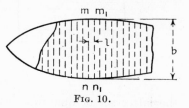

Fig. 10.

increased by a certain amount. To calculate accurately this
displacement we must consider not only the action of the bending
moment M on the hull but also the effect on this bending of a
certain change in tensile forces S distributed along the edges mn
and m_1n_1 of the bottom plate mnm_1n_1 (Fig. 10) which will be

Fig. 11.

considered as a long rectangular plate uniformly loaded by water
pressure. Owing to the fact that the plates between the consecutive frames are equally loaded, there will be no rotation at
the longitudinal edges of the plates, and they may be considered
as absolutely built in along these edges.

To determine the value of Δ, which denotes, as before, the displacement of the edge mn toward the edge m_1n_1 in Fig. 10 and
which is produced by the hull bending moment M and the tensile
reactions S per unit length along the edges mn and m_1n_1 of
bottom plate, let us imagine that the plate mnm_1n_1 is removed
and replaced by uniformly distributed forces S so that the total
force along mn and m_1n_1 is Sb (Fig. 12). We can then say that
the displacement Δ of one frame relative to another is due to

the bending moment M and to the eccentric load Sb applied to the hull without bottom plating.

If A, I and c are cross-sectional area, central moment of inertia and distance from the bottom plate to the neutral axis of the complete hull section and if A_1, I_1 and c_1 are the corresponding quantities for the hull section without bottom plates,

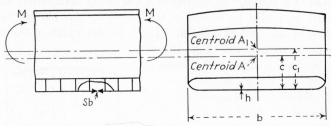

Fig. 12.

the latter set of quantities can be derived from the former by the relations

$$\left. \begin{aligned} A_1 &= A - bh, \\ c_1 &= \frac{Ac}{A_1}, \\ I_1 &= I - bhc^2 - A_1(c_1 - c)^2 \end{aligned} \right\} \qquad (a)$$

The relative displacement Δ_1 produced by the eccentrically applied forces Sb is

$$\Delta_1 = \frac{l}{E}\left(\frac{Sb}{A_1} + \frac{Sbc_1^2}{I_1}\right).$$

The displacement due to the bending moment M is

$$\Delta_2 = -\frac{Mc_1 l}{EI_1}.$$

Hence the total displacement is

$$\Delta = \Delta_1 + \Delta_2 = \frac{l}{E}\left[\frac{Sb}{A_1} + \frac{(Sbc_1 - M)c_1}{I_1}\right]. \qquad (b)$$

Substituting in this expression

$$S = \frac{4u^2 D}{l^2} = \frac{Eu^2 h^3}{3l^2(1 - \nu^2)},$$

we finally obtain

$$\Delta = \frac{u^2 h^3}{3l(1 - \nu^2)}\left(\frac{b}{A_1} + \frac{bc_1^2}{I_1}\right) - \frac{Mlc_1}{EI_1}. \qquad (c)$$

This quantity must be substituted in Eq. (23) for determining the tensile parameter u.

Let us apply this theory to a numerical example. Assume $b = 54$ ft., $I = 1{,}668$ ft.^{4}, $A = 13.5$ ft.^{2}, $c = 12.87$ ft., $h = 0.75$ in. $= 0.0625$ ft., $l = 45$ in. $= 3.75$ ft., $q = 10$ lb. per square inch, $M = 123{,}500$ ft.-tons. From Eqs. (a) we obtain

$$A_1 = 13.5 - 0.0625 \cdot 54 = 10.125 \text{ ft.}^2,$$

$$c_1 = \frac{13.5 \cdot 12.87}{10.125} = 17.15 \text{ ft.},$$

$$I_1 = 1{,}668 - 559.5 - 10.125(17.15 - 12.87)^2 = 923.1 \text{ ft.}^4$$

Substituting these values in expression (c), we calculate Δ and finally obtain

$$\frac{3\Delta l}{h^2} = 1.549u^2 - 11.49.$$

Equation (23) then becomes

$$\frac{E^2 h^8}{q^2(1 - \nu^2)^2 l^8} \frac{u^2 + 1.549u^2 - 11.49}{u^2} = U_1,$$

or

$$\frac{1.596 E h^4}{q(1 - \nu^2) l^4} \sqrt{\frac{u^2 - 4.508}{u^2}} = \sqrt{U_1}.$$

Substituting numerical values and taking logarithms of both sides, we obtain

$$3.609 + \log_{10} \sqrt{\frac{u^2 - 4.508}{u^2}} = \log_{10} (10^4 \sqrt{U_1}).$$

Using the curve in Fig. 8, this equation can be readily solved by trial-and-error method, and we obtain $u = 2.128$ and, from Fig. 5, $\psi_1(u) = 0.788$. The maximum stress is now calculated by using Eqs. (16) and (17) from which

$$\sigma_1 = \frac{30 \cdot 10^6 \cdot 4.258}{3 \cdot 0.91 \cdot 60^2} = 13{,}840 \text{ lb. per square inch,}$$

$$\sigma_2 = \tfrac{1}{2} \cdot 10 \cdot 60^2 \cdot 0.788 = 14{,}180 \text{ lb. per square inch,}$$

$$\sigma_{\max.} = \sigma_1 + \sigma_2 = 28{,}020 \text{ lb. per square inch.}$$

If the bending stress in the plate due to water pressure were neglected and if the bottom plate stress were calculated from the formula $\sigma = Mc/I$, we should arrive at a figure of only $13{,}240$ lb. per square inch.

6. An Approximate Method of Calculating the Parameter u.— In calculating the parameter u for plates the longitudinal edges of which do not move in the plane of the plate, we used the equation

$$\frac{Sl(1 - \nu^2)}{hE} = \frac{1}{2}\int_0^l \left(\frac{dw}{dx}\right)^2 dx, \qquad (a)$$

which states that the extension of an elemental strip produced by forces S is equal to the difference between the length of the arc along the deflection curve of the strip and the chord length l. In the particular cases considered in the previous articles, exact expressions for the deflections w were derived, and numerical tables and curves for the right side of the Eq. (a) were given by the use of which the equation can be readily solved. If such tables are not at hand, the solution of the equation becomes complicated, and to simplify the problem recourse should be had to an approximate method. From the discussion of bending of beams it is known[1] that, in the case of simply supported ends and when all lateral loads are acting in the same direction, the deflection curve of an elemental strip produced by a combination of a lateral load and of an axial tensile force S (Fig. 3) can be represented with sufficient accuracy by the equation

$$w = \frac{w_0}{1 + \alpha} \sin \frac{\pi x}{l}, \qquad (b)$$

in which w_0 denotes the deflection at the middle of the strip produced by the lateral load alone, and the quantity α is given by the equation

$$\alpha = \frac{S}{S_{cr}} = \frac{Sl^2}{\pi^2 D}. \qquad (c)$$

Thus, α represents the ratio of the axial force S to the Euler's value of the force for the elemental strip.

Substituting expression (b) in Eq. (a) and integrating, we obtain

$$\frac{Sl(1 - \nu^2)}{hE} = \frac{\pi^2 w_0^2}{4l(1 + \alpha)^2}.$$

Now, using notation (c) and substituting for D its expression (3), we finally obtain

$$\alpha(1 + \alpha)^2 = \frac{3w_0^2}{h^2}. \qquad (24)$$

---

[1] See author's "Strength of Materials," vol. 2, p. 417.

From this equation the quantity α can be calculated in each particular case, and the parameter u is now determined from the equation

$$u^2 = \frac{S}{D}\frac{l^2}{4} = \frac{\pi^2\alpha}{4}. \qquad (d)$$

To show the application of the approximate Eq. (24) let us take a numerical example. A long rectangular steel plate with simply supported edges and of dimensions $l = 50$ in. and $h = \frac{1}{2}$ in. is loaded with a uniformly distributed load $q = 20$ lb. per square inch. In such a case

$$w_0 = \frac{5}{384}\frac{ql^4}{D};$$

and, after substituting numerical values, Eq. (24) becomes

$$\alpha(1 + \alpha)^2 = 269.56.$$

The solution of the equation can be simplified by letting

$$1 + \alpha = x. \qquad (e)$$

Then

$$x^3 - x^2 = 269.56;$$

i.e., the quantity x is such that the difference between its cube and its square has a known value. x can be readily determined from a slide rule or a suitable table, and we find in our case

$$x = 6.8109 \qquad \text{and} \qquad \alpha = 5.8109.$$

Then, from Eq. (d)

$$u = 3.7865,$$

and from the formula (e) (see page 8)

$$\psi_0 = 0.13316.$$

For calculating direct stress and maximum bending stress we use Eqs. (10) and (11). In this way we find

$$\sigma_1 = 15,759 \text{ lb. per square inch,}$$
$$\sigma_2 = 19,974 \text{ lb. per square inch,}$$
$$\sigma_{\text{max.}} = \sigma_1 + \sigma_2 = 35,733 \text{ lb. per square inch.}$$

The calculations made in Art. 2 (page 8) give us, for this example, $\sigma_{\text{max.}} = 35,760$ lb. per square inch. Thus the accuracy of the approximate Eq. (24) is in this case very high. In general, this accuracy depends on the magnitude of u. The error increases with increase of u. Calculations show that for $u = 1.44$

the error in the maximum stress is only 0.065 of 1 per cent and that for $u = 12.29$, which corresponds to very flexible plates, it is about 0.30 of 1 per cent. These values of u will cover the range ordinarily met with in practice, and we conclude that Eq. (24) can be used with sufficient accuracy in all practical cases of uniformly loaded plates with simply supported edges.

It can also be used when the load is not uniformly distributed as, for example, in the case of a hydrostatic pressure non-uniformly distributed along the elemental strip. If the longitudinal force is found by using the approximate Eq. (24), the deflections may be obtained from Eq. (b), and the bending moment at any cross section may be found as the algebraic sum of the moment produced by the lateral load and the moment due to the longitudinal force.[1]

In the case of built-in edges the approximate expression for the deflection curve of an elemental strip can be taken in the form

$$w = \frac{w_0}{1 + \dfrac{\alpha}{4}} \cdot \frac{1}{2}\left(1 - \cos\frac{2\pi x}{l}\right), \qquad (f)$$

in which w_0 and α have the same meanings as before. Substituting this expression in Eq. (a) and integrating, we obtain for determining α the equation

$$\alpha\left(1 + \frac{\alpha}{4}\right)^2 = \frac{3w_0^2}{h^2} \qquad (25)$$

which can be solved in each particular case by the method suggested for solving Eq. (24).

When α is found, the parameter u is determined from Eq. (d); the maximum stress can be calculated by using Eqs. (16) and (17); and the maximum deflection, by using Eq. (18).

If during bending one edge moves toward the other by an amount Δ, the equation

$$\frac{Sl(1 - \nu^2)}{hE} = \frac{1}{2}\int_0^l \left(\frac{dw}{dx}\right)^2 dx - \Delta \qquad (g)$$

---

[1] More accurate values for the deflections and for the bending moments can be obtained by substituting the approximate value of the longitudinal force in Eq. (4) and integrating this equation, which gives Eqs. (12) and (9).

must be used instead of Eq. (*a*). Substituting expression (*b*) in this equation, we obtain for determining α in the case of simply supported edges the equation

$$\alpha(1 + \alpha)^2 \frac{\alpha + 12\dfrac{\Delta l}{\pi^2 h^2}}{\alpha} = \frac{3w_0^2}{h^2}. \tag{26}$$

In the case of built-in edges we use expression (*f*). Then for determining α we obtain

$$\alpha\left(1 + \frac{\alpha}{4}\right)^2 \frac{\alpha + 12\dfrac{\Delta l}{\pi^2 h^2}}{\alpha} = \frac{3w_0^2}{h^2}. \tag{27}$$

If the dimensions of the plate and the load q are given, and the displacement Δ is known, Eqs. (26) and (27) can both be readily solved in the same manner as before. If the displacement Δ is proportional to the tensile force S, the second factor on the left sides of Eqs. (26) and (27) is a constant and can be determined as was explained in the previous article (see page 20). Thus again the equations can be readily solved.

7. Long Uniformly Loaded Rectangular Plates Having a Small Initial Cylindrical Curvature.—It is seen, from the discussions in Arts. 2 and 3, that the tensile forces S contribute to the strength of the plates by counteracting the bending produced by lateral load. This action increases with the increase in deflection. A further reduction of maximum stress can be accomplished by giving a proper initial curvature to a plate. The effect on stresses and deflections of such an initial curvature can be readily investigated[1] by using the approximate method developed in the previous article.

Let us consider the case of a long rectangular plate with simply supported edges (Fig. 13), the initial curvature of which is given by the equation

$$w_1 = \delta \sin \frac{\pi x}{l}. \tag{a}$$

If tensile forces S are applied to the edges of the plate, the initial deflections (*a*) will be reduced in the ratio $1/(1 + \alpha)$,

[1] See author's paper in "Festschrift zum siebzigsten Geburtstage August Föppl," p. 74, Berlin, 1923.

where α has the same meaning as in the previous article[1] (page 24). The lateral load in combination with the forces S will produce deflections that can be expressed approximately by Eq. (b) of the previous article. Thus the total deflection of the plate, indicated in Fig. 13 by the dotted line, is

$$w = \frac{\delta}{1 + \alpha} \sin \frac{\pi x}{l} + \frac{w_0}{1 + \alpha} \sin \frac{\pi x}{l} = \frac{\delta + w_0}{1 + \alpha} \sin \frac{\pi x}{l}. \qquad (b)$$

Assuming that the longitudinal edges of the plate do not move in the plane of the plate, the tensile force S will be found from the

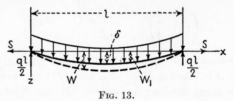

Fig. 13.

condition that the extension of the elemental strip produced by forces S is equal to the difference between the length of the arc along the deflection curve of the elemental strip and the initial length of the strip. This difference, in the case of small deflections, is given by the equation

$$\lambda = \frac{1}{2} \int_0^l \left(\frac{dw}{dx}\right)^2 dx - \frac{1}{2} \int_0^l \left(\frac{dw_1}{dx}\right)^2 dx. \qquad (c)$$

Substituting expressions (a) and (b) for w and w_1 and integrating, we obtain

$$\lambda = \frac{\pi^2}{4l} \left[\left(\frac{\delta + w_0}{1 + \alpha}\right)^2 - \delta^2 \right].$$

Putting λ equal to the extension of the strip $Sl(1 - \nu^2)/hE$ we finally obtain

$$\alpha(1 + \alpha)^2 = \frac{3(\delta + w_0)^2}{h^2} - \frac{3\delta^2(1 + \alpha)^2}{h^2}. \qquad (28)$$

If we take $\delta = 0$, this equation reduces to Eq. (24) for a plate without initial curvature.

To show the effect of the initial curvature on the maximum stress in a plate, let us apply Eq. (28) to a numerical example.

[1] See author's "Strength of Materials," vol. 2, p. 462, 1930.

Assume a steel plate having $l = 45$ in., $h = \frac{3}{8}$ in. and submitted to the action of a uniformly distributed load $q = 10$ lb. per square inch. If there is no initial deflection, $\delta = 0$ and Eq. (28) becomes

$$\alpha(1 + \alpha)^2 = 290,$$

from which

$$\alpha = 5.97 \quad \text{and} \quad u = \frac{\pi}{2}\sqrt{\alpha} = 3.83.$$

From Eq. (10) we then obtain

$$\sigma_1 = 11,300 \text{ lb. per square inch,}$$

and from Eq. (11)

$$\sigma_2 = 14,200 \text{ lb. per square inch.}$$

The maximum stress in the plate is

$$\sigma_{\text{max.}} = \sigma_1 + \sigma_2 = 25,500 \text{ lb. per square inch.}$$

Let us now assume that there is an initial deflection in the plate such that $\delta = h = \frac{3}{8}$ in. In such a case Eq. (28) gives

$$\alpha(1 + \alpha)^2 = 351.6 - 3(1 + \alpha)^2.$$

Letting

$$1 + \alpha = x,$$

we obtain

$$x^3 + 2x^2 = 351.6,$$

from which

$$x = 6.45, \qquad \alpha = 5.45, \qquad u = \frac{\pi}{2}\sqrt{\alpha} = 3.67.$$

The tensile stress, from Eq. (10), is

$$\sigma_1 = 10,200 \text{ lb. per square inch.}$$

In calculating bending stress we must consider only the change in deflections

$$w - w_1 = \frac{w_0}{1 + \alpha} \sin\frac{\pi x}{l} - \frac{\alpha\delta}{1 + \alpha} \sin\frac{\pi x}{l}. \tag{d}$$

The maximum bending stress, corresponding to the first term on the right side of Eq. (d), is the same as for a flat plate with $u = 3.67$. From Table 1 we find $\psi_0 = 0.142$, and from Eq. (11)

$$\sigma_2' = 15,300 \text{ lb. per square inch.}$$

The bending moment corresponding to the second term in Eq. (d) is

$$-D\frac{d^2}{dx^2}\left(-\frac{\alpha\delta}{1+\alpha}\sin\frac{\pi x}{l}\right) = -\frac{\alpha\pi^2\,\delta D}{(1+\alpha)l^2}\sin\frac{\pi x}{l}.$$

This moment has a negative sign, and the corresponding maximum stress of

$$\sigma_2'' = \frac{6}{h^2}\frac{\alpha\pi^2\,\delta D}{(1+\alpha)l^2} = 9,500 \text{ lb. per square inch}$$

must be subtracted from the bending stress σ_2' calculated above. Hence the maximum stress for the plate with the initial deflection is

$$\sigma_{\text{max.}} = 10,200 + 15,300 - 9,500 = 16,000 \text{ lb. per square inch.}$$

Comparison of this result with that obtained for the plane plate shows that the effect of the initial curvature is to reduce the maximum stress from 25,500 to 16,000 lb. per square inch. This result is obtained assuming the initial deflection equal to the thickness of the plate. By increasing the initial deflection, the maximum stress can be reduced still further.

8. Bending to Cylindrical Surface of Plates on Elastic Foundation.— Let us consider the problem of bending of a long uniformly loaded rectangular plate supported over the entire surface by an elastic foundation and rigidly

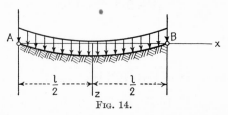

Fig. 14.

supported along the edges (Fig. 14). Cutting out from the plate an elemental strip, as before, we may consider it as a beam on an elastic foundation. Assuming that the reaction of the foundation at any point is proportional to the deflection w at that point, and using Eq. (4), we obtain by double differentiation of that equation[1]

$$D\frac{d^4w}{dx^4} = q - kw, \tag{29}$$

where q is the intensity of the load acting on the plate and k is the reaction

[1] See author's "Strength of Materials," vol. 2, p. 402, 1930.

of the foundation per unit area for a deflection equal to unity. Introducing the notation

$$\beta = \frac{l}{2}\sqrt[4]{\frac{k}{4D}}, \tag{30}$$

the general solution of Eq. (29) can be written as follows:

$$w = \frac{q}{k} + C_1 \sin\frac{2\beta x}{l}\sinh\frac{2\beta x}{l} + C_2 \sin\frac{2\beta x}{l}\cosh\frac{2\beta x}{l} + C_3 \cos\frac{2\beta x}{l}\sinh\frac{2\beta x}{l}$$
$$+ C_4 \cos\frac{2\beta x}{l}\cosh\frac{2\beta x}{l}. \tag{a}$$

The four constants of integration must now be determined from the conditions at the ends of the strip. In the case under consideration the deflection is symmetrical with respect to the middle of the strip. Thus taking the coordinate axes as shown in Fig. 14, we conclude[1] that $C_2 = C_3 = 0$. The constants C_1 and C_4 are found from the condition that the deflection and the bending moment of the strip are zero at the end $(x = l/2)$. Hence

$$\left.\begin{array}{c} (w)_{x=\frac{l}{2}} = 0, \\[2mm] \left(\dfrac{d^2w}{dx^2}\right)_{x=\frac{l}{2}} = 0. \end{array}\right\} \tag{b}$$

Substituting expression (a) for w and observing that $C_2 = C_3 = 0$, we obtain

$$\left.\begin{array}{c} \dfrac{q}{k} + C_1 \sin\beta\sinh\beta + C_4 \cos\beta\cosh\beta = 0, \\[2mm] C_1 \cos\beta\cosh\beta - C_4 \sin\beta\sinh\beta = 0, \end{array}\right\} \tag{c}$$

from which we find

$$C_1 = -\frac{q}{k}\frac{\sin\beta\sinh\beta}{\sin^2\beta\sinh^2\beta + \cos^2\beta\cosh^2\beta} = -\frac{q}{k}\frac{2\sin\beta\sinh\beta}{\cos 2\beta + \cosh 2\beta},$$
$$C_4 = -\frac{q}{k}\frac{\cos\beta\cosh\beta}{\sin^2\beta\sinh^2\beta + \cos^2\beta\cosh^2\beta} = -\frac{q}{k}\frac{2\cos\beta\cosh\beta}{\cos 2\beta + \cosh 2\beta}.$$

Substituting these values of the constants in expression (a) and using Eq. (30), we finally represent the deflection of the strip by the following equation:

$$w = \frac{ql^4}{64D\beta^4}\left(1 - \frac{2\sin\beta\sinh\beta}{\cos 2\beta + \cosh 2\beta}\sin\frac{2\beta x}{l}\sinh\frac{2\beta x}{l}\right.$$
$$\left. - \frac{2\cos\beta\cosh\beta}{\cos 2\beta + \cosh 2\beta}\cos\frac{2\beta x}{l}\cosh\frac{2\beta x}{l}\right). \tag{d}$$

[1] It is seen that the terms with coefficients C_2 and C_3 change sign when x is replaced by $-x$.

The deflection at the middle is obtained by substituting $x = 0$, which gives

$$(w)_{x=0} = \frac{ql^4}{64D\beta^4}[1 - \varphi_0(\beta)], \tag{31}$$

where

$$\varphi_0(\beta) = \frac{2 \cos \beta \cosh \beta}{\cos 2\beta + \cosh 2\beta}.$$

To get the angles of rotation of the edges of the plate, we differentiate expression (d) with respect to x and put $x = -l/2$. In this way we obtain

$$\left(\frac{dw}{dx}\right)_{x=-\frac{l}{2}} = \frac{ql^3}{24D}\varphi_1(\beta), \tag{32}$$

where

$$\varphi_1(\beta) = \frac{3}{4\beta^3} \frac{\sinh 2\beta - \sin 2\beta}{\cosh 2\beta + \cos 2\beta}.$$

The bending moment at any cross section of the strip is obtained from the equation

$$M = -D\frac{d^2w}{dx^2}.$$

Substituting expression (d) for w, we find for the middle of the strip

$$(M)_{x=0} = \frac{ql^2}{8}\varphi_2(\beta), \tag{33}$$

where

$$\varphi_2(\beta) = \frac{2}{\beta^2} \frac{\sinh \beta \sin \beta}{\cosh 2\beta + \cos 2\beta}.$$

To simplify the calculation of deflections and stresses, the numerical values of functions φ_0, φ_1 and φ_2 are given in Table 2. For small values of β, *i.e.*, for a yielding foundation, the function $(1 - \varphi_0)/\beta^4$ and φ_2 do not differ much

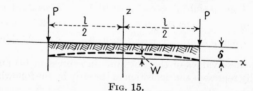

Fig. 15.

from unity. Thus the maximum deflection and bending stresses are close to those for a simply supported strip without elastic foundation. With the increase of β the effect of the foundation becomes more and more important.

Conditions similar to those represented in Fig. 14 are obtained if a long rectangular plate of width l is pressed into an elastic foundation by loads uniformly distributed along the edges and of the amount P per unit length (Fig. 15). The plate will be pressed into the elastic foundation and bent.

as shown by the dotted line.   If δ denotes the deflection at the edges of the plate, the reaction of the foundation at any point is

$$k(\delta - w) = k\delta - kw,$$

where w is given by Eq. (d) with $q = k\delta$.   The magnitude δ is then obtained from the condition that the load is balanced by the reaction of the foundation.   Hence

$$P = \frac{k\delta l}{2} - k \int_0^{\frac{l}{2}} w \, dx.$$

Plates on elastic foundation with other conditions at the longitudinal edges can also be discussed in a similar manner.

TABLE 2

β	φ_0	φ_1	φ_2	β	φ_0	φ_1	φ_2
0.1	1.000	1.000	1.000	1.6	−0.013	0.200	0.164
0.2	0.999	0.999	0.999	1.7	−0.052	0.166	0.129
0.3	0.993	0.995	0.995	1.8	−0.081	0.138	0.101
0.4	0.979	0.983	0.983	1.9	−0.102	0.116	0.079
0.5	0.950	0.961	0.959	2.0	−0.117	0.099	0.062
0.6	0.901	0.923	0.919	2.2	−0.133	0.072	0.037
0.7	0.827	0.866	0.859	2.4	−0.135	0.055	0.021
0.8	0.731	0.791	0.781	2.6	−0.127	0.043	0.011
0.9	0.619	0.702	0.689	2.8	−0.114	0.034	0.005
1.0	0.498	0.609	0.591	3.0	−0.098	0.028	0.002
1.1	0.380	0.517	0.494	3.2	−0.081	0.023	0.000
1.2	0.272	0.431	0.405	3.4	−0.064	0.019	−0.001
1.3	0.178	0.357	0.327	3.6	−0.049	0.016	−0.002
1.4	0.100	0.294	0.262	3.8	−0.035	0.014	−0.002
1.5	0.037	0.242	0.208	4.0	−0.024	0.012	−0.002

CHAPTER II

PURE BENDING OF PLATES

9. Slope and Curvature of Slightly Bent Plates.—In discussing small deflections of a plate we take the *middle plane* of the plate,

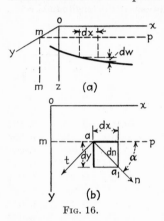

(a)

(b)

<small>FIG. 16.</small>

before bending occurs, as the xy-plane. During bending, the particles that were in the xy-plane undergo small displacements w perpendicular to the xy-plane and form the *middle surface* of the plate. These displacements of the middle surface are called *deflections* of a plate in our further discussion. Taking a normal section of the plate parallel to the xz-plane (Fig. 16a), we find that the slope of the middle surface in the x-direction is $i_x = \partial w / \partial x$. In the same manner the slope in the y-direction is $i_y = \partial w / \partial y$. Taking now any direction an in the xy-plane (Fig. 16b) making an angle α with the x-axis, we find that the difference in the deflections of the two adjacent points a and a_1 in the an direction is

$$dw = \frac{\partial w}{\partial x}dx + \frac{\partial w}{\partial y}dy$$

and that the corresponding slope is

$$\frac{\partial w}{\partial n} = \frac{\partial w}{\partial x} \cdot \frac{dx}{dn} + \frac{\partial w}{\partial y} \cdot \frac{dy}{dn} = \frac{\partial w}{\partial x} \cos \alpha + \frac{\partial w}{\partial y} \sin \alpha. \qquad (a)$$

To find the direction α_1 for which the slope is a maximum we equate to zero the derivative with respect to α of the expression (a). In this way we obtain

$$\tan \alpha_1 = \frac{\left(\dfrac{\partial w}{\partial y}\right)}{\left(\dfrac{\partial w}{\partial x}\right)}. \qquad (b)$$

Substituting the corresponding values of $\sin \alpha_1$ and $\cos \alpha_1$ in (a), we obtain for the maximum slope the expression

$$\left(\frac{\partial w}{\partial n}\right)_{\text{max.}} = \sqrt{\left(\frac{\partial w}{\partial x}\right)^2 + \left(\frac{\partial w}{\partial y}\right)^2}. \qquad (c)$$

By setting expression (a) equal to zero we obtain the direction for which the slope of the surface is zero. The corresponding angle α_2 is determined from the equation

$$\tan \alpha_2 = -\frac{\left(\dfrac{\partial w}{\partial x}\right)}{\left(\dfrac{\partial w}{\partial y}\right)}. \qquad (d)$$

From Eqs. (b) and (d) we conclude that

$$\tan \alpha_1 \cdot \tan \alpha_2 = -1$$

which shows that the directions of the zero slope and of the maximum slope are perpendicular to each other.

In determining the curvature of the middle surface of the plate we observe that the deflections of the plate are very small. In such a case the slope of the surface in any direction can be taken equal to the angle that the tangent to the surface in that direction makes with the xy-plane, and the square of the slope may be neglected compared to unity. The curvature of the surface in a plane parallel to the xz-plane (Fig. 16) is then numerically equal to

$$\frac{1}{r_x} = -\frac{\partial}{\partial x}\left(\frac{\partial w}{\partial x}\right) = -\frac{\partial^2 w}{\partial x^2}. \qquad (e)$$

We consider a curvature positive if it is convex downward. The minus sign is taken in Eq. (e), since for the deflection convex downward, as shown in the figure, the second derivative $\partial^2 w/\partial x^2$ is negative.

In the same manner we obtain for the curvature in a plane parallel to the yz-plane

$$\frac{1}{r_y} = -\frac{\partial}{\partial y}\left(\frac{\partial w}{\partial y}\right) = -\frac{\partial^2 w}{\partial y^2}. \qquad (f)$$

These expressions are similar to those used in discussing the curvature of a bent beam.

In considering the curvature of the middle surface in any direction an (Fig. 16) we obtain

$$\frac{1}{r_n} = -\frac{\partial}{\partial n}\left(\frac{\partial w}{\partial n}\right).$$

Substituting expression (a) for $\partial w/\partial n$ and observing that

$$\frac{\partial}{\partial n} = \frac{\partial}{\partial x}\cos\alpha + \frac{\partial}{\partial y}\sin\alpha,$$

we find

$$\frac{1}{r_n} = -\left(\frac{\partial}{\partial x}\cos\alpha + \frac{\partial}{\partial y}\sin\alpha\right)\left(\frac{\partial w}{\partial x}\cos\alpha + \frac{\partial w}{\partial y}\sin\alpha\right)$$

$$= -\left(\frac{\partial^2 w}{\partial x^2}\cos^2\alpha + 2\frac{\partial^2 w}{\partial x\,\partial y}\sin\alpha\cos\alpha + \frac{\partial^2 w}{\partial y^2}\sin^2\alpha\right)$$

$$= \frac{1}{r_x}\cos^2\alpha - \frac{1}{r_{xy}}\sin 2\alpha + \frac{1}{r_y}\sin^2\alpha. \qquad (g)$$

It is seen that the curvature in any direction n at a point of the middle surface can be calculated if we know at that point the curvatures

$$\frac{1}{r_x} = -\frac{\partial^2 w}{\partial x^2}, \qquad \frac{1}{r_y} = -\frac{\partial^2 w}{\partial y^2}$$

and the quantity

$$\frac{1}{r_{xy}} = \frac{\partial^2 w}{\partial x\,\partial y}, \qquad (h)$$

which is called the *twist of the surface* with respect to x- and y-axes.

If instead of the direction an (Fig. 16b) we take the direction at perpendicular to an, the curvature in this new direction will be obtained from expression (g) by substituting $\pi/2 + \alpha$ for α. Thus we obtain

$$\frac{1}{r_t} = \frac{1}{r_x}\sin^2\alpha + \frac{1}{r_{xy}}\sin 2\alpha + \frac{1}{r_y}\cos^2\alpha. \qquad (i)$$

Adding expressions (g) and (i), we find

$$\frac{1}{r_n} + \frac{1}{r_t} = \frac{1}{r_x} + \frac{1}{r_y}, \qquad (34)$$

which shows that at any point of the middle surface the sum of the curvatures in two perpendicular directions such as n and t is independent of the angle α. This sum is usually called the *average curvature* of the surface at a point.

The twist of the surface at a with respect to the an and at directions is

$$\frac{1}{r_{nt}} = \frac{d}{dt}\left(\frac{dw}{dn}\right).$$

In calculating the derivative with respect to t, we observe that the direction at is perpendicular to an. Thus we obtain the required derivative by substituting $(\pi/2) + \alpha$ for α in Eq. (*a*). In this manner we find

$$\frac{1}{r_{nt}} = \left(\frac{\partial}{\partial x}\cos\alpha + \frac{\partial}{\partial y}\sin\alpha\right)\left(-\frac{\partial w}{\partial x}\sin\alpha + \frac{\partial w}{\partial y}\cos\alpha\right)$$

$$= \frac{1}{2}\sin 2\alpha\left(-\frac{\partial^2 w}{\partial x^2} + \frac{\partial^2 w}{\partial y^2}\right) + \cos 2\alpha\frac{\partial^2 w}{\partial x\,\partial y},$$

or

$$\frac{1}{r_{nt}} = \frac{1}{2}\sin 2\alpha\left(\frac{1}{r_x} - \frac{1}{r_y}\right) + \cos 2\alpha\frac{1}{r_{xy}}. \tag{j}$$

In our further discussion we shall be interested in finding in terms of α the directions in which the curvature of the surface is a maximum or a minimum and in finding the corresponding values of the curvature. We obtain the necessary equation for determining α by equating the derivative of expression (*g*) with respect to α to zero, which gives

$$\frac{1}{r_x}\sin 2\alpha + \frac{2}{r_{xy}}\cos 2\alpha - \frac{1}{r_y}\sin 2\alpha = 0, \tag{k}$$

whence

$$\tan 2\alpha = -\frac{\dfrac{2}{r_{xy}}}{\dfrac{1}{r_x} - \dfrac{1}{r_y}}. \tag{35}$$

From this equation we find two values of α, differing by $\pi/2$. Substituting these in Eq. (*g*) we find two values of $1/r_n$, one representing the maximum and the other the minimum curvature at a point a of the surface. These two curvatures are called the *principal curvatures* of the surface; and the corresponding planes *naz* and *taz*, the *principal planes of curvature*.

Observing that the left side of Eq. (*k*) is equal to the doubled value of expression (*j*), we conclude that, if the directions an and *at* (Fig. 16) are in the principal planes, the corresponding twist $1/r_{nt}$ is equal to zero.

We can use a circle, similar to the Mohr's circle representing combined stresses, to show how the curvature and the twist of a surface vary with the angle α.[1] To simplify the discussion we assume that the coordinate planes xz and yz are taken parallel to the principal planes of curvature at the point a. Then

$$\frac{1}{r_{xy}} = 0,$$

and we obtain from Eqs. (g) and (j) for any angle α

$$\left.\begin{aligned}
\frac{1}{r_n} &= \frac{1}{r_x}\cos^2\alpha + \frac{1}{r_y}\sin^2\alpha, \\
\frac{1}{r_{nt}} &= \frac{1}{2}\left(\frac{1}{r_x} - \frac{1}{r_y}\right)\sin 2\alpha.
\end{aligned}\right\} \tag{36}$$

Taking the curvatures as abscissas and the twists as ordinates and constructing a circle on the diameter $1/r_x - 1/r_y$, as shown

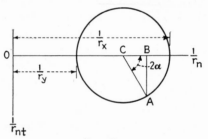

Fɪɢ. 17.

in Fig. 17, we see that the point A defined by the angle 2α has the abscissa

$$\overline{OB} = \overline{OC} + \overline{CB} = \frac{1}{2}\left(\frac{1}{r_x} + \frac{1}{r_y}\right) + \frac{1}{2}\left(\frac{1}{r_x} - \frac{1}{r_y}\right)\cos 2\alpha$$

$$= \frac{1}{r_x}\cos^2\alpha + \frac{1}{r_y}\sin^2\alpha$$

and the ordinate

$$\overline{AB} = \frac{1}{2}\left(\frac{1}{r_x} - \frac{1}{r_y}\right)\sin 2\alpha.$$

Comparing these results with formulas (36), we conclude that the coordinates of the point A define the curvature and the twist

[1] See author's "Strength of Materials," vol. 1, p. 50, 1930.

of the surface for any value of the angle α. It is seen that the maximum twist, represented by the radius of the circle, takes place when $\alpha = \pi/4$, *i.e.*, when we take the two perpendicular directions bisecting the angles between the principal planes.

In our example the curvature in any direction is positive, hence the surface is bent convex downward. If the curvatures $1/r_x$ and $1/r_y$ are both negative, the curvature in any direction is also negative, and we have a bending of the plate convex upward. Surfaces in which the curvature in all planes have like signs are called *synclastic*. Sometimes we shall deal with surfaces in which

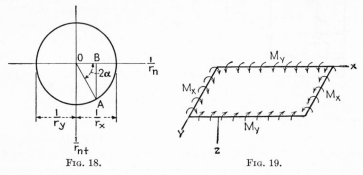

Fig. 18.   Fig. 19.

the two principal curvatures have opposite signs. A saddle is a good example. Such surfaces are called *anticlastic*. The circle in Fig. 18 represents a particular case of such surfaces when $1/r_y = -1/r_x$. It is seen that in this case the curvature becomes zero for $\alpha = \pi/4$ and for $\alpha = 3\pi/4$, and the twist becomes equal to $\pm 1/r_x$.

10. Relations between Bending Moments and Curvature in Pure Bending of Plates.—In the case of pure bending of prismatical bars a rigorous solution for stress distribution is obtained by assuming that cross sections of the bar remain plane during bending and rotate only with respect to their neutral axes so as to be always normal to the deflection curve. Combination of such bending in two perpendicular directions brings us to pure bending of plates. Let us begin with pure bending of a rectangular plate by moments that are uniformly distributed along the edges of the plate as shown in Fig. 19. We take the xy-plane to coincide with the middle plane of the plate before deflection and the x- and y-axes along the edges of the plate as shown. The z-axis, which is then perpendicular to the middle plane is taken positive downward.   We denote by M_x the bending moment per unit length acting on the edges parallel to the y-axis and by M_y the moment per unit length acting on the edges parallel to the x-axis.   These moments we consider positive when they are directed as shown in the figure, *i.e.*, when they produce compression in the upper surface of the plate and tension in the lower. The thickness of the plate we denote, as before, by h and consider

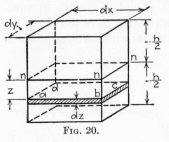

FIG. 20.

it small in comparison with the other dimensions.

Let us consider an element cut out of the plate by two pairs of planes parallel to the xz- and yz-planes as shown in Fig. 20.   Since the case shown in Fig. 19 represents the combination of two uniform bendings, the stress conditions are identical in all elements, such as shown in Fig. 20, and we have a uniform bending of the plate.   Assuming that during bending of the plate the lateral sides of the element remain plane and rotate about the neutral axes nn so as to remain normal to the deflected middle surface of the plate, it can be concluded that the middle plane of the plate does not undergo any extension during this bending, and the middle surface is therefore the *neutral surface*.[1]   Let $1/r_x$ and $1/r_y$ denote, as before, the curvatures of this neutral surface in sections parallel to the xz- and yz-planes, respectively. Then the unit elongations in the x- and y-directions of an elemental lamina *abcd* (Fig. 20), at a distance z from the neutral surface, are found, as in the case of a beam, and are equal to

$$\epsilon_x = \frac{z}{r_x}, \qquad \epsilon_y = \frac{z}{r_y}. \tag{a}$$

Using now Hooke's law [Eq. (1), page 2], the corresponding stresses in the lamina *abcd* are

$$\left.\begin{aligned}
\sigma_x &= \frac{Ez}{1-\nu^2}\left(\frac{1}{r_x} + \nu\frac{1}{r_y}\right), \\
\sigma_y &= \frac{Ez}{1-\nu^2}\left(\frac{1}{r_y} + \nu\frac{1}{r_x}\right).
\end{aligned}\right\} \tag{b}$$

[1] It will be shown in Art. 13 that this conclusion is accurate enough if the deflections of the plate are small in comparison with the thickness h.

They are proportional to the distance z of the lamina *abcd* from the neutral surface and depend on the magnitude of curvatures of the bent plate.

These normal stresses distributed over the lateral sides of the element in Fig. 20 can be reduced to couples, the magnitudes of which per unit length evidently must be equal to the external moments M_x and M_y. In this way we obtain the equations

$$\int_{-\frac{h}{2}}^{\frac{h}{2}} \sigma_x z \, dy \, dz = M_x \, dy,$$

$$\int_{-\frac{h}{2}}^{\frac{h}{2}} \sigma_y z \, dx \, dz = M_y \, dx. \tag{c}$$

Substituting expressions (*b*) for σ_x and σ_y, we obtain

$$M_x = D\left(\frac{1}{r_x} + \nu \frac{1}{r_y}\right) = -D\left(\frac{\partial^2 w}{\partial x^2} + \nu \frac{\partial^2 w}{\partial y^2}\right), \tag{37}$$

$$M_y = D\left(\frac{1}{r_y} + \nu \frac{1}{r_x}\right) = -D\left(\frac{\partial^2 w}{\partial y^2} + \nu \frac{\partial^2 w}{\partial x^2}\right), \tag{38}$$

where D is the flexural rigidity of the plate defined by Eq. (3), and w denotes small deflections of the plate in the z-direction.

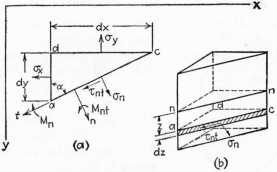

Fig. 21.

Let us now consider the stresses acting on a section of the lamina *abcd* parallel to the z-axis and inclined to the x- and y-axes. If *acd* (Fig. 21) represents a portion of the lamina cut by such a section, the stress acting on the side *ac* can be found by means of the equations of statics. Resolving this stress into a normal component σ_n and a shearing component τ_{nt}, the magnitudes of these components are obtained by projecting the forces acting on the element *acd* on the *n* and *t* directions respectively, which gives us the known equations

$$\left.\begin{aligned} \sigma_n &= \sigma_x \cos^2 \alpha + \sigma_y \sin^2 \alpha, \\ \tau_{nt} &= \tfrac{1}{2}(\sigma_y - \sigma_x) \sin 2\alpha, \end{aligned}\right\} \qquad (d)$$

in which α is the angle between the normal n and the x-axis or between the direction t and the y-axis (Fig. 21a). This angle is considered positive if measured in a clockwise direction.

Considering all laminas, such as *acd* in Fig. 21b, over the thickness of the plate, the normal stresses σ_n give us the bending moment acting on the section *ac* of the plate, the magnitude of which per unit length along *ac* is

$$M_n = \int_{-\frac{h}{2}}^{\frac{h}{2}} \sigma_n z \, dz = M_x \cos^2 \alpha + M_y \sin^2 \alpha. \qquad (39)$$

The shearing stresses τ_{nt} give us the twisting moment acting on the section *ac* of the plate, the magnitude of which per unit length of *ac* is

$$M_{nt} = -\int_{-\frac{h}{2}}^{\frac{h}{2}} \tau_{nt} z \, dz = \tfrac{1}{2} \sin 2\alpha (M_x - M_y). \qquad (40)$$

The signs of M_n and M_{nt} are chosen in such a manner that the positive values of these moments are represented by vectors in the positive directions of n and t (Fig. 21a) if the rule of the right-hand screw is used. When α is zero or π, Eq. (39) gives $M_n = M_x$. For $\alpha = \pi/2$ or $3\pi/2$, we obtain $M_n = M_y$. The moments M_{nt} become zero for these values of α. Thus we obtain the conditions shown in Fig. 19.

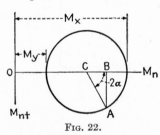

Fig. 22.

Equations (39) and (40) are similar to Eqs. (36), and by using them the bending and twisting moments can be readily calculated for any value of α. We can also use the graphical method for the same purpose and find the values of M_n and M_{nt} from the Mohr's circle which can be constructed as shown in the previous article by taking M_n as abscissa and M_{nt} as ordinate. The diameter of the circle will be equal to $M_x - M_y$, as shown in Fig. 22. Then the coordinates $\overline{OB}$ and $\overline{AB}$ of a point A, defined by the angle 2α, give us the moments M_n and M_{nt} respectively.

Let us now represent M_n and M_{nt} as functions of the curvatures and of the twist of the middle surface of the plate. Substituting in Eq. (39) for M_x and M_y their expressions (37) and (38), we find

$$M_n = D\left(\frac{1}{r_x}\cos^2\alpha + \frac{1}{r_y}\sin^2\alpha\right) + \nu D\left(\frac{1}{r_x}\sin^2\alpha + \frac{1}{r_y}\cos^2\alpha\right).$$

Using the first of the equations (36) of the previous article, we conclude that the expressions in parentheses represent the curvatures of the middle surface in the n- and t-directions respectively. Hence

$$M_n = D\left(\frac{1}{r_n} + \nu\frac{1}{r_t}\right) = -D\left(\frac{\partial^2 w}{\partial n^2} + \nu\frac{\partial^2 w}{\partial t^2}\right). \tag{41}$$

To get the corresponding expression for the twisting moment M_{nt}, let us consider the distortion of a thin lamina $abcd$ with the

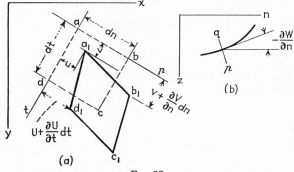

Fig. 23.

sides ab and ad parallel to the n- and t-directions and at a distance z from the middle plane (Fig. 23). During bending of the plate the points a, b, c, and d undergo small displacements. The components of the displacement of the point a in the n- and t-directions we denote by u and v respectively. Then the displacement of the adjacent point d in the n-direction is $u + (\partial u/\partial t)dt$, and the displacement of the point b in the t-direction is $v + (\partial v/\partial n)dn$. Owing to these displacements, we obtain for the shearing strain

$$\gamma_{nt} = \frac{\partial u}{\partial t} + \frac{\partial v}{\partial n}. \tag{e}$$

The corresponding shearing stress is

$$\tau_{nt} = G\left(\frac{\partial u}{\partial t} + \frac{\partial v}{\partial n}\right). \tag{f}$$

From Fig. 23b, representing the section of the middle surface made by the normal plane through the n-axis, it may be seen that the angle of rotation in counterclockwise direction of an element pq, which initially was perpendicular to the xy-plane, about an axis perpendicular to nz-plane is equal to $-\partial w/\partial n$. Owing to this rotation a point of the element at a distance z from the neutral surface has a displacement in the n-direction equal to

$$u = -z\frac{\partial w}{\partial n}.$$

Considering the normal section through the t-axis, it can be shown that the same point has a displacement in the t-direction equal to

$$v = -z\frac{\partial w}{\partial t}.$$

Substituting these values of the displacements u and v in expression (f), we find

$$\tau_{nt} = -2Gz\frac{\partial^2 w}{\partial n \, \partial t}, \tag{42}$$

and expression (40) for the twisting moment becomes

$$M_{nt} = -\int_{-\frac{h}{2}}^{\frac{h}{2}} \tau_{nt}z \, dz = \frac{Gh^3}{6}\frac{\partial^2 w}{\partial n \, \partial t} = D(1 - \nu)\frac{\partial^2 w}{\partial n \, \partial t}. \tag{43}$$

It is seen that the twisting moment for the given perpendicular directions n and t is proportional to the twist of the middle surface corresponding to those directions. When the n- and t-directions coincide with the x- and y-axes, there are only bending moments M_x and M_y acting on the sections perpendicular to those axes (Fig. 19). Hence the corresponding twist is zero, and the curvatures $1/r_x$ and $1/r_y$ are the principal curvatures of the middle surface of the plate. They can readily be calculated from Eqs. (37) and (38) if the bending moments M_x and M_y are given. The curvature in any other direction, defined by an angle α, can then be calculated by using the first of the equations (36), or it can be taken from Fig. 17.

Regarding the stresses in a plate undergoing pure bending, it can be concluded from the first of equations (*d*) that the maximum normal stress acts on those sections parallel to the *xz*- or *yz*-planes. The magnitudes of these stresses are obtained from Eq. (*b*) by substituting $z = h/2$ and by using Eqs. (37) and (38). In this way we find

$$(\sigma_x)_{\max.} = \frac{6M_x}{h^2}, \qquad (\sigma_y)_{\max.} = \frac{6M_y}{h^2}. \qquad (44)$$

If these stresses are of opposite sign, the maximum shearing stress acts in the plane bisecting the angle between the *xz*- and *yz*-planes and is equal to

$$\tau_{\max.} = \frac{1}{2}(\sigma_x - \sigma_y) = \frac{3(M_x - M_y)}{h^2}. \qquad (45)$$

If the stresses (44) are of the same sign, the maximum shear acts in the plane bisecting the angle between the *xy*- and *xz*-planes or in that bisecting the angle between the *xy*- and *yz*-planes and is equal to $\frac{1}{2}(\sigma_y)_{\max.}$ or $\frac{1}{2}(\sigma_x)_{\max.}$, depending on which of the two principal stresses $(\sigma_y)_{\max.}$ or $(\sigma_x)_{\max.}$ is greater.

11. Particular Cases of Pure Bending.—In the discussion of the previous article we started with the case of a rectangular plate along the edges of which uniformly distributed bending moments act. To obtain a general case of pure bending of plates, let us imagine that a portion of any shape is cut out from the plate considered above (Fig. 19) by a cylindrical or prismatical surface perpendicular to the plate. The conditions of bending of this portion will remain unchanged provided that bending and twisting moments that satisfy Eqs. (39) and (40) are distributed along the boundary of the isolated portion of the plate. Thus we arrive at the case of pure bending of a plate of any shape, and we conclude that pure bending of a plate is always produced if along the edges of the plate bending moments M_n and twisting moments M_{nt} are distributed in such a manner as given by Eqs. (39) and (40).

Let us take, as a first example, the particular case in which $M_x = M_y = M$. It can be concluded, from Eqs. (39) and (40), that in this case, for a plate of any shape, the bending moments are uniformly distributed along the entire boundary and twisting moments vanish. From Eqs. (37) and (38) we conclude that

$$\frac{1}{r_x} = \frac{1}{r_y} = \frac{M}{D(1 + \nu)};$$ (46)

i.e., the plate in this case is bent to a spherical surface the curvature of which is given by Eq. (46).

In the general case, when M_x is different from M_y, we put

$$M_x = M_1 \quad \text{and} \quad M_y = M_2.$$

Then, from Eqs. (37) and (38), we find

$$\left.\begin{aligned} \frac{\partial^2 w}{\partial x^2} &= -\frac{M_1 - \nu M_2}{D(1 - \nu^2)}, \\ \frac{\partial^2 w}{\partial y^2} &= -\frac{M_2 - \nu M_1}{D(1 - \nu^2)}. \end{aligned}\right\}$$ (a)

We have also

$$\frac{\partial^2 w}{\partial x \, \partial y} = 0.$$ (b)

Integrating these equations, we find

$$w = -\frac{M_1 - \nu M_2}{2D(1 - \nu^2)}x^2 - \frac{M_2 - \nu M_1}{2D(1 - \nu^2)}y^2 + C_1 x + C_2 y + C_3,$$ (c)

where C_1, C_2 and C_3 are constants of integration. These constants define the plane from which the deflections w are measured. If this plane is taken tangent to the middle surface of the plate at the origin, the constants of integration must be equal to zero, and the deflection surface is given by the equation

$$w = -\frac{M_1 - \nu M_2}{2D(1 - \nu^2)}x^2 - \frac{M_2 - \nu M_1}{2D(1 - \nu^2)}y^2.$$ (d)

Let us consider the particular case where $M_2 = -M_1$. In this case the principal curvatures, from Eqs. (a), are

$$\frac{1}{r_x} = -\frac{1}{r_y} = -\frac{\partial^2 w}{\partial x^2} = \frac{M_1}{D(1 - \nu)},$$ (e)

and we obtain an anticlastic surface the equation of which is

$$w = -\frac{M_1}{2D(1 - \nu)}(x^2 - y^2). \qquad (f)$$

Straight lines parallel to the x-axis become, after bending, parabolic curves convex downward (Fig. 24), whereas straight lines in the y-direction become parabolas convex upward. Along the lines bisecting the angles between the x- and y-axes we have $x = y$, or $x = -y$; thus deflections along these lines, as is seen from Eq. (f), are zero. All lines parallel to these bisecting lines before bending remain straight during bending, rotating only

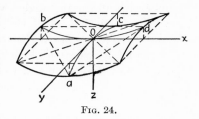

Fig. 24.

by some angle. A rectangle $abcd$ bounded by such lines will be twisted, as shown in Fig. 24. Imagine normal sections of the plate along the lines ab, bc, cd and ad. From Eqs. (39) and (40) we conclude that bending moments along these sections are zero and that twisting moments along sections ad and bc are equal to M_1 and along sections ab and cd are equal to $-M_1$.

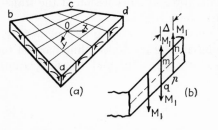
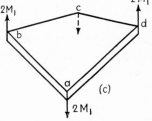

Fig. 25.

Thus the portion $abcd$ of the plate is in the condition of a plate undergoing pure bending produced by twisting moments uniformly distributed along the edges (Fig. 25a). These twisting moments are formed by the horizontal shearing stresses continuously distributed over the edge [Eq. (40)]. This horizontal stress distribution can be replaced by vertical shearing forces which produce the same effect as the actual distribution of stresses. To show this let the edge ad be divided into infinitely narrow rectangles, such as $mnpq$ in Fig. 25b. If Δ is the small width of the rectangle, the corresponding twisting couple is $M_1\Delta$ and can be formed by two vertical forces equal to M_1 acting along the vertical sides of the rectangle.   This replacement of the distributed horizontal forces by a statically equivalent system of two vertical forces cannot cause any sensible disturbance in the plate, except within a distance comparable with the thickness of the plate,[1] which is assumed small.   Proceeding in the same manner with all the rectangles, we find that all forces M_1 acting along the vertical sides of the rectangles balance one another and only two forces M_1 at the corners a and d are left.   Making the same transformation along the other edges of the plate, we conclude that the bending of the plate to the anticlastic surface shown in Fig. 25a can be produced by forces concentrated at the corners[2] (Fig. 25c).   Such an experiment is comparatively simple to perform, and was used for the experimental verification of the theory of bending of plates discussed above.[3]   In these experiments the deflections of the plate along the line bod (Fig. 24) were measured and were found to be in very satisfactory agreement with the theoretical results obtained from Eq. (f).   Some discrepancies were found only near the edges, and they were more pronounced in the case of comparatively thick plates, as would be expected from the foregoing discussion of the transformation of twisting couples along the edges.

As a last example let us consider the bending of a plate (Fig. 19) to a cylindrical surface having its generating line parallel to the y-axis.   In such a case $\partial^2 w/\partial y^2 = 0$, and we find, from Eqs. (37) and (38),

$$M_x = -D\frac{\partial^2 w}{\partial x^2}, \qquad M_y = -\nu D\frac{\partial^2 w}{\partial x^2}. \qquad (g)$$

It is seen that to produce bending of the plate to a cylindrical surface we must apply not only the moments M_x but also the moments M_y.   Without these latter moments the plate will be

[1] This follows from the so-called *Saint Venant's principle;* see author's "Theory of Elasticity," p. 31, 1934.

[2] This transformation of the force system acting along the edges was first suggested by Lord Kelvin and P. G. Tait.   See "Treatise on Natural Philosophy," vol. 1, part 2, p. 203, 1883.

[3] Such experiments were made by Dr. A. Nadai, *Forschungsarbeiten,* vols. 170, 171, Berlin, 1915; see also his book "Elastische Platten," p. 42, Berlin, 1925.

bent to an anticlastic surface.[1] The first of the equations (g) have already been used in Chap. I in discussing bending of long rectangular plates to a cylindrical surface. Although in that discussion we had bending of plates by lateral loads and there were not only bending stresses but also vertical shearing stresses acting on sections perpendicular to the x-axis, it can be concluded from a comparison with the usual beam theory that the effect of the shearing forces is negligible in the case of thin plates, and the equation developed for the case of pure bending can be used with sufficient accuracy also for lateral loading.

12. Strain Energy in Pure Bending of Plates.—If a plate is bent by uniformly distributed bending moments M_x and M_y (Fig. 19) so that the xz- and yz- planes are the principal planes of the deflection surface of the plate, the strain energy stored in an element, such as shown in Fig. 20, is obtained by calculating the work done by the moments $M_x\,dy$ and $M_y\,dx$ on the element during bending of the plate. Since the sides of the element remain plane, the work done by the moments $M_x\,dy$ is obtained by taking half the product of the moment and the angle between the corresponding sides of the element after bending. Since $-\partial^2 w/\partial x^2$ represents the curvature of the plate in the xz-plane, the angle corresponding to the moments $M_x\,dy$ is $-(\partial^2 w/\partial x^2)dx$, and the work done by these moments is

$$-\frac{1}{2}M_x\frac{\partial^2 w}{\partial x^2}dx\,dy.$$

An analogous expression is also obtained for the work produced by the moments $M_y\,dx$. Then the total work, equal to the strain energy of the element, is

$$dV = -\frac{1}{2}\left(M_x\frac{\partial^2 w}{\partial x^2} + M_y\frac{\partial^2 w}{\partial y^2}\right)dx\,dy.$$

Substituting for the moments their expressions (37) and (39), the strain energy of the elements is represented in the following form:

$$dV = \frac{1}{2}D\left[\left(\frac{\partial^2 w}{\partial x^2}\right)^2 + \left(\frac{\partial^2 w}{\partial y^2}\right)^2 + 2\nu\frac{\partial^2 w}{\partial x^2}\frac{\partial^2 w}{\partial y^2}\right]dx\,dy. \qquad (a)$$

[1] We always assume very small deflections or else bending to a developable surface. The case of bending to a non-developable surface when the deflections are not small will be discussed later; see p. 51.

Since in the case of pure bending the curvature is constant over the entire surface of the plate, the total strain energy of the plate will be obtained if we substitute the area A of the plate in place of the elementary area $dx\,dy$ in expression (a).   Then

$$V = \frac{1}{2}DA\left[\left(\frac{\partial^2 w}{\partial x^2}\right)^2 + \left(\frac{\partial^2 w}{\partial y^2}\right)^2 + 2\nu\frac{\partial^2 w}{\partial x^2}\frac{\partial^2 w}{\partial y^2}\right]. \qquad (47)$$

If the directions x and y do not coincide with the principal planes of curvature, there will act on the sides of the element (Fig. 20) not only the bending moments $M_x\,dy$ and $M_y\,dx$ but also the twisting moments $M_{xy}\,dy$ and $M_{yx}\,dx$. The strain energy due to bending moments are represented by the expression (a). In deriving the expression for the strain energy due to twisting moments $M_{xy}\,dy$ we observe that the corresponding angle of twist is equal to the rate of change of the slope $\partial w/\partial y$, as x varies, multiplied with dx; hence the strain energy due to $M_{xy}\,dy$ is

$$\frac{1}{2}M_{xy}\frac{\partial^2 w}{\partial x\,\partial y}dx\,dy,$$

which, applying Eq. (43), becomes

$$\frac{1}{2}D(1-\nu)\left(\frac{\partial^2 w}{\partial x\,\partial y}\right)^2 dx\,dy.$$

The same amount of energy will also be produced by the couples $M_{yx}\,dx$ so that the strain energy due to both twisting couples is

$$D(1-\nu)\left(\frac{\partial^2 w}{\partial x\,\partial y}\right)^2 dx\,dy. \qquad (b)$$

Since the twist does not affect the work produced by the bending moments, the total strain energy of an element of a plate is obtained by adding together the energy of bending (a) and the energy of twist (b). Thus we obtain

$$dV = \frac{1}{2}D\left[\left(\frac{\partial^2 w}{\partial x^2}\right)^2 + \left(\frac{\partial^2 w}{\partial y^2}\right)^2 + 2\nu\frac{\partial^2 w}{\partial x^2}\frac{\partial^2 w}{\partial y^2}\right]dx\,dy$$
$$+ D(1-\nu)\left(\frac{\partial^2 w}{\partial x\,\partial y}\right)^2 dx\,dy,$$

or

$$dV = \frac{1}{2}D\left\{\left(\frac{\partial^2 w}{\partial x^2} + \frac{\partial^2 w}{\partial y^2}\right)^2 - 2(1-\nu)\left[\frac{\partial^2 w}{\partial x^2}\frac{\partial^2 w}{\partial y^2} - \left(\frac{\partial^2 w}{\partial x\,\partial y}\right)^2\right]\right\}dx\,dy. \qquad (48)$$

The strain energy of the entire plate is now obtained by substituting the area A of the plate for the elemental area $dx\,dy$. Expression (48) will be used later in more complicated cases of bending of plates.

13. Limitations on the Application of the Derived Formulas.— In discussing stress distribution in the case of pure bending (Art. 10) it was assumed that the middle surface is the neutral surface of the plate. This condition can be rigorously satisfied only if the middle surface of the bent plate is a *developable surface*. Considering, for instance, pure bending of a plate to a cylindrical surface, the only limitation on the application of the theory will be the requirement that the thickness of the plate be small in comparison with the radius of curvature. In the problems of bending of plates to a cylindrical surface by lateral loading, discussed in the previous chapter, it is required that deflections be small in comparison with the width of the plate, since only under this condition will the approximate expression used for the curvature be accurate enough.

If a plate is bent to a non-developable surface, the middle surface undergoes some stretching during bending and the theory of pure bending developed previously will be accurate enough only if the stresses corresponding to this stretching of the middle surface are small in comparison with the maximum bending stresses given by Eqs. (44) or, what is equivalent, if the strain in the middle surface is small in comparison with the maximum bending strain $h/2r_{\min}$. This requirement puts an additional limitation on deflections of a plate, *viz.*, that the deflections w of the plate must be small in comparison with its thickness h.

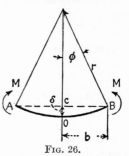

FIG. 26.

To show this, let us consider the bending of a circular plate by bending couples M uniformly distributed along the edge. The deflection surface, for small deflections, is spherical of a radius r the magnitude of which is defined by Eq. (46). Let AOB (Fig. 26) represent a diametral section of the bent circular plate, a its outer radius before bending and δ the deflection at the middle. We assume at first that there is no stretching of the middle surface of the plate in the radial direction. In such a case the arc *OB* must be equal to the initial outer radius *a* of the plate. The angle φ and the radius *b* of the plate after bending are then given by the following equations:

$$\varphi = \frac{a}{r}, \qquad b = r \sin \varphi.$$

It is seen that the assumed bending of the plate implies a compressive strain of the middle surface in the circumferential direction. The magnitude of this strain at the edge of the plate is

$$\epsilon = \frac{a - b}{a} = \frac{r\varphi - r \sin \varphi}{r\varphi}. \tag{a}$$

For small deflections we can take

$$\sin \varphi = \varphi - \frac{\varphi^3}{6}$$

which, substituted in Eq. (*a*), gives

$$\epsilon = \frac{\varphi^2}{6}. \tag{b}$$

To represent this strain as a function of the maximum deflection δ, we observe that

$$\delta = r(1 - \cos \varphi) \approx \frac{r\varphi^2}{2}.$$

Hence

$$\varphi^2 = \frac{2\delta}{r}.$$

Substituting in Eq. (*b*), we obtain

$$\epsilon = \frac{\delta}{3r}. \tag{49}$$

This represents an upper limit for the circumferential strain at the edge of the plate. It was obtained by assuming that the radial strain is zero. Under actual conditions there is some radial strain, and the circumferential compression is somewhat smaller[1] than that given by Eq. (49).

From this discussion it follows that the equations obtained in Art. 10, on the assumption that the middle surface of the bent plate is its neutral surface, are accurate provided the strain given by expression (49) is small in comparison with the maximum

---

[1] This question is discussed later; see Art. 67.

bending strain $h/2r$, or, what is equivalent, if the deflection δ is small in comparison with the thickness h of the plate. A similar conclusion can also be obtained in the more general case of pure bending of a plate when the two principal curvatures are not equal.[1] Generalizing these conclusions we can state that the equations of Art. 10 can always be applied with sufficient accuracy if the deflections of a plate from its initial plane or from a true developable surface are small in comparison with the thickness of the plate.

14. Thermal Stresses in Plates with Clamped Edges.—Equation (46) for the bending of a plate to a spherical surface can be used in calculating thermal stresses in a plate for certain cases of non-uniform heating. Assume that the variation of the temperature through the thickness of the plate follows a linear law and that the temperature does not vary in planes parallel to the surfaces of the plate. In such a case, by measuring the temperature from the temperature of the middle surface, it can be concluded that temperature expansions and contractions are proportional to the distance from the middle surface. Thus we have exactly the same condition as in the pure bending of a plate to a spherical surface. If the edges of the non-uniformly heated plate are entirely free, the plate will bend to a spherical surface.[2] Let α be the coefficient of linear expansion of the material of the plate, and let t denote the difference in temperature of the upper and lower faces of the plate. The difference between the maximum thermal expansion and the expansion at the middle surface is $\alpha t/2$, and the curvature resulting from the non-uniform heating can be found from the equation

$$\frac{\alpha t}{2} = \frac{h}{2r}, \qquad (a)$$

from which

$$\frac{1}{r} = \frac{\alpha t}{h}. \qquad (50)$$

This bending of the plate does not produce any stresses, provided the edges are free and deflections are small in comparison with the thickness of the plate.

[1] See Lord Kelvin and P. G. Tait, "Treatise on Natural Philosophy," vol. 1, part 2, p. 172, 1883.

[2] It is assumed that deflections are small in comparison with the thickness of the plate.

Assume, now, that the middle plane of the plate is free to expand but that the edges are clamped so that they cannot rotate. In such a case the non-uniform heating will produce bending moments uniformly distributed along the edges of the plate. The magnitude of these moments is such as to eliminate the curvature produced by the non-uniform heating [Eq. (50)], since only in this way can the condition at the clamped edge be satisfied. Using Eq. (46) for the curvature produced by the bending moments, we find for determining the magnitude M of the moment per unit length of the boundary the equation

$$\frac{M}{D(1 + \nu)} = \frac{\alpha t}{h},$$

from which

$$M = \frac{\alpha t D(1 + \nu)}{h}. \tag{b}$$

The corresponding maximum stress can be found from Eqs. (44) and is equal to

$$\sigma_{\text{max.}} = \frac{6M}{h^2} = \frac{6\alpha t D(1 + \nu)}{h^3}.$$

Substituting for D its expression (3), we finally obtain

$$\sigma_{\text{max.}} = \frac{\alpha t E}{2(1 - \nu)}. \tag{51}$$

It is seen that the stress is proportional to the coefficient of thermal expansion α, to the temperature difference t between the two faces of the plate and to the modulus of elasticity E. The thickness h of the plate does not enter into formula (51); but since the difference t of temperatures usually increases in proportion to the thickness of the plate, it can be concluded that greater thermal stresses are to be expected in thick plates than in thin ones.

It will be shown later (see Art. 86) that the simple formula (51) can be also used in calculating thermal stresses in non-uniformly heated thin shells, such as thin cylindrical tubes or thin spherical containers. The change in curvature during non-uniform heating of such shells is prevented by the shape of the shell itself, and the maximum bending stresses (51) are produced. Since the temperature difference t is usually proportional to the thickness of the shell, it becomes evident that thin glass containers will prove more satisfactory than thick ones in cases where thermal stresses are the controlling factor.

CHAPTER III

SYMMETRICAL BENDING OF CIRCULAR PLATES

15. Differential Equation for Symmetrical Bending of Laterally Loaded Circular Plates.[1]—If the load acting on a circular plate is symmetrically distributed about the axis perpendicular to the plate through its center, the deflection surface to which the middle plane of the plate is bent will also be symmetrical. In all points equally distant from the center of the plate the deflections will be the same, and it is sufficient to consider deflections only in one diametral section through the axis of symmetry (Fig. 27). Let us take the origin of coordinates O at the center of the undeflected plate and denote by r the radial distances of points in the middle plane of the plate and by w their deflections in the downward direction. The maximum slope of the deflection surface at any point A is then equal to $-dw/dr$, and the curvature of the middle surface of the plate in the diametral section rz for small deflections is

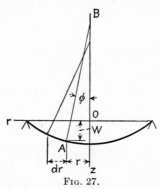

FIG. 27.

$$\frac{1}{r_n} = -\frac{d^2w}{dr^2} = \frac{d\varphi}{dr}, \qquad (a)$$

where φ is the small angle between the normal to the deflection surface at A and the axis of symmetry OB. From symmetry we conclude that $1/r_n$ is one of the principal curvatures of the deflection surface at A. The second principal curvature will be in the section through the normal AB and perpendicular to the rz plane. Observing that the normals, such as AB, for all points of the middle surface with radial distance r form a conical surface

[1] The solution of these problems of bending of circular plates was given by Poisson; see "Memoirs of the Academy," vol. 8, Paris, 1829.

55

with apex B, we conclude that the length AB is the radius of the second principal curvature which we denote by r_t. Then, from the figure, we obtain

$$\frac{1}{r_t} = -\frac{1}{r}\frac{dw}{dr} = \frac{\varphi}{r}. \tag{b}$$

Having expressions (a) and (b) for the principal curvatures, we can obtain the corresponding values of the bending moments assuming that relations (37) and (38), derived for pure bending, also hold between these moments and the curvatures.[1] Using these relations, we obtain

$$M_r = -D\left(\frac{d^2w}{dr^2} + \frac{\nu}{r}\frac{dw}{dr}\right) = D\left(\frac{d\varphi}{dr} + \frac{\nu}{r}\varphi\right), \tag{52}$$

$$M_t = -D\left(\frac{1}{r}\frac{dw}{dr} + \nu\frac{d^2w}{dr^2}\right) = D\left(\frac{\varphi}{r} + \nu\frac{d\varphi}{dr}\right), \tag{53}$$

where, as before, M_r and M_t denote the bending moments per unit length M_r along circumferential sections of the plate, such as the section made by the coni-

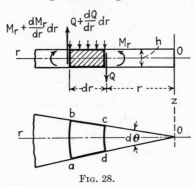

FIG. 28.

cal surface with the apex at B, and M_t along the diametral section rz of the plate.

Equations (52) and (53) contain only one variable w or φ, which can be determined from the consideration of equilibrium of an element of the plate such as element $abcd$ in Fig. 28 cut out from the plate by two cylindrical sections ab and cd and by two diametral sections ad and bc. The couple acting on the side cd of the element is

$$M_r r\, d\theta. \tag{c}$$

[1] The effect on deflections of shearing stresses acting on normal sections of the plate perpendicular to meridians, such as the section cut by the conical surface with the apex at B, is neglected here. Their effect is small in the case of plates the thickness of which is small in comparison with the diameter. Further discussion of this subject will be given in Art. 20. The stresses perpendicular to the surface of the plate are also neglected, which is justifiable in all cases when the load is not highly concentrated (see p. 76).

The corresponding couple on the side ab is

$$\left(M_r + \frac{dM_r}{dr}dr\right)(r + dr)d\theta. \qquad (d)$$

The couples on the sides ad and bc of the element are each $M_t\, dr$, and they give a resultant couple in the plane roz equal to

$$M_t\, dr\, d\theta. \qquad (e)$$

From symmetry it can be concluded that the shearing forces that may act on the element must vanish on diametral sections of the plate but that they are usually present on cylindrical sections such as sides cd and ab of the element. Denoting by Q the shearing force per unit length of cylindrical section of radius r, the total shearing force acting on the side cd of the element is $Qr\, d\theta$, and the corresponding force on the side ab is

$$\left[Q + \left(\frac{dQ}{dr}\right)dr\right](r + dr)d\theta.$$

Neglecting the small difference between the shearing forces on the two opposite sides of the element, we can state that these forces give a couple in the rz plane equal to

$$Qr\, d\theta\, dr. \qquad (f)$$

Summing up the moments (c), (d), (e) and (f) with proper signs and neglecting the moment due to the external load on the element as a small quantity of a higher order, we obtain the following equation of equilibrium of the element $abcd$:

$$\left(M_r + \frac{dM_r}{dr}dr\right)(r + dr)d\theta - M_r r\, d\theta - M_t\, dr\, d\theta + Qr\, d\theta\, dr = 0,$$

from which we find, by neglecting a small quantity of higher order,

$$M_r + \frac{dM_r}{dr}r - M_t + Qr = 0. \qquad (g)$$

Substituting expressions (52) and (53) for M_r and M_t, Eq. (g) becomes

$$\frac{d^2\varphi}{dr^2} + \frac{1}{r}\frac{d\varphi}{dr} - \frac{\varphi}{r^2} = -\frac{Q}{D}, \qquad (54)$$

or, in another form,

$$\frac{d^3w}{dr^3} + \frac{1}{r}\frac{d^2w}{dr^2} - \frac{1}{r^2}\frac{dw}{dr} = \frac{Q}{D}. \qquad (55)$$

In any particular case of a symmetrically loaded circular plate the shearing force Q can easily be calculated by dividing the load distributed within the circle of radius r by $2\pi r$; then Eq. (54) or (55) can be used to determine the slope φ and the deflection w of the plate. The integration of these equations is simplified if we observe that they can be put in the following forms:

$$\frac{d}{dr}\left[\frac{1}{r}\frac{d}{dr}(r\varphi)\right] = -\frac{Q}{D}, \tag{56}$$

$$\frac{d}{dr}\left[\frac{1}{r}\frac{d}{dr}\left(r\frac{dw}{dr}\right)\right] = \frac{Q}{D}. \tag{57}$$

If Q is represented by a function of r, these equations can be integrated without any difficulty in each particular case.

Sometimes it is advantageous to represent the right side of Eq. (57) as a function of the intensity q of the load distributed over the plate. For this purpose we multiply both sides of the equation by $2\pi r$. Then, observing that

$$Q2\pi r = \int^r q2\pi r\, dr,$$

we obtain

$$r\frac{d}{dr}\left[\frac{1}{r}\frac{d}{dr}\left(r\frac{dw}{dr}\right)\right] = \frac{1}{D}\int_0^r qr\, dr.$$

Differentiating both sides of this equation with respect to r and dividing by r, we finally obtain

$$\frac{1}{r}\frac{d}{dr}\left\{r\frac{d}{dr}\left[\frac{1}{r}\frac{d}{dr}\left(r\frac{dw}{dr}\right)\right]\right\} = \frac{q}{D}. \tag{58}$$

This equation can easily be integrated if the intensity of the load q is given as a function of r.

16. Uniformly Loaded Circular Plates.—If a circular plate of radius a carries a load of intensity q uniformly distributed over the entire surface of the plate, the magnitude of the shearing force Q at a distance r from the center of the plate is determined from the equation

$$2\pi rQ = \pi r^2 q,$$

from which

$$Q = \frac{qr}{2}. \tag{a}$$

Substituting in Eq. (57), we obtain

$$\frac{d}{dr}\left[\frac{1}{r}\frac{d}{dr}\left(r\frac{dw}{dr}\right)\right] = \frac{qr}{2D}. \tag{b}$$

By one integration we find

$$\frac{1}{r}\frac{d}{dr}\left(r\frac{dw}{dr}\right) = \frac{qr^2}{4D} + C_1, \tag{c}$$

where C_1 is a constant of integration to be found later from the conditions at the center and at the edge of the plate. Multiplying both sides of Eq. (c) by r, and making the second integration, we find

$$r\frac{dw}{dr} = \frac{qr^4}{16D} + \frac{C_1 r^2}{2} + C_2$$

and

$$\frac{dw}{dr} = \frac{qr^3}{16D} + \frac{C_1 r}{2} + \frac{C_2}{r}. \tag{59}$$

The new integration then gives

$$w = \frac{qr^4}{64D} + \frac{C_1 r^2}{4} + C_2 \log\frac{r}{a} + C_3. \tag{60}$$

Let us now calculate the constants of integration for various particular cases.

Circular Plate with Clamped Edges.—In this case the slope of the deflection surface in the radial direction must be zero for $r = 0$ and $r = a$. Hence, from Eq. (59),

$$\left(\frac{qr^3}{16D} + \frac{C_1 r}{2} + \frac{C_2}{r}\right)_{r=0} = 0,$$

$$\left(\frac{qr^3}{16D} + \frac{C_1 r}{2} + \frac{C_2}{r}\right)_{r=a} = 0.$$

From the first of these equations we conclude that $C_2 = 0$. Substituting this in the second equation, we obtain

$$C_1 = -\frac{qa^2}{8D}.$$

With these values of the constants, Eq. (59) gives the following expression for the slope:

$$\varphi = -\frac{dw}{dr} = \frac{qr}{16D}(a^2 - r^2). \tag{61}$$

Equation (60) gives

$$w = \frac{qr^4}{64D} - \frac{qa^2r^2}{32D} + C_3. \qquad (d)$$

At the edge of the plate the deflection is zero.   Hence,

$$\frac{qa^4}{64D} - \frac{qa^4}{32D} + C_3 = 0,$$

and we obtain

$$C_3 = \frac{qa^4}{64D}.$$

Substituting in Eq. (d), we find

$$w = \frac{q}{64D}(a^2 - r^2)^2. \qquad (62)$$

The maximum deflection is at the center of the plate and, from Eq. (62), is equal to

$$w_{\text{max.}} = \frac{qa^4}{64D}. \qquad (e)$$

This deflection is equal to three-eighths of the deflection of a uniformly loaded strip with built-in ends having a flexural rigidity equal to D, a width of unity, and a length equal to the diameter of the plate.

Having expression (61) for the slope, we obtain now the bending moments M_r and M_t by using expressions (52) and (53) from which we find

$$M_r = \frac{q}{16}[a^2(1 + \nu) - r^2(3 + \nu)], \qquad (63)$$

$$M_t = \frac{q}{16}[a^2(1 + \nu) - r^2(1 + 3\nu)]. \qquad (64)$$

Substituting $r = a$ in these expressions, we find for the bending moments at the boundary of the plate

$$(M_r)_{r=a} = -\frac{qa^2}{8}, \qquad (M_t)_{r=a} = -\frac{\nu qa^2}{8}. \qquad (65)$$

At the center of the plate where $r = 0$,

$$M_r = M_t = \frac{qa^2}{16}(1 + \nu). \qquad (66)$$

From expressions (65) and (66) it is seen that the maximum stress is at the boundary of the plate where

$$(\sigma_r)_{\text{max.}} = -\frac{6M_r}{h^2} = \frac{3}{4}\frac{qa^2}{h^2}. \tag{f}$$

The variation of stresses σ_r and σ_t at the lower face of the plate along the radius of the plate is shown in Fig. 29.

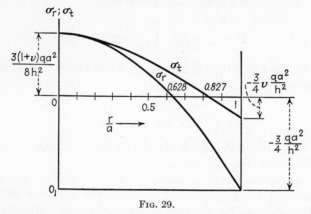

Fig. 29.

Circular Plate with Supported Edges.—In calculating deflections for this case we apply the method of superposition. It was shown that in the case of clamped edges there are negative

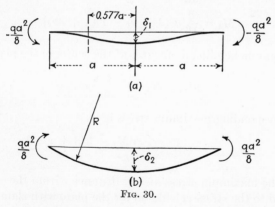

Fig. 30.

bending moments $M_r = -qa^2/8$ acting along the edge (Fig. 30a). If this case is combined with that of pure bending shown in Fig. 30b, the bending moments M_r at the edge will be eliminated, and we obtain the bending of a plate supported at the edge. The deflection surface in the case of pure bending by the moments $qa^2/8$, from Eq. (46), is

$$w = \frac{qa^2}{16D(1 + \nu)}(a^2 - r^2).$$

Adding this to the deflections (62) of the clamped plate, we find for the plate with a simply supported edge

$$w = \frac{q(a^2 - r^2)}{64D}\left(\frac{5 + \nu}{1 + \nu}a^2 - r^2\right). \tag{67}$$

Substituting $r = 0$ in this expression we obtain the deflection of the plate at the center:

$$w_{\text{max.}} = \frac{(5 + \nu)qa^4}{64(1 + \nu)D}. \tag{68}$$

For $\nu = 0.3$ this deflection is about four times as great as that for the plate with clamped edge.

In calculating bending moments in this case we must add the constant bending moment $qa^2/8$ to the moments (63) and (64) found above for the case of clamped edges. Hence in the case of supported edges

$$M_r = \frac{q}{16}(3 + \nu)(a^2 - r^2), \tag{69}$$

$$M_t = \frac{q}{16}[a^2(3 + \nu) - r^2(1 + 3\nu)]. \tag{70}$$

The maximum bending moment is at the center of the plate where

$$M_r = M_t = \frac{3 + \nu}{16}qa^2.$$

The corresponding maximum stress is

$$(\sigma_r)_{\text{max.}} = (\sigma_t)_{\text{max.}} = \frac{6M_r}{h^2} = \frac{3(3 + \nu)qa^2}{8h^2}. \tag{71}$$

To get the maximum stress at any distance r from the center we must add to the stress calculated for the plate with clamped edge the constant value

$$\frac{6}{h^2} \cdot \frac{qa^2}{8}$$

corresponding to the pure bending shown in Fig. 30*b*. The same stress is obtained also from Fig. 29 by measuring the ordinates from the horizontal axis through O_1. It may be seen that by clamping the edge a more favorable stress distribution in the plate is obtained.

17. Circular Plate with a Circular Hole at the Center.—Let us begin with a discussion of the bending of a plate by the moments M_1 and M_2 uniformly distributed along the inner and outer

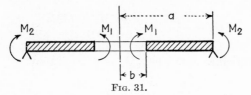

FIG. 31.

boundaries, respectively (Fig. 31). The shearing force Q vanishes in such a case, and Eq. (57) becomes

$$\frac{d}{dr}\left[\frac{1}{r}\frac{d}{dr}\left(r\frac{dw}{dr}\right)\right] = 0.$$

By integrating this equation twice we obtain

$$-\frac{dw}{dr} = \varphi = \frac{C_1 r}{2} + \frac{C_2}{r}. \tag{a}$$

Integrating again, we find the deflection

$$w = -\frac{C_1 r^2}{4} - C_2 \log\frac{r}{a} + C_3. \tag{b}$$

The constants of integration are now to be determined from the conditions at the edges. Substituting expression (*a*) into Eq. (52), we find

$$M_r = D\left[\frac{C_1}{2} - \frac{C_2}{r^2} + \nu\left(\frac{C_1}{2} + \frac{C_2}{r^2}\right)\right]. \tag{c}$$

This moment must be equal to M_1 for $r = b$ and equal to M_2 for $r = a$. Hence equations for determining constants C_1 and C_2 are

$$D\left[\frac{C_1}{2}(1 + \nu) - \frac{C_2}{b^2}(1 - \nu)\right] = M_1,$$

$$D\left[\frac{C_1}{2}(1 + \nu) - \frac{C_2}{a^2}(1 - \nu)\right] = M_2,$$

from which

$$C_1 = \frac{2(a^2 M_2 - b^2 M_1)}{(1 + \nu)D(a^2 - b^2)}, \qquad C_2 = \frac{a^2 b^2 (M_2 - M_1)}{(1 - \nu)D(a^2 - b^2)}. \qquad (d)$$

To determine the constant C_3 in Eq. (b), the deflections at the edges of the plate must be considered. Assume, for example, that the plate in Fig. 31 is supported along the outer edge. Then $w = 0$ for $r = a$, and we find, from (b),

$$C_3 = \frac{C_1 a^2}{4} = \frac{a^2(a^2 M_2 - b^2 M_1)}{2(1 + \nu)D(a^2 - b^2)}.$$

In the particular case when $M_2 = 0$ we obtain

$$C_1 = -\frac{2b^2 M_1}{(1 + \nu)D(a^2 - b^2)}, \qquad C_2 = -\frac{a^2 b^2 M_1}{(1 - \nu)D(a^2 - b^2)},$$

$$C_3 = -\frac{a^2 b^2 M_1}{2(1 + \nu)D(a^2 - b^2)};$$

and expressions (a) and (b) for the slope and the deflection become

$$\frac{dw}{dr} = \frac{a^2 b^2 M_1}{D(1 - \nu)(a^2 - b^2)}\left(\frac{1}{r} + \frac{1 - \nu}{1 + \nu} \cdot \frac{r}{a^2}\right), \qquad (72)$$

$$w = -\frac{b^2 M_1}{2(1 + \nu)D(a^2 - b^2)}(a^2 - r^2)$$
$$+ \frac{a^2 b^2 M_1}{(1 - \nu)D(a^2 - b^2)} \log \frac{r}{a}. \qquad (73)$$

As a second example we consider the case of bending of a plate by shearing forces Q_0 uniformly distributed along the inner edge (Fig. 32). The shearing force per unit length of a circumference of radius r is

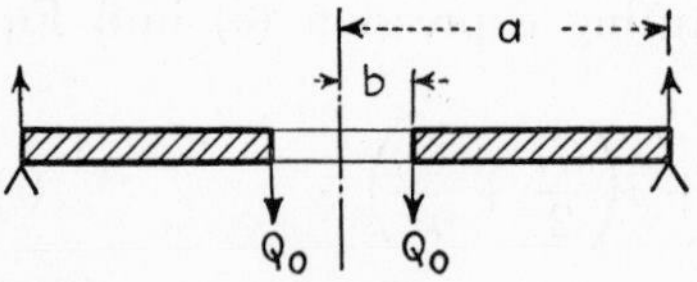

FIG. 32.

$$Q = \frac{Q_0 b}{r} = \frac{P}{2\pi r},$$

where $P = 2\pi b Q_0$ denotes the total load applied to the inner boundary of the plate. Substituting this in Eq. (57) and integrating, we obtain

$$\frac{dw}{dr} = \frac{Pr}{8\pi D}\left(2 \log \frac{r}{a} - 1\right) - \frac{C_1 r}{2} - \frac{C_2}{r} \qquad (e)$$

and

$$w = \frac{Pr^2}{8\pi D}\left(\log \frac{r}{a} - 1\right) - \frac{C_1 r^2}{4} - C_2 \log \frac{r}{a} + C_3. \qquad (f)$$

The constants of integration will now be calculated from the boundary conditions. Assuming that the plate is simply supported along the outer edge, we have

$$(w)_{r=a} = 0, \qquad -D\left(\frac{d^2w}{dr^2} + \frac{\nu}{r}\frac{dw}{dr}\right)_{r=a} = 0. \qquad (g)$$

For the inner edge of the plate we have

$$-D\left(\frac{d^2w}{dr^2} + \frac{\nu}{r}\frac{dw}{dr}\right)_{r=b} = 0. \qquad (h)$$

Substituting expressions (e) and (f) in Eqs. (g) and (h), we find

$$\left.\begin{aligned} C_1 &= \frac{P}{4\pi D}\left(\frac{1-\nu}{1+\nu} - \frac{2b^2}{a^2-b^2}\log\frac{b}{a}\right), \\ C_2 &= -\frac{(1+\nu)P}{(1-\nu)4\pi D}\cdot\frac{a^2 b^2}{a^2-b^2}\log\frac{b}{a}, \\ C_3 &= \frac{Pa^2}{8\pi D}\left(1 + \frac{1}{2}\cdot\frac{1-\nu}{1+\nu} - \frac{b^2}{a^2-b^2}\log\frac{b}{a}\right). \end{aligned}\right\} \qquad (i)$$

With these values of the constants substituted in expressions (e) and (f), we find the slope and the deflection at any point of the plate shown in Fig. 32. For the slope at the inner edge, which will be needed in the further discussion, we obtain in this way

$$\left(\frac{dw}{dr}\right)_{r=b} = \frac{Pb}{8\pi D}\left[2\log\frac{b}{a} - 1 - \frac{1-\nu}{1+\nu}\right.$$
$$\left. + \frac{2b^2}{a^2-b^2}\log\frac{b}{a}\cdot\left(1 + \frac{a^2}{b^2}\cdot\frac{1+\nu}{1-\nu}\right)\right] \qquad (j)$$

In the limiting case where b is infinitely small, $b^2 \log(b/a)$ approaches zero, and the constants of integration become

$$C_1 = \frac{1-\nu}{1+\nu}\cdot\frac{P}{4\pi D}, \qquad C_2 = 0, \qquad C_3 = \frac{Pa^2}{8\pi D}\left(1 + \frac{1}{2}\cdot\frac{1-\nu}{1+\nu}\right).$$

Substituting these values in expression (f), we obtain

$$w = \frac{P}{8\pi D}\left[\frac{3+\nu}{2(1+\nu)}(a^2-r^2) + r^2\log\frac{r}{a}\right]. \qquad (k)$$

This coincides with the deflection of a plate without a hole and loaded at the center [see Eq. (89), page 74]. Thus a very small hole at the center does not affect the deflection of the plate.

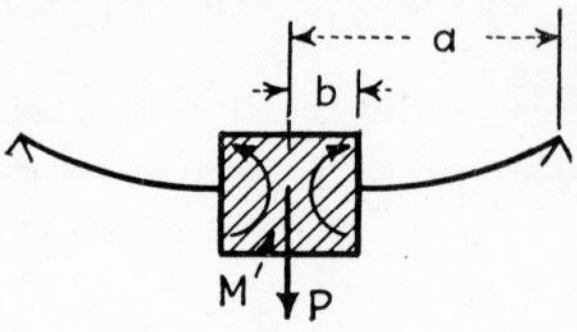

Combining the loadings shown in Figs. 31 and 32, we can obtain the solution for the case of a plate built in along the inner and uniformly loaded along the outer edge (Fig. 33). Since the slope at the built-in edge is zero in this case, using expressions (72) and (j), we obtain the following equation for determining the bending moment M_1 at the built-in edge:

Fig. 33.

$$-\frac{a^2b^2M_1}{D(1-\nu)(a^2-b^2)}\left(\frac{1}{b}+\frac{1-\nu}{1+\nu}\cdot\frac{b}{a^2}\right)=\frac{Pb}{8\pi D}\left[2\log\frac{b}{a}-1\right.$$
$$\left.-\frac{1-\nu}{1+\nu}+\frac{2b^2}{a^2-b^2}\log\frac{b}{a}\cdot\left(1+\frac{a^2}{b^2}\cdot\frac{1+\nu}{1-\nu}\right)\right],$$

from which

$$M_1=\frac{P}{8\pi\left[(1+\nu)\dfrac{a^2}{b^2}+1-\nu\right]}\left[2(1-\nu)\left(\frac{a^2}{b^2}-1\right)\right.$$
$$\left.+4(1+\nu)\frac{a^2}{b^2}\log\frac{a}{b}\right]. \quad (74)$$

Having this expression for the moment M_1, we obtain the deflections of the plate by superposing expression (73) and expression (f) in which the constants of integration are given by expressions (i).

By using the same method of superposition one can obtain also the solution for the case

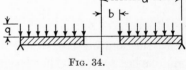

Fig. 34.

shown in Fig. 34 in which the plate is supported along the outer edge and carries a uniformly distributed load. In this case we use the solution obtained in the previous article for the plate without a hole at the center. Considering the section of this plate cut by the cylindrical surface of radius b and perpendicular to the plate, we find that along this section there act a shearing force

$Q = \pi q b^2/2\pi b = qb/2$ and a bending moment of the intensity [see Eq. (69)]

$$M_r = \frac{q}{16}(3 + \nu)(a^2 - b^2).$$

Hence to obtain the stresses and deflections for the case shown in Fig. 34, we have to superpose on stresses and deflections obtained for the plate without a hole the stresses and deflections produced by the bending moments and shearing forces shown in Fig. 35.

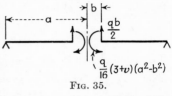

Fig. 35.

These latter quantities are obtained from expressions (72), (73),

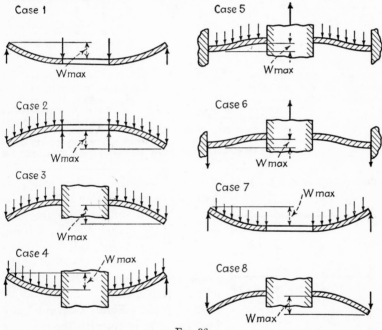

Fig. 36.

(e) and (f) with due attention being given to the sign of applied shears and moments.

Several cases of practical importance are represented in Fig. 36. In all these cases the maximum stress is given by a formula of the type

$$\sigma_{\text{max.}} = k\frac{qa^2}{h^2} \quad \text{or} \quad \sigma_{\text{max.}} = \frac{kP}{h^2}, \tag{75}$$

depending on whether the applied load is uniformly distributed over the surface or concentrated along the edge.   The numerical values of the factor k, calculated[1] for several values of the ratio a/b and for Poisson's ratio $\nu = 0.3$, are given in Table 3.

The maximum deflections in the same cases are given by formulas of the type

$$w_{\max.} = k_1 \frac{qa^4}{Eh^3} \quad \text{or} \quad w_{\max.} = k_1 \frac{Pa^2}{Eh^3}. \tag{76}$$

The coefficients k_1 are also given in Table 3.

TABLE 3.—COEFFICIENTS k AND k_1 IN EQS. (75) AND (76) FOR THE EIGHT CASES SHOWN IN FIG. 36

$a/b =$	1.25		1.5		2		3		4		5	
Case	k	k_1	k	k_1	k	k_1	k	k_1	k	k_1	k	k_1
1	1.10	0.341	1.26	0.519	1.48	0.672	1.88	0.734	2.17	0.724	2.34	0.704
2	0.66	0.202	1.19	0.491	2.04	0.902	3.34	1.220	4.30	1.300	5.10	1.310
3	0.135	0.00231	0.410	0.0183	1.04	0.0938	2.15	0.293	2.99	0.448	3.69	0.564
4	0.122	0.00343	0.336	0.0313	0.74	0.1250	1.21	0.291	1.45	0.417	1.59	0.492
5	0.090	0.00077	0.273	0.0062	0.71	0.0329	1.54	0.110	2.23	0.179	2.80	0.238
6	0.115	0.00129	0.220	0.0064	0.405	0.0237	0.703	0.062	0.933	0.092	1.13	0.114
7	0.592	0.184	0.976	0.414	1.440	0.664	1.880	0.824	2.08	0.830	2.19	0.813
8	0.227	0.00510	0.428	0.0249	0.753	0.0877	1.205	0.209	1.514	0.293	1.745	0.350

When the ratio a/b approaches unity, the values of the coefficients k and k_1 in Eqs. (75) and (76) can be obtained with sufficient accuracy by considering a radial strip as a beam with end conditions and loading as in the actual plate.   The effect of the moments M_t on bending is then entirely neglected.

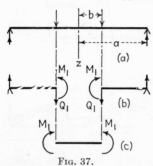

FIG. 37.

18. Circular Plate Concentrically Loaded.—We begin with the case of a simply supported plate in which the load is uniformly distributed along a circle of radius b (Fig. 37a).   Dividing the plate into two parts as shown in Figs. 37b and 37c, it may be seen that the inner portion of the plate is in the condition of pure bending produced by

[1] These calculations were made by A. M. Wahl and G. Lobo, *Trans. Am. Soc. Mech. Eng.*, vol. 52, 1930.

the uniformly distributed moments M_1, while the outer part is bent by the moments M_1 and the shearing forces Q_1. Denoting by P the total load applied, we find that

$$Q_1 = \frac{P}{2\pi b}. \tag{a}$$

The magnitude of the moment M_1 is found from the condition of continuity along the circle $r = b$, from which it follows that both portions of the plate have, at that circle, the same slope. Using Eqs. (72) and (*j*) of the previous article, we find the slope for the inner boundary of the outer portion of the plate equal to

$$\left(\frac{dw}{dr}\right)_{r=b} = \frac{a^2 b^2 M_1}{D(1-\nu)(a^2-b^2)}\left(\frac{1}{b} + \frac{1-\nu}{1+\nu}\frac{b}{a^2}\right)$$
$$+ \frac{Pb}{8\pi D}\left[2\log\frac{b}{a} - 1 - \frac{1-\nu}{1+\nu}\right.$$
$$\left.+ \frac{2b^2}{a^2-b^2}\log\frac{b}{a}\cdot\left(1 + \frac{a^2}{b^2}\cdot\frac{1+\nu}{1-\nu}\right)\right]. \tag{b}$$

The inner portion of the plate is bent to a spherical surface, the curvature of which is given by expression (46). Therefore the corresponding slope at the boundary is

$$\left(\frac{dw}{dr}\right)_{r=b} = -\frac{M_1 b}{D(1+\nu)}. \tag{c}$$

Equating expressions (*b*) and (*c*), we obtain

$$M_1 = \frac{(1-\nu)P(a^2-b^2)}{8\pi a^2} - \frac{(1+\nu)P\log\dfrac{b}{a}}{4\pi}. \tag{d}$$

Substituting this expression for M_1 in Eq. (73), we obtain deflections of the outer part of the plate due to the moments M_1. The deflections due to the forces Q_1 are obtained from Eq. (*f*) of the previous article. Adding together both these deflections, we obtain for the outer part of the plate

$$w = \frac{P}{8\pi D}\left[(a^2-r^2)\left(1 + \frac{1}{2}\cdot\frac{1-\nu}{1+\nu}\cdot\frac{a^2-b^2}{a^2}\right) + (b^2+r^2)\log\frac{r}{a}\right]. \tag{77}$$

Substituting $r = b$ in this expression, we obtain the deflection under the load:

$$(w)_{r=b} = \frac{P}{8\pi D}\left[(a^2 - b^2)\left(1 + \frac{1}{2}\cdot\frac{1 - \nu}{1 + \nu}\cdot\frac{a^2 - b^2}{a^2}\right) + 2b^2\log\frac{b}{a}\right].$$

$$(e)$$

To find the deflections of the inner portion of the plate, we add to the deflection (e) the deflections due to the pure bending of that portion of the plate. In this manner we obtain

$$
\begin{aligned}
w &= \frac{P}{8\pi D}\left[(a^2 - b^2)\left(1 + \frac{1}{2}\cdot\frac{1 - \nu}{1 + \nu}\cdot\frac{a^2 - b^2}{a^2}\right) + 2b^2\log\frac{b}{a}\right] \\
&\quad + \frac{b^2 - r^2}{2D(1 + \nu)}\left[\frac{(1 - \nu)P(a^2 - b^2)}{8\pi a^2} - \frac{(1 + \nu)P\log\dfrac{b}{a}}{4\pi}\right] \\
&= \frac{P}{8\pi D}\left[(b^2 + r^2)\log\frac{b}{a} + r^2 - b^2 + (a^2 - r^2)\frac{(3 + \nu)a^2 - (1 - \nu)b^2}{2(1 + \nu)a^2}\right] \\
&= \frac{P}{8\pi D}\left[(b^2 + r^2)\log\frac{b}{a} + (a^2 - b^2)\frac{(3 + \nu)a^2 - (1 - \nu)r^2}{2(1 + \nu)a^2}\right]. \quad (78)
\end{aligned}
$$

If the outer edge of the plate is built in, the deflections of the plate are obtained by superposing on the deflections (77) and (78) the deflections produced by the bending moments M_2 uniformly distributed along the outer edge of the plate (Fig. 38) and of such a magnitude that the slope of the deflection surface at that edge is equal to zero. From expression (77) the slope at the edge of a simply supported plate is

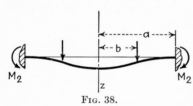

Fig. 38.

$$\left(\frac{dw}{dr}\right)_{r=a} = -\frac{P}{4\pi D}\cdot\frac{1}{1 + \nu}\cdot\frac{a^2 - b^2}{a}. \quad (f)$$

The slope produced by the moments M_2 is

$$\left(\frac{dw}{dr}\right)_{r=a} = \frac{M_2 a}{D(1 + \nu)}. \quad (g)$$

Equating the sum of expressions (f) and (g) to zero, we obtain

$$M_2 = \frac{P}{4\pi}\frac{a^2 - b^2}{a^2}.$$

Deflections produced by this moment are

$$w = \frac{M_2}{D(1 + \nu)} \frac{r^2 - a^2}{2} = \frac{P}{8\pi D(1 + \nu)} \frac{a^2 - b^2}{a^2}(r^2 - a^2). \quad (h)$$

Adding these deflections to deflections (77) and (78), we obtain, for the outer portion of a plate with a built-in edge

$$w = \frac{P}{8\pi D}\left[(a^2 - r^2)\frac{a^2 + b^2}{2a^2} + (b^2 + r^2) \log \frac{r}{a} \right]; \quad (79)$$

and for the inner portion,

$$\begin{aligned} w &= \frac{P}{8\pi D}\left[(b^2 + r^2) \log \frac{b}{a} + r^2 - b^2 + \frac{(a^2 - r^2)(a^2 + b^2)}{2a^2} \right] \\ &= \frac{P}{8\pi D}\left[(b^2 + r^2) \log \frac{b}{a} + \frac{(a^2 + r^2)(a^2 - b^2)}{2a^2} \right]. \quad (80) \end{aligned}$$

Having the deflections for the case of a load uniformly distributed along a concentric circle, any case of bending of a circular plate symmetrically loaded with respect to the center can be solved by using the method of superposition. Let us consider, for example, the case in which the load is uniformly distributed over the inner portion of the plate bounded by a circle of radius c (Fig. 39). Expression (77) is used to obtain the deflection at any point of the unloaded portion of the plate $(a > r > c)$. The deflection produced by an elementary loading distributed over a ring surface of radius b and width db (see Fig. 39) is obtained by substituting $P = 2\pi bq\,db$ in that expression, where q is the intensity of the uniform load. Integrating the expression thus obtained with respect to b, we obtain the deflection

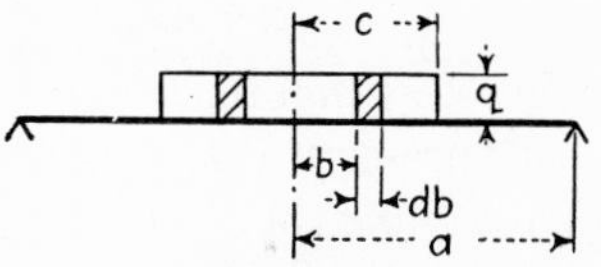

FIG. 39.

$$\begin{aligned} w = \frac{q}{4D}\int_0^c &\left\{ (a^2 - r^2)\frac{3 + \nu}{2(1 + \nu)} + r^2 \log \frac{r}{a} + b^2\left[\log \frac{r}{a} \right.\right. \\ &\left.\left. - \frac{(1 - \nu)(a^2 - r^2)}{2(1 + \nu)a^2} \right]\right\}b\,db = \frac{qc^2}{8D}\left[\frac{3 + \nu}{2(1 + \nu)}(a^2 - r^2) + r^2 \log \frac{r}{a} \right] \\ &\quad + \frac{qc^4}{16D}\left[\log \frac{r}{a} - \frac{(1 - \nu)}{2(1 + \nu)}\frac{(a^2 - r^2)}{a^2} \right]\right\}, \end{aligned}$$

or, denoting the total load $\pi c^2 q$ by P,

$$w = \frac{P}{16\pi D}\left\{\frac{3 + \nu}{1 + \nu}(a^2 - r^2) + 2r^2 \log\frac{r}{a}\right.$$
$$\left. + c^2\left[\log\frac{r}{a} - \frac{1 - \nu}{2(1 + \nu)}\frac{(a^2 - r^2)}{a^2}\right]\right\}. \quad (81)$$

Expression (78) is used to obtain the deflection at the center. Substituting $r = 0$ and $P = 2\pi bq \, db$ in this expression and integrating, we find

$$(w)_{r=0} = \frac{q}{4D}\int_0^c\left[b^2 \log\frac{b}{a} + \frac{a^2 - b^2}{2}\left(\frac{3 + \nu}{1 + \nu}\right)\right]b \, db$$
$$= \frac{P}{16\pi D}\left[\frac{3 + \nu}{1 + \nu}a^2 + c^2 \log\frac{c}{a} - \frac{7 + 3\nu}{4(1 + \nu)}c^2\right], \quad (82)$$

where $P = \pi c^2 q$.

The maximum bending moment is at the center and is found by using expression (d). Substituting $2\pi bq \, db$ for P in this expression and integrating, we find

$$M_{\text{max.}} = q\int_0^c\left(\frac{1 - \nu}{4}\cdot\frac{a^2 - b^2}{a^2} - \frac{1 + \nu}{2}\log\frac{b}{a}\right)b \, db$$
$$= \frac{P}{4\pi}\left[(1 + \nu)\log\frac{a}{c} + 1 - \frac{(1 - \nu)c^2}{4a^2}\right], \quad (83)$$

where, as before, P denotes the total load $\pi c^2 q$.[1]

Expression (81) is used to obtain the bending moments M_r and M_t at any point of the unloaded outer portion of the plate. Substituting this expression in the general formulas (52) and (53), we find

$$M_r = \frac{(1 + \nu)P}{4\pi}\log\frac{a}{r} + \frac{(1 - \nu)Pc^2}{16\pi}\left(\frac{1}{r^2} - \frac{1}{a^2}\right), \quad (84)$$

$$M_t = \frac{P}{4\pi}\left[(1 + \nu)\log\frac{a}{r} + 1 - \nu\right] - \frac{(1 - \nu)Pc^2}{16\pi}\left(\frac{1}{r^2} + \frac{1}{a^2}\right). \quad (85)$$

The maximum values of these moments are obtained at the circle $r = c$, where

$$M_r = \frac{(1 + \nu)P}{4\pi}\log\frac{a}{c} + \frac{(1 - \nu)P(a^2 - c^2)}{16\pi a^2}, \quad (86)$$

$$M_t = \frac{P}{4\pi}\left[(1 + \nu)\log\frac{a}{c} + 1 - \nu\right] - \frac{(1 - \nu)P(a^2 + c^2)}{16\pi a^2}. \quad (87)$$

---

[1] This expression applies only when c is at least several times the thickness h.   The case of a very small c is discussed in Art. 19.

The same method of calculating deflections and moments can be used also for any kind of symmetrical loading of a circular plate.

The deflection at the center of the plate can easily be calculated also for any kind of unsymmetrical loading by using the following consideration:

Owing to the complete symmetry of the plate and of its boundary conditions the deflection produced at its center by an isolated load P depends only on the magnitude of the load and on its radial distance from the center. This deflection remains unchanged if the load P is moved to another position provided the radial distance of the load from the center remains the same. The deflection remains unchanged also if the load P is replaced by several loads the sum of which is equal to P and the radial distances of which are the same as that of the load P. From this it follows that in calculating the deflection of the plate at the center we can replace an isolated load P by a load P uniformly distributed along a circle the radius of which is equal to the radial distance of the isolated load. For the load uniformly distributed along a circle of radius b the deflection at the center of a plate supported at the edges is given by Eq. (78) and is

$$(w)_{r=0} = \frac{P}{8\pi D}\left[\frac{3 + \nu}{2(1 + \nu)}(a^2 - b^2) - b^2 \log \frac{a}{b}\right].$$

This formula gives the deflection at the center of the plate produced by an isolated load P at a distance b from the center of the plate. Having this formula the deflection at the center for any other kind of loading can be obtained by using the method of superposition.[1]

19. Circular Plate Loaded at the Center.—The solution for a concentrated load acting at the center of the plate can be obtained from the discussion of the previous article by assuming that the radius c of the circle within which the load is distributed becomes infinitely small whereas the total load P remains finite. Using this assumption the maximum deflection at the center of a simply supported plate, by Eq. (82), is

$$w_{\text{max.}} = \frac{(3 + \nu)Pa^2}{16\pi(1 + \nu)D}. \tag{88}$$

[1] This method of calculating deflections at the center of the plate was indicated by Saint Venant in his translation of the "Théorie de l'élasticité des corps solides," by Clebsch, p. 363, 1883, Paris.

The deflection at any point of the plate at a distance r from the center, by Eq. (81), is

$$w = \frac{P}{16\pi D}\left[\frac{3 + \nu}{1 + \nu}(a^2 - r^2) + 2r^2 \log \frac{r}{a}\right]. \qquad (89)$$

The bending moment for points with $r > c$ may be found by neglecting the terms in Eqs. (84) and (85) which contain c^2. This gives

$$M_r = \frac{P}{4\pi}(1 + \nu) \log \frac{a}{r}, \qquad (90)$$

$$M_t = \frac{P}{4\pi}\left[(1 + \nu) \log \frac{a}{r} + 1 - \nu\right]. \qquad (91)$$

To obtain formulas for a circular plate with clamped edges we differentiate Eq. (89) and find for the slope at the boundary of a simply supported plate

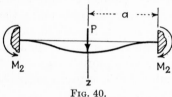

Fig. 40.

$$-\left(\frac{dw}{dr}\right)_{r=a} = \frac{Pa}{4(1 + \nu)\pi D}. \qquad (a)$$

The bending moments M_2 uniformly distributed along the clamped edge (Fig. 40) produce a bending of the plate to a spherical surface the radius of which is given by Eq. (46), and the corresponding slope at the boundary is

$$-\frac{M_2 a}{(1 + \nu)D}. \qquad (b)$$

Using (a) and (b), the condition that the built-in edge does not rotate gives

$$(M_r)_{r=a} = M_2 = -\frac{P}{4\pi}. \qquad (c)$$

Deflections produced by moments M_2 by Eq. (h) of the preceding article are

$$\frac{P(r^2 - a^2)}{8\pi D(1 + \nu)}.$$

Superposing these deflections on the deflections of a simply supported plate in Eq. (89), we obtain the following expression for the deflections of a clamped plate loaded at the center:

$$w = \frac{Pr^2}{8\pi D} \log \frac{r}{a} + \frac{P}{16\pi D}(a^2 - r^2). \qquad (92)$$

Adding Eq. (*c*) to Eqs. (90) and (91) for a simply supported plate, we obtain the following equations for the bending moment at any point not very close to the load:

$$M_r = \frac{P}{4\pi}\left[(1 + \nu) \log \frac{a}{r} - 1\right],$$ (93)

$$M_t = \frac{P}{4\pi}\left[(1 + \nu) \log \frac{a}{r} - \nu\right].$$ (94)

When r approaches zero, expressions (90), (91), (93) and (94) approach infinity and hence are not suitable for calculating the bending moments. Moreover, the assumptions that serve as the basis for the elementary theory of bending of circular plates do not hold near the point of application of a concentrated load. As the radius c of the circle over which P is distributed decreases, the intensity $P/\pi c^2$ of the pressure increases till it can no longer be neglected in comparison with the bending stresses as is done in the elementary theory. Shearing stresses which are also disregarded in the simple theory likewise increase without limit as c approaches zero, since the cylindrical surface $2\pi ch$ over which the total shear force P is distributed approaches zero.

Discarding the assumptions on which the elementary theory is based, we may obtain the stress distribution near the point of application of the load by considering that portion of the plate as a body all three dimensions of which are of the same order of magnitude. To do this imagine the central loaded portion separated from the rest of the plate by a cylindrical surface whose radius b is several times as large as the thickness h of the plate, as shown in Fig. 41. It may be assumed that the elementary theory of bending is accurate enough at a distance b from the point of application of the load P and

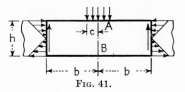

FIG. 41.

that the corresponding stresses may be calculated by means of Eq. (90). The problem of stress distribution near the center of the plate is thus reduced to the problem of a symmetrical stress distribution in a circular cylinder of height h and radius b acted upon by a load P distributed over a small circle of radius c and by reactions along the lateral boundary.[1] The

[1] Several examples of symmetrical stress distributions are discussed in the author's "Theory of Elasticity" (see p. 309). The case shown in Fig. 41 was studied by Dr. A. Nadai (see his book "Elastische Platten," p. 308) and also by Dr. S. Woinowsky-Krieger (see his paper in *Ingenieur-Archiv*, vol. 4, p. 305, 1933). The results given here are from the latter paper.

solution of this problem shows that the maximum compressive stress at the center A of the upper face of the plate can be expressed by the following approximate formula:[1]

$$\sigma_r = \sigma_t = \sigma_1 - \frac{P}{\pi c^2}\left[\frac{1+2\nu}{2} - (1+\nu)\alpha\right], \qquad (95)$$

in which σ_1 is the value of the compressive bending stress[2] obtained from the approximate theory, say, by using Eq. (83) for the case of a simply supported plate, and α is a numerical factor depending on $2c/h$, the ratio of the

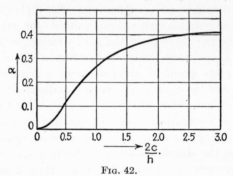

FIG. 42.

diameter of the loaded area to the thickness of the plate. Several values of this factor are given in the table below. Its variation with the ratio $2c/h$ is shown also in Fig. 42. When c approaches zero, the stress calculated by Eq. (95) approaches infinity.

TABLE 4.—VALUES OF FACTOR α IN EQ. (95)

$2c/h =$	0.10	0.25	0.50	0.75	1.00	1.50	2.00	2.50
$\alpha =$	0.0106	0.0466	0.1234	0.200	0.263	0.348	0.386	0.398

The maximum tensile stress occurs at B, the center of the lower surface of the plate (Fig. 41). When c is very small, *i.e.*, for a strong load concentration, this tensile stress is practically independent of the ratio $2c/h$ and for a simply supported plate is given by the following approximate formula:[3]

$$\sigma_{\text{max.}} = \frac{P}{h^2}\left[(1+\nu)\left(0.485\log\frac{a}{h} + 0.52\right) + 0.48\right]. \qquad (96)$$

To obtain the compressive stresses σ_r and σ_t at the center of the upper surface of a clamped plate, we must decrease the value of the compressive

[1] When c is very small, the compressive stress $P/\pi c^2$ becomes larger than the $(\sigma_{\text{max.}})$ given by Eq. (95) (see Fig. 43).

[2] This quantity should be taken with negative sign in Eq. (95).

[3] See paper by Woinowsky-Krieger, *loc. cit.*, p. 75. a is outer radius.

stress σ_1 in Eq. (95) by an amount equal to

$$\frac{P}{4\pi} \cdot \frac{6}{h^2} = \frac{3}{2} \frac{P}{\pi h^2} \tag{d}$$

on account of the action of the moments $M_2 = -P/4\pi$. The maximum tensile stress at the center of the lower surface of a clamped plate for a strong concentration of the load ($c = 0$) is found by subtracting Eq. (d) from Eq. (96). It is

$$\sigma_{\text{max.}} = \frac{P}{h^2}(1 + \nu)\left(0.485 \log \frac{a}{h} + 0.52\right). \tag{97}$$

The stress distribution across a thick circular plate ($h/a = 0.4$) with built-in edges is shown in Fig. 43. These stresses are calculated for $c = 0.1a$ and $\nu = 0.3$. For this case the maximum compressive stress σ_z normal to

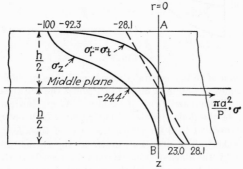

Fig. 43.

the surface of the plate is larger than the maximum compressive stress in bending given by Eq. (95). The maximum tensile stress is calculated by means of Eq. (97). It is smaller than the tensile stress given by the elementary theory of bending. The value of the latter across the thickness of the plate is shown in the figure by the dotted line. It was calculated from the equation for bending moment

$$M_{\text{max.}} = \frac{P}{4\pi}\left[(1 + \nu) \log \frac{a}{c} - \frac{(1 - \nu)c^2}{4a^2}\right] \tag{98}$$

obtained by adding the moment $M_2 = -P/4\pi$ to Eq. (83).

In determining the safe dimensions of a circular plate loaded at the center, we can usually limit our investigations to the calculation of the maximum tensile bending stresses at the bottom of the plate by means of Eqs. (96) and (97). Although the compressive stresses at the top of the plate may be many times as large as the tensile stresses at the bottom in the case of a strong concentration of the load, they do not represent a direct danger because of their highly localized character. The local yielding in the case of a ductile material will not affect the deformation of the plate in general if the tensile stresses at the bottom of the plate remain within safe limits. The compressive strength of a brittle material is usually many times greater than its tensile strength, so that a plate of such a material will also be safe if the tensile stress at the bottom is within the limit of safety.

The local disturbance produced by a concentrated load in the vicinity of its point of application must also be considered if we want an exact description of the deflection of the plate. This disturbance is mainly confined to a

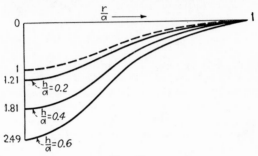

Fig. 44.

cylindrical region of radius several times h, and thus its effect on the total deflection becomes of practical importance when the thickness of the plate is not very small compared with its radius. As an illustration there are shown in Fig. 44 the deflections of circular plates with built-in edges and a central concentrated load for which the ratio of thickness to radius h/a is 0.2, 0.4 and 0.6.[1] The deflection given by the elementary theory [Eq. (94)] is shown by the dotted line. It may be seen that the discrepancy between the elementary theory and the exact solution diminishes rapidly as the ratio h/a diminishes. In the next article we shall show that this discrepancy is due principally to the effect of shearing forces which are entirely neglected in the elementary theory.

20. Corrections to the Elementary Theory of Symmetrical Bending of Circular Plates.

—The relations (37) and (38) between bending moments and curvatures, which were derived for the case of pure bending, have been used as the basis for the solution of the various problems of symmetrical bending of circular plates which have been discussed. The effect that shearing stresses and normal pressures on planes parallel to the surface of the plate have on bending has not been taken into account. Hence only the solution for a plate bent to a spherical surface and the solution for the annular plate loaded with moments uniformly distributed along the inner and outer boundaries (Fig. 31) are rigor-

[1] The curves in Fig. 44 are the results of the exact solution of Woinowsky-Krieger, *loc. cit.*, p. 75.

ous. In all other cases discussed, the formulas obtained are approximate, and their accuracy depends on the ratio of the thickness of the plate to its outer radius. More accurate formulas may be obtained by considering in an approximate manner[1] the effect of shearing stresses and lateral pressures on deflections.

Let us consider first a circular plate without a hole supported along its edge and uniformly loaded. The shearing force Q per unit length of arc along a circle of radius r is

$$Q = \tfrac{1}{2}qr.$$

From the exact solution for plates whose thickness is not assumed to be small,[2] it is known that the shearing stresses τ_{rz} vary across the thickness of the plate according to the parabolic law in the same way as in beams of narrow rectangular cross section. Hence the maximum shearing stress is at the middle surface of the plate, and its magnitude is

$$(\tau_{rz})_{\text{max.}} = -\frac{3}{2}\frac{qr}{2h}. \tag{a}$$

The corresponding shearing strain is

$$\frac{dw_1}{dr} = -\frac{3}{2}\frac{qr}{2Gh}, \tag{b}$$

where w_1 is the additional deflection of the middle surface of the plate due to the shearing stress. By integration the deflections produced by the shearing stresses are found to be

$$w_1 = \frac{3}{2}\cdot\frac{q}{4Gh}(a^2 - r^2). \tag{c}$$

At the center of the plate:

$$(w_1)_{\text{max.}} = \frac{3}{2}\cdot\frac{qa^2}{4Gh}. \tag{d}$$

[1] A rigorous theory of plates was originated by Saint Venant in his translation of Clebsch book, "Théorie de l'élasticité des corps solides," p. 337. A valuable criticism of this work is given in "History of the Theory of Elasticity," by J. Todhunter and K. Pearson, vol. 2, part 1, p. 217. Further development of the theory is due to J. H. Michell, *Proc. London Math. Soc.*, vol. 31, p. 100, 1900, and to A. E. H. Love, "Mathematical Theory of Elasticity," 4th ed., p. 465. A list of references to the new literature on this subject is given in the paper by Woinowsky-Krieger, *Ingenieur Archiv*, vol. 4, p. 203, 1933. Some examples of rigorous theory are given in Art. 25, see p. 105.

[2] See author's "Theory of Elasticity," p. 315.

The lateral pressure acting on the plate produces a negative curvature, convex upward, similar to that which occurs in a uniformly loaded beam.[1]   The pressure q per unit area produces a radial elongation of $\nu q/E$ at the upper surface of the plate.   At the middle surface of the plate this elongation is $\nu q/2E$, and at the bottom of the plate it is zero.   Assuming a straight-line relation to hold, an approximate value of the radius of curvature R can be found from the equation

$$\frac{\nu q}{2E} = \frac{h}{2R},$$

from which

$$\frac{1}{2R} = \frac{\nu q}{2hE},$$

and the negative deflection is

$$w_2 = -\frac{1}{2R}(a^2 - r^2) = -\frac{\nu q}{2hE}(a^2 - r^2). \qquad (e)$$

Adding Eqs. (c) and (e) to Eq. (67), a more exact expression for deflection is found to be

$$w = \frac{q}{64D}(a^2 - r^2)\left(\frac{5+\nu}{1+\nu}a^2 - r^2\right) + \frac{qh^2}{8D} \cdot \frac{3+\nu}{6(1-\nu^2)}(a^2 - r^2).$$

At the center of the plate this becomes

$$w_{\text{max.}} = \frac{qa^4}{64D}\left(\frac{5+\nu}{1+\nu} + \frac{4}{3} \cdot \frac{3+\nu}{1-\nu^2} \cdot \frac{h^2}{a^2}\right). \qquad (f)$$

The second term in Eq. (f) represents the correction for shearing stresses and lateral pressure.   This correction is seen to be small when the ratio of the thickness of the plate to its radius is small.   The value of this correction given by the exact solution is[2]

$$\frac{qa^4}{64D} \cdot \frac{2}{5} \cdot \frac{8+\nu+\nu^2}{1-\nu^2} \cdot \frac{h^2}{a^2} \qquad (g)$$

For $\nu = 0.3$ the exact value is about 20 per cent less than that given by Eq. (f).

In a uniformly loaded circular plate with clamped edges the negative deflection w_2 due to pressure cannot occur, and hence

---

[1] See *ibid.*, p. 42.

[2] See A. E. H. Love, "Mathematical Theory of Elasticity," 4th ed., p. 481.

only the deflection w_1 due to shear need be considered. Adding this deflection to Eq. (62), we obtain as a more accurate value of the deflection

$$w = \frac{q}{64D}\left[(a^2 - r^2)^2 + \frac{4h^2}{1 - \nu}(a^2 - r^2)\right].\qquad (h)$$

It is interesting to note that this coincides with the exact solution.[1]

Consider next the deflections produced by shearing stresses in the annular plate loaded with shearing forces uniformly distributed along the inner edge of the plate as shown in Fig. 32. The maximum shearing stress at a distance r from the center is

$$(\tau_{rz})_{\text{max.}} = -\frac{3}{2}\frac{P}{2\pi rh},$$

where P denotes the total shear load. The corresponding shear strain is

$$\frac{dw_1}{dr} = -\frac{3}{2}\frac{P}{2\pi rhG}.\qquad (i)$$

Integrating, we obtain for the deflection produced by shear

$$w_1 = \frac{3}{4}\frac{P}{\pi hG}\log\frac{a}{r} = \frac{Ph^2}{8\pi(1 - \nu)D}\log\frac{a}{r}.\qquad (j)$$

This deflection must be added to Eq. (k) on page 65 to get a more accurate value of the deflection of the plate shown in Fig. 32. When the radius b of the hole is very small, the expression for the total deflection becomes

$$w = \frac{P}{8\pi D}\left[\frac{3 + \nu}{2(1 + \nu)}(a^2 - r^2) + r^2\log\frac{r}{a}\right] + \frac{Ph^2}{8\pi(1 - \nu)D}\log\frac{a}{r}.\qquad (k)$$

The deflection at the edge of the hole is

$$w_{\text{max.}} = \frac{Pa^2}{8\pi D}\left(\frac{3 + \nu}{2(1 + \nu)} + \frac{1}{1 - \nu}\cdot\frac{h^2}{a^2}\log\frac{a}{b}\right).\qquad (l)$$

The second term in this expression represents the correction due to shear. It increases indefinitely as b approaches zero, as a consequence of our assumption that the load P is always finite. Thus when b approaches zero, the corresponding shearing stress and shearing strain become infinitely large.

[1] See *ibid.*, p. 485.

The term in Eq. (*l*) which represents the correction for shear cannot be applied to a plate without a hole. The correction for a plate without a hole may be expected to be somewhat smaller because of the wedging effect produced by the concentrated load *P* applied at the center of the upper

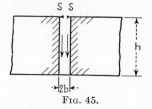

FIG. 45.

surface of the plate. Imagine that the central portion of the plate is removed by means of a cylindrical section of small radius *b* and that its action on the remainder of the plate is replaced by vertical shearing forces equivalent to *P* and by radial forces *S* representing the wedging effect of the load and distributed along the upper edge of the hole as shown in Fig. 45. It is evident that the latter forces produce stretching of the middle surface of the plate together with some deflection of the plate in the upward direction. This indicates that we must decrease the correction term in expression (*k*) to make it apply to a plate without a hole. To get an idea of the magnitude of the radial forces *S*, let us consider the plate under the two loading conditions shown in Fig. 46.

FIG. 46.

In the first case the plate is compressed by two equal and opposite forces *P* acting along the axis of symmetry *z*. In the second case the plate is subjected to uniform compression in its plane by a pressure *p* uniformly distributed over the cylindrical surface bounding the plate. As a result of lateral expansion these pressures produce an increase of the thickness of the plate by the amount

$$\Delta h = \frac{2\nu p}{E} h.$$

We can now obtain from this expression the increase Δr in the radius *r* of the plate due to the action of the forces *P* (Fig. 46*a*) by applying the reciprocal theorem to the two conditions of loading shown in Fig. 46. This gives

$$P \, \Delta h = 2\pi r h p \, \Delta r,$$

from which

$$\Delta r = \frac{P \, \Delta h}{2\pi r h p} = \frac{2\nu}{E} \frac{P}{2\pi r}. \qquad (m)$$

Let us compare this radial expansion with the radial expansion produced in a thick-walled cylinder by an internal pressure p_i. If the inner radius *b* of the cylinder is very small compared with the outer radius *r*, the increase in the outer radius by Lame's formula[1] is

[1] See author's "Strength of Materials," vol. 2, p. 533.

$$\Delta r = \frac{1 + \nu}{E} \cdot \frac{p_i b^2}{r}. \qquad (n)$$

Comparing expressions (m) and (n), we conclude that the radial expansion which the forces P in Fig. 46a produce in the plate has the same magnitude as the radial expansion produced in a plate with a small cylindrical hole at the center (Fig. 45) by internal pressure p_i whose magnitude is given by the equation

$$\frac{2\nu P}{E 2\pi r} = \frac{1 + \nu}{E} \cdot \frac{p_i b^2}{r}.$$

From this we obtain

$$p_i = \frac{\nu P}{(1 + \nu)\pi b^2}. \qquad (o)$$

Returning to the case of one concentrated force at the center of the upper surface of the plate, the action of which is illustrated by Fig. 45, we conclude that the force S per unit length of the circumference of the hole must be equal to the pressure $p_i h / 2$. Using the value of p_i from Eq. (o), we obtain

$$S = \frac{\nu P h}{2(1 + \nu)\pi b^2}. \qquad \cdot$$

These forces applied in the upper plane of the plate produce upward deflections w_1, the magnitudes of which are found by substituting

$$M_1 = \frac{Sh}{2} = \frac{\nu P h^2}{4(1 + \nu)\pi b^2}$$

in Eq. (73) and neglecting b^2 in comparison with a^2. In this manner we obtain

$$w_1 = -\frac{\nu P h^2}{8\pi(1 + \nu)^2 D} \cdot \frac{a^2 - r^2}{a^2} - \frac{\nu P h^2}{4(1 - \nu^2)\pi D} \log \frac{a}{r}. \qquad (p)$$

Adding this to expression (k), we obtain the following more accurate formula for the deflection of a plate without a hole and carrying a load P concentrated at the center of the upper surface of the plate:

$$w = \frac{P}{8\pi D}\left[\frac{3 + \nu}{2(1 + \nu)}(a^2 - r^2) + r^2 \log \frac{r}{a} \right] + \frac{P h^2}{8\pi(1 + \nu) D} \log \frac{a}{r}$$
$$- \frac{\nu P h^2}{8\pi(1 + \nu)^2 D} \cdot \frac{a^2 - r^2}{a^2} \qquad (q)$$

This equation can be used to calculate the deflection of all points of the plate that are not very close to the point of application of the load. When r is of the same order of magnitude as the thickness of the plate, Eq. (q) is no longer applicable; and to obtain a satisfactory solution the central portion of the plate must be considered as was explained in the preceding article. We can get an approximate value of the deflection of this central portion considered as a plate of small radius b by adding the deflection due to local disturbance in stress distribution near the point of application of the load to the deflection given by the elementary theory.[1]   The deflection due to local disturbance near the center is affected very little by the conditions at the edge of the plate and hence can be evaluated approximately by means of the curves in Fig. 44.   The dotted-line curve in this figure is obtained by using Eq. (92).   The additional deflections due to local stress disturbance are equal to the differences between the ordinates of the full lines and those of the dotted line.

As an example, consider a plate the radius of the inner portion of which is $b = 5h$.   The deflection of the inner portion calculated from Eq. (92) and taken as unity in Fig. 44 is

$$\delta_1 = \frac{Pb^2}{16\pi D} = \frac{P}{16\pi D}(5h)^2.$$

Using the curve $h/a = 0.2$ in Fig. 44, the additional deflection due to local stress disturbance is

$$\delta_2 = 0.21\delta_1 = 0.21\frac{P}{16\pi D}(5h)^2. \tag{r}$$

If we consider a plate for which $b = 2.5h$ and use the curve for $h/a = 0.4$ in Fig. 44, we obtain

$$\delta_2 = 0.81\frac{P}{16\pi D}(2.5h)^2, \tag{s}$$

which differs only slightly from that given in expression (r) for $b = 5h$.   It will be unsatisfactory to take b smaller than $2.5h$, since for smaller radii the edge condition of the thick plate becomes of importance and the curves in Fig. 44, calculated for a built-in edge, may not be accurate enough for our case.

Finally, to obtain the deflection of the plate under the load we proceed as follows: We calculate the deflection at a radius $r = b = 2.5h$ by using Eq. (q).   To this deflection we add the deflection of the central portion of the plate which consists of two parts: the first part, equal to

$$\frac{Pb^2}{8\pi D}\left(\frac{3 + \nu}{2(1 + \nu)} + \log\frac{a}{b}\right),$$

is calculated by using the first term of expression (q); and the second part is given by expression (s).

---

[1] In the case under consideration this deflection can be calculated by using the first term in expression (q) and substituting b for a.

CHAPTER IV

SMALL DEFLECTIONS OF LATERALLY LOADED PLATES

21. The Differential Equation of the Deflection Surface.—We assume that the load acting on a plate is normal to its surface and that deflections are small in comparison with the thickness of the plate (see Art. 13). At the boundary we assume that the edges of the plate are free to move in the plane of the plate; thus the reactive forces at the edges are normal to the plate. With these assumptions we can neglect any strain in the middle plane of the plate during bending. Taking, as before (see Art.

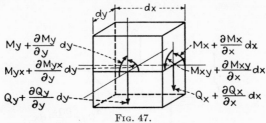

FIG. 47.

10), the coordinate axes x and y in the middle plane of the plate and the z-axis perpendicular to that plane, let us consider an element cut out of the plate by two pairs of planes parallel to the xz- and yz-planes as shown in Fig. 47. In addition to the bending moments M_x and M_y and twisting moments M_{xy} which we had when considering the pure bending of a plate (see Art. 10), there are vertical shearing forces[1] acting on the sides of the element the magnitudes of which per unit length parallel to the y- and x-axes we denote by Q_x and Q_y respectively, so that

$$Q_x = \int_{-\frac{h}{2}}^{\frac{h}{2}} \tau_{xz}\, dz, \qquad Q_y = \int_{-\frac{h}{2}}^{\frac{h}{2}} \tau_{yz}\, dz. \qquad (a)$$

Since the moments and the shearing forces are functions of the coordinates x and y, we must, in discussing the conditions of

---

[1] There will be no horizontal shearing forces and no forces normal to the sides of the element, since the strain of the middle plane of the plate is assumed negligible.

equilibrium of the element, take into consideration the small changes of these quantities when the coordinates x and y change by the small quantities dx and dy. The middle plane of the element is represented in Figs. 48a and 48b, and the directions in which the moments and forces are taken as positive are indicated.

We must also consider the load distributed over the upper surface of the plate. The intensity of this load we denote by q, so that the load acting on the element[1] is $q \, dx \, dy$.

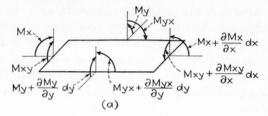

(a)

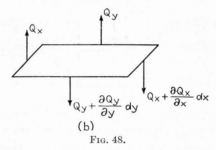

(b)

Fig. 48.

Projecting all the forces acting on the element on the z-axis we obtain the following equation of equilibrium:

$$\frac{\partial Q_x}{\partial x} dx \, dy + \frac{\partial Q_y}{\partial y} dy \, dx + q \, dx \, dy = 0,$$

from which

$$\frac{\partial Q_x}{\partial x} + \frac{\partial Q_y}{\partial y} + q = 0. \tag{b}$$

Taking moments of all the forces acting on the element with respect to the x-axis, we obtain the equation of equilibrium

$$\frac{\partial M_{xy}}{\partial x} dx \, dy - \frac{\partial M_y}{\partial y} dy \, dx + Q_y \, dx \, dy = 0. \tag{c}$$

[1] The weight of the plate itself may be considered as included in the load q.

The moment of the load q and the moment due to change in the force Q_y are neglected in this equation, since they are small quantities of a higher order than those which we retain. After simplification, Eq. (c) becomes

$$\frac{\partial M_{xy}}{\partial x} - \frac{\partial M_y}{\partial y} + Q_y = 0. \qquad (d)$$

In the same manner, by taking moments with respect to the y-axis, we obtain

$$\frac{\partial M_{yx}}{\partial y} + \frac{\partial M_x}{\partial x} - Q_x = 0. \qquad (e)$$

Since there are no forces in the x- and y-directions and no moments with respect to the z-axis, the three Eqs. (b), (d) and (e) completely define the equilibrium of the element. Let us eliminate the shearing forces Q_x and Q_y from these equations by determining them from Eqs. (d) and (e) and substituting into Eq. (b). In this manner we obtain

$$\frac{\partial^2 M_x}{\partial x^2} + \frac{\partial^2 M_{yx}}{\partial x\,\partial y} + \frac{\partial^2 M_y}{\partial y^2} - \frac{\partial^2 M_{xy}}{\partial x\,\partial y} = -q. \qquad (f)$$

Observing that $M_{yx} = -M_{xy}$, by virtue of $\tau_{xy} = \tau_{yx}$, we finally represent the equation of equilibrium (f) in the following form:

$$\frac{\partial^2 M_x}{\partial x^2} + \frac{\partial^2 M_y}{\partial y^2} - 2\frac{\partial^2 M_{xy}}{\partial x\,\partial y} = -q. \qquad (g)$$

To represent this equation in terms of the deflections w of the plate, we make the assumption here that expressions (41) and (43), developed for the case of pure bending, can be used also in the case of laterally loaded plates. This assumption is equivalent to neglecting the effect on bending of the shearing forces Q_x and Q_y and the compressive stress σ_z produced by the load q. We have already used such an assumption in the previous chapter and have seen that the errors in deflections obtained in this way are small provided the thickness of the plate is small in comparison with the dimensions of the plate in its plane. A further discussion of the same subject will be given in Art. 25 in which several examples of exact solutions of bending problems of plates will be discussed.

Using x- and y-directions instead of n and t, which we had in Eqs. (41) and (43), we obtain

$$M_x = -D\left(\frac{\partial^2 w}{\partial x^2} + \nu\frac{\partial^2 w}{\partial y^2}\right), \qquad M_y = -D\left(\frac{\partial^2 w}{\partial y^2} + \nu\frac{\partial^2 w}{\partial x^2}\right), \quad (99)$$

$$M_{xy} = -M_{yx} = D(1-\nu)\frac{\partial^2 w}{\partial x\,\partial y}. \tag{100}$$

Substituting these expressions in Eq. (g), we obtain

$$\frac{\partial^4 w}{\partial x^4} + 2\frac{\partial^4 w}{\partial x^2\,\partial y^2} + \frac{\partial^4 w}{\partial y^4} = \frac{q}{D}.^1 \tag{101}$$

It is seen that the problem of bending of plates by a lateral load q reduces to the integration of Eq. (101). If, for a particular case, a solution of this equation is found that satisfies the conditions at the boundary of the plate, the bending and twisting moments can be calculated from Eqs. (99) and (100). The corresponding normal and shearing stresses are found from Eqs. (44) and (45). Equations (d) and (e) are used to determine shearing forces Q_x and Q_y from which

$$Q_x = \frac{\partial M_{yx}}{\partial y} + \frac{\partial M_x}{\partial x} = -D\frac{\partial}{\partial x}\left(\frac{\partial^2 w}{\partial x^2} + \frac{\partial^2 w}{\partial y^2}\right). \tag{102}$$

$$Q_y = \frac{\partial M_y}{\partial y} - \frac{\partial M_{xy}}{\partial x} = -D\frac{\partial}{\partial y}\left(\frac{\partial^2 w}{\partial x^2} + \frac{\partial^2 w}{\partial y^2}\right). \tag{103}$$

The shearing stresses τ_{xz} and τ_{yz} can now be determined by assuming that they are distributed across the thickness of the plate according to the parabolic law.² Then

$$(\tau_{xz})_{\text{max.}} = \frac{3}{2}\frac{Q_x}{h}, \qquad (\tau_{yz})_{\text{max.}} = \frac{3}{2}\frac{Q_y}{h}.$$

It is seen that the stresses in a plate can be calculated provided the deflection surface for a given load distribution and for given boundary conditions is determined by integration of Eq. (101).

---

[1] This equation was obtained by Lagrange in 1811 when he was examining the memoir presented to the French Academy of Science by Sophie Germain. The history of the development of this equation is given in Todhunter and Pearson, "History of the Theory of Elasticity," vol. 1, pp. 147, 247, 348, and vol. 2, part 1, p. 263. See also the note by Saint Venant to Art. 73 of the French translation of "Théorie de l'élasticité des corps solides," by Clebsch, Paris, 1883.

[2] It will be shown in Art. 25 that in certain cases this assumption is in agreement with the exact theory of bending of plates.

22. Boundary Conditions.—We begin the discussion of boundary conditions with the case of a rectangular plate and assume that the x- and y-axes are taken parallel to the sides of the plate.

Built-in Edge.—If the edge of a plate is built in, the deflection along this edge is zero, and the tangent plane to the deflected middle surface along this edge coincides with the initial position of the middle plane of the plate. Assuming that the x-axis coincides with the built-in edge, the boundary conditions are

$$(w)_{y=0} = 0, \qquad \left(\frac{\partial w}{\partial y}\right)_{y=0} = 0. \qquad (104)$$

Simply Supported Edge.—If the edge $y = 0$ of the plate is simply supported, the deflection w along this edge must be zero. At the same time this edge can rotate freely with respect to the x-axis; *i.e.*, there are no bending moments M_y along this edge. This kind of support is represented in Fig. 49. The analytical expressions of the boundary conditions in this case are

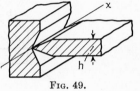

Fig. 49.

$$(w)_{y=0} = 0, \qquad \left(\frac{\partial^2 w}{\partial y^2} + \nu \frac{\partial^2 w}{\partial x^2}\right)_{y=0} = 0. \qquad (105)$$

Free Edge.—If an edge of a plate, say the edge $x = a$ (Fig. 50), is entirely free, it is natural to assume that along this edge there are no bending and twisting moments and also no vertical shearing forces, *i.e.*, that

$$(M_x)_{x=a} = 0, \qquad (M_{xy})_{x=a} = 0, \qquad (Q_x)_{x=a} = 0.$$

The boundary conditions were expressed by Poisson[1] in this form. But later on, Kirchhoff[2] proved that three boundary conditions are too many and that two conditions are sufficient for the complete determination of deflections w satisfying Eq. (101). He showed also that the two requirements of Poisson dealing with the twisting moment M_{xy} and with the shearing force Q_x must be replaced by one boundary condition. The

[1] See discussion of this subject in J. Todhunter and K. Pearson, "History of the Theory of Elasticity," vol. 1, p. 250, and in Saint Venant's translation of "Théorie de l'élasticité des corps solides," by Clebsch, final note to Art. 73, p. 689.

[2] See *J. Crelle*, vol. 40, p. 51, 1850.

physical significance of this reduction in the number of boundary conditions has been explained by Thomson and Tait.[1] These authors point out that the bending of a plate will not be changed if the horizontal forces giving the twisting couple $M_{xy}\,dy$ acting on an element of the length dy of the edge $x = a$ are replaced by two vertical forces of the magnitude M_{xy}, dy apart, as shown in Fig. 50. Such a replacement does not change the magnitude of twisting moments and produces only local changes in the stress distribution at the edge of the plate, leaving the stress condition of the rest of the plate unchanged.   We have already discussed a particular case of such a transformation of the boundary force

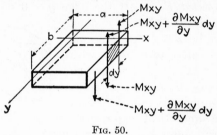

Fig. 50.

system in considering a pure bending of a plate to an anticlastic surface (page 47).   Proceeding with the foregoing replacement of twisting couples along the edge of the plate and considering two adjacent elements of the edge (Fig. 50), we find that the distribution of twisting moments M_{xy} is statically equivalent to a distribution of shearing forces of the intensity

$$Q'_x = -\left(\frac{\partial M_{xy}}{\partial y}\right)_{x=a}.$$

Hence the joint requirement regarding twisting moment M_{xy} and shearing force Q_x along the free edge $x = a$ becomes

$$V_x = \left(Q_x - \frac{\partial M_{xy}}{\partial y}\right)_{x=a} = 0. \qquad (a)$$

Substituting for Q_x and M_{xy} their expressions (102) and (100), we finally obtain for a free edge $x = a$;

$$\left[\frac{\partial^3 w}{\partial x^3} + (2 - \nu)\frac{\partial^3 w}{\partial x\,\partial y^2}\right]_{x=a} = 0. \qquad (106)$$

[1] See "Natural Philosophy," vol. 1, part 2, p. 188, 1883.   Independently the same question was explained by Boussinesq, *J. Math.*, Ser. 2, vol. 16, 1871, pp. 125–274; Ser. 3, vol. 5, pp. 329–344, Paris, 1879.

The condition that bending moments along the free edge are zero requires

$$\left(\frac{\partial^2 w}{\partial x^2} + \nu\frac{\partial^2 w}{\partial y^2}\right)_{x=a} = 0. \tag{107}$$

Equations (106) and (107) represent the two necessary boundary conditions along the free edge $x = a$ of the plate.

Transforming the twisting couples as explained in the foregoing discussion and as shown in Fig. 50, we obtain not only shearing forces Q'_x distributed along the edge $x = a$ but also two concentrated forces at the ends of that edge, as indicated in Fig.

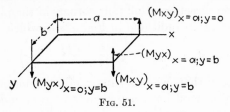

Fig. 51.

51. The magnitudes of these forces are equal to the magnitudes of the twisting couple[1] M_{xy} at the corresponding corners of the plate. Making the analogous transformation of twisting couples M_{yx} along the edge $y = b$, we shall find that in this case again,

in addition to the distributed shearing forces Q'_y, there will be concentrated forces M_{yx} at the corners. This indicates that a rectangular plate supported in some way along the edges and loaded laterally will usually produce not only reactions distributed along the boundary but also concentrated reactions at the corners.

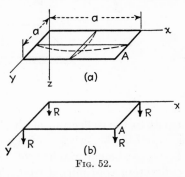

Fig. 52.

Regarding the directions of these concentrated reactions, a conclusion can be drawn if the general shape of the deflection surface is known. Take, for example, a uniformly loaded square plate simply supported along the edges. The general shape of the deflection surface is indicated in Fig. 52a by dotted lines

---

[1] The couple M_{xy} is a moment per unit length and has the dimension of a force.

representing the section of the middle surface of the plate by planes parallel to the xz- and yz-coordinate planes. Considering these lines, it may be seen that near the corner A the derivative $\partial w/\partial x$, representing the slope of the deflection surface in the x-direction, is negative and decreases numerically with increasing y. Hence $\partial^2 w/\partial x\, \partial y$ is positive at the corner A. From Eq. (100) we conclude that M_{xy} is positive and M_{yx} is negative at that corner. From this and from the directions of M_{xy} and M_{yx} in Fig. 48a it follows that both concentrated forces, indicated at the corner A in Fig. 51, have a downward direction. From symmetry we conclude also that the forces have the same magnitude and direction at all four corners of the plate. Hence the conditions are as indicated in Fig. 52b in which

$$R = 2(M_{xy})_{x=a,y=a} = 2D(1 - \nu)\left(\frac{\partial^2 w}{\partial x\, \partial y}\right)_{x=a,y=a}.$$

It can be seen that, when a square plate is uniformly loaded, the corners in general have a tendency to rise, and this is prevented by the concentrated reactions at the corners as indicated in the figure.

Elastically Supported and Elastically Built-in Edge.—If the edge $x = a$ of a rectangular plate is rigidly joined to a supporting

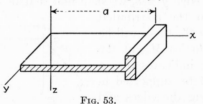

Fig. 53.

beam (Fig. 53), the deflection along this edge is not zero and is equal to the deflection of the beam. Also rotation of the edge is equal to the twisting of the beam. Let B be the flexural and C the torsional rigidity of the beam. The pressure in the z-direction transmitted from the plate to the supporting beam, from Eq. (a), is

$$-V_x = -\left(Q_x - \frac{\partial M_{xy}}{\partial y}\right)_{x=a} = D\frac{\partial}{\partial x}\left[\frac{\partial^2 w}{\partial x^2} + (2 - \nu)\frac{\partial^2 w}{\partial y^2}\right]_{x=a},$$

and the differential equation of the deflection curve of the beam is

$$B\left(\frac{\partial^4 w}{\partial y^4}\right)_{x=a} = D\frac{\partial}{\partial x}\left[\frac{\partial^2 w}{\partial x^2} + (2 - \nu)\frac{\partial^2 w}{\partial y^2}\right]_{x=a}. \qquad (108)$$

This equation represents one of the two boundary conditions of the plate along the edge $x = a$.

To obtain the second condition, the twisting of the beam should be considered. The angle of rotation[1] of any cross section of the beam is $-(\partial w/\partial x)_{x=a}$, and the rate of change of this angle along the edg is

$$-\left(\frac{\partial^2 w}{\partial x\,\partial y}\right)_{x=a}.$$

Hence the twisting moment in the beam is $-C(\partial^2 w/\partial x\partial y)_{x=a}$. This moment varies along the edge, since the plate, rigidly connected with the beam, transmits continuously distributed twisting moments to the beam. The magnitude of these applied moments per unit length is equal and opposite to the bending moments M_x in the plate. Hence, from the consideration of rotational equilibrium of an element of the beam, we obtain

$$-C\frac{\partial}{\partial y}\left(\frac{\partial^2 w}{\partial x\,\partial y}\right)_{x=a} = -(M_x)_{x=a},$$

or, substituting for M_x its expression (99),

$$-C\frac{\partial}{\partial y}\left(\frac{\partial^2 w}{\partial x\,\partial y}\right)_{x=a} = D\left(\frac{\partial^2 w}{\partial x^2} + \nu\frac{\partial^2 w}{\partial y^2}\right)_{x=a}. \tag{109}$$

This is the second boundary condition at the edge $x = a$ of the plate.

In the case of a plate with a curvilinear boundary (Fig. 54), we take at a point A of the edge the coordinate axes in the direction of the tangent t and the normal n as shown in the figure. The bending and the twisting moments at that point are

$$M_n = \int_{-\frac{h}{2}}^{\frac{h}{2}} z\sigma_n\, dz, \qquad M_{nt} = -\int_{-\frac{h}{2}}^{\frac{h}{2}} z\tau_{nt}\, dz. \tag{b}$$

Using for the stress components σ_n and τ_{nt} the known expressions[2]

---

[1] The right-hand screw rule is used for the sign of the angle.

[2] The x- and y-directions are not the principal directions as we had in the case of pure bending; hence the expressions for M_n and M_{nt} will be different from those given by Eqs. (39) and (40).

$$\sigma_n = \sigma_x \cos^2 \alpha + \sigma_y \sin^2 \alpha + 2\tau_{xy} \sin \alpha \cos \alpha,$$
$$\tau_{nt} = \tau_{xy}(\cos^2 \alpha - \sin^2 \alpha) + (\sigma_y - \sigma_x) \sin \alpha \cos \alpha,$$

we can represent expressions (b) in the following form:

$$\left.\begin{array}{l} M_n = M_x \cos^2 \alpha + M_y \sin^2 \alpha - 2M_{xy} \sin \alpha \cos \alpha, \\ M_{nt} = M_{xy}(\cos^2 \alpha - \sin^2 \alpha) + (M_x - M_y) \sin \alpha \cos \alpha. \end{array}\right\} \quad (c)$$

The shearing force Q_n at point A of the boundary will be found from the equation of equilibrium of an element of the plate shown in Fig. 54b, from which

$$Q_n \, ds = Q_x \, dy - Q_y \, dx,$$

or

$$Q_n = Q_x \cos \alpha + Q_y \sin \alpha. \qquad (d)$$

Having expressions (c) and (d), the boundary condition in each particular case can be written without difficulty.

If the curvilinear edge of the plate is built in, we have for such an edge

$$w = 0, \qquad \frac{\partial w}{\partial n} = 0. \qquad (e)$$

In the case of a simply supported edge we have

$$w = 0, \qquad M_n = 0. \qquad (f)$$

Substituting for M_n its expression from the first of equations (c) and using Eqs. (99) and (100), we can represent the boundary conditions (f) in terms of w and its derivatives.

If the edge of a plate is free, the boundary conditions are

$$M_n = 0, \qquad V_n = Q_n - \frac{\partial M_{nt}}{\partial s} = 0, \qquad (g)$$

where the term $-\partial M_{nt}/\partial s$ is obtained in the manner shown in Fig. 50 and represents the portion of the edge reaction which is due to the distribution along the edge of the twisting moment M_{nt}. Substituting expressions (c) and (d) for M_n, M_{nt} and Q_n and using Eqs. (99), (100), (102) and (103), we can represent boundary conditions (g) in the following form:

$$\left.\begin{array}{l} \nu \, \Delta w + (1 - \nu)\left(\cos^2 \alpha \dfrac{\partial^2 w}{\partial x^2} + \sin^2 \alpha \dfrac{\partial^2 w}{\partial y^2} + \sin 2\alpha \dfrac{\partial^2 w}{\partial x \, \partial y} \right) = 0 \\[2ex] \cos \alpha \dfrac{\partial}{\partial x}\Delta w + \sin \alpha \dfrac{\partial}{\partial y}\Delta w + (1 - \nu)\dfrac{\partial}{\partial s}\left[\cos 2\alpha \dfrac{\partial^2 w}{\partial x \, \partial y} \right. \\[2ex] \left. \qquad\qquad + \dfrac{1}{2} \sin 2\alpha\left(\dfrac{\partial^2 w}{\partial y^2} - \dfrac{\partial^2 w}{\partial x^2} \right) \right] = 0, \end{array}\right\} \quad (110)$$

where

$$\Delta w = \frac{\partial^2 w}{\partial x^2} + \frac{\partial^2 w}{\partial y^2}.$$

Another method of derivation of these conditions will be shown in the next article.

23. Alternate Method of Derivation of the Boundary Conditions.—The differential equation (101) of the deflection surface of a plate and the boundary conditions can be obtained by using the principle of virtual displacements together with the expression for the strain energy of a bent plate.[1] Since the effect of shearing stresses on deflections was entirely neglected in the derivation of Eq. (101), the corresponding expression for the strain energy will contain only terms depending on the action of bending and twisting moments as in the case of pure bending discussed in Art. 12. Using Eq. (48) we obtain for the strain energy in an infinitesimal element

$$dV = \frac{1}{2}D\left\{\left(\frac{\partial^2 w}{\partial x^2} + \frac{\partial^2 w}{\partial y^2}\right)^2 - 2(1-\nu)\left[\frac{\partial^2 w}{\partial x^2}\frac{\partial^2 w}{\partial y^2} - \left(\frac{\partial^2 w}{\partial x \, \partial y}\right)^2\right]\right\}dx \, dy. \quad (a)$$

The total strain energy of the plate is then obtained by integration as follows:

$$V = \frac{1}{2}D\int\int\left\{\left(\frac{\partial^2 w}{\partial x^2} + \frac{\partial^2 w}{\partial y^2}\right)^2 - 2(1-\nu)\left[\frac{\partial^2 w}{\partial x^2}\frac{\partial^2 w}{\partial y^2} - \left(\frac{\partial^2 w}{\partial x \, \partial y}\right)^2\right]\right\}dx \, dy,$$

$$\tag{111}$$

where the integration is extended over the entire surface of the plate.

Applying the principle of virtual displacement, we assume that an infinitely small variation δw of the deflections w of the plate is produced. Then the corresponding change in the strain energy of the plate must be equal to the work done by the external forces during the assumed virtual displacements. In calculating this work we must consider not only the lateral load q distributed over the surface of the plate but also the bending moments M_n and transverse forces $Q_n - (\partial M_{nt}/\partial s)$ distributed along the boundary of the plate. Hence the general equation, given by the principle of virtual displacements, is

$$\delta V = \int\int q \, \delta w \, dx \, dy - \int M_n \frac{\partial \, \delta w}{\partial n}ds + \int\left(Q_n - \frac{\partial M_{nt}}{\partial s}\right)\delta w \, ds. \quad (b)$$

The first integral on the right side of this equation represents the work of the lateral load during the displacement δw. The second, extended along the boundary of the plate, represents the work of the bending moments due to the rotation $\partial \, \delta w/\partial n$ of the edge of the plate. The minus sign follows from

[1] This is the method by which the boundary conditions were for the first time satisfactorily established by G. Kirchhoff in *J. Crelle*, vol. 40, 1850. See also his "Vorlesungen über Mathematische Physik," *Mechanik*, p. 450, 1877.

the directions chosen for M_n and the normal n indicated in Fig. 54. The third integral represents the work of the transverse forces applied along the edge of the plate.

In the calculation of the variation δV of the strain energy of the plate we use certain transformations which we shall show in detail for the first term of the expression (111). The small variation of this term is

$$\delta \int \int \left(\frac{\partial^2 w}{\partial x^2} \right)^2 dx \, dy = 2 \int \int \frac{\partial^2 w}{\partial x^2} \frac{\partial^2 \, \delta w}{\partial x^2} dx \, dy$$

$$= 2 \int \int \left[\frac{\partial}{\partial x} \left(\frac{\partial^2 w}{\partial x^2} \frac{\partial \, \delta w}{\partial x} \right) - \frac{\partial^3 w}{\partial x^3} \frac{\partial \, \delta w}{\partial x} \right] dx \, dy$$

$$= 2 \int \int \left[\frac{\partial}{\partial x} \left(\frac{\partial^2 w}{\partial x^2} \frac{\partial \, \delta w}{\partial x} \right) - \frac{\partial}{\partial x} \left(\frac{\partial^3 w}{\partial x^3} \delta w \right) + \frac{\partial^4 w}{\partial x^4} \delta w \right] dx \, dy. \quad (c)$$

In the first two terms after the last sign of equality in expression (c) the double integration can be replaced by simple integrals if we remember that for any function F of x and y the following formulas hold:

$$\left. \begin{array}{l} \displaystyle \int \int \frac{\partial F}{\partial x} dx \, dy = \int F \cos \alpha \, ds, \\[3mm] \displaystyle \int \int \frac{\partial F}{\partial y} dx \, dy = \int F \sin \alpha \, ds. \end{array} \right\} \quad (d)$$

In these expressions the simple integrals are extended along the boundary, and α is the angle between the outer normal and the x-axis, as shown in Fig. 54. Using the first of the formulas (d), we can represent expression (c) as follows

$$\delta \int \int \left(\frac{\partial^2 w}{\partial x^2} \right)^2 dx \, dy = 2 \int \int \frac{\partial^4 w}{\partial x^4} \delta w \, dx \, dy$$

$$+ 2 \int \left(\frac{\partial^2 w}{\partial x^2} \frac{\partial \, \delta w}{\partial x} - \frac{\partial^3 w}{\partial x^3} \delta w \right) \cos \alpha \, ds. \quad (e)$$

Advancing along the boundary in the direction shown in Fig. 54, we have

$$\frac{\partial \, \delta w}{\partial x} = \frac{\partial \, \delta w}{\partial n} \frac{dn}{dx} + \frac{\partial \, \delta w}{\partial s} \frac{ds}{dx} = \frac{\partial \, \delta w}{\partial n} \cos \alpha - \frac{\partial \, \delta w}{\partial s} \sin \alpha.$$

With this transformation, expression (e) becomes

$$\delta \int \int \left(\frac{\partial^2 w}{\partial x^2} \right)^2 dx \, dy = 2 \int \int \frac{\partial^4 w}{\partial x^4} \delta w \, dx \, dy$$

$$+ 2 \int \frac{\partial^2 w}{\partial x^2} \left(\frac{\partial \, \delta w}{\partial n} \cos \alpha - \frac{\partial \, \delta w}{\partial s} \sin \alpha \right) \cos \alpha \, ds - 2 \int \frac{\partial^3 w}{\partial x^3} \delta w \cos \alpha \, ds. \quad (f)$$

Integrating by parts, we have

$$\int \frac{\partial^2 w}{\partial x^2} \sin \alpha \cos \alpha \frac{\partial \, \delta w}{\partial s} ds = \left| \frac{\partial^2 w}{\partial x^2} \sin \alpha \cos \alpha \, \delta w \right|$$
$$- \int \frac{\partial}{\partial s} \left(\frac{\partial^2 w}{\partial x^2} \sin \alpha \cos \alpha \right) \delta w \, ds.$$

The first term on the right side of this expression is zero, since we are integrating along the closed boundary of the plate. Thus we obtain

$$\int \frac{\partial^2 w}{\partial x^2} \sin \alpha \cos \alpha \frac{\partial \, \delta w}{\partial s} ds = - \int \frac{\partial}{\partial s} \left(\frac{\partial^2 w}{\partial x^2} \sin \alpha \cos \alpha \right) \delta w \, ds.$$

Substituting this result in Eq. (*f*), we finally obtain the variation of the first term in the expression for the strain energy in the following form:

$$\delta \int \int \left(\frac{\partial^2 w}{\partial x^2} \right)^2 dx \, dy = 2 \int \int \frac{\partial^4 w}{\partial x^4} \delta w \, dx \, dy + 2 \int \frac{\partial^2 w}{\partial x^2} \cos^2 \alpha \frac{\partial \, \delta w}{\partial n} ds$$
$$+ 2 \int \left[\frac{\partial}{\partial s} \left(\frac{\partial^2 w}{\partial x^2} \sin \alpha \cos \alpha \right) - \frac{\partial^3 w}{\partial x^3} \cos \alpha \right] \delta w \, ds. \quad (g)$$

Transforming in similar manner the variations of the other terms of **expression** (111), we obtain

$$\delta \int \int \left(\frac{\partial^2 w}{\partial y^2} \right)^2 dx \, dy = 2 \int \int \frac{\partial^4 w}{\partial y^4} \delta w \, dx \, dy + 2 \int \frac{\partial^2 w}{\partial y^2} \sin^2 \alpha \frac{\partial \, \delta w}{\partial n} ds$$
$$- 2 \int \left[\frac{\partial}{\partial s} \left(\frac{\partial^2 w}{\partial y^2} \sin \alpha \cos \alpha \right) + \frac{\partial^3 w}{\partial y^3} \sin \alpha \right] \delta w \, ds. \quad (h)$$

$$\delta \int \int \frac{\partial^2 w}{\partial x^2} \frac{\partial^2 w}{\partial y^2} dx \, dy = 2 \int \int \frac{\partial^4 w}{\partial x^2 \, \partial y^2} \delta w \, dx \, dy + \int \left(\frac{\partial^2 w}{\partial y^2} \cos^2 \alpha \right.$$
$$+ \frac{\partial^2 w}{\partial x^2} \sin^2 \alpha \left. \right) \frac{\partial \, \delta w}{\partial n} ds - \int \left\{ \frac{\partial^3 w}{\partial x^2 \, \partial y} \sin \alpha + \frac{\partial^3 w}{\partial x \, \partial y^2} \cos \alpha \right.$$
$$+ \frac{\partial}{\partial s} \left[\left(\frac{\partial^2 w}{\partial x^2} - \frac{\partial^2 w}{\partial y^2} \right) \sin \alpha \cos \alpha \right] \left. \right\} \delta w \, ds. \quad (i)$$

$$\delta \int \int \left(\frac{\partial^2 w}{\partial x \, \partial y} \right)^2 dx \, dy = 2 \int \int \frac{\partial^4 w}{\partial x^2 \, \partial y^2} \delta w \, dx \, dy$$
$$+ 2 \int \frac{\partial^2 w}{\partial x \, \partial y} \sin \alpha \cos \alpha \frac{\partial \, \delta w}{\partial n} ds + \int \left\{ \frac{\partial}{\partial s} \left[\frac{\partial^2 w}{\partial x \, \partial y} (\sin^2 \alpha - \cos^2 \alpha) \right] \right.$$
$$- \frac{\partial^3 w}{\partial x \, \partial y^2} \cos \alpha - \frac{\partial^3 w}{\partial x^2 \, \partial y} \sin \alpha \left. \right\} \delta w \, ds. \quad (j)$$

By using these formulas the variation of the potential energy will be represented in the following form:[1]

$$\delta V = D\left\{ \iint \Delta\Delta w \cdot \delta w \; dx \; dy + \int\left[(1 - \nu)\left(\frac{\partial^2 w}{\partial x^2} \cos^2 \alpha \right.\right.\right.$$

$$\left.\left. + 2\frac{\partial^2 w}{\partial x \; \partial y} \sin \alpha \cos \alpha + \frac{\partial^2 w}{\partial y^2} \sin^2 \alpha\right) + \nu \, \Delta w\right]\frac{\partial}{\partial n}\frac{\delta w}{} ds$$

$$+ \int\left\{ (1 - \nu)\frac{\partial}{\partial s}\left[\left(\frac{\partial^2 w}{\partial x^2} - \frac{\partial^2 w}{\partial y^2}\right) \sin \alpha \cos \alpha - \frac{\partial^2 w}{\partial x \; \partial y} (\cos^2 \alpha - \sin^2 \alpha)\right]\right.$$

$$\left. - \left(\frac{\partial^3 w}{\partial x^3} + \frac{\partial^3 w}{\partial x \; \partial y^2}\right) \cos \alpha - \left(\frac{\partial^3 w}{\partial y^3} + \frac{\partial^3 w}{\partial x^2 \; \partial y}\right) \sin \alpha\right\}\delta w \; ds\right\}. \quad (112)$$

Substituting this expression in Eq. (b) and remembering that δw and $\partial\delta w/\partial n$ are arbitrary small quantities satisfying the boundary conditions, we conclude that Eq. (b) will be satisfied only if the following three equations are satisfied:

$$\iint (D\Delta\Delta w - q)\delta w \; dx \; dy = 0, \quad (k)$$

$$\int\left\{ D\left[(1 - \nu)\left(\frac{\partial^2 w}{\partial x^2} \cos^2 \alpha + 2\frac{\partial^2 w}{\partial x \; \partial y} \sin \alpha \cos \alpha + \frac{\partial^2 w}{\partial y^2} \sin^2 \alpha\right) + \nu \, \Delta w\right]\right.$$

$$\left. + M_n\right\}\frac{\partial}{\partial n}\frac{\delta w}{} ds = 0, \quad (l)$$

$$\int\left\{ D\left\{(1 - \nu)\frac{\partial}{\partial s}\left[\left(\frac{\partial^2 w}{\partial x^2} - \frac{\partial^2 w}{\partial y^2}\right) \sin \alpha \cos \alpha - \frac{\partial^2 w}{\partial x \; \partial y} (\cos^2 \alpha - \sin^2 \alpha)\right]\right.\right.$$

$$\left. - \left(\frac{\partial^3 w}{\partial x^3} + \frac{\partial^3 w}{\partial x \; \partial y^2}\right) \cos \alpha - \left(\frac{\partial^3 w}{\partial y^3} + \frac{\partial^3 w}{\partial x^2 \; \partial y}\right) \sin \alpha\right\}$$

$$\left. - \left(Q_n - \frac{\partial M_{nt}}{\partial s}\right)\right\}\delta w \; ds = 0. \quad (m)$$

The first of these equations will be satisfied only if in every point of the middle surface of the plate we have

$$D\Delta\Delta w - q = 0$$

which represents the differential equation (101) of the deflection surface of the plate.   Equations (l) and (m) give us boundary conditions.

If the plate is built in along the edge, δw and $\partial\delta w/\partial n$ are zero along the edge; and Eqs. (l) and (m) are satisfied.   In the case of a simply supported edge, $\delta w = 0$ and $M_n = 0$.   Hence Eq. (m) is satisfied, and Eq. (l) will be satisfied if

[1] The symbols $\Delta\Delta w$ stay for the left-hand side of Eq. (101).

$$(1 - \nu)\left(\frac{\partial^2 w}{\partial x^2} \cos^2 \alpha + 2\frac{\partial^2 w}{\partial x \, \partial y} \sin \alpha \cos \alpha + \frac{\partial^2 w}{\partial y^2} \sin^2 \alpha\right) + \nu \, \Delta w = 0. \quad (n)$$

In the particular case of a rectilinear edge parallel to the y-axis, $\alpha = 0$; and we obtain from Eq. (n)

$$\frac{\partial^2 w}{\partial x^2} + \nu \frac{\partial^2 w}{\partial y^2} = 0$$

as it should be for a simply supported edge.

If the edge of a plate is entirely free, the quantity δw and $\partial \, \delta w / \partial n$ in Eqs. (l) and (m) are arbitrary; furthermore, $M_n = 0$ and $Q_n - (\partial M_{nt}/\partial s) = 0$. Hence, from Eqs. (l) and (m), for a free edge we have

$$(1 - \nu)\left(\frac{\partial^2 w}{\partial x^2} \cos^2 \alpha + 2\frac{\partial^2 w}{\partial x \, \partial y} \sin \alpha \cos \alpha + \frac{\partial^2 w}{\partial y^2} \sin^2 \alpha\right) + \nu \, \Delta w = 0,$$

$$(1 - \nu)\frac{\partial}{\partial s}\left[\left(\frac{\partial^2 w}{\partial x^2} - \frac{\partial^2 w}{\partial y^2}\right) \sin \alpha \cos \alpha - \frac{\partial^2 w}{\partial x \, \partial y}(\cos^2 \alpha - \sin^2 \alpha)\right]$$
$$- \left(\frac{\partial^3 w}{\partial x^3} + \frac{\partial^3 w}{\partial x \, \partial y^2}\right) \cos \alpha - \left(\frac{\partial^3 w}{\partial y^3} + \frac{\partial^3 w}{\partial x^2 \, \partial y}\right) \sin \alpha = 0.$$

These conditions are in agreement with Eqs. (110) which were obtained previously (see page 94). In the particular case of a free rectilinear edge parallel to the y-axis, $\alpha = 0$, and we obtain

$$\frac{\partial^2 w}{\partial x^2} + \nu \frac{\partial^2 w}{\partial y^2} = 0,$$

$$\frac{\partial^3 w}{\partial x^3} + (2 - \nu)\frac{\partial^3 w}{\partial x \, \partial y^2} = 0.$$

These equations coincide with Eqs. (106) and (107) obtained previously.

In the case when given moments M_n and transverse forces $Q_n - (\partial M_{nt}/\partial s)$ are distributed along the edge of a plate, the corresponding boundary conditions again can be easily obtained by using Eqs. (l) and (m).

24. Reduction of the Problem of Bending of a Plate to That of Deflection of a Membrane.

There are cases in which it is advantageous to replace the differential equation (101) of the fourth order developed for a plate by two equations of the second order which represent the deflections of a membrane.[1] This replacement can easily be done if we write Eq. (101) in the following form:

$$\left(\frac{\partial^2}{\partial x^2} + \frac{\partial^2}{\partial y^2}\right)\left(\frac{\partial^2 w}{\partial x^2} + \frac{\partial^2 w}{\partial y^2}\right) = \frac{q}{D} \qquad (a)$$

[1] This method of investigating bending of plates was introduced by Dr. H. Marcus in his book "Die Theorie elastischer Gewebe," Berlin, 1923.

and observe that by adding together the two expressions (99) for bending moments (see page 88) we have

$$M_x + M_y = -D(1 + \nu)\left(\frac{\partial^2 w}{\partial x^2} + \frac{\partial^2 w}{\partial y^2}\right). \qquad (b)$$

Introducing a new notation

$$M = \frac{M_x + M_y}{1 + \nu} = -D\left(\frac{\partial^2 w}{\partial x^2} + \frac{\partial^2 w}{\partial y^2}\right), \qquad (113)$$

the two Eqs. (*a*) and (*b*) can be represented in the following form:

$$\left.\begin{array}{c} \dfrac{\partial^2 M}{\partial x^2} + \dfrac{\partial^2 M}{\partial y^2} = -q, \\[2mm] \dfrac{\partial^2 w}{\partial x^2} + \dfrac{\partial^2 w}{\partial y^2} = -\dfrac{M}{D}. \end{array}\right\} \qquad (114)$$

Both these equations are of the same kind as that obtained for a uniformly stretched and laterally loaded membrane.[1]

The solution of these equations is very much simplified in the case of a simply supported plate of polygonal shape, in which case along each rectilinear portion of the boundary we have $\partial^2 w/\partial s^2 = 0$ since $w = 0$ at the boundary. Observing that $M_n = 0$ at a simply supported edge, we conclude also that $\partial^2 w/\partial n^2 = 0$ at the boundary. Hence we have [see Eq. (34)]

$$\frac{\partial^2 w}{\partial s^2} + \frac{\partial^2 w}{\partial n^2} = \frac{\partial^2 w}{\partial x^2} + \frac{\partial^2 w}{\partial y^2} = -\frac{M}{D} = 0 \qquad (c)$$

at the boundary. It must be seen that the solution of the plate problem reduces in this case to the integration of the two Eqs. (114) in succession. We begin with the first of these equations and find its solution satisfying the condition $M = 0$ at the boundary.[2] Substituting this solution in the second equation and integrating it, we find the deflections w. Both problems are of the same kind as the problem of the deflection of a uniformly stretched and laterally loaded membrane having zero deflection at the boundary. This latter problem is much simpler than the plate problem, and it can always be solved with sufficient accuracy

---

[1] See author's "Theory of Elasticity," p. 239, 1934.

[2] Note that if the plate is not of a polygonal shape, M generally does not vanish at the boundary when $M_n = 0$.

by using an approximate method of integration such as Ritz's or the method of finite differences. Some examples of the application of the latter method will be discussed later (see page 180). Several applications of Ritz's method are given in discussing torsional problems.[1]

A simply supported plate of polygonal shape, bent by moments M_n uniformly distributed along the boundary, is another simple case of the application of Eqs. (114). Equations (114) in such a case become

$$\left.\begin{array}{l}\dfrac{\partial^2 M}{\partial x^2} + \dfrac{\partial^2 M}{\partial y^2} = 0, \\[2mm] \dfrac{\partial^2 w}{\partial x^2} + \dfrac{\partial^2 w}{\partial y^2} = -\dfrac{M}{D}.\end{array}\right\} \tag{115}$$

Along a rectilinear edge we have again $\partial^2 w/\partial s^2 = 0$. Hence

$$M_n = -D\frac{\partial^2 w}{\partial n^2},$$

and we have at the boundary

$$\frac{\partial^2 w}{\partial x^2} + \frac{\partial^2 w}{\partial y^2} = \frac{\partial^2 w}{\partial n^2} = -\frac{M_n}{D} = -\frac{M}{D}.$$

This boundary condition and the first of the equations (115) will be satisfied if we take for the quantity M the constant value $M = M_n$ at all points of the plate, which means that the sum of the bending moments M_x and M_y remains constant over the entire surface of the plate. The deflections of the plate will then be found from the second of the equations (115),[2] which becomes

$$\frac{\partial^2 w}{\partial x^2} + \frac{\partial^2 w}{\partial y^2} = -\frac{M_n}{D}. \tag{d}$$

It may be concluded from this that, in the case of bending of a simply supported polygonal plate by moments M_n uniformly distributed along the boundary, the deflection surface of the plate is the same as that of a uniformly stretched membrane with a uniformly distributed load. There are many cases for which the solutions of the membrane problem are known. These can be

---

[1] See *ibid.*, p. 253.

[2] This was shown first by S. Woinowsky-Krieger, *Ingenieur-Archiv*, vol. 4, p. 254, 1933.

immediately applied in discussing the corresponding plate problems.

Take, for example, a simply supported equilateral triangular plate (Fig. 55) bent by moments M_n uniformly distributed along the boundary. The deflection surface of the plate is the same as that of a uniformly stretched and uniformly loaded membrane.

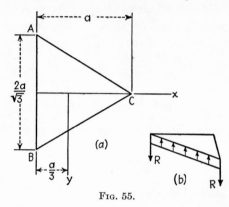

Fɪɢ. 55.

The latter can be easily obtained experimentally by stretching a soap film on the triangular boundary and loading it uniformly by air pressure.[1]

The analytical expression of the deflection surface is also comparatively simple in this case. We take the product of the left sides of the equations of the three sides of the triangle:

$$\left(x + \frac{a}{3}\right)\left(\frac{x}{\sqrt{3}} + y - \frac{2a}{3\sqrt{3}}\right)\left(\frac{x}{\sqrt{3}} - y - \frac{2a}{3\sqrt{3}}\right)$$
$$= \frac{x^3 - 3y^2x}{3} - \frac{a(x^2 + y^2)}{3} + \frac{4a^3}{3 \cdot 27}.$$

This expression evidently becomes zero at the boundary. Hence the boundary condition $w = 0$ for the membrane is satisfied if we take for deflections the expression

$$w = N\left[\frac{x^3 - 3y^2x}{3} - \frac{a(x^2 + y^2)}{3} + \frac{4a^3}{3 \cdot 27}\right], \qquad (e)$$

where N is a constant factor the magnitude of which we choose

---

[1] Such experiments are used in solving torsional problems; see author's "Theory of Elasticity," p. 260.

in such a manner as to satisfy Eq. (d).   In this way we obtain the required solution:

$$w = \frac{M_n}{4aD}\left[x^3 - 3y^2x - a(x^2 + y^2) + \frac{4}{27}a^3 \right]. \qquad (f)$$

Substituting $x = y = 0$ in this expression, we obtain the deflection at the centroid of the triangle

$$w_0 = \frac{M_n a^2}{27D}. \qquad (g)$$

The expressions for the bending and twisting moments, from Eqs. (99) and (100), are

$$\left.\begin{aligned}
M_x &= \frac{M_n}{2}\left[1 + \nu - (1 - \nu)\frac{3x}{a} \right], \\
M_y &= \frac{M_n}{2}\left[1 + \nu + \frac{(1 - \nu)3x}{a} \right] \\
M_{xy} &= -\frac{3(1 - \nu)M_n y}{2a}.
\end{aligned}\right\} \qquad (h)$$

Shearing forces, from Eqs. (102) and (103), are

$$Q_x = Q_y = 0.$$

Along the boundary, from Eq. (d) (Art. 22), the shearing force $Q_n = 0$, and the bending moment is equal to M_n.   The twisting moment along the side BC (Fig. 55) from Eqs. (c) of Art. 22 is

$$M_{nt} = \frac{3(1 - \nu)M_n}{4a}(y - \sqrt{3}x).$$

The vertical reactions acting on the plate along the side BC (Fig. 55) are

$$V_n = Q_n - \frac{\partial M_{nt}}{\partial s} = -\frac{3(1 - \nu)}{2a}M_n. \qquad (i)$$

From symmetry we conclude that the same uniformly distributed reactions also act along the two other sides of the plate.   These forces are balanced by the concentrated reactions at the corners of the triangular plate, the magnitude of which can be found as was explained on page 90 and is equal to

$$R = 2(M_{nt})_{x=\frac{2}{3}a, y=0} = (1 - \nu)\sqrt{3}M_n. \qquad (j)$$

The distribution of the reactive forces along the boundary is shown in Fig. 55b. The maximum bending stresses are at the corners and act on the planes bisecting the angles. The magnitude of the corresponding bending moment, from Eqs. (h), is

$$(M_y)_{\text{max.}} = (M_y)_{x=\frac{2}{3}a} = \frac{M_n(3 - \nu)}{2}. \tag{k}$$

This method of determining the bending of simply supported polygonal plates by moments uniformly distributed along the boundary can be applied to the calculation of the thermal stresses produced in such plates by non-uniform heating. In discussing thermal stresses in clamped plates it was shown in Art. 14 [Eq. (b)] that non-uniform heating produces uniformly distributed bending moments along the boundary of the plate which prevent any bending of the plate. The magnitude of these moments is[1]

$$M_n = \frac{\alpha t D(1 + \nu)}{h}. \tag{l}$$

To get thermal stresses in the case of a simply supported plate we need only superpose on stresses produced in pure bending by the moments (l) the stresses that are produced in a plate with simply supported edges by the bending moments $-\alpha t D(1 + \nu)/h$ uniformly distributed along the boundary. The solution of the latter problem, as was already explained, can be obtained without much difficulty in the case of a plate of polygonal shape.[2]

Take again, as an example, the equilateral triangular plate. If the edges of the plate are clamped, the bending moments due to non-uniform heating are

$$M_x' = M_y' = \frac{\alpha t D(1 + \nu)}{h}. \tag{m}$$

To get the bending moments M_x and M_y for a simply supported plate we must superpose on the moments (m) the moments that will be obtained from Eqs. (h) by letting $M_n = -\alpha t D(1 + \nu)/h$. In this way we finally obtain

[1] It is assumed that the upper surface of the plate is kept at a higher temperature than the lower one and that the plate thus has the tendency to bend convexly upward.

[2] See dissertation by J. L. Maulbetsch, *J. Appl. Mech.*, vol. 2, p. 141, 1935.

$$M_x = \frac{\alpha t D(1 + \nu)}{h} - \frac{\alpha t D(1 + \nu)}{2h}\left[1 + \nu - (1 - \nu)\frac{3x}{a}\right]$$

$$= \frac{\alpha t E h^2}{24}\left(1 + \frac{3x}{a}\right)$$

$$M_y = \frac{\alpha t D(1 + \nu)}{h} - \frac{\alpha t D(1 + \nu)}{2h}\left[1 + \nu + (1 - \nu)\frac{3x}{a}\right]$$

$$= \frac{\alpha t E h^2}{24}\left(1 - \frac{3x}{a}\right),$$

$$M_{xy} = \frac{1}{8}\frac{\alpha t E h^2 y}{a}.$$

The reactive forces can now be obtained from Eqs. (i) and (j) by substitution of $M = -\alpha t D(1 + \nu)/h$. Hence we find

$$V_n = Q_n - \frac{\partial M_{nt}}{\partial s} = \frac{\alpha t E h^2}{8a}, \qquad R = -\frac{\sqrt{3}\alpha t E h^2}{12}.$$

The results obtained for moments and reactive forces due to non-uniform heating are represented in Figs. 56a and 56b, respectively.

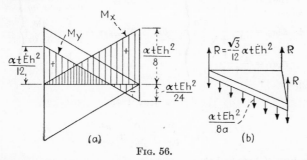

FIG. 56.

25. Exact Theory of Plates.—The differential equation (101) which, together with the boundary conditions, defines the deflections of plates was derived (see Art. 21) by neglecting the effect on bending of normal stresses σ_z and shearing stresses τ_{xz} and τ_{yz}. This means that in the derivation each thin layer of the plate parallel to the middle plane was considered to be in a state of plane stress in which only the stress components σ_x, σ_y and τ_{xy} may be different from zero. One of the simplest cases of this kind is that of pure bending. The deflection surface in this case is a second-degree function in x and y [see Eq. (c), Art. 11] that satisfies Eq. (101). The stress components σ_x, σ_y, and τ_{xy} are proportional to z and independent of x and y.

There are other cases of bending in which a plane stress distribution takes place and Eq. (101) holds rigorously. Take, for example, a circular plate

with a central circular hole bent by moments M_r uniformly distributed along
the boundary of the hole (Fig. 57).   Each thin layer of the plate cut out by
two adjacent planes parallel to the middle plane is in the same stress condition as a thick-walled cylinder subjected to a uniform internal pressure or
tension (Fig. 57b).   The sum $\sigma_r + \sigma_t$ of the two principal stresses is constant
in such a case,[1] and it can be concluded that the deformation of the layer in
the z-direction is also constant and does not interfere with the deformation
of adjacent layers.   Hence we have again a planar stress distribution, and
Eq. (101) holds.

Let us discuss now the general question regarding the shape of the deflection surface of a plate when bending results in a planar stress distribution.
To answer this question it is necessary to consider the three differential
equations of equilibrium together with the six compatibility conditions.   If
body forces are neglected, these equations are[2]

$$\left.\begin{aligned}
\frac{\partial \sigma_x}{\partial x} + \frac{\partial \tau_{xy}}{\partial y} + \frac{\partial \tau_{xz}}{\partial z} &= 0, \\[1em]
\frac{\partial \sigma_y}{\partial y} + \frac{\partial \tau_{xy}}{\partial x} + \frac{\partial \tau_{yz}}{\partial z} &= 0, \\[1em]
\frac{\partial \sigma_z}{\partial z} + \frac{\partial \tau_{xz}}{\partial x} + \frac{\partial \tau_{yz}}{\partial y} &= 0.
\end{aligned}\right\} \tag{a}$$

$$\left.\begin{aligned}
\Delta_1 \sigma_x &= -\frac{1}{1+\nu}\frac{\partial^2 \theta}{\partial x^2}, \\[1em]
\Delta_1 \sigma_y &= -\frac{1}{1+\nu}\frac{\partial^2 \theta}{\partial y^2}, \\[1em]
\Delta_1 \sigma_z &= -\frac{1}{1+\nu}\frac{\partial^2 \theta}{\partial z^2}.
\end{aligned}\right\} \ (b)
\qquad
\left.\begin{aligned}
\Delta_1 \tau_{xy} &= -\frac{1}{1+\nu}\frac{\partial^2 \theta}{\partial x\,\partial y}, \\[1em]
\Delta_1 \tau_{xz} &= -\frac{1}{1+\nu}\frac{\partial^2 \theta}{\partial x\,\partial z}, \\[1em]
\Delta_1 \tau_{yz} &= -\frac{1}{1+\nu}\frac{\partial^2 \theta}{\partial y\,\partial z}.
\end{aligned}\right\} \tag{c}$$

in which
$$\theta = \sigma_x + \sigma_y + \sigma_z$$
and
$$\Delta_1 = \frac{\partial^2}{\partial x^2} + \frac{\partial^2}{\partial y^2} + \frac{\partial^2}{\partial z^2}.$$

Adding Eqs. (b), we find that

$$\frac{\partial^2 \theta}{\partial x^2} + \frac{\partial^2 \theta}{\partial y^2} + \frac{\partial^2 \theta}{\partial z^2} = \Delta_1 \theta = 0; \tag{d}$$

i.e., the sum of the three normal stress components represents a harmonic
function.   In the case of a planar stress $\tau_{xz} = \tau_{yz} = \sigma_z = 0$, and it can be
concluded from the last two of the equations (c) and the last of the equations
(b) that $\partial\theta/\partial z$ must be a constant, say β.   Hence the general expression
for θ in the case of planar stress is

$$\theta = \theta_0 + \beta z, \tag{e}$$

[1] See author's "Theory of Elasticity," p. 57, 1934.
[2] See *ibid.*, pp. 195 and 198.

where θ_0 is a plane harmonic function, *i.e.*,

$$\frac{\partial^2 \theta_0}{\partial x^2} + \frac{\partial^2 \theta_0}{\partial y^2} = \Delta \theta_c = 0.$$

We see that in the case of planar stress the function θ consists of two parts; θ_0 independent of z and βz proportional to z. The first part does not vary through the thickness of the plate. It depends on deformation of the plate in its own plane and can be omitted if we are interested only in bending of plates. Thus we can take in our further discussion

$$\theta = \beta z. \tag{f}$$

Equations of equilibrium (a) will be satisfied in the case of a planar stress distribution if we take

$$\sigma_x = \frac{\partial^2 \varphi}{\partial y^2}, \qquad \sigma_y = \frac{\partial^2 \varphi}{\partial x^2}, \qquad \tau_{xy} = -\frac{\partial^2 \varphi}{\partial x \partial y}, \tag{g}$$

where φ is the stress function. Let us consider now the general form of this function.

Substituting expressions (g) in Eq. (f), we obtain

$$\frac{\partial^2 \varphi}{\partial x^2} + \frac{\partial^2 \varphi}{\partial y^2} = \beta z. \tag{h}$$

Furthermore, from the first of the equations (b) we conclude that

$$\Delta_1 \frac{\partial^2 \varphi}{\partial y^2} = 0 \qquad \text{or} \qquad \frac{\partial^2}{\partial y^2} \Delta_1 \varphi = 0,$$

which, by using Eq. (h), can be put in the following form:

$$\frac{\partial^2}{\partial y^2}\left(\frac{\partial^2 \varphi}{\partial z^2}\right) = 0. \tag{i}$$

In the same manner, from the second and the third of the equations (b), we find

$$\frac{\partial^2}{\partial x^2}\left(\frac{\partial^2 \varphi}{\partial z^2}\right) = 0, \qquad \frac{\partial^2}{\partial x \partial y}\left(\frac{\partial^2 \varphi}{\partial z^2}\right) = 0. \tag{j}$$

From Eqs. (i) and (j) it follows that $\partial^2 \varphi / \partial z^2$ is a linear function of x and y. This function may be taken to be zero without affecting the magnitudes of the stress components given by expressions (g). In such a case the general expression of the stress function is

$$\varphi = \varphi_0 + \varphi_1 z,$$

where φ_0 is a plane harmonic function and φ_1 satisfies the equation

$$\frac{\partial^2 \varphi_1}{\partial x^2} + \frac{\partial^2 \varphi_1}{\partial y^2} = \beta. \tag{k}$$

Since we are not interested in the deformations of plates in their plane, we can omit φ_0 in our further discussion and take as a general expression for the stress function

$$\varphi = \varphi_1 z. \tag{l}$$

Substituting this in Eqs. (g), the stress components can now be calculated, and the displacements can be found from the equations

$$\left.\begin{array}{lll}\dfrac{\partial u}{\partial x} = \dfrac{1}{E}(\sigma_x - \nu\sigma_y), & \dfrac{\partial v}{\partial y} = \dfrac{1}{E}(\sigma_y - \nu\sigma_x), & \dfrac{\partial w}{\partial z} = -\dfrac{\nu}{E}(\sigma_x + \sigma_y), \\[2mm] \dfrac{\partial u}{\partial y} + \dfrac{\partial v}{\partial x} = \dfrac{1}{G}\tau_{xy}, & \dfrac{\partial u}{\partial z} + \dfrac{\partial w}{\partial x} = 0, & \dfrac{\partial v}{\partial z} + \dfrac{\partial w}{\partial y} = 0.\end{array}\right\} \quad (m)$$

For the displacements w perpendicular to the plate we obtain in this way[1]

$$w = -\frac{\beta}{2E}(x^2 + y^2 + \nu z^2) + \frac{1 + \nu}{E}\varphi_1,$$

and the deflection of the middle surface of the plate is

$$w = -\frac{\beta}{2E}(x^2 + y^2) + \frac{1 + \nu}{E}\varphi_1. \quad (n)$$

The corresponding stress components, from Eqs. (g) and (l), are

$$\sigma_x = z\frac{\partial^2\varphi_1}{\partial y^2}, \qquad \sigma_y = z\frac{\partial^2\varphi_1}{\partial x^2}, \qquad \tau_{xy} = -z\frac{\partial^2\varphi_1}{\partial x\partial y},$$

and the bending and twisting moments are

$$\left.\begin{array}{l}M_x = \displaystyle\int_{-\frac{h}{2}}^{\frac{h}{2}}\sigma_x z\,dz = \dfrac{h^3}{12}\dfrac{\partial^2\varphi_1}{\partial y^2}, \qquad M_y = \displaystyle\int_{-\frac{h}{2}}^{\frac{h}{2}}\sigma_y z\,dz = \dfrac{h^3}{12}\dfrac{\partial^2\varphi_1}{\partial x^2}, \\[4mm] \qquad M_{xy} = -\displaystyle\int_{-\frac{h}{2}}^{\frac{h}{2}}\tau_{xy} z\,dz = \dfrac{h^3}{12}\dfrac{\partial^2\varphi_1}{\partial x\,\partial y}.\end{array}\right\} \quad (o)$$

For the curvatures and the twist of a plate, we find from Eq. (n)

$$\frac{\partial^2 w}{\partial x^2} = -\frac{\beta}{E} + \frac{1 + \nu}{E}\frac{\partial^2\varphi_1}{\partial x^2}, \qquad \frac{\partial^2 w}{\partial y^2} = -\frac{\beta}{E} + \frac{1 + \nu}{E}\frac{\partial^2\varphi_1}{\partial y^2},$$

$$\frac{\partial^2 w}{\partial x\,\partial y} = \frac{1 + \nu}{E}\frac{\partial^2\varphi_1}{\partial x\,\partial y},$$

from which, by using Eqs. (k) and (o), we obtain

$$\left.\begin{array}{l}\dfrac{\partial^2 w}{\partial x^2} + \nu\dfrac{\partial^2 w}{\partial y^2} = -\dfrac{1 - \nu^2}{E}\dfrac{\partial^2\varphi_1}{\partial y^2} = -\dfrac{M_x}{D}, \\[4mm] \dfrac{\partial^2 w}{\partial y^2} + \nu\dfrac{\partial^2 w}{\partial x^2} = -\dfrac{1 - \nu^2}{E}\dfrac{\partial^2\varphi_1}{\partial x^2} = -\dfrac{M_y}{D}, \\[4mm] \dfrac{\partial^2 w}{\partial x\,\partial y} = \dfrac{12(1 + \nu)}{Eh^3}M_{xy} = \dfrac{M_{xy}}{(1 - \nu)D}.\end{array}\right\} \quad (p)$$

[1] Several examples of calculating u, v, and w from Eqs. (m) are given in the author's "Theory of Elasticity."

From this analysis it may be concluded that, in the case of bending of plates resulting in a planar stress distribution, the deflections w [see Eq. (n)] rigorously satisfy Eq. (101) and also Eqs. (99) and (100) representing bending and twisting moments. If a solution of Eq. (k) is taken in the form of a function of the second degree in x and y, the deflection surface (n) is also of the second degree which represents the deflection for pure bending. Generally we can conclude, from Eq. (k), that the deflection of the plate in the case of a planar stress distribution is the same as that of a uniformly stretched and uniformly loaded membrane. The plate shown in Fig. 57 represents a particular case of such bending, *viz.*,

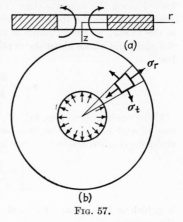

(a)

(b)

Fɪɢ. 57.

the case for which the solution of Eq. (k), given in polar coordinates, is

$$\varphi_1 = Ar^2 + B \log r + C,$$

where A, B and C are constants that must be chosen so as to satisfy the boundary conditions.

Plates of a polygonal shape simply supported and bent by moments uniformly distributed along the boundary (see Art. 24) represent another example of bending in which the deflection surface has a form satisfying Eq. (n), and Eqs. (99), (100) and (101) hold rigorously. In all these cases, as we may see from Eqs. (k) and (o), we have

$$M_x + M_y = \frac{h^3}{12}\left(\frac{\partial^2 \varphi_1}{\partial x^2} + \frac{\partial^2 \varphi_1}{\partial y^2}\right) = \frac{\beta h^3}{12};$$

i.e., the sum of the bending moments in two perpendicular directions remains constant over the entire plate.

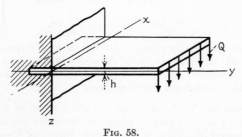

Fɪɢ. 58.

Let us consider now the case in which bending of a plate results in a generalized planar stress distribution, *i.e.*, one in which the normal stress component σ_z, is zero at all points of the plate and the shearing stress components τ_{xz} and τ_{yz} are zero on the surfaces $z = \pm h/2$ of the plate. The deflection of a rectangular plate clamped along one edge and uniformly loaded along the opposite edge (Fig. 58) represents an example of such a bending. From the theory of bending of rectangular beams we know that in this case $\sigma_z = 0$ at all points of the plate and τ_{xz} is zero on the surfaces of the plate and varies along the depth of the plate according to the parabolic law

$$\tau_{xz} = \frac{6Q}{h^3}\left(\frac{h^2}{4} - z^2\right).$$

Using again general Eqs. (a), (b), and (c) and proceeding as in the previous case of a planar stress distribution, we find[1] that the general expression for the deflection surface in this case has the form

$$w = \frac{1}{E}\left[\frac{h^2\varphi}{4} + (1 + \nu)\varphi_1\right], \qquad (q)$$

in which φ is a planar harmonic function of x and y, and φ_1 satisfies the equation

$$\frac{\partial^2\varphi_1}{\partial x^2} + \frac{\partial^2\varphi_1}{\partial y^2} = -\frac{1 - \nu}{1 + \nu}\varphi.$$

It can be concluded that in this case again the differential equation (101) holds with $q = 0$.

The equations for the bending and twisting moments and for the shearing forces in this case are

$$\left.\begin{array}{l}
M_x = -D\left(\dfrac{\partial^2 w}{\partial x^2} + \nu\dfrac{\partial^2 w}{\partial y^2}\right) + \dfrac{8 + \nu}{40}Dh^2\dfrac{\partial^2}{\partial y^2}\Delta w, \\[3mm]
M_y = -D\left(\dfrac{\partial^2 w}{\partial y^2} + \nu\dfrac{\partial^2 w}{\partial x^2}\right) + \dfrac{8 + \nu}{40}Dh^2\dfrac{\partial^2}{\partial x^2}\Delta w, \\[3mm]
M_{xy} = D(1 - \nu)\dfrac{\partial^2 w}{\partial x\,\partial y} + \dfrac{8 + \nu}{40}Dh^2\dfrac{\partial^2}{\partial x\,\partial y}\Delta w, \\[3mm]
Q_x = -D\dfrac{\partial}{\partial x}\Delta w, \qquad Q_y = -D\dfrac{\partial}{\partial y}\Delta w.
\end{array}\right\} \qquad (r)$$

It can be seen that the expressions for the shearing forces coincide with expressions (102) and (103) given by the approximate theory but that the expressions for moments are different, the second terms of those expressions representing the effect of the shearing forces.

<hr>

[1] The rigorous solution for this case was given by Saint Venant; see his translation of Clebsch's book: "Théorie de l'élasticité des corps solides," p. 337. A general discussion of the rigorous theory of bending of plates was given by J. H. Michell, *Proc. London Math. Soc.*, vol. 31, p. 100, 1900. See also the book by A. E. H. Love, "The Mathematical Theory of Elasticity," p. 473, 1927. The results given in our further discussion are taken from the latter book.

These correction terms can be obtained in an elementary way by using the same reasoning as in the case of bending of beams. Considering the curvature in the xz-plane, we can state that the total curvature is produced by two factors, the bending moments M_x, M_y and the shearing force Q_x. The curvature produced by the bending moments is obtained by subtracting from the total curvature $-\partial^2 w/\partial x^2$ the portion $-\partial(kQ_x/hG)/\partial x$ produced by the shearing force.[1] Substituting $-(\partial^2 w/\partial x^2) + [\partial(kQ_x/hG)/\partial x]$ and $-(\partial^2 w/\partial y^2) + [\partial(kQ_y/hG)/\partial y]$ for $-\partial^2 w/\partial x^2$ and $-\partial^2 w/\partial y^2$ in Eqs. (99) and using the last two equations of the system (r), we find for the bending moments the expressions

$$M_x = -D\left(\frac{\partial^2 w}{\partial x^2} + \nu\frac{\partial^2 w}{\partial y^2}\right) + \frac{k\,Dh^2}{6}\frac{\partial^2}{\partial y^2}\Delta w,$$

$$M_y = -D\left(\frac{\partial^2 w}{\partial y^2} + \nu\frac{\partial^2 w}{\partial x^2}\right) + \frac{k\,Dh^2}{6}\frac{\partial^2}{\partial x^2}\Delta w.$$

These equations coincide with the first two equations of the system (r) if we take

$$\frac{k}{6} = \frac{8 + \nu}{40}.$$

For $\nu = 0.3$ this gives $k = 1.245$.

From the theory of bending of beams we know that the correction due to the action of the shearing force is small and can be neglected if the depth h is small in comparison with the span of the beam. The same conclusion also holds in the case of plates.

The exact expressions for stress components are

$$
\left.
\begin{aligned}
\sigma_x &= -\frac{Ez}{1-\nu^2}\left(\frac{\partial^2 w}{\partial x^2} + \frac{\partial^2 w}{\partial y^2}\right) + \frac{E}{1-\nu^2}\left(\frac{h^2 z}{4} - \frac{2-\nu}{6}z^3\right)\frac{\partial^2}{\partial y^2}\Delta w, \\
\sigma_y &= -\frac{Ez}{1-\nu^2}\left(\frac{\partial^2 w}{\partial y^2} + \nu\frac{\partial^2 w}{\partial x^2}\right) + \frac{E}{1-\nu^2}\left(\frac{h^2 z}{4} - \frac{2-\nu}{6}z^3\right)\frac{\partial^2}{\partial x^2}\Delta w, \\
\tau_{xy} &= -\frac{Ez}{1+\nu}\frac{\partial^2 w}{\partial x\,\partial y} - \frac{E}{1-\nu^2}\left(\frac{h^2 z}{4} - \frac{2-\nu}{6}z^3\right)\frac{\partial^2}{\partial x\,\partial y}\Delta w, \\
\tau_{xz} &= -\frac{E(h^2 - 4z^2)}{8(1-\nu^2)}\frac{\partial}{\partial x}\Delta w, \qquad \tau_{yz} = -\frac{E(h^2 - 4z^2)}{8(1-\nu^2)}\frac{\partial}{\partial y}\Delta w, \qquad \sigma_z = 0.
\end{aligned}
\right\}
\quad (s)
$$

The second terms on the right sides of the equations for σ_x, σ_y and τ_{xy} are the corrections due to the effect of shearing forces on bending. It is seen that the stresses σ_x, σ_y and τ_{xy} are no longer proportional to the distance z from the middle plane but contain a term proportional to z^3. Shearing stresses τ_{xz} and τ_{yz} vary according to the same parabolic law as for rectangular beams. In the case of a plane stress distribution, Δw is a constant, and formulas (s) coincide with those given by the approximate theory.

[1] k is a numerical factor that in the case of beams depends on the shape of the cross section.

The problem of a uniformly loaded plate can also be treated rigorously in the same way. Thus it can be shown that the general expression for deflections in this case is obtained by adding to expression (q) the term

$$\frac{1}{64}\frac{q}{D}(x^2 + y^2)\left(x^2 + y^2 - \frac{2h^2}{1 - \nu}\right), \qquad (t)$$

which again satisfies Eq. (101) of the approximate theory. The equations for bending moments do not coincide with Eqs. (99) of the approximate theory but contain some additional correction terms. If the thickness of the plate is small in comparison with the other dimensions, these terms are small and can be neglected.

In all previous cases general solutions of plate bending problems were discussed without considering the boundary conditions. There exist also rigorous solutions of several problems in which boundary conditions are also considered. All these solutions indicate that the elementary theory of plates is accurate enough for practical applications.[1]

---

[1] In recent times the rigorous theory of plates has attracted the interest of engineers, and several important papers in this field have been published. We shall mention here the following papers: S. Woinowsky-Krieger, *Ingenieur-Archiv*, vol. 4, pp. 203 and 305, 1933. B. Galerkin, *Compt. rend. acad. sci. Paris*, vol. 190, p. 1047; vol. 193, p. 568; vol. 194, p. 1440. G. D. Birkhoff, *Phil. Mag.*, vol. 43, p. 953, 1922. C. A. Garabedian, *Trans. Am. Math. Soc.*, vol. 25, p. 343, 1923; *Compt. rend.*, Paris, vols. 178 (1924), 180 (1925), 186 (1928), 195 (1932). R. Archie Higdon and D. L. Holl, *Duke Math. J.*, vol. 3, p. 18, 1937.

CHAPTER V

SIMPLY SUPPORTED RECTANGULAR PLATES

26. Simply Supported Rectangular Plates under Sinusoidal Load.—Taking the coordinate axes as shown in Fig. 59, we assume that the load distributed over the surface of the plate is given by the expression

$$q = q_0 \sin \frac{\pi x}{a} \sin \frac{\pi y}{b}, \qquad (a)$$

in which q_0 represents the intensity of the load at the center of the plate. The differential equation (101) for the deflection surface in this case becomes

F<small>IG</small>. 59.

$$\frac{\partial^4 w}{\partial x^4} + 2 \frac{\partial^4 w}{\partial x^2\,\partial y^2} + \frac{\partial^4 w}{\partial y^4} = \frac{q_0}{D} \sin \frac{\pi x}{a} \sin \frac{\pi y}{b}. \qquad (b)$$

The boundary conditions, for simply supported edges are

$$
\begin{aligned}
w = 0, \qquad M_x = 0 \qquad &\text{for} \qquad x = 0 \qquad \text{and} \qquad x = a; \\
w = 0, \qquad M_y = 0 \qquad &\text{for} \qquad y = 0 \qquad \text{and} \qquad y = b.
\end{aligned}
$$

Using expression (99) for bending moments and observing that since $w = 0$ at the edges, $\partial^2 w/\partial x^2 = 0$ and $\partial^2 w/\partial y^2 = 0$ for the edges parallel to the x- and y-axes, respectively, we can represent the boundary conditions in the following form:

$$
\left.
\begin{aligned}
(1)\ w = 0, \quad (2)\ \frac{\partial^2 w}{\partial x^2} = 0 \qquad &\text{for} \qquad x = 0 \qquad \text{and} \qquad x = a, \\
(3)\ w = 0, \quad (4)\ \frac{\partial^2 w}{\partial y^2} = 0 \qquad &\text{for} \qquad y = 0 \qquad \text{and} \qquad y = b.
\end{aligned}
\right\} \quad (c)
$$

It may be seen that all boundary conditions are satisfied if we take for deflections the expression

$$w = C \sin \frac{\pi x}{a} \sin \frac{\pi y}{b}, \qquad (d)$$

113

in which the constant C must be chosen so as to satisfy Eq. (b). Substituting expression (d) into Eq. (b), we find

$$\pi^4\left(\frac{1}{a^2} + \frac{1}{b^2}\right)^2 C = \frac{q_0}{D},$$

and we conclude that the deflection surface satisfying Eq. (b) and boundary conditions (c) is

$$w = \frac{q_0}{\pi^4 D\left(\dfrac{1}{a^2} + \dfrac{1}{b^2}\right)^2} \sin\frac{\pi x}{a} \sin\frac{\pi y}{b}. \tag{e}$$

Having this expression and using Eqs. (99) and (100), we find

$$\left.\begin{aligned}
M_x &= \frac{q_0}{\pi^2\left(\dfrac{1}{a^2} + \dfrac{1}{b^2}\right)^2}\left(\frac{1}{a^2} + \frac{\nu}{b^2}\right) \sin\frac{\pi x}{a} \sin\frac{\pi y}{b}, \\
M_y &= \frac{q_0}{\pi^2\left(\dfrac{1}{a^2} + \dfrac{1}{b^2}\right)^2}\left(\frac{\nu}{a^2} + \frac{1}{b^2}\right) \sin\frac{\pi x}{a} \sin\frac{\pi y}{b}, \\
M_{xy} &= \frac{q_0(1 - \nu)}{\pi^2\left(\dfrac{1}{a^2} + \dfrac{1}{b^2}\right)^2 ab} \cos\frac{\pi x}{a} \cos\frac{\pi y}{b}.
\end{aligned}\right\} \tag{f}$$

It is seen that the maximum deflection and the maximum bending moments are at the center of the plate. Substituting $x = a/2$, $y = b/2$ in Eqs. (e) and (f), we obtain

$$w_{\text{max.}} = \frac{q_0}{\pi^4 D\left(\dfrac{1}{a^2} + \dfrac{1}{b^2}\right)^2}, \tag{116}$$

$$(M_x)_{\text{max.}} = \frac{q_0}{\pi^2\left(\dfrac{1}{a^2} + \dfrac{1}{b^2}\right)^2}\left(\frac{1}{a^2} + \frac{\nu}{b^2}\right),$$

$$(M_y)_{\text{max.}} = \frac{q_0}{\pi^2\left(\dfrac{1}{a^2} + \dfrac{1}{b^2}\right)^2}\left(\frac{\nu}{a^2} + \frac{1}{b^2}\right). \tag{117}$$

In the particular case of a square plate, $a = b$, and the foregoing formulas become

$$w_{\text{max.}} = \frac{q_0 a^4}{4\pi^4 D}, \qquad (M_x)_{\text{max.}} = (M_y)_{\text{max.}} = \frac{(1 + \nu)q_0 a^2}{4\pi^2}. \tag{118}$$

We use Eqs. (102) and (103) to calculate the shearing forces and obtain

$$Q_x = \frac{q_0}{\pi a\left(\dfrac{1}{a^2} + \dfrac{1}{b^2}\right)} \cos \frac{\pi x}{a} \sin \frac{\pi y}{b},$$

$$Q_y = \frac{q_0}{\pi b\left(\dfrac{1}{a^2} + \dfrac{1}{b^2}\right)} \sin \frac{\pi x}{a} \cos \frac{\pi y}{b}. \quad (g)$$

To find the reactive forces at the supported edges of the plate we proceed as was explained in Art. 22.   For the edge $x = a$ we find

$$V_x = \left(Q_x - \frac{\partial M_{xy}}{\partial y}\right)_{x=a} = -\frac{q_0}{\pi a\left(\dfrac{1}{a^2} + \dfrac{1}{b^2}\right)^2}\left(\frac{1}{a^2} + \frac{2 - \nu}{b^2}\right) \sin \frac{\pi y}{b}.$$

$$(h)$$

In the same manner, for the edge $y = b$

$$V_y = \left(Q_y - \frac{\partial M_{xy}}{\partial x}\right)_{y=b} = -\frac{q_0}{\pi b\left(\dfrac{1}{a^2} + \dfrac{1}{b^2}\right)^2}\left(\frac{1}{b^2} + \frac{2 - \nu}{a^2}\right) \sin \frac{\pi x}{a}.$$

$$(i)$$

Hence the pressure distribution follows a sinusoidal law.   The minus sign indicates that the reactions on the plate act upward. From symmetry it may be concluded that formulas (h) and (i) represent also pressure distributions along the sides $x = 0$ and $y = 0$, respectively.   The resultant of distributed pressures is

$$\frac{2q_0}{\pi\left(\dfrac{1}{a^2} + \dfrac{1}{b^2}\right)^2}\left[\frac{1}{a}\left(\frac{1}{a^2} + \frac{2 - \nu}{b^2}\right)\int_0^b \sin \frac{\pi y}{b}dy\right.$$

$$\left. + \frac{1}{b}\left(\frac{1}{b^2} + \frac{2 - \nu}{a^2}\right)\int_0^a \sin \frac{\pi x}{a}dx\right] = \frac{4q_0 ab}{\pi^2} + \frac{8q_0(1 - \nu)}{\pi^2 ab\left(\dfrac{1}{a^2} + \dfrac{1}{b^2}\right)^2}. \quad (j)$$

Observing that

$$\frac{4q_0 ab}{\pi^2} = \int_0^a \int_0^b q_0 \sin \frac{\pi x}{a} \sin \frac{\pi y}{b}dx\,dy, \quad (k)$$

it can be concluded that the sum of the distributed reactions is larger than the total load on the plate given by expression (k).

This result can be easily explained if we note that, proceeding as was described in Art. 22, we obtain not only the distributed reactions but also reactions concentrated at the corners of the plate. These concentrated reactions are equal, from symmetry; and their magnitude, as may be seen from Fig. 51, is

$$R = 2(M_{xy})_{x=a,y=b} = \frac{2q_0(1 - \nu)}{\pi^2 ab\left(\dfrac{1}{a^2} + \dfrac{1}{b^2}\right)^2}. \qquad (l)$$

The positive sign indicates that the reactions act downward. Their sum is exactly equal to the second term in expression (j).

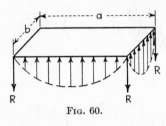

Fig. 60.

The distributed and the concentrated reactions which act on the plate and keep the load defined by Eq. (a) in equilibrium are shown graphically in Fig. 60. It may be seen that the corners of the plate have a tendency to rise up under the action of the applied load and that the concentrated forces R must be applied to prevent this.

The maximum bending stress is at the center of the plate. Assuming that $a > b$, we find that at the center $M_y > M_x$. Hence the maximum bending stress is

$$(\sigma_y)_{\text{max.}} = \frac{6(M_y)_{\text{max.}}}{h^2} = \frac{6q_0}{\pi^2 h^2\left(\dfrac{1}{a^2} + \dfrac{1}{b^2}\right)^2}\left(\frac{\nu}{a^2} + \frac{1}{b^2}\right).$$

The maximum shearing stress will be at the middle of the longer sides of the plate. Assuming that the total transverse force $V_y = Q_y - \dfrac{\partial M_{xy}}{\partial x}$ is distributed along the thickness of the plate according to the parabolic law and using Eq. (i), we obtain

$$(\tau_{yz})_{\text{max.}} = \frac{3q_0}{2\pi bh\left(\dfrac{1}{a^2} + \dfrac{1}{b^2}\right)^2}\left(\frac{1}{b^2} + \frac{2 - \nu}{a^2}\right).$$

If the sinusoidal load distribution is given by the equation

$$q = q_0 \sin \frac{m\pi x}{a} \sin \frac{n\pi y}{b}, \qquad (m)$$

where m and n are integer numbers, we can proceed as before, and we shall obtain for the deflection surface the following expression:

$$w = \frac{q_0}{\pi^4 D\left(\dfrac{m^2}{a^2} + \dfrac{n^2}{b^2}\right)^2} \sin \frac{m\pi x}{a} \sin \frac{n\pi y}{b}, \qquad (119)$$

from which the expressions for bending and twisting moments can be readily obtained by differentiation.

27. Navier Solution for Simply Supported Rectangular Plates. The solution of the previous article can be used in calculating deflections produced in a simply supported rectangular plate by any kind of loading given by the equation

$$q = f(x,y). \qquad (a)$$

For this purpose we represent the function $f(x,y)$ in the form of a double trigonometric series:[1]

$$f(x,y) = \sum_{m=1}^{\infty} \sum_{n=1}^{\infty} a_{mn} \sin \frac{m\pi x}{a} \sin \frac{n\pi y}{b}. \qquad (b)$$

To calculate any particular coefficient $a_{m'n'}$ of this series we multiply both sides of Eq. (b) by $\sin \dfrac{n'\pi y}{b} dy$ and integrate from 0 to b. Observing that

$$\int_0^b \sin \frac{n\pi y}{b} \sin \frac{n'\pi y}{b} dy = 0, \qquad \text{when} \qquad n \neq n',$$

$$\int_0^b \sin \frac{n\pi y}{b} \sin \frac{n'\pi y}{b} dy = \frac{b}{2}, \qquad \text{when} \qquad n = n',$$

we find in this way

$$\int_0^b f(x,y) \sin \frac{n'\pi y}{b} dy = \frac{b}{2} \sum_{m=1}^{\infty} a_{mn'} \sin \frac{m\pi x}{a}. \qquad (c)$$

---

[1] The first solution of the problem of bending of simply supported rectangular plates and the use for this purpose of double trigonometric series is due to Navier, who presented a paper on this subject to the French Academy in 1820. The abstract of the paper was published in *Bull. soc. phil.-math.*, Paris, 1823. The manuscript is in the library of l'École des Ponts et Chaussées.

Multiplying both sides of Eq. (c) by $\sin \dfrac{m'\pi x}{a} dx$ and integrating from 0 to a, we obtain

$$\int_0^a \int_0^b f(x,y) \sin \frac{m'\pi x}{a} \sin \frac{n\pi y}{b} dx\, dy = \frac{ab}{4} a_{m'n'},$$

from which

$$a_{m'n'} = \frac{4}{ab} \int_0^a \int_0^b f(x,y) \sin \frac{m'\pi x}{a} \sin \frac{n'\pi y}{b} dx\, dy. \tag{120}$$

Performing the integration indicated in expression (120) for a given load distribution, *i.e.*, for a given $f(x,y)$, we find the coefficients of series (b) and represent in this way the given load as a sum of partial sinusoidal loadings. The deflection produced by each partial loading was discussed in the previous article, and the total deflection will be obtained by summation of such terms as are given by Eq. (119). Hence we find

$$w = \frac{1}{\pi^4 D} \sum_{m=1}^{\infty} \sum_{n=1}^{\infty} \frac{a_{mn}}{\left(\dfrac{m^2}{a^2} + \dfrac{n^2}{b^2}\right)^2} \sin \frac{m\pi x}{a} \sin \frac{n\pi y}{b}. \tag{121}$$

Take the case of a load uniformly distributed over the entire surface of the plate as an example of the application of the general solution (121). In such a case

$$f(x,y) = q_0$$

where q_0 is the intensity of the uniformly distributed load. From formula (120) we obtain in this case

$$a_{mn} = \frac{4q_0}{ab} \int_0^a \int_0^b \sin \frac{m\pi x}{a} \sin \frac{n\pi y}{b} dx\, dy = \frac{16q_0}{\pi^2 mn},$$

where m and n are odd integers. If m or n or both of them are even numbers, $a_{mn} = 0$. Substituting in Eq. (121), we find

$$w = \frac{16q_0}{\pi^6 D} \sum_{m=1}^{\infty} \sum_{n=1}^{\infty} \frac{\sin \dfrac{m\pi x}{a} \sin \dfrac{n\pi y}{b}}{mn\left(\dfrac{m^2}{a^2} + \dfrac{n^2}{b^2}\right)^2}, \tag{122}$$

where $m = 1, 3, 5, \ldots$ and $n = 1, 3, 5, \ldots$.

In the case of a uniform load we have a deflection surface symmetrical with respect to the axes $x = a/2, y = b/2$; and quite naturally all terms with even numbers for m or n in series (122) vanish, since they are unsymmetrical with respect to the above-mentioned axes. The maximum deflection of the plate is at its center and is found by substituting $x = a/2, y = b/2$ in formula (122), giving

$$w_{\text{max.}} = \frac{16q_0}{\pi^6 D} \sum_{m=1}^{\infty} \sum_{n=1}^{\infty} \frac{(-1)^{\frac{m+n}{2}-1}}{mn\left(\frac{m^2}{a^2} + \frac{n^2}{b^2}\right)^2}. \tag{123}$$

This is a rapidly converging series, and a satisfactory approximation is obtained by taking only the first term of the series which, for example, in the case of a square plate gives

$$w_{\text{max.}} = \frac{4q_0 a^4}{\pi^6 D},$$

or, by substituting expression (3) for D and assuming $\nu = 0.3$,

$$w_{\text{max.}} = 0.0454 \frac{q_0 a^4}{E h^3}.$$

This result is about $2\frac{1}{2}$ per cent in error (see table on page 133).

From expression (123) it may be seen that the deflections of two plates that have the same thickness and the same value of the ratio a/b increase as the fourth power of the length of the sides.

The expressions for bending and twisting moments can be obtained from the general solution (122) by using Eqs. (99) and (100). The series obtained in this way are not so rapidly convergent as series (122), and in the further discussion (see Art. 29) another form of solution will be given more suitable for numerical calculations. Since the moments are expressed by the second derivatives of series (122), their maximum values, if we keep q_0 and D the same, are proportional to the square of linear dimensions. Since the total load on the plate, equal to $q_0 ab$, is also proportional to the square of the linear dimensions, we conclude that, for two plates of equal thickness and of the same value of the ratio a/b, the maximum bending moments and hence the maximum stresses are equal if the total loads on the two plates are equal.[1]

By using the general expression (120) for the coefficients of the trigonometric series (b), Navier also obtained solutions for the case where the load is uniformly distributed over a rectangle with sides parallel to the sides of the plate and for the case of a concentrated load. The corresponding series are not convenient for numerical calculations, and another form of solution of these problems will be discussed later.

28. Application of the Strain Energy Method in Calculating Deflections.—From the discussion in the previous article it is seen that the deflection of a simply supported rectangular plate (Fig. 59) can always be represented in the form of a double trigonometric series

$$w = \sum_{m=1}^{\infty} \sum_{n=1}^{\infty} a_{mn} \sin \frac{m\pi x}{a} \sin \frac{n\pi y}{b}. \tag{a}$$

The coefficients a_{mn} may be considered as the coordinates defining the shape of the deflection surface, and for their determination the principle of virtual displacements may be used. In the application of this principle we need the expression for strain energy

$$V = \frac{1}{2} D \int_0^a \int_0^b \left\{ \left(\frac{\partial^2 w}{\partial x^2} + \frac{\partial^2 w}{\partial y^2} \right)^2 - 2(1 - \nu) \left[\frac{\partial^2 w}{\partial x^2} \frac{\partial^2 w}{\partial y^2} - \left(\frac{\partial^2 w}{\partial x \, \partial y} \right)^2 \right] \right\} dx \, dy. \tag{b}$$

Substituting series (a) for w, the first term under the integral sign in (b) becomes

$$\frac{1}{2} D \int_0^a \int_0^b \left[\sum_{m=1}^{\infty} \sum_{n=1}^{\infty} a_{mn} \left(\frac{m^2 \pi^2}{a^2} + \frac{n^2 \pi^2}{b^2} \right) \sin \frac{m\pi x}{a} \sin \frac{n\pi y}{b} \right]^2 dx \, dy.$$

$$\tag{c}$$

Observing that

$$\int_0^a \sin \frac{m\pi x}{a} \sin \frac{m'\pi x}{a} dx = \int_0^b \sin \frac{n\pi y}{b} \sin \frac{n'\pi y}{b} dy = 0,$$

[1] This conclusion was established by Mariotte in the paper "Traité du mouvement des eaux" published in 1686. See Mariotte's scientific papers, nouvelle ed., vol. 2, p. 467, 1740.

if $m \neq m'$ and $n \neq n'$, we conclude that in calculating the integral (c) we have to consider only the squares of terms of the infinite series in the parentheses.   Using the formula

$$\int_0^a \int^b \sin^2 \frac{m\pi x}{a} \sin^2 \frac{n\pi y}{b} dx\, dy = \frac{ab}{4},$$

the calculation of the integral (c) gives

$$\frac{\pi^4 ab}{8} D \sum_{m=1}^{\infty} \sum_{n=1}^{\infty} a_{mn}^2 \left(\frac{m^2}{a^2} + \frac{n^2}{b^2} \right)^2.$$

From the fact that

$$\int_0^a \int_0^b \sin^2 \frac{m\pi x}{a} \sin^2 \frac{n\pi y}{b} dx\, dy$$

$$= \int_0^a \int_0^b \cos^2 \frac{m\pi x}{a} \cos^2 \frac{n\pi y}{b} dx\, dy = \frac{ab}{4}$$

it can be concluded that the second term under the integral sign in expression (b) is zero after integration.   Hence the total strain energy in this case is given by expression (c) and is

$$V = \frac{\pi^4 ab}{8} D \sum_{m=1}^{\infty} \sum_{n=1}^{\infty} a_{mn}^2 \left(\frac{m^2}{a^2} + \frac{n^2}{b^2} \right)^2. \qquad (124)$$

Let us consider the deflection of the plate (Fig. 59) by a concentrated force P perpendicular to the plate and applied at a point $x = \xi$, $y = \eta$.   To get a virtual displacement satisfying boundary conditions we give to any coefficient $a_{m'n'}$ of series (a) an infinitely small variation $\delta a_{m'n'}$.   As a result of this the deflection (a) undergoes a variation

$$\delta w = \delta a_{m'n'} \sin \frac{m'\pi x}{a} \sin \frac{n'\pi y}{b},$$

and the concentrated load P produces a virtual work

$$P\, \delta a_{m'n'} \sin \frac{m'\pi \xi}{a} \sin \frac{n'\pi \eta}{b}.$$

From the principle of virtual displacements it follows that this work must be equal to the change in potential energy (124) due to the variation $\delta a_{m'n'}$.   Hence

$$P \, \delta a_{m'n'} \sin \frac{m'\pi\xi}{a} \sin \frac{n'\pi\eta}{b} = \frac{\partial V}{\partial a_{m'n'}} \delta a_{m'n'}.$$

Substituting expression (124) for V, we obtain

$$P \, \delta a_{m'n'} \sin \frac{m'\pi\xi}{a} \sin \frac{n'\pi\eta}{b} = \frac{\pi^4 ab}{4} D a_{m'n'} \left(\frac{m'^2}{a^2} + \frac{n'^2}{b^2} \right)^2 \delta a_{m'n'}, \quad (d)$$

from which

$$a_{m'n'} = \frac{4P \sin \dfrac{m'\pi\xi}{a} \sin \dfrac{n'\pi\eta}{b}}{\pi^4 ab D \left(\dfrac{m'^2}{a^2} + \dfrac{n'^2}{b^2} \right)^2}.$$

Substituting this into expression (a), we find the deflection of the plate in the following form:

$$w = \frac{4P}{\pi^4 ab D} \sum_{m=1}^{\infty} \sum_{n=1}^{\infty} \frac{\sin \dfrac{m\pi\xi}{a} \sin \dfrac{n\pi\eta}{b}}{\left(\dfrac{m^2}{a^2} + \dfrac{n^2}{b^2} \right)^2} \sin \frac{m\pi x}{a} \sin \frac{n\pi y}{b}. \quad (125)$$

The series converges rapidly, and we can get the deflection at any given point with sufficient accuracy by taking only the first few terms of the series. Let us, for example, calculate the deflection at the middle when the load is also applied at the middle. In such a case $\xi = x = a/2, \eta = y = b/2$, and series (125) gives

$$w_{\text{max.}} = \frac{4P}{\pi^4 ab D} \sum_{m=1}^{\infty} \sum_{n=1}^{\infty} \frac{1}{\left(\dfrac{m^2}{a^2} + \dfrac{n^2}{b^2} \right)^2}, \quad (e)$$

where $m = 1, 3, 5, \ldots, n = 1, 3, 5, \ldots$. In the case of a square plate, expression (e) becomes

$$w_{\text{max.}} = \frac{4Pa^2}{\pi^4 D} \sum_{m=1}^{\infty} \sum_{n=1}^{\infty} \frac{1}{(m^2 + n^2)^2}.$$

Taking the first four terms of the series, we find that $w_{\text{max.}} = 0.01121 Pa^2/D$ which is about $3\frac{1}{2}$ per cent less than the correct value (see table, page 158).

Having expression (125) for the deflection under a concentrated force, we can get the deflection of the plate under any kind of loading by using the method of superposition. Take, as an example, a uniformly loaded plate. The load distributed over an infinitely small element $d\xi\,d\eta$ of the plate is $qd\xi\,d\eta$, and the deflection produced by this elemental load is obtained by substituting $qd\xi\,d\eta$, in place of P, in Eq. (125). To get the deflection of the plate under the action of the total load we have only to form the summation of the deflections produced by elemental loads. Hence we obtain

$$w = \frac{4q}{\pi^4 abD}\int_0^a\int_0^b\left\{\sum_{m=1}^{\infty}\sum_{n=1}^{\infty}\frac{\sin\dfrac{m\pi\xi}{a}\sin\dfrac{n\pi\eta}{b}}{\left(\dfrac{m^2}{a^2}+\dfrac{n^2}{b^2}\right)^2}\right.$$

$$\left.\sin\frac{m\pi x}{a}\sin\frac{n\pi y}{b}\right\}d\xi\,d\eta. \quad (f)$$

After integration we obtain formula (122) of Navier's solution.

Instead of using the principle of virtual displacements in calculating coefficients a_{mn} in expression (a) for the deflection, we can obtain the same result from the consideration of the total energy of the system. If a system is in a position of stable equilibrium, its total energy is a minimum. Applying this statement to the investigation of bending of plates, we observe that the total energy in such cases consists of two parts, the strain energy of bending, given by expression (b), and the potential energy of the load distributed over the plate. Defining the position of the element $q\,dx\,dy$ of the load by its vertical distance w from the horizontal plane xy, the corresponding potential energy may be taken equal to $-wq\,dx\,dy$, and the potential energy of the total load is

$$-\int\int wq\,dx\,dy.$$

The total energy of the system then is

$$I = \int\int\left\{\frac{D}{2}\left\{\left(\frac{\partial^2 w}{\partial x^2}+\frac{\partial^2 w}{\partial y^2}\right)^2\right.\right.$$

$$\left.\left.- 2(1-\nu)\left[\frac{\partial^2 w}{\partial x^2}\frac{\partial^2 w}{\partial y^2}-\left(\frac{\partial^2 w}{\partial x\,\partial y}\right)^2\right]\right\}-wq\right\}dx\,dy. \quad (g)$$

The problem of bending of a plate reduces in each particular case to that of finding a function w of x and y that satisfies the given boundary conditions and makes the integral (g) a minimum. If we proceed with this problem by the use of the calculus of variations, we obtain for w the partial differential equation (101) which was derived before from the consideration of the equilibrium of an element of the plate. The integral (g), however, can be used advantageously in an approximate investigation of bending of plates. For that purpose we replace the problem of variational calculus with that of finding the minimum of a certain function by assuming that the deflection w can be represented in the form of a series

$$w = a_1\varphi_1(x,y) + a_2\varphi_2(x,y) + a_3\varphi_3(x,y) + \cdots + a_n\varphi_n(x,y), \quad (i)$$

in which the functions φ_1, φ_2, . . . , φ_n are chosen so as to be suitable[1] for representation of the deflection surface w and at the same time to satisfy boundary conditions. Substituting expression (i) in the integral (g), we obtain, after integration, a function of second degree in the coefficients a_1, a_2, ... These coefficients must now be chosen so as to make the integral (g) a minimum, from which it follows that

$$\frac{\partial I}{\partial a_1} = 0, \qquad \frac{\partial I}{\partial a_2} = 0, \qquad \cdots , \frac{\partial I}{\partial a_n} = 0. \qquad (j)$$

This is a system of n linear equations in a_1, a_2, . . . , a_n, and these quantities can readily be calculated in each particular case. If the functions φ are of such a kind that series (i) can represent any arbitrary function within the boundary of the plate,[2] this method of calculating deflections w brings us to a closer and closer approximation as the number n of the terms of the series increases, and by taking n infinitely large we obtain an exact solution of the problem.

[1] From experience we usually know approximately the shape of the deflection surface, and we should be guided by this information in choosing suitable functions φ.

[2] We have seen that a double trigonometrical series (a) possesses this property with respect to deflections w of a simply supported rectangular plate. Hence it can be used for obtaining an exact solution of the problem. The method of solving the bending problems of plates by the use of the integral (g) was developed by W. Ritz; see *J. reine angew. Math.*, vol. 135, 1908; and *Ann. Physik* (4), vol. 28, p. 737, 1909.

Applying the method to the case of a simply supported rectangular plate, we take the deflection in the form of the trigonometric series (a). Then by using expression (124) for the strain energy, the integral (g) is represented in the following form:

$$I = \frac{\pi^4 abD}{8} \sum_{m=1}^{\infty} \sum_{n=1}^{\infty} a_{mn}^2 \left(\frac{m^2}{a^2} + \frac{n^2}{b^2}\right)^2$$

$$- \int_0^a \int_0^b q \sum_{m=1}^{\infty} \sum_{n=1}^{\infty} a_{mn} \sin \frac{m\pi x}{a} \sin \frac{n\pi y}{b} dx \, dy, \quad (k)$$

and Eqs. (j) have the form

$$\frac{\pi^4 abD}{4} a_{mn} \left(\frac{m^2}{a^2} + \frac{n^2}{b^2}\right)^2 - \int_0^a \int_0^b q \sin \frac{m\pi x}{a} \sin \frac{n\pi y}{b} dx \, dy = 0. \quad (l)$$

In the case of a load P applied at a point with the coordinates ξ, η, the intensity q of the load is zero in all points except the point ξ, η, in which we have to put $q \, dx \, dy = P$. Then Eq. (l) coincides with Eq. (d) previously derived by the use of the principle of virtual displacements. Several further applications of this method of calculating deflections will be given later in the discussion of plates with boundary conditions other than those of simply supported edges.

29. Alternate Solution for Simply Supported and Uniformly Loaded Rectangular Plates.—In discussing problems of bending of rectangular plates that have two opposite edges simply supported, M. Levy[1] suggested taking the solution in the form of a series

$$w = \sum_{m=1}^{\infty} Y_m \sin \frac{m\pi x}{a}, \quad (a)$$

where Y_m is a function of y only. It is assumed that the sides $x = 0$ and $x = a$ (Fig. 61) are simply supported. Hence each term of series (a) satisfies the boundary conditions $w = 0$ and

---

[1] See *Compt. rend.*, vol. 129, pp. 535–539, 1899. The solution was applied to several particular cases of bending of rectangular plates by E. Estanave, "Thèses," Paris, 1900; in this paper the transformation of the double series of the Navier solution to the simple series of M. Levy is shown.

$\partial^2 w / \partial x^2 = 0$ at these two sides. It remains to determine Y_m in such a form as to satisfy the boundary conditions on the sides $y = \pm b/2$ and also the equation of the deflection surface

$$\frac{\partial^4 w}{\partial x^4} + 2 \frac{\partial^4 w}{\partial x^2 \, \partial y^2} + \frac{\partial^4 w}{\partial y^4} = \frac{q}{D}. \qquad (b)$$

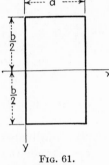

FIG. 61.

In applying this method to uniformly loaded and simply supported rectangular plates, a further simplification can be made by taking the solution of Eq. (b) in the form[1]

$$w = w_1 + w_2 \qquad (c)$$

and letting

$$w_1 = \frac{q}{24D}(x^4 - 2ax^3 + a^3 x); \qquad (d)$$

i.e., w_1 represents the deflection of a uniformly loaded strip parallel to the x-axis. It satisfies Eq. (b) and also the boundary conditions at the edges $x = 0$ and $x = a$.

The expression w_2 evidently has to satisfy the equation

$$\frac{\partial^4 w_2}{\partial x^4} + 2 \frac{\partial^4 w_2}{\partial x^2 \, \partial y^2} + \frac{\partial^4 w_2}{\partial y^4} = 0 \qquad (e)$$

and must be chosen in such a manner as to make the sum (c) satisfy all boundary conditions of the plate. Taking w_2 in the form of the series (a) in which from symmetry $m = 1, 3, 5, \ldots$ and substituting it into Eq. (e), we obtain

$$\sum_{m=1}^{\infty} \left(Y_m^{\mathrm{IV}} - 2 \frac{m^2 \pi^2}{a^2} Y_m'' + \frac{m^4 \pi^4}{a^4} Y_m \right) \sin \frac{m \pi x}{a} = 0.$$

This equation can be satisfied for all values of x only if the function Y_m satisfies the equation

$$Y_m^{\mathrm{IV}} - 2 \frac{m^2 \pi^2}{a^2} Y_m'' + \frac{m^4 \pi^4}{a^4} Y_m = 0. \qquad (f)$$

[1] This form of solution was used by A. Nadai, *Forschungsarbeiten*, Nos. 170 and 171, Berlin, 1915; see also his book "Elastische Platten," Berlin, 1925.

The general integral of this equation is

$$Y_m = \frac{qa^4}{D}\left(A_m \cosh \frac{m\pi y}{a} + B_m \frac{m\pi y}{a} \sinh \frac{m\pi y}{a} \right.$$
$$\left. + C_m \sinh \frac{m\pi y}{a} + D_m \frac{m\pi y}{a} \cosh \frac{m\pi y}{a} \right). \quad (g)$$

Observing that the deflection surface of the plate is symmetrical with respect to the x-axis (Fig. 61), we keep in the expression (g) only even functions of y and let the integration constants $C_m = D_m = 0$.

The deflection surface (c) is then represented by the following expression:

$$w = \frac{q}{24D}(x^4 - 2ax^3 + a^3x)$$
$$+ \frac{qa^4}{D}\sum_{m=1}^{\infty}\left(A_m \cosh \frac{m\pi y}{a} + B_m \frac{m\pi y}{a} \sinh \frac{m\pi y}{a} \right) \sin \frac{m\pi x}{a}, \quad (h)$$

which satisfies Eq. (b) and also the boundary conditions at the sides $x = 0$ and $x = a$. It remains now to adjust the constants of integration A_m and B_m in such a manner as to satisfy the boundary conditions

$$w = 0, \qquad \frac{\partial^2 w}{\partial y^2} = 0 \qquad (i)$$

on the sides $y = \pm b/2$. We begin by developing expression (d) in a trigonometric series, which gives[1]

$$\frac{q}{24D}(x^4 - 2ax^3 + a^3x) = \frac{4qa^4}{\pi^5 D}\sum_{m=1}^{\infty} \frac{1}{m^5} \sin \frac{m\pi x}{a},$$

where $m = 1, 3, 5, \ldots$. The deflection surface (h) will now be represented in the form

$$w = \frac{qa^4}{D}\sum_{m=1}^{\infty}\left(\frac{4}{\pi^5 m^5} + A_m \cosh \frac{m\pi y}{a} + B_m \frac{m\pi y}{a} \sinh \frac{m\pi y}{a} \right) \sin \frac{m\pi x}{a},$$
$$(j)$$

where $m = 1, 3, 5, \ldots$. Substituting this expression in the

[1] See author's "Strength of Materials," vol. 2, p. 420, 1930.

boundary conditions (i) and using the notation

$$\frac{m\pi b}{2a} = \alpha_m, \qquad (k)$$

we obtain the following equations for determining the constants A_m and B_m:

$$\frac{4}{\pi^5 m^5} + A_m \cosh \alpha_m + \alpha_m B_m \sinh \alpha_m = 0,$$

$$(A_m + 2B_m) \cosh \alpha_m + \alpha_m B_m \sinh \alpha_m = 0,$$

from which

$$A_m = -\frac{2(\alpha_m \tanh \alpha_m + 2)}{\pi^5 m^5 \cosh \alpha_m}, \qquad B_m = \frac{2}{\pi^5 m^5 \cosh \alpha_m}. \qquad (l)$$

Substituting these values of the constants in Eq. (j), we obtain the deflection surface of the plate, satisfying Eq. (b) and the boundary conditions, in the following form:

$$w = \frac{4qa^4}{\pi^5 D} \sum_{m=1,3,5,\cdots}^{\infty} \frac{1}{m^5} \left[1 - \frac{(\alpha_m \tanh \alpha_m + 2)}{2 \cosh \alpha_m} \cosh \frac{2\alpha_m y}{b} \right.$$
$$\left. + \frac{\alpha_m}{2 \cosh \alpha_m} \frac{2y}{b} \sinh \frac{2\alpha_m y}{b} \right] \sin \frac{m\pi x}{a}, \qquad (126)$$

from which the deflection at any point can be calculated by using tables of hyperbolic functions.[1] The maximum deflection is obtained at the middle of the plate ($x = a/2$, $y = 0$), where

$$w_{\text{max.}} = \frac{4qa^4}{\pi^5 D} \sum_{m=1,3,5,\cdots}^{\infty} \frac{(-1)^{\frac{m-1}{2}}}{m^5} \left(1 - \frac{\alpha_m \tanh \alpha_m + 2}{2 \cosh \alpha_m} \right). \qquad (m)$$

The summation of the first series of terms represents the deflection of the middle of a uniformly loaded strip. Hence we can represent expression (m) in the following form:

$$w_{\text{max.}} = \frac{5}{384} \frac{qa^4}{D} - \frac{4qa^4}{\pi^5 D} \sum_{m=1,3,5,\cdots}^{\infty} \frac{(-1)^{\frac{m-1}{2}}}{m^5} \cdot \frac{\alpha_m \tanh \alpha_m + 2}{2 \cosh \alpha_m}. \qquad (127)$$

The series in this expression converges very rapidly,[2] and suffi-

[1] See, for instance, C. F. Becker and C. E. van Orstrand, "Hyperbolic Functions," Washington, 1909; or K. Hayashi. "Fünfst. Tafeln der Kreis- und Hyperbelfunktionen," Berlin, 1928.

[2] We assume that $b \geqq a$, as in Fig. 61.

cient accuracy is obtained by taking only the first term.   Taking a square plate as an example, we have from Eq. (*k*) that

$$\alpha_1 = \frac{\pi}{2}, \qquad \alpha_3 = \frac{3\pi}{2}, \qquad \cdots ,$$

and Eq. (127) gives

$$w_{\text{max.}} = \frac{5}{384}\frac{qa^4}{D} - \frac{4qa^4}{\pi^5 D}(0.68562 - 0.00025 + \cdots) = 0.00406\frac{qa^4}{D}.$$

It is seen that the second term of the series in the parentheses is negligible and that by taking only the first term the formula for deflection is obtained correct to three significant figures.

Substituting expression (3) for *D* in formula (127), we can represent the maximum deflection of a plate in the form

$$w_{\text{max.}} = \alpha\frac{qa^4}{Eh^3}, \tag{128}$$

where α is a numerical factor depending on the ratio b/a of the sides of the plate and on Poisson's ratio ν.   Values of α calculated for $\nu = 0.3$ are given in Table 5.   To obtain α for a material with a different value of ν the values of α given in the table must be multiplied by $(1 - \nu^2)/0.91$.

The bending moments M_x and M_y are calculated by means of expression (*h*).   Substituting the algebraic portion of this expression in Eqs. (99), we find that

$$M_x' = \frac{qx(a - x)}{2}, \qquad M_y' = \nu\frac{qx(a - x)}{2}. \tag{n}$$

The substitution of the series of expression (*h*) in the same equations gives

$$\left.\begin{aligned}
M_x'' &= (1 - \nu)qa^2\pi^2\sum_{m=1}^{\infty} m^2\bigg[A_m \cosh\frac{m\pi y}{a} \\
&\quad + B_m\bigg(\frac{m\pi y}{a}\sinh\frac{m\pi y}{a} - \frac{2\nu}{1 - \nu}\cosh\frac{m\pi y}{a}\bigg)\bigg]\sin\frac{m\pi x}{a}, \\
M_y'' &= -(1 - \nu)qa^2\pi^2\sum_{m=1}^{\infty} m^2\bigg[A_m \cosh\frac{m\pi y}{a} \\
&\quad + B_m\bigg(\frac{m\pi y}{a}\sinh\frac{m\pi y}{a} + \frac{2}{1 - \nu}\cosh\frac{m\pi y}{a}\bigg)\bigg]\sin\frac{m\pi x}{a}.
\end{aligned}\right\} \tag{o}$$

The total bending moments are obtained by summations of expressions (n) and (o). The maximum values of these moments are at the center of the plate $(x = a/2, \ y = 0)$, for which point we obtain

$$(M_x)_{\text{max.}} = \frac{qa^2}{8} + (1 - \nu)qa^2\pi^2 \sum_{m=1}^{\infty} (-1)^{\frac{m-1}{2}} m^2 \left(A_m - \frac{2\nu}{1 - \nu} B_m \right),$$

$$(M_y)_{\text{max.}} = \nu\frac{qa^2}{8} - (1 - \nu)qa^2\pi^2 \sum_{m=1}^{\infty} (-1)^{\frac{m-1}{2}} m^2 \left(A_m + \frac{2}{1 - \nu} B_m \right),$$

where A_m and B_m are given by expressions (l). Again we have series that converge very rapidly. We can represent the maximum moments in the form

$$(M_x)_{\text{max.}} = \beta qa^2, \qquad (M_y)_{\text{max.}} = \beta_1 qa^2. \qquad (p)$$

The numerical factors β and β_1 depending on the ratio a/b of the sides of the plate and on the magnitude of ν are given in Table 5 for $\nu = 0.3$. From the table it is seen that, as the ratio b/a increases, the maximum deflection and the maximum moments of the plate rapidly approach the values calculated for a uniformly loaded strip or for a plate bent to a cylindrical surface obtained by making $b/a = \infty$. For $b/a = 3$ the difference between the deflection of the strip and the plate is about $6\frac{1}{2}$ per cent. For $b/a = 5$ this difference is less than $\frac{1}{2}$ per cent. The differences between the maximum bending moments for the same ratios of b/a are 5 and $\frac{1}{3}$ per cent, respectively. It may be concluded from this comparison that for $b/a > 3$ the calculations for a plate can be replaced by those for a strip without substantial error.

Expression (h) can be used also for calculating shearing forces and reactions at the boundary. Forming the second derivatives of this expression, we find

$$\Delta w = \frac{\partial^2 w}{\partial x^2} + \frac{\partial^2 w}{\partial y^2}$$

$$= -\frac{qx(a - x)}{2D} + \frac{2\pi^2 qa^2}{D} \sum_{m=1}^{\infty} m^2 B_m \cosh \frac{m\pi y}{a} \sin \frac{m\pi x}{a}.$$

Substituting this in Eqs. (102) and (103), we obtain

$$Q_x = \frac{q(a - 2x)}{2} - 2\pi^3 qa \sum_{m=1}^{\infty} m^3 B_m \cosh \frac{m\pi y}{a} \cos \frac{m\pi x}{a},$$

$$Q_y = -2\pi^3 qa \sum_{m=1}^{\infty} m^3 B_m \sinh \frac{m\pi y}{a} \sin \frac{m\pi x}{a}.$$

For the sides $x = a$ and $y = b/2$ we find

$$(Q_x)_{x=a} = -\frac{qa}{2} + 2\pi^3 qa \sum_{m=1}^{\infty} m^3 B_m \cosh \frac{m\pi y}{a}$$

$$= -\frac{qa}{2} + \frac{4qa}{\pi^2} \sum_{m=1,3,5,\cdots}^{\infty} \frac{\cosh \dfrac{m\pi y}{a}}{m^2 \cosh \alpha_m},$$

$$(Q_y)_{y=\frac{b}{2}} = -2\pi^3 qa \sum_{m=1}^{\infty} m^3 B_m \sinh \alpha_m \sin \frac{m\pi x}{a}$$

$$= -\frac{4qa}{\pi^2} \sum_{m=1,3,5,\cdots}^{\infty} \frac{\tanh \alpha_m}{m^2} \sin \frac{m\pi x}{a}.$$

These shearing forces have their numerical maximum value at the middle of the sides, where

$$\left.\begin{array}{l} (Q_x)_{x=a,y=0} = -\dfrac{qa}{2} + \dfrac{4qa}{\pi^2} \displaystyle\sum_{m=1,3,5,\cdots}^{\infty} \dfrac{1}{m^2 \cosh \alpha_m} = -\gamma qa, \\[4mm] (Q_y)_{x=\frac{a}{2},y=\frac{b}{2}} = -\dfrac{4qa}{\pi^2} \displaystyle\sum_{m=1,3,5,\cdots}^{\infty} \dfrac{(-1)^{\frac{m-1}{2}}}{m^2} \tanh \alpha_m = -\gamma_1 qa. \end{array}\right\} \quad (q)$$

The numerical factors γ and γ_1 are also given in Table 5.

The reactive forces along the side $x = a$ are given by the expression

$$V_x = \left(Q_x - \frac{\partial M_{xy}}{\partial y}\right)_{x=a} = -\frac{qa}{2} + \frac{4qa}{\pi^2} \sum_{m=1,3,5,\cdots}^{\infty} \frac{\cosh \dfrac{m\pi y}{a}}{m^2 \cosh \alpha_m}$$

$$+ \frac{2(1-\nu)qa}{\pi^2} \sum_{m=1,3,5,\cdots}^{\infty} \frac{1}{m^2 \cosh^2 \alpha_m}$$

$$\left(-\alpha_m \sinh \alpha_m \cosh \frac{m\pi y}{a} + \frac{m\pi y}{a} \cosh \alpha_m \sinh \frac{m\pi y}{a}\right).$$

The maximum numerical value of this pressure is at the middle of the side ($y = 0$) at which point we find

$$(V_x)_{x=a,y=0} = -qa\left[\frac{1}{2} - \frac{4}{\pi^2} \sum_{m=1,3,5,\cdots}^{\infty} \frac{1}{m^2 \cosh \alpha_m}\right.$$

$$\left.+ \frac{2(1-\nu)}{\pi^2} \sum_{m=1,3,5,\cdots}^{\infty} \frac{\alpha_m \sinh \alpha_m}{m^2 \cosh^2 \alpha_m}\right] = -\delta qa, \quad (r)$$

where δ is a numerical factor depending on ν and on the ratio b/a, which can readily be obtained by summing up the rapidly converging series that occur in expression (r). Numerical values

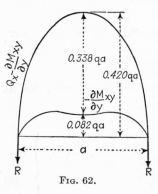

FIG. 62.

of δ, and of δ_1, which corresponds to the middle of the sides parallel to the x-axis, are given in Table 5. The distribution of the pressures (r) along the sides of a square plate is shown in Fig. 62. The portion of the pressures produced by the twisting moments M_{xy} is also shown. These latter pressures are balanced by reactive forces concentrated at the corners of the plate. The magnitude of these forces is given by the expression

$$R = 2(M_{xy})_{x=a,y=\frac{b}{2}} = 2D(1-\nu)\left(\frac{\partial^2 w}{\partial x\, \partial y}\right)_{x=a,y=\frac{b}{2}}$$

$$= \frac{4(1-\nu)qa^2}{\pi^3} \sum_{m=1,3,5,\cdots}^{\infty} \frac{1}{m^3 \cosh \alpha_m}[(1 + \alpha_m \tanh \alpha_m) \sinh \alpha_m$$

$$- \alpha_m \cosh \alpha_m] = nqa^2.$$

The forces are directed downward and prevent the corners of a plate from rising up during bending. The values of the coefficient n are given in the last column of the Table 5.

TABLE 5.—NUMERICAL FACTORS α, β, γ, δ, n FOR UNIFORMLY LOADED AND SIMPLY SUPPORTED RECTANGULAR PLATES
($\nu = 0.3$)

b/a	$w_{\max.}$ $= \alpha \dfrac{qa^4}{Eh^3}$	$(M_x)_{\max.}$ $= \beta qa^2$	$(M_y)_{\max.}$ $= \beta_1 qa^2$	$(Q_x)_{\max.}$ $= \gamma qa$	$(Q_y)_{\max.}$ $= \gamma_1 qa$	$(V_x)_{\max.}$ $= \delta qa$	$(V_y)_{\max.}$ $= \delta_1 qa$	R $= n qa^2$
	α	β	β_1	γ	γ_1	δ	δ_1	n
1.0	0.0443	0.0479	0.0479	0.338	0.338	0.420	0.420	0.065
1.1	0.0530	0.0553	0.0494	0.360	0.347	0.440	0.440	0.070
1.2	0.0616	0.0626	0.0501	0.380	0.353	0.455	0.453	0.074
1.3	0.0697	0.0693	0.0504	0.397	0.357	0.468	0.464	0.079
1.4	0.0770	0.0753	0.0506	0.411	0.361	0.478	0.471	0.083
1.5	0.0843	0.0812	0.0499	0.424	0.363	0.486	0.480	0.085
1.6	0.0906	0.0862	0.0493	0.435	0.365	0.491	0.485	0.086
1.7	0.0964	0.0908	0.0486	0.444	0.367	0.496	0.488	0.088
1.8	0.1017	0.0948	0.0479	0.452	0.368	0.499	0.491	0.090
1.9	0.1064	0.0985	0.0471	0.459	0.369	0.502	0.494	0.091
2.0	0.1106	0.1017	0.0464	0.465	0.370	0.503	0.496	0.092
3.0	0.1336	0.1189	0.0404	0.493	0.372	0.505	0.498	0.093
4.0	0.1400	0.1235	0.0384	0.498	0.372	0.502	0.500	0.094
5.0	0.1416	0.1246	0.0375	0.500	0.372	0.501	0.500	0.095
∞	0.1422	0.1250	0.0375	0.500	0.372	0.500	0.500	0.095

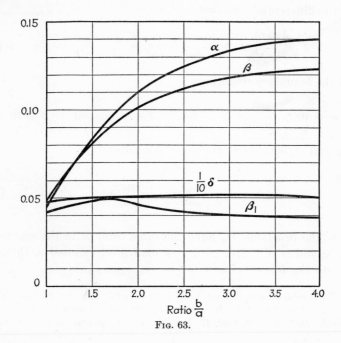

FIG. 63.

The values of the factors α, β, β_1, δ as functions of the ratio b/a are represented by the curves in Fig. 63.

30. Simply Supported Rectangular Plates under Hydrostatic Pressure.—Assume that a simply supported rectangular plate is loaded as shown in Fig. 64. Proceeding as in the case of a uniformly distributed load, we take the deflection of the plate in the form[1]

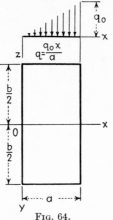

FIG. 64.

$$w = w_1 + w_2, \qquad (a)$$

in which

$$w_1 = \frac{q_0}{360D}\left(\frac{3x^5}{a} - 10ax^3 + 7ax^3\right)$$

$$= \frac{2q_0 a^4}{D\pi^5} \sum_{m=1,2,3,\cdots}^{\infty} \frac{(-1)^{m+1}}{m^5} \sin\frac{m\pi x}{a} \quad (b)$$

represents the deflection of a strip under the triangular load. This expression satisfies the differential equation

$$\frac{\partial^4 w}{\partial x^4} + 2\frac{\partial^4 w}{\partial x^2\,\partial y^2} + \frac{\partial^4 w}{\partial y^4} = \frac{q}{D} = \frac{q_0 x}{aD} \qquad (c)$$

and the boundary conditions

$$w = 0, \qquad \frac{\partial^2 w}{\partial x^2} = 0 \qquad \text{for} \qquad x = 0 \qquad \text{and} \qquad x = a.$$

The part w_2 is taken in the form of a series

$$w_2 = \sum_{m=1}^{\infty} Y_m \sin\frac{m\pi x}{a}, \qquad (d)$$

where the functions Y_m have the same form as in the previous article, and $m = 1, 2, 3, \ldots$. Substituting expressions (b) and (d) into Eq. (a), we obtain

[1] This problem was discussed by E. Estanave, *loc. cit.*, p. 125. The numerical tables of deflections and moments were calculated by B. G. Galerkin, *Bull. Polytech. Inst.*, St. Petersburg, vols. 26 and 27, 1918.

$$w = \frac{q_0 a^4}{D} \sum_{m=1}^{\infty} \left[\frac{2(-1)^{m+1}}{\pi^5 m^5} + A_m \cosh \frac{m\pi y}{a} \right.$$

$$\left. + B_m \frac{m\pi y}{a} \sinh \frac{m\pi y}{a} \right] \sin \frac{m\pi x}{a}, \quad (e)$$

where the constants A_m and B_m are to be determined from the conditions

$$w = 0, \qquad \frac{\partial^2 w}{\partial y^2} = 0 \qquad \text{for} \qquad y = \pm \frac{b}{2}.$$

From these conditions we find

$$\frac{2(-1)^{m+1}}{\pi^5 m^5} + A_m \cosh \alpha_m + B_m \alpha_m \sinh \alpha_m = 0,$$

$$(2B_m + A_m) \cosh \alpha_m + B_m \alpha_m \sinh \alpha_m = 0.$$

In these equations we use, as before, the notation

$$\alpha_m = \frac{m\pi b}{2a}.$$

Solving them, we find

$$A_m = -\frac{(2 + \alpha_m \tanh \alpha_m)(-1)^{m+1}}{\pi^5 m^5 \cosh \alpha_m}, \qquad B_m = \frac{(-1)^{m+1}}{\pi^5 m^5 \cosh \alpha_m}, \quad (f)$$

The deflection of the plate along the x-axis is

$$(w)_{y=0} = \frac{q_0 a^4}{D} \sum_{m=1}^{\infty} \left[\frac{2(-1)^{m+1}}{\pi^5 m^5} + A_m \right] \sin \frac{m\pi x}{a}.$$

For a square plate $a = b$, and we find

$$(w)_{y=0} = \frac{q_0 a^4}{D} \left(0.002055 \sin \frac{\pi x}{a} - 0.000177 \sin \frac{2\pi x}{a} \right.$$

$$\left. + 0.000025 \sin \frac{3\pi x}{a} - \cdots \right). \quad (g)$$

The deflection at the center of the plate is

$$(w)_{x=\frac{a}{2}, y=0} = 0.00203 \frac{q_0 a^4}{D} \qquad (h)$$

which is one-half the deflection of a uniformly loaded plate (see page 129) as it should be. By equating the derivative of expression (g) to zero, we find that the maximum deflection is at the point $x = 0.557a$. This maximum deflection, which is 0.00206 $q_0 a^4/D$, differs only very little from the deflection at the middle as given by formula (h). The point of maximum deflection approaches the center of the plate as the ratio b/a increases. For $b/a = \infty$, as for a strip [see expression (b)], the maximum deflection is at the point $x = 0.5193a$. When $b/a < 1$, the point of maximum deflection moves away from the center of the plate as the ratio b/a decreases. The deflections at several points along the x-axis (Fig. 64) are given in Table 6. It is seen

TABLE 6.—NUMERICAL FACTOR α FOR DEFLECTIONS OF A SIMPLY SUPPORTED
RECTANGULAR PLATE; PRESSURE $q = q_0 x/a$
($\nu = 0.3,\ b > a$)

$$w = \alpha \frac{q_0 a^4}{Eh^3}, \qquad y = 0$$

b/a	$x = 0.25a$	$x = 0.50a$	$x = 0.60a$	$x = 0.75a$
1	0.0143	0.0221	0.0220	0.0177
1.1	0.0173	0.0265	0.0264	0.0210
1.2	0.0203	0.0308	0.0305	0.0241
1.3	0.0231	0.0348	0.0344	0.0271
1.4	0.0257	0.0385	0.0380	0.0298
1.5	0.0281	0.0421	0.0414	0.0323
1.6	0.0303	0.0453	0.0444	0.0346
1.7	0.0323	0.0482	0.0472	0.0366
1.8	0.0342	0.0508	0.0497	0.0385
1.9	0.0358	0.0532	0.0519	0.0402
2.0	0.0373	0.0553	0.0539	0.0417
3.0	0.0454	0.0668	0.0647	0.0498
4.0	0.0477	0.0700	0.0679	0.0521
5.0	0.0482	0.0708	0.0687	0.0527
∞	0.0484	0.0711	0.0690	0.0529

that, as the ratio b/a increases, the deflections approach the values calculated for a strip. For $b/a = 4$ the differences in these values are about $1\frac{1}{2}$ per cent. We can always calculate the deflection of a plate for which $b/a > 4$ with satisfactory accuracy by using formula (b) for the deflection of a strip under triangular load. The bending moments M_x and M_y are found by substituting expression (e) for deflections in Eqs. (99). Along the x-axis ($y = 0$) the expression for M_x becomes

$$(M_x)_{y=0} = q_0 a^2 \sum_{m=1}^{\infty} \frac{2(-1)^{m+1}}{\pi^3 m^3} \sin \frac{m\pi x}{a}$$

$$+ q_0 a^2 \pi^2 \sum_{m=1}^{\infty} m^2 [(1 - \nu)A_m - 2\nu B_m] \sin \frac{m\pi x}{a}. \quad (i)$$

The first sum on the right side of this expression represents the bending moment for a strip under the action of a triangular load and is equal to $\dfrac{q_0}{6}\left(ax - \dfrac{x^3}{a} \right)$. Using expressions ($f$) for the constants A_m and B_m in the second sum, we obtain

$$(M_x)_{y=0} = \frac{q_0(a^2 x - x^3)}{6a}$$

$$- \frac{q_0 a^2}{\pi^3} \sum_{m=1}^{\infty} \frac{(-1)^{m+1}}{m^3 \cosh \alpha_m} [2 + (1 - \nu)\alpha_m \tanh \alpha_m] \sin \frac{m\pi x}{a}. \quad (j)$$

The series thus obtained converges rapidly, and a sufficiently accurate value of M_x can be realized by taking only the first few terms. In this way the bending moment at any point of the x-axis can be represented by the equation

$$(M_x)_{y=0} = \beta q_0 a^2, \quad (k)$$

where β is a numerical factor depending on the abscissa x of the point. In a similar manner we get

$$(M_y)_{y=0} = \beta_1 q_0 a^2. \quad (l)$$

The numerical values of the factors β and β_1 in formulas (k) and (l) are given in Table 7. It is seen that for $b \gtrless 4a$ the moments are very close to the values of the moments in a strip under a triangular load.

Equations (102) and (103) are used to calculate shearing forces. From the first of these equations, by using expression (j), we obtain for points on the x-axis

$$(Q_x)_{y=0} = -D\frac{\partial}{\partial x}\left(\frac{\partial^2 w}{\partial x^2} + \frac{\partial^2 w}{\partial y^2}\right)_{y=0}$$

$$= \frac{q_0(a^2 - 3x^2)}{6a} - \frac{2q_0 a}{\pi^2}\sum_{m=1}^{\infty}\frac{(-1)^{m+1}}{m^2 \cosh \alpha_m} \cos \frac{m\pi x}{a}.$$

The general expressions for shearing forces Q_x and Q_y are

$$Q_x = \frac{q_0(a^2 - 3x^2)}{6a} - \frac{2q_0 a}{\pi^2}\sum_{m=1}^{\infty}\frac{(-1)^{m+1}\cosh \dfrac{m\pi y}{a}}{m^2 \cosh \alpha_m} \cos \frac{m\pi x}{a}, \qquad (m)$$

$$Q_y = -\frac{2q_0 a}{\pi^2}\sum_{m=1}^{\infty}\frac{(-1)^{m+1}\sinh \dfrac{m\pi y}{a}}{m^2 \cosh \alpha_m} \sin \frac{m\pi x}{a}. \qquad (n)$$

The magnitude of the vertical reactions V_x and V_y along the boundary are obtained by combining the shearing forces with the

TABLE 7.—NUMERICAL FACTORS β AND β_1 FOR BENDING MOMENTS OF
SIMPLY SUPPORTED RECTANGULAR PLATES UNDER HYDROSTATIC
PRESSURE $q = q_0 x/a$
($\nu = 0.3$, $b > a$)

b/a	$M_x = \beta a^2 q_0$, $y = 0$				$M_y = \beta_1 a^2 q_0$, $y = 0$			
	$x = 0.25a$	$x = 0.50a$	$x = 0.60a$	$x = 0.75a$	$x = 0.25a$	$x = 0.50a$	$x = 0.60a$	$x = 0.75a$
1.0	0.0132	0.0239	0.0264	0.0259	0.0149	0.0239	0.0245	0.0207
1.1	0.0156	0.0276	0.0302	0.0289	0.0155	0.0247	0.0251	0.0211
1.2	0.0179	0.0313	0.0338	0.0318	0.0158	0.0250	0.0254	0.0213
1.3	0.0200	0.0346	0.0371	0.0344	0.0160	0.0252	0.0255	0.0213
1.4	0.0221	0.0376	0.0402	0.0367	0.0160	0.0253	0.0254	0.0212
1.5	0.0239	0.0406	0.0429	0.0388	0.0159	0.0249	0.0252	0.0210
1.6	0.0256	0.0431	0.0454	0.0407	0.0158	0.0246	0.0249	0.0207
1.7	0.0272	0.0454	0.0476	0.0424	0.0155	0.0243	0.0246	0.0205
1.8	0.0286	0.0474	0.0496	0.0439	0.0153	0.0239	0.0242	0.0202
1.9	0.0298	0.0492	0.0513	0.0452	0.0150	0.0235	0.0238	0.0199
2.0	0.0309	0.0508	0.0529	0.0463	0.0148	0.0232	0.0234	0.0197
3.0	0.0369	0.0594	0.0611	0.0525	0.0128	0.0202	0.0207	0.0176
4.0	0.0385	0.0617	0.0632	0.0541	0.0120	0.0192	0.0196	0.0168
5.0	0.0389	0.0623	0.0638	0.0546	0.0118	0.0187	0.0193	0.0166
∞	0.0391	0.0625	0.0640	0.0547	0.0117	0.0187	0.0192	0.0165

derivatives of the twisting moments. Along the sides $x = 0$ and $x = a$ these reactions can be represented in the form

$$V_x = \left(Q_x - \frac{\partial M_{xy}}{\partial y} \right)_{x=0, x=a} = \pm \delta q_0 a, \qquad (o)$$

and along the sides $y = \pm b/2$ in the form

$$V_y = \left(Q_y - \frac{\partial M_{xy}}{\partial x} \right)_{y = \pm \frac{b}{2}} = \mp \delta_1 q_0 b, \qquad (p)$$

in which δ and δ_1 are numerical factors depending on the ratio b/a and on the coordinates of the points taken on the boundary. Several values of these factors are given in Table 8.

TABLE 8.—NUMERICAL FACTORS δ AND δ_1 FOR REACTIONS OF SIMPLY SUPPORTED RECTANGULAR PLATES UNDER HYDROSTATIC PRESSURE $q = q_0 x/a$ ($\nu = 0.3$, $b > a$)

	Reactions $\delta q_0 a$				Reactions $\delta_1 q_0 b$			
	$x = 0$		$x = a$		$y = \pm b/2$			
b/a	$y = 0$	$y = 0.25b$	$y = 0$	$y = 0.25b$	$x = 0.25a$	$x = 0.50a$	$x = 0.60a$	$x = 0.75a$
1.0	0.126	0.098	0.294	0.256	0.115	0.210	0.234	0.239
1.1	0.136	0.107	0.304	0.267	0.110	0.199	0.221	0.224
1.2	0.144	0.114	0.312	0.276	0.105	0.189	0.208	0.209
1.3	0.150	0.121	0.318	0.284	0.100	0.178	0.196	0.196
1.4	0.155	0.126	0.323	0.292	0.095	0.169	0.185	0.184
1.5	0.159	0.132	0.327	0.297	0.090	0.160	0.175	0.174
1.6	0.162	0.136	0.330	0.302	0.086	0.151	0.166	0.164
1.7	0.164	0.140	0.332	0.306	0.082	0.144	0.157	0.155
1.8	0.166	0.143	0.333	0.310	0.078	0.136	0.149	0.147
1.9	0.167	0.146	0.334	0.313	0.074	0.130	0.142	0.140
2.0	0.168	0.149	0.335	0.316	0.071	0.124	0.135	0.134
3.0	0.169	0.163	0.336	0.331	0.048	0.083	0.091	0.089
4.0	0.168	0.167	0.334	0.334	0.036	0.063	0.068	0.067
5.0	0.167	0.167	0.334	0.335	0.029	0.050	0.055	0.054
∞	0.167	0.167	0.333	0.333				

The magnitude of concentrated forces that must be applied to prevent the corners of the plate rising up during bending can be found from the values of the twisting moments M_{xy} at the corners. Since the load is not symmetrical, the reactions R_1 at $x = 0$ and $y = \pm b/2$ are different from the reactions R_2 at $x = a$ and $y = \pm b/2$. These reactions can be represented in the following form:

$$R_1 = n_1 q_0 ab, \qquad R_2 = n_2 q_0 ab. \qquad (q)$$

The values of the numerical factors n_1 and n_2 are given in Table 9.

TABLE 9.—NUMERICAL FACTORS n_1 AND n_2 IN EQS. (q) FOR REACTIVE FORCES R_1 AND R_2 AT THE CORNERS OF SIMPLY SUPPORTED RECTANGULAR PLATES UNDER HYDROSTATIC PRESSURE $q = q_0 x/a$
$(\nu = 0.3, b > a)$

b/a	1.0	1.1	1.2	1.3	1.4	1.5	1.6	1.7	1.8	1.9	2.0	3.0	4.0	5.0
n_1	0.026	0.026	0.026	0.026	0.025	0.024	0.023	0.022	0.021	0.021	0.020	0.014	0.010	0.008
n_2	0.039	0.038	0.037	0.036	0.035	0.033	0.032	0.030	0.029	0.028	0.026	0.018	0.014	0.011

Since a uniform load q_0 is obtained by superposing the two triangular loads $q = q_0 x/a$ and $q_0(a - x)/a$, it can be concluded

TABLE 10.—NUMERICAL FACTORS α FOR DEFLECTIONS OF SIMPLY SUPPORTED RECTANGULAR PLATES UNDER HYDROSTATIC PRESSURE $q = q_0 x/a$
$(\nu = 0.3, b < a)$

a/b	$w = \alpha \dfrac{q_0 b^4}{Eh^3}, \quad y = 0$			
	$x = 0.25a$	$x = 0.50a$	$x = 0.60a$	$x = 0.75a$
∞	0.0355	0.0711	0.0853	0.1066
5	0.0355	0.0708	0.0850	0.1054
4	0.0355	0.0700	0.0820	0.0908
3	0.0350	0.0688	0.0756	0.0772
2	0.0315	0.0553	0.0592	0.0537
1.9	0.0307	0.0532	0.0566	0.0508
1.8	0.0295	0.0508	0.0536	0.0474
1.7	0.0285	0.0482	0.0506	0.0441
1.6	0.0272	0.0453	0.0472	0.0406
1.5	0.0256	0.0421	0.0436	0.0370
1.4	0.0238	0.0385	0.0397	0.0332
1.3	0.0217	0.0348	0.0355	0.0294
1.2	0.0195	0.0308	0.0312	0.0255
1.1	0.0167	0.0265	0.0268	0.0217
1.0	0.0143	0.0221	0.0220	0.0177

that for corresponding values of b/a the sum $n_1 + n_2$ of the factors given in Table 9 multiplied by b/a must equal the corresponding value of n, the last column in Table 5.

If the relative dimensions of the plate are such that a in Fig. 64 is greater than b, then more rapidly converging series will be obtained by representing w_1 and w_2 by the following expressions:

$$w_1 = \frac{q_0 x}{a} \cdot \frac{1}{384D}(16y^4 - 24b^2y^2 + 5b^4), \qquad (r)$$

$$w_2 = \sum_{m=1}^{\infty} X_{2m-1} \cos \frac{(2m-1)\pi y}{b}. \qquad (s)$$

The first of these expressions is the deflection of a narrow strip parallel to the y-axis, supported at $y = \pm b/2$ and carrying a uniformly distributed load of intensity $q_0 x/a$. This expression satisfies the differential equation (c) and also the boundary con-

TABLE 11.—NUMERICAL FACTORS β AND β_1 FOR BENDING MOMENTS IN SIMPLY SUPPORTED RECTANGULAR PLATES UNDER HYDROSTATIC PRESSURE $q = q_0 x/a$

$(\nu = 0.3, b < a)$

a/b	$M_x = \beta b^2 q_0,$	$y = 0$			$M_y = \beta_1 b^2 q_0,$	$y = 0$		
	$x = 0.25a$	$x = 0.50a$	$x = 0.60a$	$x = 0.75a$	$x = 0.25a$	$x = 0.50a$	$x = 0.60a$	$x = 0.75a$
∞	0.0094	0.0187	0.0225	0.0281	0.0312	0.0625	0.0750	0.0937
5.0	0.0094	0.0187	0.0230	0.0309	0.0312	0.0623	0.0742	0.0877
4.0	0.0094	0.0192	0.0237	0.0326	0.0312	0.0617	0.0727	0.0820
3.0	0.0096	0.0202	0.0256	0.0345	0.0309	0.0594	0.0678	0.0715
2.0	0.0108	0.0232	0.0285	0.0348	0.0284	0.0508	0.0554	0.0523
1.9	0.0111	0.0235	0.0288	0.0345	0.0278	0.0492	0.0533	0.0498
1.8	0.0115	0.0239	0.0291	0.0341	0.0269	0.0474	0.0509	0.0470
1.7	0.0117	0.0243	0.0293	0.0337	0.0261	0.0454	0.0485	0.0442
1.6	0.0120	0.0246	0.0294	0.0331	0.0251	0.0431	0.0457	0.0412
1.5	0.0123	0.0249	0.0294	0.0324	0.0239	0.0406	0.0428	0.0381
1.4	0.0126	0.0253	0.0292	0.0315	0.0225	0.0376	0.0396	0.0348
1.3	0.0129	0.0252	0.0290	0.0304	0.0209	0.0346	0.0360	0.0314
1.2	0.0131	0.0250	0.0284	0.0291	0.0192	0.0313	0.0323	0.0279
1.1	0.0134	0.0247	0.0276	0.0276	0.0169	0.0276	0.0285	0.0245
1.0	0.0132	0.0239	0.0264	0.0259	0.0149	0.0239	0.0245	0.0207

ditions $w = 0$ and $\partial^2 w/\partial y^2 = 0$ at $y = \pm b/2$. Expression (s) represents an infinite series each term of which also satisfies the conditions at the edges $y = \pm b/2$. The functions X_{2m-1} of x are chosen in such a manner that each of them satisfies the homogeneous equation (e) of the previous article (see page 126) and so that expression (a) satisfies the boundary conditions at the edges $x = 0$ and $x = a$. Since the method of determining

TABLE 12.—NUMERICAL FACTORS δ AND δ_1 FOR REACTIONS IN SIMPLY SUPPORTED RECTANGULAR PLATES UNDER HYDROSTATIC PRESSURE $q = q_0 x/a$
($\nu = 0.3$, $b < a$)

	Reactions $\delta q_0 a$				Reactions $\delta_1 q_0 b$			
	$x = 0$		$x = a$		$y = \pm b/2$			
a/b	$y = 0$	$y = b/4$	$y = 0$	$y = b/4$	$x = 0.25a$	$x = 0.50a$	$x = 0.60a$	$x = 0.75a$
∞	......	......	......	......	0.125	0.250	0.300	0.375
5.0	0.008	0.006	0.092	0.076	0.125	0.250	0.301	0.379
4.0	0.013	0.010	0.112	0.093	0.125	0.251	0.301	0.377
3.0	0.023	0.018	0.143	0.119	0.125	0.252	0.304	0.368
2.0	0.050	0.038	0.197	0.166	0.127	0.251	0.296	0.337
1.9	0.055	0.041	0.205	0.172	0.127	0.251	0.294	0.331
1.8	0.060	0.045	0.213	0.179	0.128	0.249	0.291	0.325
1.7	0.066	0.050	0.221	0.187	0.127	0.248	0.288	0.318
1.6	0.073	0.055	0.230	0.195	0.127	0.245	0.284	0.311
1.5	0.080	0.060	0.240	0.204	0.127	0.243	0.279	0.302
1.4	0.088	0.067	0.250	0.213	0.126	0.239	0.273	0.292
1.3	0.097	0.074	0.260	0.223	0.124	0.234	0.266	0.281
1.2	0.106	0.081	0.271	0.233	0.122	0.227	0.257	0.269
1.1	0.116	0.090	0.282	0.244	0.120	0.220	0.247	0.255
1.0	0.126	0.090	0.294	0.256	0.115	0.210	0.234	0.239

TABLE 13.—NUMERICAL FACTORS n_1 AND n_2 IN EQS. (q) FOR REACTIVE FORCES R_1 AND R_2 AT THE CORNERS OF SIMPLY SUPPORTED RECTANGULAR PLATES UNDER HYDROSTATIC PRESSURE $q = q_0 x/a$
($\nu = 0.3$, $b < a$)

a/b	5	4	3	2	1.9	1.8	1.7	1.6	1.5	1.4	1.3	1.2	1.1	1.0
n_1	0.002	0.004	0.006	0.013	0.014	0.016	0.017	0.018	0.020	0.021	0.023	0.024	0.025	0.026
n_2	0.017	0.020	0.025	0.033	0.034	0.035	0.036	0.037	0.037	0.038	0.039	0.039	0.039	0.039

the functions X_{2m-1} is similar to that already used in determining the functions Y_m, we shall limit ourselves to giving only the final numerical results which are represented by Tables 10, 11, 12 and 13. The notations in these tables are the same as in the previous tables for the hydrostatic pressure.

31. Simply Supported Rectangular Plate under a Load in the Form of a Triangular Prism.—Assume that the intensity of the load is represented by an isosceles triangle as shown in Fig. 65a. The deflection surface can again be represented in the form

$$w = w_1 + w_2, \qquad (a)$$

in which w_1 represents the deflection of a simply supported strip parallel to the x-axis, and w_2 has the same form as in the previous article [Eq. (d)]. To represent the deflection w_1 in the form of a trigonometric series we observe that the deflection produced by a concentrated force P applied at a distance ξ from the left end of a strip is[1]

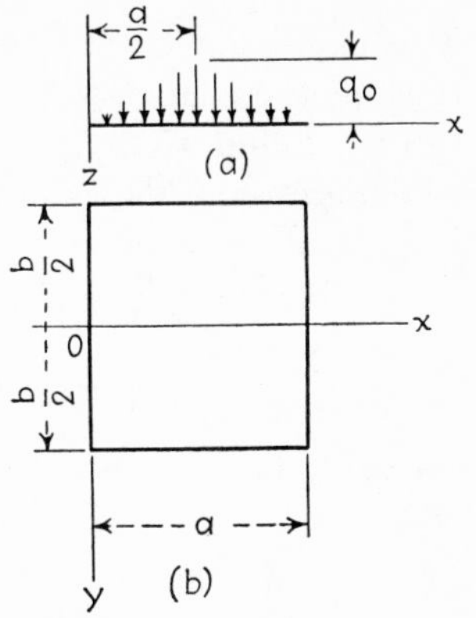

Fig. 65.

$$\frac{2Pa^3}{D\pi^4} \sum_{m=1}^{\infty} \frac{1}{m^4} \sin \frac{m\pi\xi}{a} \sin \frac{m\pi x}{a}. \qquad (b)$$

Substituting $q\,d\xi$ for P and using $q = 2q_0\xi/a$ for $\xi < a/2$ and $q = 2q_0(a - \xi)/a$ for $\xi > a/2$, the deflection of the strip by an elemental load is obtained. The deflection produced by the total load on the strip is now obtained by integration in the following form:

$$w_1 = \frac{4q_0a^2}{D\pi^4} \sum_{m=1}^{\infty} \frac{1}{m^4} \sin \frac{m\pi x}{a} \left[\int_0^{\frac{a}{2}} \xi \sin \frac{m\pi\xi}{a} d\xi \right.$$

$$\left. + \int_{\frac{a}{2}}^{a} (a - \xi) \sin \frac{m\pi\xi}{a} d\xi \right] = \frac{8q_0a^4}{D\pi^6} \sum_{m=1,3,5,\cdots}^{\infty} \frac{(-1)^{\frac{m-1}{2}}}{m^6} \sin \frac{m\pi x}{a}. \qquad (c)$$

[1] See author's "Strength of Materials," vol. 2, p. 419, 1930.

Substituting this in Eq. (*a*) and using Eq. (*d*) of the previous article, we obtain

$$w = \frac{q_0 a^4}{D} \sum_{m=1,3,5,\cdots}^{\infty} \left[\frac{8(-1)^{\frac{m-1}{2}}}{\pi^6 m^6} \right.$$

$$\left. + A_m \cosh \frac{m\pi y}{a} + B_m \frac{m\pi y}{a} \sinh \frac{m\pi y}{a} \right] \sin \frac{m\pi x}{a}. \quad (d)$$

This expression satisfies Eq. (101) and also the boundary conditions at the edges $x = 0$ and $x = a$. The constants A_m and B_m can be found from the conditions along the edges $y = \pm b/2$, which are the same as in the previous article and which give

$$\left. \begin{array}{c} \dfrac{8(-1)^{\frac{m-1}{2}}}{\pi^6 m^6} + A_m \cosh \alpha_m + B_m \alpha_m \sinh \alpha_m = 0, \\[2mm] (2B_m + A_m) \cosh \alpha_m + B_m \alpha_m \sinh \alpha_m = 0, \end{array} \right\} \quad (e)$$

where, as before, we use the notation

$$\alpha_m = \frac{m\pi b}{2a}.$$

Solving Eqs. (*e*), we find

$$A_m = -\frac{4(2 + \alpha_m \tanh \alpha_m)(-1)^{\frac{m-1}{2}}}{\pi^6 m^6 \cosh \alpha_m} \qquad B_m = \frac{4(-1)^{\frac{m-1}{2}}}{\pi^6 m^6 \cosh \alpha_m}. \quad (f)$$

To obtain the deflection of the plate along the *x*-axis we put $y = 0$ in expression (*d*). Then

$$(w)_{y=0} = \frac{q_0 a^4}{D} \sum_{m=1,3,5,\cdots}^{\infty} \left[\frac{8(-1)^{\frac{m-1}{2}}}{\pi^6 m^6} + A_m \right] \sin \frac{m\pi x}{a}.$$

The maximum deflection is at the center of the plate, where

$$w_{\max.} = \frac{q_0 a^4}{D} \sum_{m=1,3,5,\cdots}^{\infty} \left(\frac{8}{\pi^6 m^6} + A_m (-1)^{\frac{m-1}{2}} \right).$$

It can be represented in the form

$$w_{\max.} = \alpha \frac{q_0 a^4}{E h^3},$$

in which α is a numerical factor depending on the magnitude of the ratio b/a and on the value of Poisson's ratio ν.   Several values of this factor are given in Table 14.[1]

Using expression (d) and proceeding as in the previous article, we can readily obtain the expressions for bending moments M_x and M_y.   The maximum values of these moments in this case are evidently at the center of the plate and can be represented in the following form:

$$(M_x)_{\text{max.}} = \beta q_0 a^2, \qquad (M_y)_{\text{max.}} = \beta_1 q_0 a^2.$$

The values of the numerical factors β and β_1 are also given in Table 14.   In the same table are given also numerical factors γ, γ_1, δ, δ_1 and n for calculating (1) shearing forces $(Q_x)_{\text{max.}} = \gamma q_0 a$, $(Q_y)_{\text{max.}} = \gamma_1 q_0 b$ at the middle of the sides $x = 0$ and $y = -b/2$

TABLE 14.—NUMERICAL FACTORS α, β, γ, δ, n FOR SIMPLY SUPPORTED RECTANGULAR PLATES UNDER A LOAD IN FORM OF A TRIANGULAR PRISM
($\nu = 0.3$, $b > a$)

b/a	$w_{\text{max.}}$ $= \alpha\dfrac{q_0 a^4}{Eh^3}$	$(M_x)_{\text{max.}}$ $= \beta q_0 a^2$	$(M_y)_{\text{max.}}$ $= \beta_1 q_0 a^2$	$(Q_x)_{\text{max.}}$ $= \gamma q_0 a$	$(Q_y)_{\text{max.}}$ $= \gamma_1 q_0 b$	$(V_x)_{\text{max.}}$ $= \delta q_0 a$	$(V_y)_{\text{max.}}$ $= \delta_1 q_0 b$	R $= n q_0 a b$
	α	β	β_1	γ	γ_1	δ	δ_1	n
1.0	0.0287	0.0340	0.0317	0.199	0.315	0.147	0.250	0.038
1.1	0.0343	0.0390	0.0326	0.212	0.297	0.161	0.232	0.038
1.2	0.0398	0.0436	0.0330	0.222	0.280	0.173	0.216	0.037
1.3	0.0449	0.0479	0.0332	0.230	0.265	0.184	0.202	0.036
1.4	0.0497	0.0518	0.0331	0.236	0.250	0.193	0.189	0.035
1.5	0.0542	0.0554	0.0329	0.241	0.236	0.202	0.178	0.034
1.6	0.0582	0.0586	0.0325	0.246	0.224	0.208	0.168	0.033
1.7	0.0619	0.0615	0.0321	0.247	0.212	0.214	0.158	0.031
1.8	0.0652	0.0641	0.0316	0.249	0.201	0.220	0.150	0.030
1.9	0.0682	0.0664	0.0311	0.251	0.191	0.224	0.142	0.029
2.0	0.0709	0.0685	0.0306	0.252	0.183	0.228	0.135	0.028
3.0	0.0855	0.0794	0.0270	0.253	0.122	0.245	0.090	0.019
∞	0.0910	0.0833	0.0250	0.250	.....	0.250		

of the plate, (2) reactive forces $V_x = \left(Q_x - \dfrac{\partial M_{xy}}{\partial y}\right)_{\text{max.}} = \delta q_0 a$,

$$V_y = \left(Q_y - \frac{\partial M_{xy}}{\partial x}\right)_{\text{max.}} = \delta_1 q_0 b$$

[1] The tables are taken from the paper by B. G. Galerkin, *loc. cit.*, p. 134.

at the same points and (3) concentrated reactions $R = nq_0ab$ at the corners of the plate which are acting downward and prevent the corners of the plate from rising. All these values are given for $b > a$. When $b < a$, a better convergency can be obtained by taking the portion w_1 of the deflection of the plate in the form of the deflection of a strip parallel to the y-direction. We omit the derivations and give only the numerical results assembled in Table 15.

Combining the load shown in Fig. 65a with the uniform load

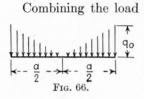

FIG. 66.

of intensity q_0, the load shown in Fig. 66 is obtained. Information regarding deflections and stresses in this latter case can be obtained by combining the data of Table 5 with those of Table 14 or 15.

TABLE 15.—NUMERICAL FACTORS α, β, γ, δ, n FOR SIMPLY SUPPORTED RECTANGULAR PLATES UNDER A LOAD IN FORM OF A TRIANGULAR PRISM ($\nu = 0.3$, $b < a$)

a/b	$w_{max.}$ $= \alpha \dfrac{q_0b^4}{Eh^3}$	$(M_x)_{max.}$ $= \beta q_0b^2$	$(M_y)_{max.}$ $= \beta_1 q_0b^2$	$(Q_x)_{max.}$ $= \gamma q_0a$	$(Q_y)_{max.}$ $= \gamma_1 q_0b$	$(V_x)_{max.}$ $= \delta q_0a$	$(V_y)_{max.}$ $= \delta_1 q_0b$	R $= nq_0ab$
	α	β	β_1	γ	γ_1	δ	δ_1	n
∞	0.1422	0.0375	0.1250	.....	0.500	.....	0.500	
3.0	0.0968	0.0387	0.0922	0.045	0.442	0.027	0.410	0.010
2.0	0.0749	0.0392	0.0707	0.091	0.412	0.057	0.365	0.023
1.9	0.0716	0.0392	0.0681	0.098	0.407	0.062	0.358	0.024
1.8	0.0681	0.0391	0.0651	0.106	0.402	0.098	0.350	0.026
1.7	0.0642	0.0390	0.0609	0.115	0.396	0.074	0.342	0.028
1.6	0.0600	0.0388	0.0585	0.124	0.389	0.081	0.332	0.029
1.5	0.0555	0.0386	0.0548	0.135	0.381	0.090	0.322	0.031
1.4	0.0507	0.0382	0.0508	0.146	0.371	0.099	0.311	0.033
1.3	0.0456	0.0376	0.0464	0.158	0.360	0.109	0.298	0.035
1.2	0.0401	0.0368	0.0418	0.171	0.347	0.120	0.284	0.036
1.1	0.0345	0.0356	0.0369	0.185	0.332	0.133	0.268	0.037
1.0	0.0287	0.0340	0.0317	0.199	0.315	0.147	0.250	0.038

32. Partially Loaded Simply Supported Rectangular Plate.— Let us consider a plate loaded only over the shaded portion *prst* (Fig. 67), the sides of which are parallel to the x-axis.[1] Then the differential equation for the loaded portion of the plate is

---

[1] This case was discussed by B. G. Galerkin, *Messenger of Math.*, vol. 55, p. 26, 1925.

$$\frac{\partial^4 w}{\partial x^4} + 2\frac{\partial^4 w}{\partial x^2\, \partial y^2} + \frac{\partial^4 w}{\partial y^4} = \frac{q}{D}. \qquad (a)$$

For the unloaded portions we have the equation

$$\frac{\partial^4 w}{\partial x^4} + 2\frac{\partial^4 w}{\partial x^2\, \partial y^2} + \frac{\partial^4 w}{\partial y^4} = 0. \qquad (b)$$

The deflection surface of the loaded portion of the plate we take again in the form

$$w = w_1 + w_2, \qquad (c)$$

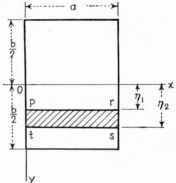

Fig. 67.

in which w_1 satisfies Eq. (a) and w_2 satisfies Eq. (b). Assuming that the intensity of the load q is a function of x only, we may consider the loaded portion $prst$ as a strip and take the deflection of the strip for the deflection w_1. Representing this deflection by a trigonometric series, as was explained in the previous article, we obtain

$$w_1 = \sum_{m=1}^{\infty} a_m \sin \frac{m\pi x}{a}, \qquad (d)$$

where a_m are numerical coefficients depending on the load distribution. For deflections w_2 we take the general expression given in Art. 29. Then the total deflections of the loaded portion of the plate, represented by Eq. (c), become

$$w = \sum_{m=1}^{\infty} \left(a_m + A_m \cosh \frac{m\pi y}{a} + B_m \sinh \frac{m\pi y}{a} \right.$$
$$\left. + C_m \frac{m\pi y}{a} \sinh \frac{m\pi y}{a} + D_m \frac{m\pi y}{a} \cosh \frac{m\pi y}{a} \right) \sin \frac{m\pi x}{a}. \qquad (e)$$

For the unloaded portion of the plate below the line ts we can take the deflection surface in the following form:

$$w' = \sum_{m=1}^{\infty}\left(A'_m \cosh\frac{m\pi y}{a} + B'_m \sinh\frac{m\pi y}{a} + C'_m\frac{m\pi y}{a}\sinh\frac{m\pi y}{a}\right.$$

$$\left. + D'_m\frac{m\pi y}{a}\cosh\frac{m\pi y}{a}\right)\sin\frac{m\pi x}{a}; \quad (f)$$

and, similarly, for the unloaded portion of the plate above the line *pr* we take

$$w'' = \sum_{m=1}^{\infty}\left(A''_m \cosh\frac{m\pi y}{a} + B''_m \sinh\frac{m\pi y}{a} + C''_m\frac{m\pi y}{a}\sinh\frac{m\pi y}{a}\right.$$

$$\left. + D''_m\frac{m\pi y}{a}\cosh\frac{m\pi y}{a}\right)\sin\frac{m\pi x}{a}. \quad (g)$$

Expression (*e*) satisfies the differential equation (*a*), and expressions (*f*) and (*g*) satisfy the differential equation (*b*). Moreover, all three expressions satisfy the boundary conditions $w = 0$ and $\partial^2 w/\partial x^2 = 0$ for the sides $x = 0$ and $x = a$.

It is necessary now to choose the constants $A_m, B_m, \ldots , C''_m,$ D''_m in such a manner that the boundary conditions at $y = \pm b/2$ and the continuity conditions along the lines *ts* and *pr* are satisfied. To represent all these conditions in a simpler form let us introduce the following notations:

$$\frac{m\pi\eta_1}{a} = 2\beta_m, \qquad \frac{m\pi\eta_2}{a} = 2\gamma_m, \qquad (h)$$

in which η_1 and η_2 are the distances of the edges of the loaded strip from the *x*-axis. Considering the line *ts*, we conclude, from the continuity conditions along this line, that

$$w' = w \quad \text{and} \quad \frac{\partial w'}{\partial y} = \frac{\partial w}{\partial y} \quad \text{for} \quad y = \eta_2. \quad (i)$$

Since there are no concentrated moments or concentrated forces applied along the line *st*, the bending moments M_y and shearing forces Q_y must be continuous at this line. Hence

$$\frac{\partial^2 w}{\partial y^2} = \frac{\partial^2 w'}{\partial y^2} \quad \text{and} \quad \frac{\partial^3 w}{\partial y^3} = \frac{\partial^3 w'}{\partial y^3} \quad \text{for} \quad y = \eta_2. \quad (j)$$

Substituting expressions (*e*) and (*f*) into Eqs. (*i*) and (*j*) and using notations (h), we can represent these equations in the following form:

$$\left.\begin{array}{l}
(A_m - A'_m) \cosh 2\gamma_m + (B_m - B'_m) \sinh 2\gamma_m \\
\quad + (C_m - C'_m)2\gamma_m \sinh 2\gamma_m + (D_m - D'_m)2\gamma_m \cosh 2\gamma_m \\
\hspace{8cm} + a_m = 0, \\
(A_m - A'_m) \sinh 2\gamma_m + (B_m - B'_m) \cosh 2\gamma_m \\
\quad + (C_m - C'_m)(\sinh 2\gamma_m + 2\gamma_m \cosh 2\gamma_m) \\
\quad\quad + (D_m - D'_m)(\cosh 2\gamma_m + 2\gamma_m \sinh 2\gamma_m) = 0, \\
(A_m - A'_m) \cosh 2\gamma_m + (B_m - B'_m) \sinh 2\gamma_m \\
\quad + (C_m - C'_m)(2 \cosh 2\gamma_m + 2\gamma_m \sinh 2\gamma_m) \\
\quad\quad + (D_m - D'_m)(2 \sinh 2\gamma_m + 2\gamma_m \cosh 2\gamma_m) = 0, \\
(A_m - A'_m) \sinh 2\gamma_m + (B_m - B'_m) \cosh 2\gamma_m \\
\quad + (C_m - C'_m)(3 \sinh 2\gamma_m + 2\gamma_m \cosh 2\gamma_m) \\
\quad\quad + (D_m - D'_m)(3 \cosh 2\gamma_m + 2\gamma_m \sinh 2\gamma_m) = 0.
\end{array}\right\} \quad (k)$$

From these equations we find

$$\left.\begin{array}{l}
A_m - A'_m = a_m(\gamma_m \sinh 2\gamma_m - \cosh 2\gamma_m), \\
B_m - B'_m = -a_m(\gamma_m \cosh 2\gamma_m - \sinh 2\gamma_m), \\
C_m - C'_m = \dfrac{a_m}{2} \cosh 2\gamma_m, \\
D_m - D'_m = -\dfrac{a_m}{2} \sinh 2\gamma_m.
\end{array}\right\} \quad (l)$$

We obtain four similar equations also for the boundary line pr $(y = \eta_1)$. Subtracting them from Eqs. (l), we find

$$\left.\begin{array}{l}
A'_m - A''_m = 2a_m \sinh (\gamma_m - \beta_m)\Big[\sinh (\gamma_m + \beta_m) \\
\quad - \dfrac{\gamma_m + \beta_m}{2} \cosh (\gamma_m + \beta_m) \\
\quad\quad - \dfrac{\gamma_m - \beta_m}{2} \sinh (\gamma_m + \beta_m) \coth (\gamma_m - \beta_m)\Big], \\
B'_m - B''_m = 2a_m \sinh (\gamma_m - \beta_m)\Big[- \cosh (\gamma_m + \beta_m) \\
\quad + \dfrac{\gamma_m + \beta_m}{2} \sinh (\gamma_m + \beta_m) \\
\quad\quad + \dfrac{\gamma_m - \beta_m}{2} \cosh (\gamma_m + \beta_m) \coth (\gamma_m - \beta_m)\Big], \\
C'_m - C''_m = -a_m \sinh (\gamma_m + \beta_m) \sinh (\gamma_m - \beta_m), \\
D'_m - D''_m = a_m \sinh (\gamma_m - \beta_m) \cosh (\gamma_m + \beta_m).
\end{array}\right\} \quad (m)$$

To these four equations containing eight constants A_m^i, . . . ,
D_m'' we add four equations representing the boundary conditions
at the edges $y = \pm b/2$. For $y = +b/2$ we have $w' = 0$ and
$\partial^2 w'/\partial y^2 = 0$, since the deflection and the moment M_y along this
edge are zero. Substituting expression (f) in these conditions,
we obtain

$$\left. \begin{array}{r} A_m' \cosh \alpha_m + B_m' \sinh \alpha_m + C_m' \alpha_m \sinh \alpha_m \\ + D_m' \alpha_m \cosh \alpha_m = 0, \\ C_m' \cosh \alpha_m + D_m' \sinh \alpha_m = 0, \end{array} \right\} \quad (n)$$

where, as before,

$$\alpha_m = \frac{m\pi b}{2a}.$$

Similarly, for the edge $y = -b/2$ we obtain

$$\left. \begin{array}{r} A_m'' \cosh \alpha_m - B_m'' \sinh \alpha_m + C_m'' \alpha_m \sinh \alpha_m \\ - D_m'' \alpha_m \cosh \alpha_m = 0, \\ C_m'' \cosh \alpha_m - D_m'' \sinh \alpha_m = 0. \end{array} \right\} \quad (o)$$

Equations (o) and (n), together with Eqs. (m), are sufficient to
determine the eight constants A_m', . . . , D_m'', and we find for
them the following values:

$$A_m' = \frac{a_m \sinh (\gamma_m - \beta_m)}{\cosh \alpha_m} \left[\sinh (\alpha_m + \beta_m + \gamma_m) \right.$$
$$- \frac{\gamma_m + \beta_m}{2} \cosh (\alpha_m + \beta_m + \gamma_m)$$
$$- \frac{\gamma_m - \beta_m}{2} \coth (\gamma_m - \beta_m) \sinh (\alpha_m + \beta_m + \gamma_m)$$
$$\left. - \alpha_m \frac{\cosh (\gamma_m + \beta_m)}{2 \cosh \alpha_m} \right],$$

$$A_m'' = \frac{a_m \sinh (\gamma_m - \beta_m)}{\cosh \alpha_m} \left[\sinh (\alpha_m - \beta_m - \gamma_m) \right.$$
$$+ \frac{\gamma_m + \beta_m}{2} \cosh (\alpha_m - \beta_m - \gamma_m)$$
$$- \frac{\gamma_m - \beta_m}{2} \coth (\gamma_m - \beta_m) \sinh (\alpha_m - \gamma_m - \beta_m)$$
$$\left. - \alpha_m \frac{\cosh (\gamma_m + \beta_m)}{2 \cosh \alpha_m} \right],$$

$$B'_m = \frac{a_m \sinh (\gamma_m - \beta_m)}{\sinh \alpha_m} \bigg[- \sinh (\alpha_m + \beta_m + \gamma_m)$$

$$+ \frac{\gamma_m + \beta_m}{2} \cosh (\alpha_m + \beta_m + \gamma_m)$$

$$+ \frac{\gamma_m - \beta_m}{2} \coth (\gamma_m - \beta_m) \sinh (\alpha_m + \beta_m + \gamma_m)$$

$$- \alpha_m \frac{\sinh (\gamma_m + \beta_m)}{2 \sinh \alpha_m} \bigg].$$

$$B''_m = \frac{a_m \sinh (\gamma_m - \beta_m)}{\sinh \alpha_m} \bigg[\sinh (\alpha_m - \beta_m - \gamma_m)$$

$$+ \frac{\gamma_m + \beta_m}{2} \cosh (\alpha_m - \beta_m - \gamma_m)$$

$$- \frac{\gamma_m - \beta_m}{2} \coth (\gamma_m - \beta_m) \sinh (\alpha_m - \beta_m - \gamma_m)$$

$$- \alpha_m \frac{\sinh (\gamma_m + \beta_m)}{2 \sinh \alpha_m} \bigg],$$

$$C'_m = - \frac{a_m}{2 \cosh \alpha_m} \sinh (\gamma_m - \beta_m) \sinh (\alpha_m + \beta_m + \gamma_m),$$

$$C''_m = - \frac{a_m}{2 \cosh \alpha_m} \sinh (\gamma_m - \beta_m) \sinh (\alpha_m - \beta_m - \gamma_m),$$

$$D'_m = \frac{a_m}{2 \sinh \alpha_m} \sinh (\gamma_m - \beta_m) \sinh (\alpha_m + \beta_m + \gamma_m),$$

$$D''_m = - \frac{a_m}{2 \sinh \alpha_m} \sinh (\gamma_m - \beta_m) \sinh (\alpha_m - \beta_m - \gamma_m).$$

Substituting A'_m, B'_m, C'_m and D'_m in Eqs. (*l*), we find

$$A_m = - \frac{a_m \cosh (\gamma_m + \beta_m)}{\cosh \alpha_m} \bigg[\cosh (\alpha_m - \gamma_m + \beta_m)$$

$$- \frac{\gamma_m + \beta_m}{2} \tanh (\gamma_m + \beta_m) \cosh (\alpha_m - \gamma_m + \beta_m)$$

$$+ \frac{\gamma_m - \beta_m}{2} \sinh (\alpha_m - \gamma_m + \beta_m) + \alpha_m \frac{\sinh (\gamma_m - \beta_m)}{2 \cosh \alpha_m} \bigg],$$

$$B_m = \frac{a_m \sinh (\gamma_m + \beta_m)}{\sinh \alpha_m} \bigg[\sinh (\alpha_m - \gamma_m + \beta_m)$$

$$- \frac{\gamma_m + \beta_m}{2} \coth (\gamma_m + \beta_m) \sinh (\alpha_m - \gamma_m + \beta_m)$$

$$+ \frac{\gamma_m - \beta_m}{2} \cosh (\alpha_m - \gamma_m + \beta_m) - \alpha_m \frac{\sinh (\gamma_m - \beta_m)}{2 \sinh \alpha_m} \bigg],$$

$$C_m = \frac{a_m \cosh\ (\gamma_m + \beta_m)}{2 \cosh\ \alpha_m} \cosh\ (\alpha_m - \gamma_m + \beta_m),$$

$$D_m = -\frac{a_m \sinh\ (\gamma_m + \beta_m)}{2 \sinh\ \alpha_m} \sinh\ (\alpha_m - \gamma_m + \beta_m).$$

Thus all constants entering in expressions (*e*), (*f*) and (*g*) are determined, and we can now calculate the deflection at any point of the plate. Since the coefficients a_m in the series (*d*) diminish rapidly as m increases, only a few terms of series (*e*), (*f*) and (*g*) need be calculated to get deflections with a very high degree of accuracy.

As an example of the application of our general solution, let us consider the symmetrical case in which a uniform load q is distributed over the rectangle *prst* (Fig. 68). The maximum deflection and the maximum bending moment in this case are at the center of the plate and are found by using expression (*e*) for the deflection of the loaded portion of the plate. From symmetry it may be concluded that the deflection surface must be an even function of y. Hence B_m and D_m in expression (*e*) equal zero, and the deflection surface is

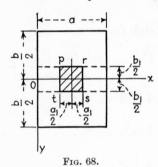

Fig. 68.

$$w = \sum_{m=1,3,5,\cdots}^{\infty} \left(a_m + A_m \cosh \frac{m\pi y}{a} + C_m \frac{m\pi y}{a} \sinh \frac{m\pi y}{a} \right) \sin \frac{m\pi x}{a},$$

$$(p)$$

where, from symmetry, m includes only the consecutive odd numbers 1, 3, 5, . . .

Using Eq. (*b*) of the previous article, we represent the deflections w_1 of the strip [Eq. (*d*)] in the following form:

$$w_1 = \frac{2qa^3}{D\pi^4} \sum_{m=1,3,5,\cdots}^{\infty} \frac{1}{m^4} \sin \frac{m\pi x}{a} \int_{\frac{1}{2}(a-a_1)}^{\frac{1}{2}(a+a_1)} \sin \frac{m\pi\xi}{a} d\xi$$

$$= \frac{4qa^4}{D\pi^5} \sum_{m=1,3,5,\cdots}^{\infty} \frac{(-1)^{\frac{m-1}{2}}}{m^5} \sin \frac{m\pi a_1}{2a} \sin \frac{m\pi x}{a}. \quad (q)$$

Hence,

$$a_m = \frac{4qa^4(-1)^{\frac{m-1}{2}}}{D\pi^5 m^5} \sin \frac{m\pi a_1}{2a}. \tag{r}$$

As a particular case, when $a_1 = a$, we have a strip uniformly loaded along its entire length, and its deflection is

$$w_1 = \frac{4qa^4}{D\pi^5} \sum_{m=1,3,5,\cdots}^{\infty} \frac{1}{m^5} \cdot \sin \frac{m\pi x}{a}. \tag{s}$$

For symmetrical loading, $\eta_2 = -\eta_1 = b_1/2$, and Eqs. (h) become

$$\gamma_m = -\beta_m = \frac{m\pi b_1}{4a} \tag{t}$$

which gives

$$\left.\begin{aligned}
A_m &= -\frac{a_m}{\cosh \alpha_m}\Bigg[\cosh (\alpha_m - 2\gamma_m) \\
&\quad + \gamma_m \sinh (\alpha_m - 2\gamma_m) + \alpha_m \frac{\sinh 2\gamma_m}{2 \cosh \alpha_m}\Bigg], \\
C_m &= \frac{a_m}{2 \cosh \alpha_m} \cosh (\alpha_m - 2\gamma_m).
\end{aligned}\right\} \tag{u}$$

Substituting this and expression (r) in Eq. (p), we obtain

$$w = \frac{4qa^4}{D\pi^5} \sum_{m=1,3,5,\cdots}^{\infty} \frac{(-1)^{\frac{m-1}{2}}}{m^5} \sin \frac{m\pi a_1}{2a}\Bigg\{1 - \frac{\cosh \frac{m\pi y}{a}}{\cosh \alpha_m}$$

$$\left[\cosh (\alpha_m - 2\gamma_m) + \gamma_m \sinh (\alpha_m - 2\gamma_m) + \alpha_m \frac{\sinh 2\gamma_m}{2 \cosh \alpha_m}\right]$$

$$+ \frac{\cosh (\alpha_m - 2\gamma_m)}{2 \cosh \alpha_m} \frac{m\pi y}{a} \sinh \frac{m\pi y}{a}\Bigg\} \sin \frac{m\pi x}{a}. \tag{129}$$

From this equation the deflection at any point of the loaded portion of the plate can be calculated.

In the particular case where $a_1 = a$ and $b_1 = b$ we have, from Eq. (t), $\gamma_m = \alpha_m/2$. Expressions (u) become

$$A_m = -\frac{a_m}{\cosh \alpha_m}\left(1 + \frac{\alpha_m}{2} \tanh \alpha_m\right), \qquad C_m = \frac{a_m}{2 \cosh \alpha_m};$$

and Eq. (129) coincides with Eq. (126) (page 128) derived for a uniformly loaded rectangular plate.

The maximum deflection of the plate is at the center and is obtained by substituting $y = 0$, $x = a/2$ in formula (129), which gives

$$w_{\text{max.}} = \frac{4qa^4}{D\pi^5} \sum_{m=1,3,5,\cdots}^{\infty} \frac{1}{m^5} \sin \frac{m\pi a_1}{2a} \Bigg\{ 1 - \frac{1}{\cosh \alpha_m}$$

$$\left[\cosh (\alpha_m - 2\gamma_m) + \gamma_m \sinh (\alpha_m - 2\gamma_m) + \alpha_m \frac{\sinh 2\gamma_m}{2 \cosh \alpha_m} \right] \Bigg\}.$$

$$(130)$$

As a particular example let us consider the case where $a_1 = a$ and b_1 is very small. This case represents a uniform distribution of load along the x-axis. Considering γ_m as small in Eq. (130) and retaining only small terms of the first order, we obtain, using the notation $qb_1 = q_0$,

$$w_{\text{max.}} = \frac{q_0 a^3}{D\pi^4} \sum_{m=1,3,5,\cdots}^{\infty} \frac{(-1)^{\frac{m-1}{2}}}{m^4} \left(\tanh \alpha_m - \frac{\alpha_m}{\cosh^2 \alpha_m} \right). \quad (131)$$

For a square plate this equation gives

$$w_{\text{max.}} = 0.655 \frac{q_0 a^3}{D\pi^4} = 0.0736 \frac{q_0 a^3}{Eh^3}.$$

In the general case the maximum deflection can be represented in the forms

$$w_{\text{max.}} = \alpha \frac{q_0 a^3}{Eh^3} \text{ for } a < b \qquad \text{and} \qquad w_{\text{max.}} = \alpha \frac{q_0 b^3}{Eh^3} \text{ for } a > b.$$

Several values of the coefficient α are given in Table 16.

Returning to the general case where b_1 is not necessarily small and a_1 may have any value, the expressions for the bending moments M_x and M_y can be derived by using Eq. (129). The maximum values of these moments occur at the center of the plate and can be represented by the formulas

$$(M_x)_{\text{max.}} = \beta a_1 b_1 q = \beta P, \qquad (M_y)_{\text{max.}} = \beta_1 a_1 b_1 q = \beta_1 P,$$

where $P = a_1 b_1 q$ is the total load. The values of the numerical factors β for a square plate and for various sizes of the loaded rectangle are given in Table 17. The coefficients β_1 can also be

TABLE 16.—DEFLECTIONS OF SIMPLY SUPPORTED RECTANGULAR PLATES UNIFORMLY LOADED ALONG THE AXIS OF SYMMETRY PARALLEL TO THE DIMENSION a

$(\nu = 0.3)$

$w_{max.} = \alpha \dfrac{q_0 a^3}{E h^3}$	$b/a =$	2	1.5	1.4	1.3	1.2	1.1	1.0
	$\alpha =$	0.1078	0.0995	0.0963	0.0922	0.0872	0.0810	0.0736
$w_{max.} = \alpha \dfrac{q_0 b^3}{E h^3}$	$a/b =$	1.1	1.2	1.3	1.4	1.5	2.0	∞
	$\alpha =$	0.876	0.1011	0.1138	0.1257	0.1366	0.1779	0.2275

TABLE 17.—COEFFICIENTS β FOR $(M_x)_{max.}$ IN SIMPLY SUPPORTED PARTIALLY LOADED SQUARE PLATES

$(\nu = 0.3)$

$a_1/a =$	0	0.1	0.2	0.3	0.4	0.5	0.6	0.7	0.8	0.9	1.0
b_1/a					Coefficients β in Eq. $(M_x)_{max.} = \beta P$						
0	∞	0.321	0.251	0.209	0.180	0.158	0.141	0.125	0.112	0.102	0.092
0.1	0.378	0.284	0.232	0.197	0.170	0.150	0.134	0.120	0.108	0.098	0.088
0.2	0.308	0.254	0.214	0.184	0.161	0.142	0.127	0.114	0.103	0.093	0.084
0.3	0.262	0.225	0.195	0.168	0.151	0.134	0.120	0.108	0.098	0.088	0.080
0.4	0.232	0.203	0.179	0.158	0.141	0.126	0.113	0.102	0.092	0.084	0.076
0.5	0.208	0.185	0.164	0.146	0.131	0.116	0.106	0.096	0.087	0.079	0.071
0.6	0.188	0.168	0.150	0.135	0.121	0.109	0.099	0.090	0.081	0.074	0.067
0.7	0.170	0.153	0.137	0.124	0.112	0.101	0.091	0.083	0.076	0.069	0.062
0.8	0.155	0.140	0.126	0.114	0.103	0.094	0.085	0.077	0.070	0.063	0.057
0.9	0.141	0.127	0.115	0.104	0.094	0.086	0.078	0.070	0.064	0.058	0.053
1.0	0.127	0.115	0.105	0.095	0.086	0.078	0.071	0.064	0.058	0.053	0.048

TABLE 18.—COEFFICIENTS β AND β_1 FOR $(M_x)_{max.}$ AND $(M_y)_{max.}$ IN PARTIALLY LOADED RECTANGULAR PLATES WITH $b = 1.4a$. $(\nu = 0.3)$

$a_1/a =$	0	0.2	0.4	0.6	0.8	1.0	0	0.2	0.4	0.6	0.8	1.0
b_1/a	Coefficient β in Eq. $(M_x)_{max.} = \beta P$						Coefficient β_1 in Eq. $(M_y)_{max.} = \beta_1 P$					
0	∞	0.276	0.208	0.163	0.134	0.110	∞	0.299	0.230	0.183	0.151	0.125
0.2	0.332	0.239	0.186	0.152	0.125	0.103	0.246	0.208	0.175	0.147	0.124	0.102
0.4	0.261	0.207	0.168	0.138	0.115	0.095	0.177	0.157	0.138	0.119	0.101	0.083
0.6	0.219	0.181	0.151	0.126	0.105	0.086	0.138	0.125	0.111	0.097	0.083	0.069
0.8	0.187	0.158	0.134	0.112	0.094	0.078	0.112	0.102	0.091	0.080	0.069	0.058
1.0	0.162	0.139	0.118	0.100	0.084	0.070	0.093	0.085	0.077	0.068	0.058	0.049
1.2	0.141	0.122	0.104	0.089	0.075	0.062	0.079	0.072	0.065	0.058	0.050	0.042
1.4	0.123	0.106	0.091	0.077	0.065	0.054	0.068	0.062	0.056	0.050	0.043	0.036

obtained from this table by interchanging the positions of the letters a_1 and b_1.

The numerical factors β and β_1 for plates with the ratios $b = 1.4a$ and $b = 2a$ are given in Tables 18 and 19, respectively.

TABLE 19.—COEFFICIENTS β AND β_1 FOR $(M_x)_{\max}$. AND $(M_y)_{\max}$. IN PARTIALLY LOADED RECTANGULAR PLATES WITH $b = 2a$. ($\nu = 0.3$)

a_1/a =	0	0.2	0.4	0.6	0.8	1.0	0	0.2	0.4	0.6	0.8	1.0
b_1/a	Coefficient β in Eq. $(M_x)_{\max}$. $= \beta P$						Coefficient β_1 in Eq. $(M_y)_{\max}$. $= \beta_1 P$					
0	∞	0.289	0.220	0.175	0.144	0.118	∞	0.294	0.225	0.179	0.148	0.122
0.2	0.347	0.252	0.199	0.163	0.135	0.111	0.242	0.203	0.170	0.143	0.120	0.099
0.4	0.275	0.221	0.181	0.150	0.125	0.103	0.172	0.152	0.133	0.114	0.097	0.081
0.6	0.233	0.195	0.164	0.138	0.115	0.095	0.133	0.120	0.106	0.093	0.079	0.066
0.8	0.203	0.174	0.148	0.126	0.106	0.088	0.107	0.097	0.087	0.076	0.065	0.054
1.0	0.179	0.155	0.134	0.115	0.097	0.080	0.089	0.081	0.073	0.064	0.055	0.046
1.2	0.161	0.141	0.122	0.105	0.089	0.074	0.074	0.068	0.061	0.054	0.046	0.039
1.4	0.144	0.127	0.111	0.096	0.081	0.068	0.064	0.058	0.052	0.046	0.040	0.033
1.6	0.130	0.115	0.101	0.087	0.074	0.062	0.056	0.051	0.046	0.040	0.035	0.029
1.8	0.118	0.104	0.091	0.079	0.067	0.056	0.049	0.045	0.041	0.036	0.031	0.026
2.0	0.107	0.094	0.083	0.072	0.061	0.051	0.044	0.041	0.037	0.032	0.028	0.023

33. Concentrated Load on a Simply Supported Rectangular Plate.

The solution of the previous article can be used in discussing the problem of bending of simply supported rectangular plates under a concentrated load. This kind of loading can be obtained by making the sides a_1 and b_1 of the loaded rectangle of the previous article very small[1] and taking $q a_1 b_1 = P$. Let us begin with the simple case in which the load acts at a point A on the x-axis, which is the axis of symmetry (Fig. 69). The deflection of the strip along the x-axis in this case is

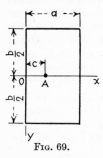

FIG. 69.

$$w_1 = \frac{2Pa^3}{b_1 D\pi^4} \sum_{m=1}^{\infty} \frac{1}{m^4} \sin \frac{m\pi c}{a} \sin \frac{m\pi x}{a},$$

[1] The problem of a concentrated force acting on a rectangular plate has been discussed by several authors. See the author's paper in *Bauingenieur*, p. 51, 1922. See also A. Nadai, *Bauingenieur*, p. 11, 1921; and B. G. Galerkin, *loc. cit.*, p. 146.

where c is the coordinate of the point of application of the concentrated load P and b_1 is the width of the strip. From this we obtain the following expression for the coefficients in series (d) of the previous article:

$$a_m = \frac{2Pa^3}{b_1 D\pi^4} \frac{\sin \frac{m\pi c}{a}}{m^4}.$$

Substituting this into Eq. (p) of the previous article and using expressions (u) of the same article for the constants A_m and C_m, we obtain the following equation for the deflection surface of the strip of width b_1:

$$
\begin{aligned}
w = \frac{2Pa^3}{b_1 \, D\pi^4} \sum_{m=1}^{\infty} \frac{\sin \frac{m\pi c}{a}}{m^4} &\left\{ 1 - \frac{\cosh \frac{m\pi y}{a}}{\cosh \alpha_m} \left[\cosh (\alpha_m - 2\gamma_m) \right.\right. \\
&+ \left. \gamma_m \sinh (\alpha_m - 2\gamma_m) + \alpha_m \frac{\sinh 2\gamma_m}{2 \cosh \alpha_m} \right] \\
&+ \left. \frac{m\pi y}{2a \cosh \alpha_m} \sinh \frac{m\pi y}{a} \cosh (\alpha_m - 2\gamma_m) \right\} \sin \frac{m\pi x}{a}. \quad (a)
\end{aligned}
$$

In order to obtain the deflection for the case of a concentrated force, b_1 in this expression must be assumed to be very small. Then γ_m, given by expression (t) of the previous article, is also very small, and we can put

$$
\begin{aligned}
\cosh (\alpha_m - 2\gamma_m) &= \cosh \alpha_m - 2\gamma_m \sinh \alpha_m, \\
\sinh (\alpha_m - 2\gamma_m) &= \sinh \alpha_m - 2\gamma_m \cosh \alpha_m, \\
\sin 2\gamma_m &= 2\gamma_m.
\end{aligned}
$$

Substituting these in expression (a) and omitting the terms containing γ_m to powers higher than the first, we obtain

$$
\begin{aligned}
w = \frac{2Pa^3}{b_1 \, D\pi^4} \sum_{m=1}^{\infty} \frac{\sin \frac{m\pi c}{a}}{m^4} &\left[1 - \cosh \frac{m\pi y}{a} \left(1 - \gamma_m \tanh \alpha_m \right.\right. \\
&+ \left.\left. \frac{\alpha_m \gamma_m}{\cosh^2 \alpha_m} \right) + \frac{m\pi y}{2a} \sinh \frac{m\pi y}{a} (1 - 2\gamma_m \tanh \alpha_m) \right] \sin \frac{m\pi x}{a}. \quad (b)
\end{aligned}
$$

Taking $y = 0$ in this expression, we obtain the deflection of the plate along the x-axis in the following form:

$$(w)_{y=0} = \frac{Pa^2}{2D\pi^3} \sum_{m=1}^{\infty} \frac{\sin \dfrac{m\pi c}{a}}{m^3} \left(\tanh \alpha_m - \frac{\alpha_m}{\cosh^2 \alpha_m} \right) \sin \frac{m\pi x}{a}. \quad (c)$$

This series converges rapidly, and the first few terms give us the deflections with sufficient accuracy. In the particular case of a load P applied at the center of the plate, the maximum deflection, which is at the center, is obtained by substituting $x = c = a/2$ in expression (c), which gives

$$w_{\max.} = \frac{Pa^2}{2D\pi^3} \sum_{m=1,3,5,\,\cdots}^{\infty} \frac{1}{m^3} \left(\tanh \alpha_m - \frac{\alpha_m}{\cosh^2 \alpha_m} \right) = \alpha \frac{Pa^2}{Eh^3}. \quad (132)$$

Values of the numerical factor α for various values of the ratio b/a are given in Table 20.

TABLE 20.—FACTOR α FOR DEFLECTION (132) OF A CENTRALLY LOADED
RECTANGULAR PLATE
($\nu = 0.3$)

b/a	1.0	1.1	1.2	1.4	1.6	1.8	2.0	3.0	∞
α	0.1265	0.1381	0.1478	0.1621	0.1714	0.1769	0.1803	0.1846	0.1849

It is seen that the maximum deflection rapidly approaches that of an infinitely long plate[1] as the length of the plate increases. The comparison of the maximum deflection of a square plate with that of a centrally loaded circular plate inscribed in the square (see page 73) indicates that the deflection of the circular plate is larger than that of the corresponding square plate. This result may be attributed to the action of the reactive forces concentrated at the corners of the square plate which have the tendency to produce deflection of the plate convex upward.

To determine the bending moments in the loaded portion of the plate we calculate the second derivatives of expression (b) which, for $y = 0$, become

---

[1] The deflection of plates by a concentrated load was investigated experimentally by M. Bergsträsser; see *Forschungsarbeiten*, vol. 302, Berlin, 1928.

$$\left(\frac{\partial^2 w}{\partial x^2}\right)_{y=0} = -\frac{P}{2D\pi}\sum_{m=1}^{\infty}\frac{\sin\dfrac{m\pi c}{a}}{m}\left(\tanh\alpha_m - \frac{\alpha_m}{\cosh^2\alpha_m}\right)\sin\frac{m\pi x}{a},$$

$$\left(\frac{\partial^2 w}{\partial y^2}\right)_{y=0} = -\frac{P}{2D\pi}\sum_{m=1}^{\infty}\frac{\sin\dfrac{m\pi c}{a}}{m}\left(\tanh\alpha_m + \frac{\alpha_m}{\cosh^2\alpha_m}\right)\sin\frac{m\pi x}{a}.$$

Substituting these derivatives into expressions (99) for the bending moments, we obtain

$$\left.\begin{aligned}
(M_x)_{y=0} &= \frac{P}{2\pi}\sum_{m=1}^{\infty}\frac{\sin\dfrac{m\pi c}{a}}{m}\Bigg[(1+\nu)\tanh\alpha_m \\
&\qquad\qquad - \frac{(1-\nu)\alpha_m}{\cosh^2\alpha_m}\Bigg]\sin\frac{m\pi x}{a}, \\
(M_y)_{y=0} &= \frac{P}{2\pi}\sum_{m=1}^{\infty}\frac{\sin\dfrac{m\pi c}{a}}{m}\Bigg[(1+\nu)\tanh\alpha_m \\
&\qquad\qquad + \frac{(1-\nu)\alpha_m}{\cosh^2\alpha_m}\Bigg]\sin\frac{m\pi x}{a}.
\end{aligned}\right\} \quad (d)$$

When b is very large in comparison with a, we can put

$$\tanh\alpha_m \approx 1, \qquad \frac{\alpha_m}{\cosh^2\alpha_m} \approx 0.$$

Then

$$M_x = M_y = \frac{(1+\nu)P}{2\pi}\sum_{m=1}^{\infty}\frac{1}{m}\sin\frac{m\pi c}{a}\sin\frac{m\pi x}{a}. \qquad (e)$$

This series does not converge rapidly enough for a satisfactory calculation of the moments in the vicinity of the point of application of the load P, so it is necessary to derive another form of representation of the moments near that point. From the discussion of bending of a circular plate by a force applied at the center (see Art. 19) we know that the shearing forces and bending moments become infinitely large at the point of application of the load. We have similar conditions also in the case of a rectangular plate. The stress distribution within a circle of small radius with its center at the point of application of the load is substantially the same as that near the center of a centrally loaded circular plate. The bending stress at a point within this circle may be considered as consisting of two parts, one of which is the same as that in the case of a centrally loaded circular plate of radius a, while the other represents the difference between the stresses in a circular and those in a rectangular plate. As the distance r between the point of application of the load and the point under consideration becomes smaller and smaller, the first part of the stresses varies as log (a/r) and becomes infinite at the center, whereas the second part, representing the effect of the difference in the boundary conditions of the two plates, remains continuous.

To obtain the expressions for bending moments in the vicinity of the point of application of the load we use the first of the equations (114) (see page 100). In the case under consideration the entire surface of the plate, with the exception of the point of application of the load P, is free from load, and the equation becomes

$$\frac{\partial^2 M}{\partial x^2} + \frac{\partial^2 M}{\partial y^2} = 0. \qquad (f)$$

At the boundary the quantity $M = (M_x + M_y)/(1 + \nu)$ is zero, since the rectilinear edges of the plate are simply supported. Thus the problem of determining M reduces to one of finding a solution of Eq. (f) which is zero at the boundary and varies as log (a/r) at the point of application of the load. This solution is known and for an infinitely long plate can be represented in the following form:

$$M = \frac{C}{4\pi} \log \frac{\cosh \dfrac{\pi y}{a} - \cos \dfrac{\pi(x - c)}{a}}{\cosh \dfrac{\pi y}{a} - \cos \dfrac{\pi(x + c)}{a}}, \qquad (g)$$

where C is a constant. By calculating the second derivatives $\partial^2 M/\partial x^2$ and $\partial^2 M/\partial y^2$ it can be shown that expression (g) satisfies Eq. (f). It is seen also that for $x = 0$ and $x = a$, i.e., along the supported edges of the plate, the expression for which the logarithm is to be taken becomes equal to unity. Hence M is zero at the boundary as it should be. For points close to the point of application of the load the quantities y and $(x - c)$ are small, and we can take $\cosh \dfrac{\pi y}{a} = 1 + \dfrac{\pi^2 y^2}{2a^2}$, $\cos \dfrac{\pi(x-c)}{a} = 1 - \dfrac{\pi^2(x-c)^2}{2a^2}$.

Expression (g) can then be represented in the following form:

$$M = \frac{C}{4\pi} \log \frac{1 + \dfrac{\pi^2 y^2}{2a^2} - 1 + \dfrac{\pi^2(x-c)^2}{2a^2}}{1 - \cos \dfrac{2\pi c}{a}}$$

$$= \frac{C}{4\pi} \log \left(\frac{\pi r}{2a \sin \dfrac{\pi c}{a}} \right)^2 = \frac{C}{2\pi} \log \frac{\pi r}{2a \sin \dfrac{\pi c}{a}}, \quad (h)$$

in which

$$r = \sqrt{y^2 + (x-c)^2}$$

represents the distance of a point under consideration from the point of application of the load P.

In order to determine the constant C, consider the equilibrium of a small circular element cut out from the plate by a cylindrical surface of small radius r with its axis along the line of application of the load. The shearing force Q_r along the boundary of this element is found from the condition of equilibrium to be

$$2\pi r Q_r = -P,$$

from which

$$Q_r = -\frac{P}{2\pi r}. \tag{i}$$

The shearing force Q_r can also be determined from the equation[1]

$$Q_r = -D\frac{\partial}{\partial r}\left(\frac{\partial^2 w}{\partial r^2} + \frac{\partial^2 w}{\partial t^2}\right) = -D\frac{\partial}{\partial r}\left(\frac{\partial^2 w}{\partial x^2} + \frac{\partial^2 w}{\partial y^2}\right) = \frac{\partial M}{\partial r}.$$

Substituting for M its expression (h), we find

$$Q_r = \frac{C}{2\pi r}. \tag{j}$$

It follows from this equation and from Eq. (i) that $C = -P$, and

[1] This equation coincides with Eq. (102) when the r- and t-directions coincide with the x- and y-axes.

we obtain for points close to the point of application of the load[1]

$$M = -\frac{P}{2\pi} \log \frac{\pi r}{2a \sin \frac{\pi c}{a}} = \frac{P}{2\pi} \log \frac{2a \sin \frac{\pi c}{a}}{\pi r}. \qquad (133)$$

For the other points, by using expression (g), we have

$$M = -\frac{P}{4\pi} \log \frac{\cosh \frac{\pi y}{a} - \cos \frac{\pi(x - c)}{a}}{\cosh \frac{\pi y}{a} - \cos \frac{\pi(x + c)}{a}}. \qquad (134)$$

The expressions for the bending moments M_x and M_y can be derived by using Eqs. (133) and (134). We begin with the points along the x-axis. For these points $M_x = M_y$, and by using Eq. (134) we obtain

$$(M_x)_{y=0} = (M_y)_{y=0} = \frac{M(1 + \nu)}{2}$$

$$= -\frac{P(1 + \nu)}{8\pi} \log \frac{1 - \cos \frac{\pi(x - c)}{a}}{1 - \cos \frac{\pi(x + c)}{a}}. \qquad (135)$$

In the particular case of the load applied at the center of the plate, $c = a/2$, and we obtain

$$(M_x)_{y=0} = (M_y)_{y=0} = -\frac{P(1 + \nu)}{8\pi} \log \frac{1 - \sin \frac{\pi x}{a}}{1 + \sin \frac{\pi x}{a}}. \qquad (136)$$

To obtain the bending moments at points that are not on the x-axis, let us consider the deflection surface of the plate below that axis. The general expression for this surface is given by Eq. (f) of the previous article (see page 148). The constants in this

---

[1] This expression can readily be obtained also by summation of series (e). For this purpose we replace the products of sines by the differences of cosines

and use the series $-\frac{1}{2} \log 2(1 - \cos \varphi) = \sum_{m=1,2,3,\,\cdots}^{\infty} \frac{1}{m} \cos \varphi.$

equation for an infinitely long plate are obtained from the general expressions on pages 150, 151 and can be put in the following form:

$$A'_m = a_m(1 - \gamma_m \coth 2\gamma_m) \sinh 2\gamma_m,$$
$$B'_m = -a_m(1 - \gamma_m \coth 2\gamma_m) \sinh 2\gamma_m,$$
$$D'_m = -C'_m = \tfrac{1}{2}a_m \sinh 2\gamma_m.$$

With these values of the constants and with the assumption that $\gamma_m = m\pi b_1/4a$ is infinitely small, the required deflection surface of the plate becomes

$$w' = \frac{Pa^2}{2\pi^3 D} \sum_{m=1}^{\infty} \frac{1}{m^3} \sin \frac{m\pi c}{a} \sin \frac{m\pi x}{a}\left(1 + \frac{m\pi y}{a}\right)e^{-\frac{m\pi y}{a}}. \quad (137)$$

The value of a_m given on page 157 has been introduced. By forming the second derivatives of these expressions we find

$$M = -D\left(\frac{\partial^2 w}{\partial x^2} + \frac{\partial^2 w}{\partial y^2}\right) = \frac{P}{\pi}\sum_{m=1}^{\infty} \frac{1}{m} \sin \frac{m\pi c}{a} \sin \frac{m\pi x}{a} e^{-\frac{m\pi y}{a}}.$$

We find also

$$2D\frac{\partial^2 w}{\partial x^2} = -M + y\frac{\partial M}{\partial y},$$
$$2D\frac{\partial^2 w}{\partial y^2} = -M - y\frac{\partial M}{\partial y}.$$

Hence

$$\left.\begin{aligned}
M_x &= -D\left(\frac{\partial^2 w}{\partial x^2} + \nu\frac{\partial^2 w}{\partial y^2}\right) = \frac{1}{2}\left[(1 + \nu)M - (1 - \nu)y\frac{\partial M}{\partial y}\right], \\
M_y &= -D\left(\frac{\partial^2 w}{\partial y^2} + \nu\frac{\partial^2 w}{\partial x^2}\right) = \frac{1}{2}\left[(1 + \nu)M + (1 - \nu)y\frac{\partial M}{\partial y}\right].
\end{aligned}\right\} \quad (138)$$

For points close to the point of application of the load P we can substitute for M its expression (133); then

$$\left.\begin{aligned}
M_x &= \frac{1}{2}\left[(1 + \nu)\frac{P}{2\pi} \log \frac{2a \sin \frac{\pi c}{a}}{\pi r} + \frac{(1 - \nu)Py^2}{2\pi r^2}\right], \\
M_y &= \frac{1}{2}\left[(1 + \nu)\frac{P}{2\pi} \log \frac{2a \sin \frac{\pi c}{a}}{\pi r} - \frac{(1 - \nu)Py^2}{2\pi r^2}\right].
\end{aligned}\right\} \quad (139)$$

It is interesting to compare this result with that for a centrally loaded, simply supported circular plate (see Art. 19). Taking a radius r under an angle α to the x-axis, we find, from Eqs. (90) and (91), for a circular plate

$$
\left.
\begin{aligned}
M_x &= M_n \cos^2 \alpha + M_t \sin^2 \alpha \\
&= \frac{P}{4\pi}(1 + \nu) \log \frac{a}{r} + (1 - \nu)\frac{P}{4\pi} \cdot \frac{y^2}{r^2}, \\
M_y &= M_n \sin^2 \alpha + M_t \cos^2 \alpha \\
&= \frac{P}{4\pi}(1 + \nu) \log \frac{a}{r} + (1 - \nu)\frac{P}{4\pi}\frac{x^2}{r^2}.
\end{aligned}
\right\} \quad (k)
$$

The first terms of expressions (139) and (k) will coincide if we take the outer radius of the circular plate equal to

$$
(2a/\pi) \sin (\pi c/a).
$$

Under this condition the moments M_x are the same for both cases. The moment M_y for the long rectangular plate is obtained from that of the circular plate by subtraction of the constant quantity[1] $(1 - \nu)P/4\pi$. From this it can be concluded that in a long rectangular plate the stress distribution around the point of application of the load is obtained by superposing on the stresses of a centrally loaded circular plate with radius $(2a/\pi) \sin (\pi c/a)$ a simple bending produced by the moments $M_y = -(1 - \nu)P/4\pi$.

It may be assumed that the same relation between the moments of circular and long rectangular plates also holds in the case of a load P uniformly distributed over a circular area of small radius e. In such a case, for the center of a circular plate we obtain from Eq. (83), by neglecting the term containing c^2,

$$
M_{\max.} = \frac{P}{4\pi}\left[(1 + \nu) \log \frac{a}{e} + 1 \right].
$$

Hence near the center of the loaded circular area of a long rectangular plate we obtain from Eqs. (139)

$$
\left.
\begin{aligned}
M_x &= \frac{1}{2}\left\{ \frac{P}{2\pi}\left[(1 + \nu) \log \frac{2a \sin \dfrac{\pi c}{a}}{\pi e} + 1 \right] + \frac{(1 - \nu)Py^2}{2\pi r^2} \right\}, \\
M_y &= \frac{1}{2}\left\{ \frac{P}{2\pi}\left[(1 + \nu) \log \frac{2a \sin \dfrac{\pi c}{a}}{\pi e} + 1 \right] - \frac{(1 - \nu)Py^2}{2\pi r^2} \right\}.
\end{aligned}
\right\} \quad (140)
$$

[1] We observe that $x^2 = r^2 - y^2$.

From this comparison of a long rectangular plate with a circular plate it may be concluded that all information regarding the local stresses at the point of application of the load P, derived for a circular plate by using the thick plate theory (see Art. 19), can also be applied in the case of a long rectangular plate.

When the plate is not very long, Eqs. (d) should be used instead of Eq. (e) in the calculation of the moments M_x and M_y along the x-axis. Because of the fact that tanh α_m approaches unity rapidly and cosh α_m becomes a large number when m increases, the differences between the sums of series (d) and the sum of series (e) can easily be calculated, and the moments M_x and M_y along the x-axis and close to the point of application of the load can be represented in the following form:

$$
\left.
\begin{aligned}
M_x &= \frac{(1+\nu)P}{2\pi}\sum_{m=1}^{\infty}\frac{1}{m}\sin\frac{m\pi c}{a}\sin\frac{m\pi x}{a} + \gamma_1\frac{P}{4\pi} \\
&= \frac{P(1+\nu)}{4\pi}\log\frac{2a\sin\dfrac{\pi c}{a}}{\pi r} + \gamma_1\frac{P}{4\pi}, \\
M_y &= \frac{(1+\nu)P}{2\pi}\sum_{m=1}^{\infty}\frac{1}{m}\sin\frac{m\pi c}{a}\sin\frac{m\pi x}{a} + \gamma_2\frac{P}{4\pi} \\
&= \frac{P(1+\nu)}{4\pi}\log\frac{2a\sin\dfrac{\pi c}{a}}{\pi r} + \gamma_2\frac{P}{4\pi},
\end{aligned}
\right\}
\quad (141)
$$

in which γ_1 and γ_2 are numerical factors the magnitudes of which depend on the ratio b/a. Several values of these factors for the case of central application of the load are given in Table 21.

TABLE 21.—FACTORS γ_1 AND γ_2 IN EQS. (141)

b/a	1.0	1.2	1.4	1.6	1.8	2.0	∞
γ_1	−0.565	−0.350	−0.211	−0.125	−0.073	−0.042	0
γ_2	+0.135	+0.115	+0.085	+0.057	+0.037	+0.023	0

Again the stress distribution near the point of application of the load is substantially the same as for a centrally loaded circular plate of radius $(2a/\pi)\sin(\pi c/a)$. To get the bending moments

M_x and M_y near the load we have only to superpose on the moments of the circular plate the uniform bending by the moments $M'_x = \gamma_1 P/4\pi$ and $M'_y = -(1 - \nu - \gamma_2)P/4\pi$. Assuming that this conclusion holds also when the load P is uniformly distributed over a circle of a small radius e, we obtain for the center of the circle

$$\left.\begin{array}{l} M_x = \dfrac{P}{4\pi}\left[(1 + \nu) \log \dfrac{2a \sin \dfrac{\pi c}{a}}{\pi e} + 1 \right] + \dfrac{\gamma_1 P}{4\pi}, \\[3em] M_y = \dfrac{P}{4\pi}\left[(1 + \nu) \log \dfrac{2a \sin \dfrac{\pi c}{a}}{\pi e} + 1 \right] - (1 - \nu - \gamma_2)\dfrac{P}{4\pi}. \end{array}\right\} \quad (142)$$

If the load P is applied at a point that is not on the axis of symmetry, the general expressions (e), (f), and (g) of the previous article should be used. As an example, let us determine the deflection under a load P applied at a point whose x- and y-coordinates are c and η, respectively. The general expressions for the constants $A_m, \ldots, D_m$, given on page 151, can be put in another form by substituting

$$\gamma_m + \beta_m = \frac{m\pi\eta}{a}, \qquad \gamma_m - \beta_m = \frac{m\pi b_1}{2a}$$

and treating b_1 as very small. Then omitting all the terms containing b_1 to a power higher than the first and making $y = \eta$ in expression (e) of the previous article, we obtain the following result for the deflection of the loaded strip ($y = \eta$):

$$w = \frac{Pa^2}{2D\pi^3}\sum_{m=1}^{\infty} \frac{\sin\dfrac{m\pi x}{a}\sin\dfrac{m\pi c}{a}}{m^3}\left[\cosh^2\frac{m\pi\eta}{a}\left(\tanh \alpha_m - \frac{\alpha_m}{\cosh^2 \alpha_m}\right)\right.$$

$$- \sinh^2\frac{m\pi\eta}{a}\left(\coth \alpha_m + \frac{\alpha_m}{\sinh^2 \alpha_m}\right)$$

$$\left. - \frac{2m\pi\eta}{a}\sinh\frac{m\pi\eta}{a}\cosh\frac{m\pi\eta}{a}(\tanh \alpha_m - \coth \alpha_m)\right]. \quad (143)$$

By making $y = 0$ in this expression we obtain expression (c) which was obtained before for the load applied at the axis of symmetry. When the plate is very long, $\tanh \alpha_m \approx \coth \alpha_m \approx 1$, and $\sinh^2 \alpha_m \approx \cosh^2 \alpha_m$ become very large; and when η is not large in comparison with a, Eq. (143) gives

$$ w = \frac{Pa^2}{2D\pi^3} \sum_{m=1}^{\infty} \frac{\sin \dfrac{m\pi x}{a} \sin \dfrac{m\pi c}{a}}{m^3}, $$

which can also be obtained from Eq. (c) for the symmetrically loaded plate.

34. Rectangular Plates of Infinite Length with Simply Supported Edges.—In our previous discussions infinitely long plates have been considered in several cases. The deflections and moments in such plates were usually obtained from the corresponding solutions for a finite plate by letting the length of the plate increase indefinitely. In some cases it is advantageous to obtain solutions for an infinitely long plate first and combine them in such a way as to obtain the solution for a finite plate. Several examples of this method of solution will be given in this article. We begin with the case of an infinitely long plate of width a loaded along the x-axis as shown in Fig. 70. Since the deflection surface is symmetrical with respect to the x-axis, we need consider only the portion of the plate corresponding to positive values of y in our further discussion. Since the load is distributed only along the x-axis, the deflection w of the plate satisfies the equation

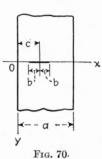

Fig. 70.

$$ \frac{\partial^4 w}{\partial x^4} + 2\frac{\partial^4 w}{\partial x^2\, \partial y^2} + \frac{\partial^4 w}{\partial y^4} = 0. \tag{a} $$

We take the solution of this equation in the form

$$ w = \sum_{m=1}^{\infty} Y_m \sin \frac{m\pi x}{a}, \tag{b} $$

which satisfies the boundary conditions along the simply supported longitudinal edges of the plate. To satisfy Eq. (a), functions Y_m must be chosen so as to satisfy the equation

$$Y_m^{\mathrm{IV}} - 2\frac{m^2\pi^2}{a^2}Y_m'' + \frac{m^4\pi^4}{a^4}Y_m = 0.$$

Taking the solution of this equation in the form

$$Y_m = A_m e^{\frac{m\pi y}{a}} + B_m\frac{m\pi y}{a}e^{\frac{m\pi y}{a}} + C_m e^{-\frac{m\pi y}{a}} + D_m\frac{m\pi y}{a}e^{-\frac{m\pi y}{a}} \qquad (c)$$

and observing that the deflections and their derivatives approach zero at a large distance from the x-axis, it may be concluded that the constants A_m and B_m should be taken equal to zero. Hence solution (b) can be represented as follows:

$$w = \sum_{m=1}^{\infty}\left(C_m + D_m\frac{m\pi y}{a}\right)e^{-\frac{m\pi y}{a}}\sin\frac{m\pi x}{a}. \qquad (d)$$

From the condition of symmetry we have

$$\left(\frac{\partial w}{\partial y}\right)_{y=0} = 0.$$

This condition is satisfied by taking $C_m = D_m$ in expression (d). Then

$$w = \sum_{m=1}^{\infty}C_m\left(1 + \frac{m\pi y}{a}\right)e^{-\frac{m\pi y}{a}}\sin\frac{m\pi x}{a}. \qquad (e)$$

The constants C_m can be readily calculated in each particular case provided the load distribution along the x-axis is given.

As an example, assume that the load is uniformly distributed along the entire width of the plate. The intensity of loading can then be represented by the following trigonometric series:

$$q = \frac{4}{\pi}q_0\sum_{m=1,3,5,\cdots}^{\infty}\frac{1}{m}\sin\frac{m\pi x}{a},$$

in which q_0 is the load per unit length. Since the load is equally divided between the two halves of the plate, we see that

$$(Q_y)_{y=0} = -D\frac{\partial}{\partial y}\left(\frac{\partial^2 w}{\partial x^2} + \frac{\partial^2 w}{\partial y^2}\right)_{y=0} = -\frac{2}{\pi}q_0\sum_{m=1,3,5,\cdots}^{\infty}\frac{1}{m}\sin\frac{m\pi x}{a}. \qquad (f)$$

Substituting expression (e) for w, we obtain

$$\frac{2D\pi^3}{a^3}\sum_{m=1}^{\infty} C_m m^3 \sin\frac{m\pi x}{a} = \frac{2q_0}{\pi}\sum_{m=1,3,5,\cdots}^{\infty}\frac{1}{m}\sin\frac{m\pi x}{a},$$

from which

$$C_m = \frac{q_0 a^3}{D\pi^4 m^4}, \text{ where } m = 1, 3, 5, \cdots$$

Hence

$$w = \frac{q_0 a^3}{\pi^4 D}\sum_{m=1,3,5,\cdots}^{\infty}\frac{1}{m^4}\left(1 + \frac{m\pi y}{a}\right)e^{-\frac{m\pi y}{a}}\sin\frac{m\pi x}{a}. \qquad (g)$$

The deflection is a maximum at the center of the plate ($x = a/2$, $y = 0$), where

$$(w)_{\text{max.}} = \frac{q_0 a^3}{\pi^4 D}\sum_{m=1,3,5,\cdots}^{\infty}\frac{(-1)^{\frac{m-1}{2}}}{m^4} = \frac{5\pi q_0 a^3}{24\cdot 64 D}. \qquad (h)$$

The same result can be obtained by setting $\tanh \alpha_m = 1$ and $\cosh \alpha_m = \infty$ in Eq. (131) (see page 154).

As another example of the application of solution (e), consider a load of length $2b$ uniformly distributed along a portion of the x-axis (Fig. 70). Representing this load distribution by a trigonometric series, we obtain

$$q = \frac{4q_0}{\pi}\sum_{m=1}^{\infty}\frac{1}{m}\sin\frac{m\pi c}{a}\sin\frac{m\pi b}{a}\sin\frac{m\pi x}{a},$$

where q_0 is the intensity of the load along the loaded portion of the x-axis. The equation for determining the constants C_m, corresponding to Eq. (f), is

$$D\frac{\partial}{\partial y}\left(\frac{\partial^2 w}{\partial x^2} + \frac{\partial^2 w}{\partial y^2}\right)_{y=0} = \frac{2q_0}{\pi}\sum_{m=1}^{\infty}\frac{1}{m}\sin\frac{m\pi c}{a}\sin\frac{m\pi b}{a}\sin\frac{m\pi x}{a}.$$

Substituting expression (e) for w, we obtain

$$\frac{2D\pi^3}{a^3}\sum_{m=1}^{\infty} C_m m^3 \sin\frac{m\pi x}{a} = \frac{2q_0}{\pi}\sum_{m=1}^{\infty}\frac{1}{m}\sin\frac{m\pi c}{a}\sin\frac{m\pi b}{a}\sin\frac{m\pi x}{a},$$

from which

$$C_m = \frac{q_0 a^3}{\pi^4 \, D m^4} \sin \frac{m\pi c}{a} \sin \frac{m\pi b}{a}.$$

Expression (*e*) for the deflections then becomes

$$w = \frac{q_0 a^3}{\pi^4 D} \sum_{m=1}^{\infty} \frac{1}{m^4} \sin \frac{m\pi c}{a} \sin \frac{m\pi b}{a} \left(1 + \frac{m\pi y}{a} \right) e^{-\frac{m\pi y}{a}} \sin \frac{m\pi x}{a}. \quad (i)$$

The particular case of a concentrated force applied at a distance *c* from the origin is obtained by making the length 2*b* of the loaded portion of the *x*-axis infinitely small. Substituting

$$2 b q_0 = P \qquad \text{and} \qquad \sin \frac{m\pi b}{a} \approx \frac{m\pi b}{a}$$

in Eq. (*i*), we obtain

$$w = \frac{P a^2}{2 \pi^3 D} \sum_{m=1}^{\infty} \frac{1}{m^3} \sin \frac{m\pi c}{a} \left(1 + \frac{m\pi y}{a} \right) e^{-\frac{m\pi y}{a}} \sin \frac{m\pi x}{a}, \quad (144)$$

an expression that coincides with expression (137) of the previous article.

We can obtain various other cases of loading by integrating expression (*i*) for the deflection of a long plate under a load distributed along a portion 2*b* of the *x*-axis. As an example, consider the case of a load of intensity *q* uniformly distributed over a rectangle with sides equal to 2*b* and 2*d* (shown shaded in Fig. 71). Taking an infinitesimal element of load of magnitude $q 2 b \, du$ at a distance *u* from the *x*-axis, the corresponding deflection produced by this load at points with $y > u$ is obtained by substituting $q \, du$ for q_0 and $y - u$ for y in expression (*i*). The deflection produced by the entire load, at points for which $y \geqq d$, is now obtained by integration as follows:

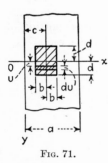

Fig. 71.

$$w = \frac{qa^3}{\pi^4 D} \sum_{m=1}^{\infty} \frac{1}{m^4} \sin\frac{m\pi c}{a} \sin\frac{m\pi b}{a} \sin\frac{m\pi x}{a}$$

$$\int_{-d}^{d} \left[1 + \frac{m\pi(y - u)}{a} \right] e^{-\frac{m\pi(y-u)}{a}} \, du$$

$$= \frac{qa^3}{\pi^4 D} \sum_{m=1}^{\infty} \frac{1}{m^4} \sin\frac{m\pi c}{a} \sin\frac{m\pi b}{a} \sin\frac{m\pi x}{a}$$

$$\left[\left(\frac{2a}{m\pi} + y - d \right) e^{-\frac{m\pi(y-d)}{a}} - \left(\frac{2a}{m\pi} + y + d \right) e^{-\frac{m\pi(y+d)}{a}} \right]. \quad (j)$$

By a proper change of the limits of integration the deflection at points with $y < d$ can also be obtained. Let us consider the deflection along the x-axis (Fig. 71). The deflection produced by the upper half of the load is obtained from expression (j) by substituting the quantity $d/2$ for y and for d. By doubling the result obtained in this way we also take into account the action of the lower half of the load and finally obtain

$$(w)_{y=0} = \frac{2qa^3}{\pi^4 D} \sum_{m=1}^{\infty} \frac{1}{m^4} \sin\frac{m\pi c}{a} \sin\frac{m\pi b}{a} \sin\frac{m\pi x}{a}$$

$$\left[\frac{2a}{m\pi} - \left(d + \frac{2a}{m\pi} \right) e^{-\frac{m\pi d}{a}} \right]. \quad (k)$$

When $d = \infty$, the load, indicated in Fig. 71, is expanded along the entire length of the plate; and the deflection surface is a cylindrical one. The corresponding deflection, from expression (k), is

$$(w)_{y=0} = \frac{4qa^4}{\pi^5 D} \sum_{m=1}^{\infty} \frac{1}{m^5} \sin\frac{m\pi c}{a} \sin\frac{m\pi b}{a} \sin\frac{m\pi x}{a}. \quad (l)$$

Making $b = c = a/2$ in this expression, we obtain

$$(w)_{y=0} = \frac{4qa^4}{\pi^5 D} \sum_{m=1,3,5,\cdots}^{\infty} \frac{1}{m^5} \sin\frac{m\pi x}{a}$$

which represents the deflection curve of a uniformly loaded strip.

The following expressions for bending moments produced by the load uniformly distributed along a portion $2b$ of the x-axis are readily obtained from expression (i) for deflection w:

$$\left. \begin{aligned} M_x &= \frac{q_0 a}{\pi^2} \sum_{m=1}^{\infty} \frac{1}{m^2} \sin \frac{m\pi c}{a} \sin \frac{m\pi b}{a} \sin \frac{m\pi x}{a} \\ &\qquad\qquad \left[1 + \nu + (1 - \nu)\frac{m\pi y}{a} \right] e^{-\frac{m\pi y}{a}}, \\ M_y &= \frac{q_0 a}{\pi^2} \sum_{m=1}^{\infty} \frac{1}{m^2} \sin \frac{m\pi c}{a} \sin \frac{m\pi b}{a} \sin \frac{m\pi x}{a} \\ &\qquad\qquad \left[1 + \nu - (1 - \nu)\frac{m\pi y}{a} \right] e^{-\frac{m\pi y}{a}}. \end{aligned} \right\} \quad (m)$$

These moments have their maximum values on the x-axis, where

$$\begin{aligned} (M_x)_{y=0} &= (M_y)_{y=0} \\ &= \frac{q_0 a(1 + \nu)}{\pi^2} \sum_{m=1}^{\infty} \frac{1}{m^2} \sin \frac{m\pi c}{a} \sin \frac{m\pi b}{a} \sin \frac{m\pi x}{a}. \quad (n) \end{aligned}$$

In the particular case when $c = b = a/2$, *i.e.*, when the load is distributed along the entire width of the plate,

$$(M_x)_{y=0} = (M_y)_{y=0} = \frac{q_0 a(1 + \nu)}{\pi^2} \sum_{m=1,3,5,\cdots}^{\infty} \frac{1}{m^2} \sin \frac{m\pi x}{a}.$$

The maximum moment is at the center of the plate where

$$(M_x)_{\text{max.}} = (M_y)_{\text{max.}} = \frac{q_0 a(1 + \nu)}{\pi^2} \sum_{m=1,3,5,\cdots}^{\infty} \frac{(-1)^{\frac{m-1}{2}}}{m^2} = \frac{\pi q_0 a(1 + \nu)}{32}.$$

When b is very small, *i.e.*, in the case of a concentrated load, we put

$$\sin \frac{m\pi b}{a} \approx \frac{m\pi b}{a} \qquad \text{and} \qquad 2bq_0 = P.$$

Then, from expression (n), we obtain

$$(M_x)_{y=0} = (M_y)_{y=0} = \frac{P(1 + \nu)}{2\pi} \sum_{m=1}^{\infty} \frac{1}{m} \sin \frac{m\pi c}{a} \sin \frac{m\pi x}{a}, \quad (o)$$

which coincides with expression (e) of the previous article.

In the case of a load q uniformly distributed over the area of a rectangle (Fig. 71), the bending moments for the portion of the plate for which $y \geqq d$ are obtained by integration of expressions (m) as follows:

$$
\begin{aligned}
M_x &= \frac{qa}{\pi^2}\sum_{m=1}^{\infty}\frac{1}{m^2}\sin\frac{m\pi c}{a}\sin\frac{m\pi b}{a}\sin\frac{m\pi x}{a} \\
&\quad \int_{-d}^{+d}\left[1+\nu+(1-\nu)\frac{m\pi(y-u)}{a}\right]e^{-\frac{m\pi(y-u)}{a}}\,du \\
&= \frac{qa}{\pi^2}\sum_{m=1}^{\infty}\frac{1}{m^2}\sin\frac{m\pi c}{a}\sin\frac{m\pi b}{a}\sin\frac{m\pi x}{a} \\
&\quad \left\{\left[\frac{2a}{m\pi}+(1-\nu)(y-d)\right]e^{-\frac{m\pi(y-d)}{a}}\right. \\
&\quad \left.-\left[\frac{2a}{m\pi}+(1-\nu)(y+d)\right]e^{-\frac{m\pi(y+d)}{a}}\right\}; \\
M_y &= \frac{qa}{\pi^2}\sum_{m=1}^{\infty}\frac{1}{m^2}\sin\frac{m\pi c}{a}\sin\frac{m\pi b}{a}\sin\frac{m\pi x}{a} \\
&\quad \left\{\left[\frac{2\nu a}{m\pi}-(1-\nu)(y-d)\right]e^{-\frac{m\pi(y-d)}{a}}\right. \\
&\quad \left.-\left[\frac{2\nu a}{m\pi}-(1-\nu)(y+d)\right]e^{-\frac{m\pi(y+d)}{a}}\right\}.
\end{aligned}
\tag{145}
$$

The moments for the portion of the plate for which $y < d$ can be calculated in a similar manner. To obtain the moments along the x-axis, we have only to substitute $d/2$ for d and y in formulas (145) and double the results thus obtained. Hence

$$
\begin{aligned}
(M_x)_{y=0} &= \frac{2qa}{\pi^2}\sum_{m=1}^{\infty}\frac{1}{m^2}\sin\frac{m\pi c}{a}\sin\frac{m\pi b}{a}\sin\frac{m\pi x}{a} \\
&\quad \left\{\frac{2a}{m\pi}-\left[\frac{2a}{m\pi}+(1-\nu)d\right]e^{-\frac{m\pi d}{a}}\right\}; \\
(M_y)_{y=0} &= \frac{2qa}{\pi^2}\sum_{m=1}^{\infty}\frac{1}{m^2}\sin\frac{m\pi c}{a}\sin\frac{m\pi b}{a}\sin\frac{m\pi x}{a} \\
&\quad \left\{\frac{2\nu a}{m\pi}-\left[\frac{2\nu a}{m\pi}-(1-\nu)d\right]e^{-\frac{m\pi d}{a}}\right\}.
\end{aligned}
\tag{146}
$$

When d is very small, Eqs. (146) coincide with Eq. (n) if we observe that $2qd$ must be replaced in such a case by q_0. When d is very large, we have the deflection of the plate to a cylindrical surface, and Eqs. (146) become

$$(M_x)_{y=0} = \frac{4qa^2}{\pi^3}\sum_{m=1}^{\infty}\frac{1}{m^3}\sin\frac{m\pi c}{a}\sin\frac{m\pi b}{a}\sin\frac{m\pi x}{a},$$

$$(M_y)_{y=0} = \frac{4\nu qa^2}{\pi^3}\sum_{m=1}^{\infty}\frac{1}{m^3}\sin\frac{m\pi c}{a}\sin\frac{m\pi b}{a}\sin\frac{m\pi x}{a}.$$

The expressions for the deflections and bending moments in a plate of finite length can be obtained from the corresponding quantities in an infinitely long plate by using the *method of images*.[1] Let us begin with the case of a concentrated force P

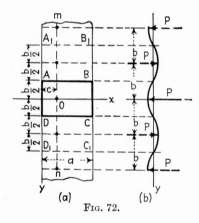

(a)   (b)

Fig. 72.

applied on the axis of symmetry x of the rectangular plate with sides a and b in Fig. 72a. If we now imagine the plate prolonged in both the positive and the negative y-directions and loaded with a series of forces P applied along the line mn at a distance b from one another and in alternate directions as shown in Fig. 72b, the deflections of such an infinitely long plate are evidently equal to zero along the lines A_1B_1, AB, CD, C_1D_1, . . . The bending moments along the same lines are also zero, and we may consider the given plate $ABCD$ as a portion of the infinitely long plate loaded as shown in Fig. 72b. Hence the deflection and the stresses produced in the given plate at the point of application O of the concentrated force can be calculated by using formulas derived for infinitely long plates. From Eq. (144) we find that the deflection produced at the x-axis of the infi-

[1] This method was used by Dr. A. Nadai, see *Z. angew. Math. Mech.*, vol. 2, p. 1, 1922; and by M. T. Huber, see *Z. angew. Math. Mech.*, vol. 6, p. 228, 1926.

nitely long plate by the load P applied at the point O is

$$w_1 = \frac{Pa^2}{2\pi^3 D} \sum_{m=1}^{\infty} \frac{1}{m^3} \sin \frac{m\pi c}{a} \sin \frac{m\pi x}{a}.$$

The two adjacent forces P applied at the distances b from the point O (Fig. 72b) produce at the x-axis the deflection

$$w_2 = -\frac{Pa^2}{\pi^3 D} \sum_{m=1}^{\infty} \frac{1}{m^3} \sin \frac{m\pi c}{a}(1 + 2\alpha_m)e^{-2\alpha_m} \sin \frac{m\pi x}{a},$$

in which, as before,

$$\alpha_m = \frac{m\pi b}{2a}.$$

The forces P at the distance $2b$ from the point O produce at the x-axis the deflection

$$w_3 = \frac{Pa^2}{\pi^3 D} \sum_{m=1}^{\infty} \frac{1}{m^3} \sin \frac{m\pi c}{a}(1 + 4\alpha_m)e^{-4\alpha_m} \sin \frac{m\pi x}{a},$$

and so on. The total deflection at the x-axis will be given by the summation

$$w = w_1 + w_2 + w_3 + \cdots . \qquad (p)$$

Observing that

$$\tanh \alpha_m = \frac{1 - e^{-2\alpha_m}}{1 + e^{-2\alpha_m}} = 1 - 2e^{-2\alpha_m} + 2e^{-4\alpha_m} \cdots ,$$

$$\frac{1}{\cosh^2 \alpha_m} = \frac{4}{(e^{\alpha_m} + e^{-\alpha_m})^2} = \frac{4e^{-2\alpha_m}}{(1 + e^{-2\alpha_m})^2}$$
$$= 4e^{-2\alpha_m}(1 - 2e^{-2\alpha_m} + 3e^{-4\alpha_m} - 4e^{-6\alpha_m} + \cdots),$$

we can bring expression (p) into coincidence with expression (c) of the previous article.

In calculating the stresses around the point of application of the load in the plate of finite length b we use Eq. (139) or (140) and calculate corrections corresponding to the action of the auxiliary forces shown in Fig. 72b by using Eqs. (138). Since the values of M entering into these equations diminish rapidly as the distances of the forces from the point O increase, it will be necessary to consider only the first few forces near the point O.

The same method can be used when the point of application of P is not on the axis of symmetry (Fig. 73a). The deflections and moments can be calculated by introducing a system of auxiliary

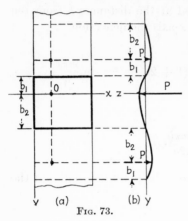

forces and using the formulas derived for an infinitely long plate. If the load is distributed over a rectangle, formulas (145) and (146) can be used for calculating the bending moments produced by actual and auxiliary loads.

35. Thermal Stresses in Simply Supported Rectangular Plates.—Let us assume that the upper surface of a rectangular plate is kept at a higher temperature than the lower surface so that

Fig. 73.

the plate has a tendency to bend convexly upward because of non-uniform heating. Because of the constraint along the simply supported edges of the plate, which prevents the edges from leaving the plane of the supports, the non-uniform heating of the plate produces certain reactions along the boundary of the plate and certain bending stresses at a distance from the edges. The method described in Art. 24 will be used in calculating these stresses.[1] We assume first that the edges of the plate are clamped. In such a case the non-uniform heating produces uniformly distributed bending moments along the boundary whose magnitude is (see page 54)

$$M_n = \frac{\alpha t D(1 + \nu)}{h}, \tag{a}$$

where t is the difference between the temperatures of the upper and the lower surfaces of the plate and α is the coefficient of thermal expansion. To get the bending moments M_x and M_y for a simply supported plate (Fig. 61), we must superpose on the uniformly distributed moments given by Eq. (a) the moments that are produced in a simply supported rectangular plate by the

[1] See paper by J. L. Maulbetsch, *loc. cit.*, p. 104.

moments $M'_n = -\alpha t D(1 + \nu)/h$ uniformly distributed along the edges. We shall use Eqs. (114) (see page 100) in discussing this latter problem. Since the curvature in the direction of an edge is zero in the case of simply supported edges, we have $M'_t = \nu M'_n$. Hence at the boundary

$$M = \frac{M_x + M_y}{1 + \nu} = \frac{M'_n + M'_t}{1 + \nu} = -\frac{\alpha t D(1 + \nu)}{h}. \qquad (b)$$

Thus the first of the equations (114) is satisfied by taking M constant along the entire plate and equal to its boundary value (b). Then the second of the equations (114) gives

$$\frac{\partial^2 w}{\partial x^2} + \frac{\partial^2 w}{\partial y^2} = \frac{\alpha t(1 + \nu)}{h}. \qquad (c)$$

Hence the deflection surface of the plate produced by non-uniform heating is the same as that of a uniformly stretched and uniformly loaded rectangular membrane and is obtained by finding the solution of Eq. (c) that satisfies the condition that $w = 0$ at the boundary.

Proceeding as before, we take the deflection surface of the plate in the form

$$w = w_1 + w_2, \qquad (d)$$

in which w_1 is the deflection of a perfectly flexible string loaded uniformly and stretched axially in such a way that the intensity of the load divided by the axial force is equal to $-\alpha t(1 + \nu)/h$. In such a case the deflection curve is a parabola which can be represented by a trigonometric series as follows:

$$w_1 = -\frac{\alpha t(1 + \nu)}{h} \frac{x(a - x)}{2}$$

$$= -\frac{\alpha t(1 + \nu)}{h} \frac{4a^2}{\pi^3} \sum_{m=1,3,5,\cdots}^{\infty} \frac{\sin \dfrac{m\pi x}{a}}{m^3}. \qquad (e)$$

This expression satisfies Eq. (c). The deflection w_2, which must satisfy the equation

$$\frac{\partial^2 w_2}{\partial x^2} + \frac{\partial^2 w_2}{\partial y^2} = 0, \qquad (f)$$

can be taken in the form of the series

$$w_2 = \sum_{m=1,3,5,\cdots}^{\infty} Y_m \sin \frac{m\pi x}{a}, \tag{g}$$

in which Y_m is a function of y only. Substituting (g) in Eq. (f), we find

$$Y_m'' - \frac{m^2\pi^2}{a^2} Y_m = 0.$$

Hence,

$$Y_m = A_m \sinh \frac{m\pi y}{a} + B_m \cosh \frac{m\pi y}{a}. \tag{h}$$

From the symmetry of the deflection surface with respect to the x-axis it may be concluded that Y_m must be an even function of y. Hence the constant A_m in the expression (h) must be taken equal to zero, and we finally obtain

$$w = w_1 + w_2 = \sum_{m=1,3,5,\cdots}^{\infty} \sin \frac{m\pi x}{a} \left[-\frac{\alpha t(1+\nu)}{h} \frac{4a^2}{\pi^3 m^3} \right. $$
$$\left. + B_m \cosh \frac{m\pi y}{a} \right]. \tag{i}$$

This expression satisfies the boundary conditions $w = 0$ at the edges $x = 0$ and $x = a$. To satisfy the same condition at the edges $y = \pm b/2$, we must have

$$B_m \cosh \frac{m\pi b}{2a} - \frac{\alpha t(1+\nu)}{h} \cdot \frac{4a^2}{\pi^3 m^3} = 0.$$

Substituting the value of B_m obtained from this equation in Eq. (i), we find that

$$w = -\frac{\alpha t(1+\nu)4a^2}{\pi^3 h} \sum_{m=1,3,5,\cdots}^{\infty} \frac{\sin \frac{m\pi x}{a}}{m^3} \left(1 - \frac{\cosh \frac{m\pi y}{a}}{\cosh \alpha_m} \right), \tag{j}$$

in which, as before, $\alpha_m = m\pi b/2a$.

Having this expression for the deflections w, we can find the corresponding values of bending moments; and, combining them with the moments (a), we finally obtain

$$\left.\begin{aligned}
M_x &= \frac{\alpha t D(1+\nu)}{h} - D\left(\frac{\partial^2 w}{\partial x^2} + \nu\frac{\partial^2 w}{\partial y^2}\right) \\
&= \frac{4D\alpha t(1-\nu^2)}{\pi h}\sum_{m=1,3,5,\cdots}^{\infty}\frac{\sin\dfrac{m\pi x}{a}\cosh\dfrac{m\pi y}{a}}{m\cosh\alpha_m}, \\
M_y &= \frac{\alpha t D(1+\nu)}{h} - D\left(\frac{\partial^2 w}{\partial y^2} + \nu\frac{\partial^2 w}{\partial x^2}\right) \\
&= \frac{\alpha t(1-\nu^2)D}{h} - \frac{4D\alpha t(1-\nu^2)}{\pi h}\sum_{m=1,3,5,\cdots}^{\infty}\frac{\sin\dfrac{m\pi x}{a}\cosh\dfrac{m\pi y}{a}}{m\cosh\alpha_m}.
\end{aligned}\right\} \quad (k)$$

The sum of the series that appears in these expressions can be readily found if we put it in the following form:

$$\sum_{m=1,3,5,\cdots}^{\infty}\frac{\sin\dfrac{m\pi x}{a}\cosh\dfrac{m\pi y}{a}}{m\cosh\alpha_m}$$

$$= \sum_{m=1,3,5,\cdots}^{\infty}\left(\frac{\sin\dfrac{m\pi x}{a}\cosh\dfrac{m\pi y}{a}}{m\cosh\alpha_m} - \frac{e^{\frac{m\pi y}{a}}\sin\dfrac{m\pi x}{a}}{me^{\alpha_m}}\right)$$

$$+ \sum_{m=1,3,5,\cdots}^{\infty}\frac{e^{\frac{m\pi y}{a}}}{me^{\alpha_m}}\sin\frac{m\pi x}{a}. \quad (l)$$

The first series on the right side of this equation converges rapidly, since $\cosh(m\pi y/a)$ and $\cosh\alpha_m$ rapidly approach $e^{\frac{m\pi y}{a}}$ and e^{α_m} as m increases. The second series can be represented as follows.[1]

$$\sum_{m=1,3,5,\cdots}^{\infty}\frac{e^{\frac{m\pi y}{a}}\sin\dfrac{m\pi x}{a}}{me^{\alpha_m}} = \frac{1}{2}\arctan\left[\frac{\sin\dfrac{\pi x}{a}}{\sinh\left(\dfrac{\pi b}{2a} - \dfrac{\pi y}{a}\right)}\right]. \quad (m)$$

[1] See W. E. Byerly, "Elementary Treatise on Fourier Series and Spherical, Cylindrical and Ellipsoidal Harmonics," p. 100, Boston, 1893. The result can be easily obtained by using the known series

$$\frac{1}{2}\arctan\frac{2x\sin\varphi}{1-x^2} = x\sin\varphi + \frac{x^3}{3}\sin 3\varphi + \frac{x^5}{5}\sin 5\varphi + \cdots.$$

The bending moments M_x and M_y have their maximum values at the boundary. These values are

$$(M_x)_{y=\pm\frac{b}{2}} = (M_y)_{x=0, x=a} = \frac{\alpha t(1 - \nu^2)D}{h} = Eh^2\frac{\alpha t}{12}. \qquad (n)$$

It is seen that these moments are obtained by multiplying the value of M_n in formula (a) by $(1 - \nu)$. The same conclusion is reached if we observe that the moments M'_n which were applied along the boundary produce in the perpendicular direction the moments

$$M'_t = \nu M'_n = -\nu\frac{\alpha t D(1 + \nu)}{h}$$

which superposed on the moment (a) give the value (n).

36. Application of Finite Differences Equations to the Bending of Simply Supported Rectangular Plates.—In our previous discussion (see Art. 24) it was shown that the differential equation for the bending of plates can be replaced by two equations each of which has the form of the equation for the deflection of a uniformly stretched membrane. It was mentioned also that this latter equation can be solved with sufficient accuracy by replacing it by a finite differences equation. To illustrate this method of solution let us begin with the case of a uniformly loaded long rectangular plate. At a considerable distance from the short sides of the plate the deflection surface in this case may be considered cylindrical. Then, by taking the x-axis parallel to the short sides of the plate, the differential equations (114) become

$$\left.\begin{aligned} \frac{\partial^2 M}{\partial x^2} &= -q, \\ \frac{\partial^2 w}{\partial x^2} &= -\frac{M}{D}. \end{aligned}\right\} \qquad (a)$$

Both these equations have the same form as the equation for the deflection of a stretched and laterally loaded flexible string.

Let AB (Fig. 74a) represent the deflection curve of a string stretched by forces S and uniformly loaded with a vertical load of intensity q. In deriving the equation of this curve we consider the equilibrium of an infinitesimal element mn. The tensile forces at points m and n have the directions of tangents to the deflection curve at these points; and, by projecting these forces and also the

load $q\,dx$ on the z-axis, we obtain

$$-S\frac{dw}{dx} + S\left(\frac{dw}{dx} + \frac{\partial^2 w}{\partial x^2}dx\right) + q\,dx = 0, \qquad (b)$$

from which

$$\frac{\partial^2 w}{\partial x^2} = -\frac{q}{S}. \qquad (c)$$

This equation has the same form as Eqs. (a) derived for an infinitely long plate. The deflection curve is now obtained by integrating Eq. (c) which gives the parabolic curve

$$w = \frac{4\,\delta\,x(a-x)}{a^2}, \qquad (d)$$

satisfying the conditions $w = 0$ at the ends and having a deflection δ at the middle.

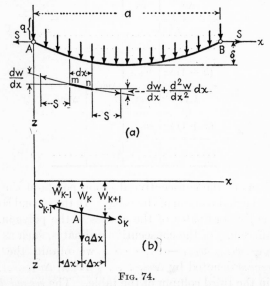

Fig. 74.

The same problem can be solved graphically by replacing the uniform load by a system of equidistant concentrated forces $q\Delta x$, Δx being the distance between two adjacent forces, and constructing the funicular polygon for these forces. If A (Fig. 74b) is one of the apexes of this funicular polygon and S_{k-1} and S_k are the tensile forces in the two adjacent sides of the polygon, the horizontal projections of these forces are equal to S and the sum of their vertical projections is in equilibrium with the load $q \, \Delta x$, which gives

$$-S\frac{w_k - w_{k-1}}{\Delta x} + S\frac{w_{k+1} - w_k}{\Delta x} + q \, \Delta x = 0. \qquad (e)$$

In this equation w_{k-1}, w_k and w_{k+1} are the ordinates corresponding to the three consecutive apexes of the funicular polygon, and $(w_k - w_{k-1})/\Delta x$ and $(w_{k+1} - w_k)/\Delta x$ are the slopes of the two adjacent sides of the polygon. Equation (e) can be used in calculating the consecutive ordinates w_1, w_2, . . . , w_{k-1}, w_k, w_{k+1}, . . . , w_n of the funicular polygon. For this purpose let us construct Table (f).

0	w_0		
		Δw_0	
Δx	w_1		
. . . .	. . . . . .	. . . . . .	. . . . . .
. . . .	. . . . . .	. . . . . .	. . . . . .
$(k-1)\Delta x$	w_{k-1}		
		Δw_{k-1}	
$k\Delta x$	w_k		$\Delta^2 w_k$
		Δw_k	
$(k+1)\Delta x$	w_{k+1}		
. . . .	. . . . . .	. . . . . .	. . . . . .

$$(f)$$

The abscissas of the consecutive division points of the span are entered in the first column of the table. In the second column are the consecutive ordinates of the apexes of the polygon. Forming the differences of the consecutive ordinates, such as $w_1 - w_0$, · · · , $w_k - w_{k-1}$, $w_{k+1} - w_k$, · · · , we obtain the so-called *first differences* denoted by Δw_0, . . . , Δw_{k-1}, Δw_k, . . . , which we enter in the third column of the table. The *second differences* are obtained by forming the differences between the consecutive numbers of the third column. For example, for the point k with the abscissa $k\Delta x$ the second difference is

$$\Delta^2 w_k = \Delta w_k - \Delta w_{k-1} = w_{k+1} - w_k - (w_k - w_{k-1})$$
$$= w_{k+1} - 2w_k + w_{k-1}. \qquad (g)$$

With this notation Eq. (e) can be written in the following form:

$$\frac{\Delta^2 w}{\Delta x^2} = -\frac{q}{S}. \tag{h}$$

This is a finite differences equation which corresponds to the differential equation (c) and approaches it closer and closer as the number of division points of the span increases.

In a similar manner the differential equations (a) can be replaced by the following finite differences equations:

$$\left.\begin{array}{l} \dfrac{\Delta^2 M}{\Delta x^2} = -q, \\[2mm] \dfrac{\Delta^2 w}{\Delta x^2} = -\dfrac{M}{D}. \end{array}\right\} \tag{i}$$

To illustrate the application of these equations in calculating the deflections of the plate let us divide the span, say, into eight equal parts, *i.e.*, let $\Delta x = \frac{1}{8}a$. Then Eqs. (i) become

$$\Delta^2 M = -\frac{qa^2}{64},$$

$$\Delta^2 w = -\frac{Ma^2}{64D}.$$

Forming the second differences for the consecutive division points w_1, w_2, w_3 and w_4 in accordance with Eq. (g) and observing that in our case $w_0 = 0$ and $M_0 = 0$ and from symmetry $w_3 = w_5$ and $M_3 = M_5$, we obtain the two following groups of linear equations:

$$\left.\begin{array}{ll} M_2 - 2M_1 = -\dfrac{qa^2}{64}, & w_2 - 2w_1 = -\dfrac{M_1 a^2}{64D}, \\[2mm] M_3 - 2M_2 + M_1 = -\dfrac{qa^2}{64}, & w_3 - 2w_2 + w_1 = -\dfrac{M_2 a^2}{64D}, \\[2mm] M_4 - 2M_3 + M_2 = -\dfrac{qa^2}{64}, & w_4 - 2w_3 + w_2 = -\dfrac{M_3 a^2}{64D}, \\[2mm] M_3 - 2M_4 + M_3 = -\dfrac{qa^2}{64}, & w_3 - 2w_4 + w_3 = -\dfrac{M_4 a^2}{64D}. \end{array}\right\} \tag{j}$$

Solving the first group, we obtain the following values for M:

$$M_1 = \frac{7}{2}\frac{qa^2}{64}, \qquad M_2 = 6\frac{qa^2}{64}, \qquad M_3 = \frac{15}{2}\frac{qa^2}{64}, \qquad M_4 = 8\frac{qa^2}{64}. \tag{k}$$

These values coincide exactly with the values of the bending moments for a uniformly loaded strip, calculated from the known equation

$$M = \frac{qa}{2}x - \frac{qx^2}{2}.$$

Substituting the values (k) for the moments in the second group of Eqs. (j), we obtain

$$w_2 - 2w_1 = -\tfrac{7}{2}N,$$
$$w_3 - 2w_2 + w_1 = -6N,$$
$$w_4 - 2w_3 + w_2 = -\tfrac{15}{2}N,$$
$$w_3 - 2w_4 + w_3 = -8N,$$

where

$$N = \frac{qa^4}{64^2 D}.$$

Solving these equations, we obtain the following deflections at the division points:

$$w_1 = 21N, \qquad w_2 = 38.5N, \qquad w_3 = 50N, \qquad w_4 = 54N. \qquad (l)$$

The exact values of these deflections as obtained from the known equation

$$w = \frac{qx}{24D}(a^3 - 2ax^2 + x^3),$$

for the deflection of a uniformly loaded strip of length a, for purposes of comparison, are

$$w_1 = 20.7N, \qquad w_2 = 38N, \qquad w_3 = 49.4N, \qquad w_4 = 53.3N.$$

It is seen that by dividing the span into eight parts, the error in the magnitude of the maximum deflection as obtained from the finite differences equations (i) is about 1.25 per cent. By increasing the number of division points the accuracy of our calculations can be increased; but this will require more work, since the number of equations in the system (j) increases as we increase the number of divisions.

Let us consider next a rectangular plate of finite length. In this case the deflections are functions of both x and y, and Eqs. (a) must be replaced by the general equations (114). In replacing these equations by the finite differences equations we have to consider the differences corresponding to the changes of both the coordinates x and y. We shall use the following notations for the first differences at a point A_{mn} with coordinates $m\Delta x$ and $n\Delta y$. The notation used in designating adjacent points is shown in Fig. 75.

$$\Delta_x w_{m-1,n} = w_{m,n} - w_{m-1,n}, \qquad \Delta_x w_{m,n} = w_{m+1,n} - w_{m,n},$$
$$\Delta_y w_{m,n-1} = w_{m,n} - w_{m,n-1}, \qquad \Delta_y w_{m,n} = w_{m,n+1} - w_{m,n}.$$

Having the first differences, we can form the three kinds of second differences as follows:

$$
\left.
\begin{aligned}
\Delta_{xx} w_{mn} &= \Delta_x w_{mn} - \Delta_x w_{m-1,n} = w_{m+1,n} - w_{mn} \\
&\quad - (w_{mn} - w_{m-1,n}) = w_{m+1,n} - 2w_{mn} + w_{m-1,n}, \\
\Delta_{yy} w_{mn} &= \Delta_y w_{mn} - \Delta_y w_{m,n-1} = w_{m,n+1} - w_{mn} \\
&\quad - (w_{mn} - w_{m,n-1}) = w_{m,n+1} - 2w_{mn} + w_{m,n-1}, \\
\Delta_{xy} w_{mn} &= \Delta_y w_{mn} - \Delta_y w_{m-1,n} = w_{m,n+1} - w_{mn} \\
&\quad - (w_{m-1,n+1} - w_{m-1,n}) = w_{m,n+1} - w_{mn} - w_{m-1,n+1} + w_{m-1,n}.
\end{aligned}
\right\} \quad (m)
$$

With these notations the differential equations (114) will be

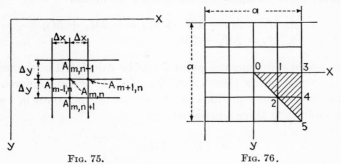

Fig. 75.   Fig. 76.

replaced by the following differences equations:

$$
\left.
\begin{aligned}
\frac{\Delta_{xx} M}{\Delta x^2} + \frac{\Delta_{yy} M}{\Delta y^2} &= -q, \\
\frac{\Delta_{xx} w}{\Delta x^2} + \frac{\Delta_{yy} w}{\Delta y^2} &= -\frac{M}{D}.
\end{aligned}
\right\} \quad (n)
$$

In the case of a simply supported rectangular plate M and w are equal to zero at the boundary, and we can solve Eqs. (n) in succession without any difficulty.

To illustrate the process of calculating moments and deflections let us take the very simple case of a uniformly loaded square plate (Fig. 76). A rough approximation for M and w

will be obtained by dividing the plate into 16 small squares as shown in the figure, and by taking $\Delta x = \Delta y = \frac{a}{4}$ in Eqs. (n).

It is evident from symmetry that the calculations need be extended over an area of one-eighth of the plate only, as shown in the figure by the shaded triangle. In this area we have to make the calculations only for the three points 0, 1, 2, for which M and w are different from zero. At the remaining points 3, 4, 5, these quantities are zero from the boundary conditions. Beginning with the first of the equations (n) and considering the center of the plate, point 0, we find the following values of the second differences for this point by using Eqs. (m) and the conditions of symmetry:

$$\Delta_{xx}M_0 = 2M_1 - 2M_0,$$
$$\Delta_{yy}M_0 = 2M_1 - 2M_0,$$

in which M_1 and M_0 are the values of M at points 1 and 0, respectively. Similarly for the point 1 we obtain

$$\Delta_{xx}M_1 = M_3 - 2M_1 + M_0 = -2M_1 + M_0,$$
$$\Delta_{yy}M_1 = 2M_2 - 2M_1.$$

The second differences at point 2 can be calculated in the same way. Substituting these expressions for the second differences in the first of the equations (n), we obtain for the points 0, 1 and 2 the following three equations:

$$4M_1 - 4M_0 = -\frac{qa^2}{16},$$

$$2M_2 - 4M_1 + M_0 = -\frac{qa^2}{16},$$

$$-4M_2 + 2M_1 = -\frac{qa^2}{16},$$

from which we find

$$M_0 = \frac{9}{2}\frac{qa^2}{64}, \qquad M_1 = \frac{7}{2}\frac{qa^2}{64}, \qquad M_2 = \frac{11}{4}\frac{qa^2}{64}.$$

Substituting these values of moments in the second of the equations (n), we obtain the following three equations for calculating deflections w_0, w_1 and w_2:

$$4w_1 - 4w_0 = -\tfrac{9}{2}N,$$
$$2w_2 - 4w_1 + w_0 = -\tfrac{7}{2}N,$$
$$-4w_2 + 2w_1 = -\tfrac{11}{4}N,$$

where

$$N = \frac{qa^4}{16 \cdot 64D}.$$

From these equations we find the following values of the deflections:

$$w_0 = \tfrac{66}{16}N, \qquad w_1 = \tfrac{48}{16}N, \qquad w_2 = \tfrac{35}{16}N.$$

For the deflection at the center we obtain

$$w_0 = \frac{66}{16}N = \frac{66qa^4}{16 \cdot 16 \cdot 64D} = 0.00403\frac{qa^4}{D} = 0.0440\frac{qa^4}{Eh^3}.$$

Comparing this with the value $0.0443qa^4/Eh^3$ given in Table 5, it can be concluded that the error of the calculated maximum deflection is less than 1 per cent. For the bending moment at the center of the plate we find

$$M_x = M_y = \frac{M_0(1 + \nu)}{2} = \frac{1.3}{2} \cdot \frac{9}{2}\frac{qa^2}{64} = 0.0457qa^2,$$

which is less than the exact value $0.0479qa^2$ by about $4\tfrac{1}{2}$ per cent. It can be seen that in this case a small number of subdivisions of the plate gives an accuracy sufficient for practical applications. By taking twice the number of subdivisions, *i.e.*, by making $\Delta x = \Delta y = \tfrac{1}{8}a$, the value of the bending moment will differ from the exact value by less than 1 per cent.

From this simple example it can be seen that the use of the differences equations gives us a satisfactory result in the case of simply supported and uniformly loaded rectangular plates and may be applied in practical cases.[1]

[1] Many numerical examples of this kind may be found in the book by Dr. H. Marcus, "Die Theorie elastischer Gewebe," 2d ed., Berlin, 1932; see also N. J. Nielsen, "Bestemmelse af spaendinger i Plader," Copenhagen, 1920. A method of successive approximations in using the finite differences equation was developed by H. Liebman, "Die angenäherte Ermittlung harmonischer Funktionen und Konformer Abbildungen," *Sitzungsb., Münchener Akad.*, p. 385, 1918. The convergency of this method was discussed by F. Wolf, *Z. angew. Math. Mech.*, vol. 6, p. 118, 1926; and by R. Courant, *Z. angew. Math. Mech.*, vol. 6, p. 322, 1926.

37. Bending of Anisotropic Plates.—In our previous discussions we have assumed that the elastic properties of the material of the plate are the same in all directions.   There are, however, cases in which an anisotropic material must be assumed if we wish to bring the theory of plates into agreement with experiments.[1]   Let us assume that the material of the plate has three planes of symmetry with respect to its elastic properties.   Taking these planes as the coordinate planes, the relations between the stress and strain components for a case of plane stress in the xy-plane can be represented by the following equations:

$$\left. \begin{aligned} \sigma_x &= E_x' \epsilon_x + E'' \epsilon_y, \\ \sigma_y &= E_y' \epsilon_y + E'' \epsilon_x, \\ \tau_{xy} &= G\gamma_{xy}. \end{aligned} \right\} \qquad (a)$$

It is seen that in the case of plane stress, four constants E_x', E_y', E'' and G are needed to characterize the elastic properties of a material.

Considering the bending of a plate made of such a material, we assume, as before, that linear elements perpendicular to the middle plane (xy-plane) of the plate before bending remain straight and normal to the deflection surface of the plate after bending.   Hence we can use our previous expressions for the components of strain:

$$\epsilon_x = -z\frac{\partial^2 w}{\partial x^2}, \qquad \epsilon_y = -z\frac{\partial^2 w}{\partial y^2}, \qquad \gamma_{xy} = -2z\frac{\partial^2 w}{\partial x\,\partial y}. \qquad (b)$$

The corresponding stress components, from Eqs. (a), are

$$\left. \begin{aligned} \sigma_x &= -z\left(E_x'\frac{\partial^2 w}{\partial x^2} + E''\frac{\partial^2 w}{\partial y^2} \right), \\ \sigma_y &= -z\left(E_y'\frac{\partial^2 w}{\partial y^2} + E''\frac{\partial^2 w}{\partial x^2} \right), \\ \tau_{xy} &= -2Gz\frac{\partial^2 w}{\partial x\,\partial y}. \end{aligned} \right\} \qquad (c)$$

With these expressions for stress components the bending and twisting moments are

[1] The case of a plate of an anisotropic material has been discussed by J. Boussinesq, *J. math.*, 3d series, vol. 5, 1879. See also Saint Venant's translation of the book "Théorie de l'élasticité des corps solides," by A. Clebsch, note **73**, p. 693.

$$M_x = \int_{-\frac{h}{2}}^{\frac{h}{2}} \sigma_x z \, dz = -\left(D_x \frac{\partial^2 w}{\partial x^2} + D_1 \frac{\partial^2 w}{\partial y^2}\right),$$

$$M_y = \int_{-\frac{h}{2}}^{\frac{h}{2}} \sigma_y z \, dz = -\left(D_y \frac{\partial^2 w}{\partial y^2} + D_1 \frac{\partial^2 w}{\partial x^2}\right), \qquad (147)$$

$$M_{xy} = -\int_{-\frac{h}{2}}^{\frac{h}{2}} \tau_{xy} z \, dz = 2D_{xy} \frac{\partial^2 w}{\partial x \, \partial y},$$

in which

$$D_x = \frac{E_x' h^3}{12}, \qquad D_y = \frac{E_y' h^3}{12}, \qquad D_1 = \frac{E'' h^3}{12}, \qquad D_{xy} = \frac{G h^3}{12}. \qquad (d)$$

Substituting expressions (147) in the differential equation of equilibrium (98), we obtain the following equation for anisotropic plates:

$$D_x \frac{\partial^4 w}{\partial x^4} + 2(D_1 + 2D_{xy}) \frac{\partial^4 w}{\partial x^2 \, \partial y^2} + D_y \frac{\partial^4 w}{\partial y^4} = q.$$

Introducing the notation

$$H = D_1 + 2D_{xy}, \qquad (e)$$

we obtain

$$D_x \frac{\partial^4 w}{\partial x^4} + 2H \frac{\partial^4 w}{\partial x^2 \, \partial y^2} + D_y \frac{\partial^4 w}{\partial y^4} = q. \qquad (148)$$

In the particular case of isotropy we have

$$E_x' = E_y' = \frac{E}{1 - \nu^2}, \qquad E'' = \frac{\nu E}{1 - \nu^2}, \qquad G = \frac{E}{2(1 + \nu)}.$$

Hence

$$D_x = D_y = \frac{Eh^3}{12(1 - \nu^2)};$$

$$H = D_1 + 2D_{xy} = \frac{h^3}{12}\left(\frac{\nu E}{1 - \nu^2} + \frac{E}{1 + \nu}\right) = \frac{Eh^3}{12(1 - \nu^2)}, \qquad (f)$$

and Eq. (148) reduces to our previous Eq. (101).

Equation (148) can be used in the investigation of the bending of plates of non-homogeneous material, such as reinforced concrete slabs,[1] which have different flexural rigidities in two

[1] The application of the theory of anisotropic plates to reinforced concrete slabs is due to M. T. Huber, who published a series of papers on

mutually perpendicular directions. The quantities D_x, D_y and D_1 can be calculated approximately for a reinforced concrete slab by the methods used in investigating the bending of reinforced concrete beams, or they can be obtained with greater accuracy by experiment. The torsional rigidity D_{xy} can be calculated approximately by taking the concrete only into account and using its shear modulus G, or a more accurate value can be obtained by direct test, as shown in Fig. 25c.

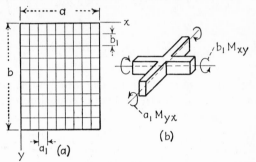

Fig. 77.

Equation (148) can also be applied to the gridwork system shown in Fig. 77. This consists of two systems of parallel beams spaced equal distances apart in the x- and y-directions and rigidly connected at their points of intersection. The beams are supported at the ends, and the load is applied normal to the xy-plane. If the distances a_1 and b_1 between the beams are small in comparison with the dimensions a and b of the grid, and if the flexural rigidity of each of the beams parallel to the x-axis is equal to B_1 and that of each of the beams parallel to y-axis is equal to B_2, we can substitute in Eq. (148)

$$D_x = \frac{B_1}{b_1}, \qquad D_y = \frac{B_2}{a_1}.$$

The quantity D_1 in this case is zero, and the quantity D_{xy} can be expressed in terms of the torsional rigidities C_1 and C_2 of the

this subject. See *Z. Österr. Ing. u. Archit. Ver.*, p. 557, 1914. The principal results are collected in his books: "Teorya Plyt," Lwow, 1922, and "Probleme der Statik technisch wichtiger orthotroper Platten," Warszawa, 1929. Abstracts of his papers are given in *Comptes rendus* v. 170, pp. 511 and 1305, 1920; and v. 180, p. 1243, 1925.

beams parallel to the x- and y-axes, respectively. For this purpose we consider the twist of an element as shown in Fig. 77b and obtain the following relations between the twisting moments and the twist $\partial^2 w/\partial x\,\partial y$:

$$M_{xy} = \frac{C_1}{b_1}\frac{\partial^2 w}{\partial x\,\partial y}, \qquad M_{yx} = -\frac{C_2}{a_1}\frac{\partial^2 w}{\partial x\,\partial y}.$$

Substituting these expressions in the equation of equilibrium (f) on page 87, we find that in the case of the system represented in Fig. 77a the differential equation of the deflection surface is

$$\frac{B_1}{b_1}\frac{\partial^4 w}{\partial x^4} + \left(\frac{C_1}{b_1} + \frac{C_2}{a_1}\right)\frac{\partial^4 w}{\partial x^2\,\partial y^2} + \frac{B_2}{a_1}\frac{\partial^4 w}{\partial y^4} = q, \qquad (148')$$

which is of the same form as Eq. 148.

Equation (148) can be solved by the methods used in the case of an isotropic plate. Let us apply the Navier method (see Art. 27) and assume that the plate is uniformly loaded. Taking the coordinate axes as shown in Fig. 59 and representing the load in the form of a double trigonometric series, the differential equation (148) becomes

$$D_x\frac{\partial^4 w}{\partial x^4} + 2H\frac{\partial^4 w}{\partial x^2\,\partial y^2} + D_y\frac{\partial^4 w}{\partial y^4}$$

$$= \frac{16q_0}{\pi^2} \sum_{m=1,3,5,\cdots}^{\infty} \sum_{n=1,3,5,\cdots}^{\infty} \frac{1}{mn}\sin\frac{m\pi x}{a}\sin\frac{n\pi y}{b}. \qquad (g)$$

A solution of this equation that satisfies the boundary conditions can be taken in the form of the double trigonometrical series

$$w = \sum_{m=1,3,5,\cdots}^{\infty} \sum_{n=1,3,5,\cdots}^{\infty} a_{mn}\sin\frac{m\pi x}{a}\sin\frac{n\pi y}{b}. \qquad (h)$$

Substituting this series in Eq. (g), we find the following expression for the coefficients a_{mn}:

$$a_{mn} = -\frac{16q_0}{\pi^6}\frac{1}{mn\left(\dfrac{m^4}{a^4}D_x + \dfrac{2m^2 n^2}{a^2 b^2}H + \dfrac{n^4}{b^4}D_y\right)}.$$

Hence the solution of Eq. (g) is

$$w = \frac{16q_0}{\pi^6} \sum_{m=1,3,5,\cdots}^{\infty} \sum_{n=1,3,5,\cdots}^{\infty} \frac{\sin \dfrac{m\pi x}{a} \sin \dfrac{n\pi y}{b}}{mn\left(\dfrac{m^4}{a^4}D_x + \dfrac{2m^2n^2}{a^2b^2}H + \dfrac{n^4}{b^4}D_y\right)}. \qquad (i)$$

In the case of an isotropic material $D_x = D_y = H = D$, and this solution coincides with that given on page 118.

As a second example let us consider an infinitely long plate (Fig. 70) and assume that the load is distributed along the x-axis following the sinusoidal relation

$$q = q_0 \sin \frac{m\pi x}{a}. \qquad (j)$$

In this case Eq. (148) for the unloaded portions of the plate becomes

$$D_x \frac{\partial^4 w}{\partial x^4} + 2H \frac{\partial^4 w}{\partial x^2\, \partial y^2} + D_y \frac{\partial^4 w}{\partial y^4} = 0. \qquad (k)$$

A solution of this equation, satisfying the boundary conditions at the sides parallel to the y-axis, can be taken in the following form:

$$w = Y_m \sin \frac{m\pi x}{a}, \qquad (l)$$

where Y_m is a function of y only. Substituting this in Eq. (k), we obtain the following equation for determining the function Y_m:

$$D_y Y_m^{\text{IV}} - 2H \frac{m^2\pi^2}{a^2} Y_m^{\text{II}} + D_x \frac{m^4\pi^4}{a^4} Y_m = 0. \qquad (m)$$

The roots of the corresponding characteristic equation are

$$r_{1,2,3,4} = \pm \frac{m\pi}{a} \sqrt{\frac{H}{D_y} \pm \sqrt{\frac{H^2}{D_y^2} - \frac{D_x}{D_y}}}. \qquad (n)$$

We have to consider the following three cases:

$$(1)\ H^2 > D_x D_y, \qquad (2)\ H^2 = D_x D_y, \qquad (3)\ H^2 < D_x D_y. \qquad (o)$$

In the first case all the roots of Eq. (n) are real. Considering the part of the plate with positive y and observing that the deflection w and its derivatives must vanish at large distances from the load, we can retain only the negative roots.   Using the notations

$$\left.\begin{array}{l} \alpha = -\dfrac{a}{\pi}\dfrac{1}{\sqrt{\sqrt{\dfrac{H}{D_y}} - \sqrt{\dfrac{H^2}{D_y^2} - \dfrac{D_x}{D_y}}}} = -\dfrac{a}{\pi}\sqrt{\dfrac{H}{D_x} + \sqrt{\dfrac{H^2}{D_x^2} - \dfrac{D_y}{D_x}}}, \\[4em] \beta = -\dfrac{a}{\pi}\dfrac{1}{\sqrt{\sqrt{\dfrac{H}{D_y}} + \sqrt{\dfrac{H^2}{D_y^2} - \dfrac{D_x}{D_y}}}} = -\dfrac{a}{\pi}\sqrt{\dfrac{H}{D_x} - \sqrt{\dfrac{H^2}{D_x^2} - \dfrac{D_y}{D_x}}}, \end{array}\right\} \quad (p)$$

the integral of Eq. (m) becomes

$$Y_m = A_m e^{-\frac{my}{\alpha}} + B_m e^{-\frac{my}{\beta}};$$

and expression (l) can be represented in the form

$$w = \left(A_m e^{-\frac{my}{\alpha}} + B_m e^{-\frac{my}{\beta}}\right)\sin\frac{m\pi x}{a}.$$

From symmetry we conclude that along the x-axis

$$\left(\frac{\partial w}{\partial y}\right)_{y=0} = 0,$$

and we find

$$B_m = -\frac{\beta}{\alpha}A_m$$

and

$$w = A_m\left(e^{-\frac{my}{\alpha}} - \frac{\beta}{\alpha}e^{-\frac{my}{\beta}}\right)\sin\frac{m\pi x}{a}. \qquad (q)$$

The coefficient A_m is obtained from the condition relating to the shearing force Q_y along the x-axis, which gives

$$-\frac{\partial}{\partial y}\left(D_y\frac{\partial^2 w}{\partial y^2} + H\frac{\partial^2 w}{\partial x^2}\right) = -\frac{q_0}{2}\sin\frac{m\pi x}{a}.$$

Substituting for w its expression (q), we obtain

$$A_m = \frac{q_0\alpha^3\beta^2}{2m^3 D_y(\alpha^2 - \beta^2)} = \frac{\alpha q_0 a^4}{2\pi^4 m^3 D_x(\alpha^2 - \beta^2)};$$

and the final expression (q) for the deflection becomes

$$w = \frac{q_0 a^4}{2\pi^4 m^3 D_x(\alpha^2 - \beta^2)}(\alpha e^{-\frac{my}{\alpha}} - \beta e^{-\frac{my}{\beta}}) \sin \frac{m\pi x}{a}. \qquad (r)$$

In the second of the three cases (o) the characteristic equation has two double roots, and the function Y_m has the same form as in the case of an isotropic plate (Art. 34). In the third of the cases (o) the roots of the characteristic equation are imaginary, and Y_m is expressed by trigonometric functions.

Having the deflection surface for the sinusoidal load (j), the deflection for any other kind of load along the x-axis can be obtained by expanding the load in the series

$$q = \sum_{m=1}^{\infty} a_m \sin \frac{m\pi x}{a}$$

and using the solution obtained for the load (j) for each term of this series. Hence, for $H^2 > D_x D_y$ the general solution is

$$w = \frac{a^4}{2\pi^4 D_x(\alpha^2 - \beta^2)} \sum_{m=1}^{\infty} \frac{a_m}{m^3} (\alpha e^{-\frac{m\pi y}{\alpha}} - \beta e^{-\frac{m\pi y}{\beta}}) \sin \frac{m\pi x}{a}, \qquad (s)$$

in which α and β have the meanings given by Eqs. (p).

Having this solution, the deflection of the plate by a load distributed over a rectangular area can be obtained by integration, as was shown in the case of an isotropic plate (see Art. 34). By applying the method of images the solutions obtained for an infinitely long plate can be used in the investigation of the bending of plates of finite dimensions.[1]

38. Rectangular Plates of Variable Thickness.[2]—In deriving the differential equation of equilibrium of plates of variable thickness, we assume that there is no abrupt variation in thickness so that the expressions for bending and twisting moments derived for plates of constant thickness apply with sufficient accuracy to this case also. Then

---

[1] Several examples of this kind are worked out in the books by Huber, *loc. cit.*, p. 190.

[2] This problem was discussed by R. Gran Olsson, *Ingenieur-Archiv*, vol. 5, p. 363, 1934; see also M. Eric Reissner, *J. Math. Phys.*, vol. 16, p. 43, 1937.

$$M_x = -D\left(\frac{\partial^2 w}{\partial x^2} + \nu\frac{\partial^2 w}{\partial y^2}\right), \qquad M_y = -D\left(\frac{\partial^2 w}{\partial y^2} + \nu\frac{\partial^2 w}{\partial y^2}\right),$$

$$M_{xy} = -M_{yx} = D(1-\nu)\frac{\partial^2 w}{\partial x\,\partial y}. \qquad\qquad (a)$$

Substititing these expressions in the differential equation of equilibrium of an element (Eq. (g), page 87),

$$\frac{\partial^2 M_x}{\partial x^2} - 2\frac{\partial^2 M_{xy}}{\partial x\,\partial y} + \frac{\partial^2 M_y}{\partial y^2} = -q, \qquad (b)$$

and observing that the flexural rigidity D is no longer a constant but a function of the coordinates x and y, we obtain

$$D\Delta\Delta w + 2\frac{\partial D}{\partial x}\frac{\partial}{\partial x}\Delta w + 2\frac{\partial D}{\partial y}\frac{\partial}{\partial y}\Delta w$$
$$+ \Delta D\,\Delta w - (1-\nu)\left(\frac{\partial^2 D}{\partial x^2}\frac{\partial^2 w}{\partial y^2} - 2\frac{\partial^2 D}{\partial x\,\partial y}\frac{\partial^2 w}{\partial x\,\partial y} + \frac{\partial^2 D}{\partial y^2}\frac{\partial^2 w}{\partial x^2}\right) = q, \quad (149)$$

where, as before, we employ the notation

$$\Delta = \frac{\partial^2}{\partial x^2} + \frac{\partial^2}{\partial y^2}.$$

As a particular example of the application of Eq. (149) let us consider the case in which the flexural rigidity D is a linear function of y expressed in the form

$$D = D_0 + D_1 y, \qquad (c)$$

where D_0 and D_1 are constants.

In such a case Eq. (149) becomes

$$(D_0 + D_1 y)\Delta\Delta w + 2D_1\frac{\partial}{\partial y}\Delta w = q,$$

or

$$\Delta[(D_0 + D_1 y)\Delta w] = q. \qquad (150)$$

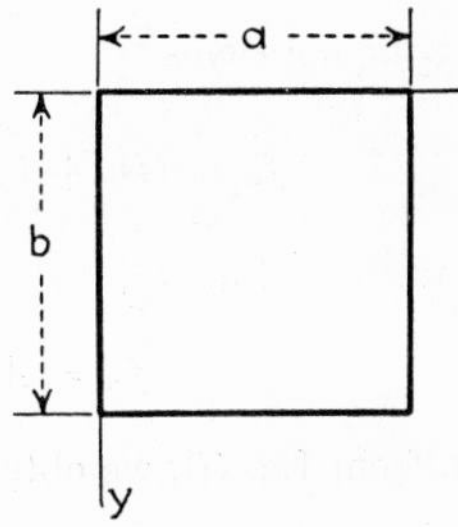

Fig. 78.

Let us consider the case in which the intensity of the load q is proportional to the flexural rigidity D. We shall assume the deflection of the plate (Fig. 78) in the form

$$w = w_1 + w_2$$

and let w_1 equal the deflection of a strip parallel to the x-axis cut from the plate and loaded with a load of intensity

$$q = q_0\left(1 + \frac{D_1}{D_0}y\right). \qquad (d)$$

This deflection can be represented, as before, by the trigonometric series

$$w_1 = \frac{4q_0\left(1 + \frac{D_1}{D_0}y\right)a^4}{(D_0 + D_1y)\pi^5} \sum_{m=1,3,5,\cdots}^{\infty} \frac{1}{m^5} \sin \frac{m\pi x}{a} = \frac{4q_0 a^4}{\pi^5 D_0} \sum_{m=1,3,5,\cdots}^{\infty} \frac{1}{m^5} \sin \frac{m\pi x}{a}. \tag{e}$$

By substitution we can readily show that this expression for w_1 satisfies Eq. (150). It satisfies also the boundary conditions $w = 0$ and $\partial^2 w/\partial x^2 = 0$ along the supported edges $x = 0$ and $x = a$.

The deflection w_2 must then satisfy the homogeneous equation

$$\Delta[(D_0 + D_1y)\Delta w] = 0. \tag{f}$$

We take it in the form of a series

$$w_2 = \sum_{m=1,3,5,\cdots}^{\infty} Y_m \sin \frac{m\pi x}{a}. \tag{g}$$

Substituting this series in Eq. (f), we find that the functions Y_m satisfy the following ordinary differential equation:

$$\left(\frac{\partial^2}{\partial y^2} - \frac{m^2\pi^2}{a^2}\right)\left[(D_0 + D_1y)\left(Y_m'' - \frac{m^2\pi^2}{a^2}Y_m\right)\right] = 0. \tag{h}$$

Using the notations

$$f_m = (D_0 + D_1y)\left(Y_m'' - \frac{m^2\pi^2}{a^2}Y_m\right), \qquad \frac{m\pi}{a} = \alpha_m, \tag{i}$$

we find, from Eq. (h),

$$f_m = A_m e^{\alpha_m y} + B_m e^{-\alpha_m y}.$$

Then, from Eq. (i), we obtain

$$Y_m'' - \alpha_m^2 Y_m = \frac{A_m e^{\alpha_m y} + B_m e^{-\alpha_m y}}{D_0 + D_1y}. \tag{j}$$

The general solution of this equation is

$$Y_m = C_m e^{\alpha_m y} + D_m e^{-\alpha_m y} + g_m, \tag{k}$$

in which g_m is a particular integral of Eq. (j). To find this particular integral we use the Lagrange method of variation of constants; i.e., we assume that g_m has the form

$$g_m = E_m e^{\alpha_m y} + F_m e^{-\alpha_m y}, \tag{l}$$

in which E_m and F_m are functions of y. These functions have to be determined from the following equations.[1]

$$E'_m e^{\alpha_m y} + F'_m e^{-\alpha_m y} = 0,$$

$$E'_m e^{\alpha_m y} - F'_m e^{-\alpha_m y} = \frac{A_m e^{\alpha_m y} + B_m e^{-\alpha_m y}}{\alpha_m (D_0 + D_1 y)},$$

from which

$$E'_m = \frac{A_m + B_m e^{-2\alpha_m y}}{2\alpha_m (D_0 + D_1 y)},$$

$$F'_m = -\frac{A_m e^{2\alpha_m y} + B_m}{2\alpha_m (D_0 + D_1 y)}.$$

Integrating these equations, we find

$$E_m = \int \frac{A_m + B_m e^{-2\alpha_m y}}{2\alpha_m (D_0 + D_1 y)} dy = \frac{A_m}{2\alpha_m D_1} \log \frac{2\alpha_m}{D_1}(D_0 + D_1 y)$$

$$+ \frac{B_m}{2\alpha_m D_1} e^{\frac{2\alpha_m D_0}{D_1}} \int \frac{e^{\frac{-2\alpha_m(D_0 + D_1 y)}{D_1}} d[2\alpha_m(D_0 + D_1 y)]}{2\alpha_m(D_0 + D_1 y)},$$

$$F_m = -\int \frac{A_m e^{2\alpha_m y} + B_m}{2\alpha_m (D_0 + D_1 y)} dy = -\frac{B_m}{2\alpha_m D_1} \log \frac{2\alpha_m}{D_1}(D_0 + D_1 y)$$

$$- \frac{A_m}{2\alpha_m D_1} e^{\frac{-2\alpha_m D_0}{D_1}} \int \frac{e^{\frac{2\alpha_m(D_0 + D_1 y)}{D_1}} d[2\alpha_m(D_0 + D_1 y)]}{2\alpha_m(D_0 + D_1 y)}.$$

Substituting these expressions in Eqs. (*l*) and (*k*) and using the notations[2]

$$E_i(u) = \int_{-\infty}^{u} \frac{e^u}{u} du, \qquad E_i(-u) = \int_{\infty}^{u} \frac{e^{-u}}{u} du,$$

we represent functions Y_m in the following form:

$$Y_m = A'_m \left\{ \log \frac{2\alpha_m}{D_1}(D_0 + D_1 y) - e^{\frac{-2\alpha_m}{D_1}(D_0 + D_1 y)} E_i \left[\frac{2\alpha_m(D_0 + D_1 y}{D_1} \right] \right\} e^{\alpha_m y}$$

$$- B'_m \left\{ e^{\frac{-2\alpha_m}{D_1}(D_0 + D_1 y)} \log \frac{2\alpha_m}{D_1}(D_0 + D_1 y) - E_i \left[\frac{-2\alpha_m(D_0 + D_1 y)}{D_1} \right] \right\} e^{\alpha_m y}$$

$$+ C_m e^{\alpha_m y} + D_m e^{-\alpha_m y}. \qquad (m)$$

The four constants of integration A'_m, B'_m, C_m, D_m are obtained from the boundary conditions along the sides $y = 0$ and $y = b$. In the case of simply supported edges these are

---

[1] E'_m and F'_m in these equations are the derivatives with respect to y of E_m and F_m.

[2] The integral $E_i(u)$ is the so-called *exponential integral* and is a tabulated function; see, for instance, Jahnke-Emde, "Tables of Functions," 2d ed., p. 83, Berlin, 1933.

$$(w)_{y=0} = 0, \qquad \left(\frac{\partial^2 w}{\partial y^2}\right)_{y=0} = 0,$$

$$(w)_{y=b} = 0, \qquad \left(\frac{\partial^2 w}{\partial y^2}\right)_{y=b} = 0.$$

The numerical results for a simply supported square plate obtained by taking only the first two terms of the series (g) are shown in Fig. 79.[1]   The

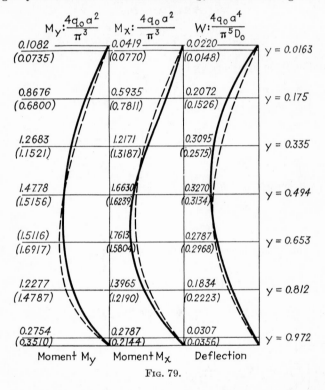

$$M_y : \frac{4q_0 a^2}{\pi^3} \qquad M_x : \frac{4q_0 a^2}{\pi^3} \qquad W : \frac{4q_0 a^4}{\pi^5 D_0}$$

Moment M_y	Moment M_x	Deflection	
0.1082	0.0419	0.0220	$y = 0.0163$
(0.0735)	(0.0770)	(0.0148)	
0.8676	0.5935	0.2072	$y = 0.175$
(0.6800)	(0.7811)	(0.1526)	
1.2683	1.2171	0.3095	$y = 0.335$
(1.1521)	(1.3187)	(0.2575)	
1.4778	1.6630	0.3270	$y = 0.494$
(1.5156)	(1.6239)	(0.3134)	
(1.5116)	1.7613	0.2787	$y = 0.653$
(1.6917)	(1.5804)	(0.2968)	
1.2277	1.3965	0.1834	$y = 0.812$
(1.4787)	(1.2190)	(0.2223)	
0.2754	0.2787	0.0307	$y = 0.972$
(0.3510)	(0.2144)	(0.0356)	

Fig. 79.

deflections and the moments M_x and M_y along the line $x = a/2$ for the plate of variable thickness are shown by full lines; the same quantities calculated for a plate of constant flexural rigidity $D = \frac{1}{2}(D_0 + D_1 b)$ are shown by dotted lines. It was assumed in the calculation that $D_1 b = 7D_0$ and $\nu = 0.16$.

[1] These results are taken from R. Gran Olsson's paper, *loc. cit.*, p. 194.

CHAPTER VI

RECTANGULAR PLATES WITH VARIOUS EDGE CONDITIONS

39. Bending of Rectangular Plates by Moments Distributed along the Edges.—Let us consider a rectangular plate supported along the edges and bent by moments distributed along the edges $y = \pm b/2$ (Fig. 80). The deflections w must satisfy the homogeneous differential equation

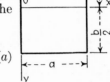

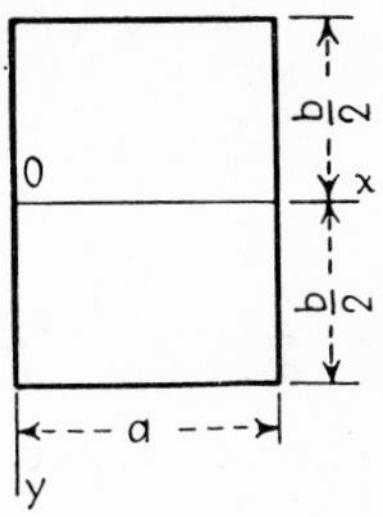

$$\frac{\partial^4 w}{\partial x^4} + 2\frac{\partial^4 w}{\partial x^2 \partial y^2} + \frac{\partial^4 w}{\partial y^4} = 0 \qquad (a)$$

and the following boundary conditions.

Fig. 80.

$$w = 0, \qquad \frac{\partial^2 w}{\partial x^2} = 0 \text{ for } x = 0 \text{ and } x = a; \qquad (b)$$

$$w = 0 \text{ for } y = \pm\frac{b}{2}; \qquad (c)$$

$$-D\left(\frac{\partial^2 w}{\partial y^2}\right)_{y=\frac{b}{2}} = f_1(x), \qquad -D\left(\frac{\partial^2 w}{\partial y^2}\right)_{y=-\frac{b}{2}} = f_2(x); \qquad (d)$$

in which f_1 and f_2 represent the bending moment distributions along the edges $y = \pm b/2$.

We take the solution of Eq. (a) in the form of the series

$$w = \sum_{m=1}^{\infty} Y_m \sin \frac{m\pi x}{a}, \qquad (e)$$

each term of which satisfies the boundary conditions (b). The functions Y_m we take, as before, in the form

$$Y_m = A_m \sinh \frac{m\pi y}{a} + B_m \cosh \frac{m\pi y}{a} + C_m \frac{m\pi y}{a} \sinh \frac{m\pi y}{a}$$

$$+ D_m \frac{m\pi y}{a} \cosh \frac{m\pi y}{a} \qquad (f)$$

which satisfies Eq. (a).

To simplify the discussion let us begin with the two particular cases:

1. The symmetrical case in which $(M_y)_{y=b/2} = (M_y)_{y=-b/2}$.
2. The antisymmetrical case in which $(M_y)_{y=b/2} = -(M_y)_{y=-b/2}$.
The general case can be obtained by combining these two particular cases.

In the case of symmetry Y_m must be an even function of y, and it is necessary to put $A_m = D_m = 0$ in expression (f). Then we obtain, from Eq. (e),

$$w = \sum_{m=1}^{\infty}\left(B_m \cosh\frac{m\pi y}{a} + C_m\frac{m\pi y}{a}\sinh\frac{m\pi y}{a}\right)\sin\frac{m\pi x}{a}. \quad (g)$$

To satisfy the boundary condition (c) we must put

$$B_m \cosh\alpha_m + C_m\alpha_m \sinh\alpha_m = 0,$$

where, as before,

$$\alpha_m = \frac{m\pi b}{2a}.$$

Hence,

$$B_m = -C_m\alpha_m \tanh\alpha_m,$$

and the deflection in the symmetrical case is

$$w = \sum_{m=1}^{\infty}C_m\left(\frac{m\pi y}{a}\sinh\frac{m\pi y}{a} - \alpha_m \tanh\alpha_m \cosh\frac{m\pi y}{a}\right)\sin\frac{m\pi x}{a}.$$

$$(h)$$

We use the boundary conditions (d) to determine the constants C_m. Representing the distribution of bending moments along the edges $y = \pm b/2$ by a trigonometric series, we have in the case of symmetry

$$f_1(x) = f_2(x) = \sum_{m=1}^{\infty}E_m \sin\frac{m\pi x}{a}, \quad (i)$$

where the coefficients E_m can be calculated in the usual way for each particular case. For instance, in the case of a uniform distribution of the bending moments we have (see page 168)

$$(M_y)_{y=\frac{b}{2}} = \frac{4M_0}{\pi} \sum_{m=1,3,5,\cdots}^{\infty} \frac{1}{m} \sin \frac{m\pi x}{a}. \tag{j}$$

Substituting expressions (h) and (i) into condition (d), we obtain

$$-2D \sum_{m=1}^{\infty} \frac{m^2\pi^2}{a^2} C_m \cosh \alpha_m \sin \frac{m\pi x}{a} = \sum_{m=1}^{\infty} E_m \sin \frac{m\pi x}{a},$$

from which

$$C_m = -\frac{a^2 E_m}{2Dm^2\pi^2 \cosh \alpha_m}$$

and

$$w = \frac{a^2}{2\pi^2 D} \sum_{m=1}^{\infty} \frac{\sin \frac{m\pi x}{a}}{m^2 \cosh \alpha_m} E_m \left(\alpha_m \tanh \alpha_m \cosh \frac{m\pi y}{a} \right.$$
$$\left. - \frac{m\pi y}{a} \sinh \frac{m\pi y}{a} \right). \tag{151}$$

In the particular case of uniformly distributed moments of intensity M_0 we obtain, by using expression (j),

$$w = \frac{2M_0 a^2}{\pi^3 D} \sum_{m=1,3,5,\cdots}^{\infty} \frac{1}{m^3 \cosh \alpha_m} \left(\alpha_m \tanh \alpha_m \cosh \frac{m\pi y}{a} \right.$$
$$\left. - \frac{m\pi y}{a} \sinh \frac{m\pi y}{a} \right) \sin \frac{m\pi x}{a}.$$

The deflection along the axis of symmetry ($y = 0$) is

$$(w)_{y=0} = \frac{2M_0 a^2}{\pi^3 D} \sum_{m=1,3,5,\cdots}^{\infty} \frac{1}{m^3} \frac{\alpha_m \tanh \alpha_m}{\cosh \alpha_m} \sin \frac{m\pi x}{a}. \tag{k}$$

When a is very large in comparison with b, we can put

$$\tanh \alpha_m \approx \alpha_m$$

and $\cosh \alpha_m \approx 1$. Then, by using series (j), we obtain

$$(w)_{y=0} = \frac{M_0 b^2}{2\pi D} \sum_{m=1,3,5,\cdots}^{\infty} \frac{1}{m} \sin \frac{m\pi x}{a} = \frac{1}{8} \frac{M_0 b^2}{D}.$$

This is the deflection at the middle of a strip of length b bent by two equal and opposite couples applied at the ends.

When a is small in comparison with b, $\cosh \alpha_m$ is a large number, and the deflection of the plate along the x-axis is very small.

For any given ratio between the length of the sides of the rectangle the deflection at the center of the plate, from expression (k), is

$$(w)_{y=0,\ x=\frac{a}{2}} = \frac{2M_0a^2}{\pi^3D} \sum_{m=1,3,5,\cdots}^{\infty} (-1)^{\frac{m-1}{2}} \frac{1}{m^3} \frac{\alpha_m \tanh \alpha_m}{\cosh \alpha_m}.$$

For a square plate we obtain from this series

$$(w)_{y=0,\ x=\frac{a}{2}} = 0.0368\frac{M_0a^2}{D}.$$

It is seen that the deflection of a strip of length a is about three and one-half times that of a square plate of dimension a. Having expression (151) for deflections, we can obtain the slope of the deflection surface at the boundary by differentiation and we can calculate the bending moments by forming the second derivatives of w.

Let us consider now the antisymmetrical case in which

$$f_1(x) = -f_2(x) = \sum_{m=1}^{\infty} E_m \sin \frac{m\pi x}{a}.$$

In this case the deflection surface is an odd function of y, and we must put $B_m = C_m = 0$ in expression (f). Hence,

$$w = \sum_{m=1}^{\infty}\left(A_m \sinh \frac{m\pi y}{a} + D_m\frac{m\pi y}{a} \cosh \frac{m\pi y}{a} \right) \sin \frac{m\pi x}{a}.$$

From the boundary conditions (c) it follows that

$$A_m \sinh \alpha_m + D_m\alpha_m \cosh \alpha_m = 0,$$

whence

$$D_m = -\frac{1}{\alpha_m} \tanh \alpha_m A_m,$$

and

$$w = \sum_{m=1}^{\infty} A_m \left(\sinh \frac{m\pi y}{a} - \frac{1}{\alpha_m} \tanh \alpha_m \frac{m\pi y}{a} \cosh \frac{m\pi y}{a} \right) \sin \frac{m\pi x}{a}.$$

The constants A_m are obtained from conditions (d), from which it follows that

$$\frac{2\pi^2 D}{a^2} \sum_{m=1}^{\infty} A_m \frac{m^2}{\alpha_m} \sinh \alpha_m \tanh \alpha_m \sin \frac{m\pi x}{a} = \sum_{m=1}^{\infty} E_m \sin \frac{m\pi x}{a}.$$

Hence,

$$A_m = \frac{a^2}{2\pi^2 D} E_m \frac{\alpha_m}{m^2 \sinh \alpha_m \tanh \alpha_m},$$

and

$$w = \frac{a^2}{2\pi^2 D} \sum_{m=1}^{\infty} \frac{E_m}{m^2 \sinh \alpha_m} \left(\alpha_m \coth \alpha_m \sinh \frac{m\pi y}{a} \right.$$

$$\left. - \frac{m\pi y}{a} \cosh \frac{m\pi y}{a} \right) \sin \frac{m\pi x}{a}. \quad (152)$$

We can obtain the deflection surface for the general case represented by the boundary conditions (d) from solutions (151) and (152) for the symmetrical and the antisymmetrical cases. For this purpose we split the given moment distributions into a symmetrical moment distribution M_y' and an antisymmetrical distribution M_y'', as follows:

$$(M_y')_{y=\frac{b}{2}} = (M_y')_{y=-\frac{b}{2}} = \tfrac{1}{2}[f_1(x) + f_2(x)],$$
$$(M_y'')_{y=\frac{b}{2}} = -(M_y'')_{y=-\frac{b}{2}} = \tfrac{1}{2}[f_1(x) - f_2(x)].$$

These moments can be represented, as before, by the trigonometric series

$$\left.\begin{aligned} (M_y')_{y=\frac{b}{2}} &= \sum_{m=1}^{\infty} E_m' \sin \frac{m\pi x}{a}, \\ (M_y'')_{y=\frac{b}{2}} &= \sum_{m=1}^{\infty} E_m'' \sin \frac{m\pi x}{a}; \end{aligned}\right\} \qquad (l)$$

and the total deflection is obtained by using expressions (151) and (152) and superposing the deflections produced by each of the two foregoing moment distributions (l).   Hence

$$
w = \frac{a^2}{2\pi^2 D} \sum_{m=1}^{\infty} \frac{\sin \frac{m\pi x}{a}}{m^2} \left[\frac{E'_m}{\cosh \alpha_m} \left(\alpha_m \tanh \alpha_m \cosh \frac{m\pi x}{a} \right. \right.
$$

$$
\left. - \frac{m\pi y}{a} \sinh \frac{m\pi y}{a} \right) + \frac{E''_m}{\sinh \alpha_m} \left(\alpha_m \coth \alpha_m \sinh \frac{m\pi y}{a} \right.
$$

$$
\left. \left. - \frac{m\pi y}{a} \cosh \frac{m\pi y}{a} \right) \right]. \quad (153)
$$

If the bending moments $M_y = \sum_{m=1}^{\infty} E_m \sin \frac{m\pi x}{l}$ are distributed only along the edge $y = b/2$, we have $f_2(x) = 0$, $E'_m = E''_m = \frac{1}{2} E_m$; and the deflection in this case becomes

$$
w = \frac{a^2}{4\pi^2 D} \sum_{m=1}^{\infty} \frac{E_m \sin \frac{m\pi x}{a}}{m^2} \left[\frac{1}{\cosh \alpha_m} \left(\alpha_m \tanh \alpha_m \cosh \frac{m\pi y}{a} \right. \right.
$$

$$
\left. - \frac{m\pi y}{a} \sinh \frac{m\pi y}{a} \right) + \frac{1}{\sinh \alpha_m} \left(\alpha_m \coth \alpha_m \sinh \frac{m\pi y}{a} \right.
$$

$$
\left. \left. - \frac{m\pi y}{a} \cosh \frac{m\pi y}{a} \right) \right]. \quad (154)
$$

Solutions (151) to (154) of this article will be applied in the investigation of plates with various edge conditions.

40. Rectangular Plates with Two Opposite Edges Simply Supported and the Other Two Edges Clamped.—Assume that the edges $x = 0$ and $x = a$ of the rectangular plate, shown in Fig. 80, are simply supported and that the other two edges are clamped.   The deflection of the plate under any lateral load can be obtained by first solving the problem on the assumption that all edges are simply supported and then applying bending moments along the edges $y = \pm b/2$ of such a magnitude as to eliminate the rotations produced along these edges by the action of the lateral load.   In this manner many problems can be solved by combining the solutions given in Chap. V with the solution of the previous article.

Uniformly Loaded Plates.—Assuming that the edges of the plate are simply supported, the deflection is [see Eq. (126), page 128]

$$w = \frac{4qa^4}{\pi^5 D} \sum_{m=1,3,5,\cdots}^{\infty} \frac{1}{m^5} \sin\frac{m\pi x}{a}\left(1 - \frac{\alpha_m \tanh \alpha_m + 2}{2 \cosh \alpha_m}\cosh\frac{m\pi y}{a}\right.$$

$$\left. + \frac{1}{2 \cosh \alpha_m}\frac{m\pi y}{a}\sinh\frac{m\pi y}{a}\right), \quad (a)$$

and the slope of the deflection surface along the edge $y = b/2$ is

$$\left(\frac{\partial w}{\partial y}\right)_{y=\frac{b}{2}} = \frac{2qa^3}{\pi^4 D} \sum_{m=1,3,5,\cdots}^{\infty} \frac{1}{m^4} \sin\frac{m\pi x}{a}$$

$$[\alpha_m - \tanh \alpha_m(1 + \alpha_m \tanh \alpha_m)]. \quad (b)$$

To eliminate this slope and thus to satisfy the actual boundary conditions we distribute along the edges $y = \pm b/2$ the bending moments M_y given by the series

$$(M_y)_{y=\pm b/2} = \sum_{m=1,3,5,\cdots}^{\infty} E_m \sin\frac{m\pi x}{a}, \quad (c)$$

and we determine the coefficients E_m so as to make the slope produced by these moments equal and opposite to that given by expression (b). Using expression (151)[1] for the deflection produced by the moments, we find that the corresponding slope along the edge $y = b/2$ is

$$\frac{a}{2\pi D} \sum_{m=1,3,5,\cdots}^{\infty} \frac{\sin\dfrac{m\pi x}{a}}{m} E_m[\tanh \alpha_m(\alpha_m \tanh \alpha_m - 1) - \alpha_m]. \quad (d)$$

Equating the negative of this quantity to expression (b), we find that

$$E_m = \frac{4qa^2}{\pi^3 m^3}\cdot\frac{\alpha_m - \tanh \alpha_m(1 + \alpha_m \tanh \alpha_m)}{\alpha_m - \tanh \alpha_m(\alpha_m \tanh \alpha_m - 1)}. \quad (e)$$

---

[1] From the symmetry of the deflection surface produced by the uniform load it can be concluded that only odd numbers 1, 3, 5, . . . must be taken for m in expression (151).

Hence the bending moments along the built-in edges are

$$(M_y)_{y=\pm b/2} = \frac{4qa^2}{\pi^3} \sum_{m=1,3,5,\cdots}^{\infty} \frac{\sin\dfrac{m\pi x}{a}}{m^3} \frac{\alpha_m - \tanh\alpha_m(1 + \alpha_m\tanh\alpha_m)}{\alpha_m - \tanh\alpha_m(\alpha_m\tanh\alpha_m - 1)}. \quad (f)$$

The maximum numerical value of this moment occurs at the middle of the sides, where $x = a/2$. Series (f) converges rapidly,

TABLE 22.—CONSTANTS α, β, β_1 AND β_2 FOR A RECTANGULAR PLATE WITH TWO EDGES SIMPLY SUPPORTED AND TWO EDGES CLAMPED; $\nu = 0.3$

$$b > a$$

$\dfrac{b}{a}$	$x = \dfrac{a}{2}, y = 0$ $w_{\max.} = \alpha\dfrac{qa^4}{Eh^3}$	$x = \dfrac{a}{2}, y = \dfrac{b}{2}$ $M_y = \beta qa^2$	$x = \dfrac{a}{2}, y = 0$ $M_x = \beta_1 qa^2$	$x = \dfrac{a}{2}, y = 0$ $M_y = \beta_2 qa^2$
	α	β	β_1	β_2
1	0.0209	−0.070	0.024	0.033
1.1	0.0274	−0.079	0.031	0.037
1.2	0.0340	−0.087	0.038	0.040
1.3	0.0424	−0.094	0.045	0.043
1.4	0.0502	−0.100	0.052	0.045
1.5	0.0582	−0.105	0.059	0.046
1.6	0.0658	−0.109	0.065	0.047
1.7	0.0730	−0.112	0.071	0.047
1.8	0.0799	−0.115	0.077	0.048
1.9	0.0863	−0.117	0.082	0.048
2.0	0.0987	−0.119	0.087	0.047
3.0	0.1276	−0.125	0.114	0.042
∞	0.1422	−0.125	0.125	0.038

$$b < a$$

$\dfrac{a}{b}$	$w_{\max.} = \alpha\dfrac{qb^4}{Eh^3}$	$x = \dfrac{a}{2}, y = \dfrac{b}{2}$ $M_y = \beta qb^2$	$x = \dfrac{a}{2}, y = 0$ $M_x = \beta_1 qb^2$	$x = \dfrac{a}{2}, y = 0$ $M_y = \beta_2 qb^2$
∞	0.0284	−0.083	0.013	0.042
2	0.0284	−0.084	0.014	0.042
1.5	0.0270	−0.083	0.017	0.041
1.4	0.0262	−0.081	0.019	0.040
1.3	0.0255	−0.079	0.020	0.039
1.2	0.0243	−0.077	0.022	0.037
1.1	0.0228	−0.074	0.023	0.036

and the maximum moment can be readily calculated in each particular case. For example, the first three terms of series (*f*) give $-0.070qa^2$ as the maximum moment in a square plate. In the general case this moment can be represented by the formula βqa^2, where β is a numerical factor the magnitude of which depends on the ratio a/b of the sides of the plate. Several values of this coefficient are given in Table 22.

Substituting the values (*e*) of the coefficients E_m in expression (151), we obtain the deflection surface produced by the moments M_y distributed along the edges

$$w_1 = -\frac{2qa^4}{\pi^5 D} \sum_{m=1,3,5,\cdots}^{\infty} \frac{\sin \dfrac{m\pi x}{a}}{m^5 \cosh \alpha_m}$$
$$\frac{\alpha_m - \tanh \alpha_m (1 + \alpha_m \tanh \alpha_m)}{\alpha_m - \tanh \alpha_m (\alpha_m \tanh \alpha_m - 1)} \left(\frac{m\pi y}{a} \sinh \frac{m\pi y}{a} \right.$$
$$\left. - \alpha_m \tanh \alpha_m \cosh \frac{m\pi y}{a} \right). \quad (g)$$

The deflection at the center is obtained by substituting $x = a/2$, $y = 0$ in expression (*g*). Then

$$(w_1)_{\text{max.}} = \frac{2qa^4}{\pi^5 D} \sum_{m=1,3,5,\cdots}^{\infty} \frac{(-1)^{\frac{m-1}{2}}}{m^5} \frac{\alpha_m \tanh \alpha_m}{\cosh \alpha_m}$$
$$\frac{\alpha_m - \tanh \alpha_m (1 + \alpha_m \tanh \alpha_m)}{\alpha_m - \tanh \alpha_m (\alpha_m \tanh \alpha_m - 1)}.$$

This is a very rapidly converging series, and the deflection can be obtained with a high degree of accuracy by taking only a few terms. In the case of a square plate, for example, the first term alone gives the deflection correct to three significant figures, and we obtain, for $\nu = 0.3$,

$$w_1 = 0.0234 \frac{qa^4}{Eh^3}.$$

Subtracting this deflection from the deflection produced at the center by uniform load (Table 5, page 133), we obtain finally for the deflection of a uniformly loaded square plate with two simply supported and two clamped edges the value

$$w = 0.0209 \frac{qa^4}{Eh^3}.$$

In the general case the deflection at the center can be represented by the formula

$$w = \alpha \frac{qa^4}{Eh^3}.$$

Several values of the numerical factor α are given in Table 22.

Substituting expression (g) for deflections in the known formulas (99) for the bending moments, we obtain

$$M_x = -\frac{2qa^2}{\pi^3} \sum_{m=1,3,5,\cdots}^{\infty} \frac{\sin\dfrac{m\pi x}{a}}{m^3 \cosh \alpha_m} \cdot \frac{\alpha_m - \tanh \alpha_m(1 + \alpha_m \tanh \alpha_m)}{\alpha_m - \tanh \alpha_m(\alpha_m \tanh \alpha_m - 1)}$$

$$\left\{ (1 - \nu)\frac{m\pi y}{a} \sinh \frac{m\pi y}{a} \right.$$

$$\left. - [2\nu + (1 - \nu)\alpha_m \tanh \alpha_m] \cosh \frac{m\pi y}{a} \right\}, \quad (h)$$

$$M_y = \frac{2qa^2}{\pi^3} \sum_{m=1,3,5,\cdots}^{\infty} \frac{\sin\dfrac{m\pi x}{a}}{m^3 \cosh \alpha_m} \cdot \frac{\alpha_m - \tanh \alpha_m(1 + \alpha_m \tanh \alpha_m)}{\alpha_m - \tanh \alpha_m(\alpha_m \tanh \alpha_m - 1)}$$

$$\left\{ (1 - \nu)\frac{m\pi y}{a} \sinh \frac{m\pi y}{a} \right.$$

$$\left. + [2 - (1 - \nu)\alpha_m \tanh \alpha_m] \cosh \frac{m\pi y}{a} \right\}. \quad (i)$$

The values of these moments at the center of the plate are

$$M_x = \frac{2qa^2}{\pi^3} \sum_{m=1,3,5,\cdots}^{\infty} \frac{(-1)^{\frac{m-1}{2}}}{m^3 \cosh \alpha_m}$$

$$\frac{\alpha_m - \tanh \alpha_m(1 + \alpha_m \tanh \alpha_m)}{\alpha_m - \tanh \alpha_m(\alpha_m \tanh \alpha_m - 1)}[2\nu + (1 - \nu)\alpha_m \tanh \alpha_m],$$

$$M_y = \frac{2qa^2}{\pi^3} \sum_{m=1,3,5,\cdots}^{\infty} \frac{(-1)^{\frac{m-1}{2}}}{m^3 \cosh \alpha_m}$$

$$\frac{\alpha_m - \tanh \alpha_m(1 + \alpha_m \tanh \alpha_m)}{\alpha_m - \tanh \alpha_m(\alpha_m \tanh \alpha_m - 1)}[2 - (1 - \nu)\alpha_m \tanh \alpha_m].$$

These series converge rapidly so that sufficiently accurate values for the moments are found by taking only the first two terms in the series. Superposing these moments on the moments in a simply supported plate (Table 5), the final values of the moments at the center of the plate can be represented as follows:

$$M_x = \beta_1 q a^2, \qquad M_y = \beta_2 q a^2, \qquad (j)$$

where β_1 and β_2 are numerical factors the magnitude of which depends on the ratio b/a. Several values of these coefficients are given in Table 22.

Taking the case of a square plate, we find that at the center the moments are

$$M_x = 0.0244 q a^2 \qquad \text{and} \qquad M_y = 0.0332 q a^2.$$

They are smaller than the moments $M_x = M_y = 0.0479 q a^4$ at the center of the simply supported square plate. But the moments M_y at the middle of the built-in edges are, as we have seen, larger than the value $0.0479 q a^2$. Hence, because of the constraint of the two edges, the magnitude of the maximum stress in the plate is increased. When the built-in sides of a rectangular plate are the longer sides $(b < a)$, the bending moments at the middle of these sides and the deflections at the center of the plate rapidly approach the corresponding values for a strip with built-in ends as the ratio b/a decreases.

Plates under Hydrostatic Pressure.—The deflection surface of a simply supported rectangular plate submitted to the action of a hydrostatic pressure, as shown in Fig. 64 (Art. 30), is

$$w = \frac{q_0 a^4}{\pi^5 D} \sum_{m=1}^{\infty} \frac{(-1)^{m+1}}{m^5} \left(2 - \frac{2 + \alpha_m \tanh \alpha_m}{\cosh \alpha_m} \cosh \frac{m\pi y}{a} \right.$$
$$\left. + \frac{1}{\cosh \alpha_m} \frac{m\pi y}{a} \sinh \frac{m\pi y}{a} \right) \sin \frac{m\pi x}{a}.$$

The slope of the deflection surface along the edge $y = b/2$ is

$$\left(\frac{\partial w}{\partial y} \right)_{y = \frac{b}{2}} = \frac{q_0 a^3}{\pi^4 D} \sum_{m=1}^{\infty} \frac{(-1)^{m+1}}{m^4} [\alpha_m - \tanh \alpha_m (1 + \alpha_m \tanh \alpha_m)]. \qquad (k)$$

This slope is eliminated by distributing the moments M_y given by series (c) along the edges $y = \pm b/2$ and determining the coefficients E_m of that series so as to make the slope produced by the moments equal and opposite to that given by expression (k). In this way we obtain

$$E_m = \frac{2q_0a^2(-1)^{m+1}}{\pi^3m^3} \frac{\alpha_m - \tanh \alpha_m(1 + \alpha_m \tanh \alpha_m)}{\alpha_m - \tanh \alpha_m(\alpha_m \tanh \alpha_m - 1)}.$$

Substituting this in series (c), the expression for bending moments along the built-in edges is found to be

$$(M_y)_{y=\pm b/2} = \frac{2q_0a^2}{\pi^3} \sum_{m=1}^{\infty} \frac{(-1)^{m+1} \sin \dfrac{m\pi x}{a}}{m^3}$$

$$\frac{\alpha_m - \tanh \alpha_m(1 + \alpha_m \tanh \alpha_m)}{\alpha_m - \tanh \alpha_m(\alpha_m \tanh \alpha_m - 1)}. \quad (l)$$

The terms in series (l) for which m is even vanish at the middle of the built-in sides where $x = a/2$, and the value of the series, as it should, becomes equal to one-half that for a uniformly loaded plate [see Eq. (f)]. The series converges rapidly, and the value of the bending moment at any point of the edge can be readily obtained. Several values of this moment are given in Table 23.

TABLE 23.—BENDING MOMENTS M_y ALONG THE BUILT-IN EDGES

b/a	$x = a/4$	$x = a/2$	$x = 3a/4$
∞	$-0.039q_0a^2$	$-0.062q_0a^2$	$-0.055q_0a^2$
2	$-0.037q_0a^2$	$-0.060q_0a^2$	$-0.053q_0a^2$
$\frac{3}{2}$	$-0.032q_0a^2$	$-0.052q_0a^2$	$-0.048q_0a^2$
1	$-0.020q_0a^2$	$0.035q_0a^2$	$-0.035q_0a^2$
$\frac{2}{3}$	$-0.021q_0b^2$	$0.041q_0b^2$	$-0.048q_0b^2$
$\frac{1}{2}$	$-0.021q_0b^2$	$0.042q_0b^2$	$-0.062q_0b^2$
0	$-0.021q_0b^2$	$-0.042q_0b^2$	$-0.062q_0b^2$

Concentrated Force Acting on the Plate.[1]—In this case again the deflection of the plate is obtained by superposing on the deflection of a simply supported plate (Art. 33) the deflection produced by moments distributed along the clamped edges. Taking the case of a centrally loaded plate and assuming that the edges $y = \pm b/2$ are clamped, we obtain the following

[1] See author's paper, *loc. cit.*, p. 156.

expression for the deflection under the load

$$w_{\text{max.}} = \frac{Pb^2}{2\pi^3 D}\left[\frac{a^2}{b^2}\sum_{m=1,3,5,\cdots}^{\infty}\frac{1}{m^3}\left(\tanh\alpha_m - \frac{\alpha_m}{\cosh^2\alpha_m}\right)\right.$$

$$\left. - \frac{\pi^2}{4}\sum_{m=1,3,5,\cdots}^{\infty}\frac{1}{m}\cdot\frac{\tanh^2\alpha_m}{\sinh\alpha_m\cosh\alpha_m + \alpha_m}\right]. \quad (m)$$

The first sum in the parentheses corresponds to the deflection of a simply supported plate [see Eq. (132), page 158], and the second represents the deflection due to the action of the moments along the clamped edges. For the ratios $b/a = 2, 1, \frac{1}{2}$ and $\frac{1}{3}$ the values of the expression in the parentheses in Eq. (m) are 0.238, 0.436, 0.448 and 0.449, respectively.

To obtain the maximum stress under the load we have to superpose on the stresses calculated for the simply supported plate the stresses produced by the following moments:

$$\left.\begin{array}{l} M_x = -P\displaystyle\sum_{m=1,3,5,\cdots}^{\infty}\frac{b}{4a}\cdot\frac{\tanh\alpha_m}{\sinh\alpha_m\cosh\alpha_m + \alpha_m} \\ \qquad\qquad\qquad [2\nu + (1-\nu)\alpha_m\tanh\alpha_m], \\[2mm] M_y = -P\displaystyle\sum_{m=1,3,5,\cdots}^{\infty}\frac{b}{4a}\cdot\frac{\tanh\alpha_m}{\sinh\alpha_m\cosh\alpha_m + \alpha_m} \\ \qquad\qquad\qquad [2 - (1-\nu)\alpha_m\tanh\alpha_m]. \end{array}\right\} \quad (n)$$

For a square plate these moments are

$$M_x = -0.0505P, \qquad M_y = -0.0308P.$$

The moment M_y at the middle of the clamped edges of a square plate is

$$M_y = -0.166P.$$

The calculations show that this moment changes only slightly as the length of the clamped edges increases and becomes equal to $-0.168P$ when $a/b = 2$.

41. Rectangular Plates with Three Edges Simply Supported and One Edge Built In.—Let us consider a rectangular plate built in along the edge $y = b/2$ and simply supported along the other edges (Fig. 80). The deflection of the plate under any lateral load can be obtained by combining the solution for the plate with all sides simply supported, with solution (154) for the case where bending moments are distributed along one side of the plate.

Uniformly Loaded Plates.—The slope along the edge $y = b/2$ produced by a uniformly distributed load is

$$\left(\frac{\partial w}{\partial y}\right)_{y=\frac{b}{2}} = \frac{2qa^3}{\pi^4 D} \sum_{m=1,3,5,\cdots}^{\infty} \frac{1}{m^4} \sin \frac{m\pi x}{a}$$
$$[\alpha_m - \tanh \alpha_m(1 + \alpha_m \tanh \alpha_m)]. \quad (a)$$

The moments $M_y = \Sigma E_m \sin (m\pi x/a)$ distributed along the side $y = b/2$ produce the slope[1] [see Eq. (154)]

$$\left(\frac{\partial w_1}{\partial y}\right)_{y=\frac{b}{2}} = \frac{a}{4\pi D} \sum_{m=1,3,5,\cdots}^{\infty} \frac{1}{m} \sin \frac{m\pi x}{a} E_m(\alpha_m \tanh^2 \alpha_m$$
$$- \tanh \alpha_m + \alpha_m \coth^2 \alpha_m - \coth \alpha_m - 2\alpha_m). \quad (b)$$

From the condition of constraint these two slopes are equal in magnitude and of opposite signs. Hence,

$$E_m = -\frac{8qa^2}{\pi^3 m^3}$$
$$\frac{\alpha_m - \tanh \alpha_m(1 + \alpha_m \tanh \alpha_m)}{\alpha_m \tanh^2 \alpha_m - \tanh \alpha_m + \alpha_m \coth^2 \alpha_m - \coth \alpha_m - 2\alpha_m}, \quad (c)$$

and the expression for the bending moments along the side $y = b/2$ is

$$(M_y)_{y=\frac{b}{2}} = \frac{8qa^2}{\pi^3} \sum_{m=1,3,5,\cdots}^{\infty} \frac{1}{m^3} \sin \frac{m\pi x}{a}$$
$$\frac{\alpha_m - \tanh \alpha_m(1 + \alpha_m \tanh \alpha_m)}{\alpha_m - \tanh \alpha_m(\alpha_m \tanh \alpha_m - 1) + \alpha_m - \coth \alpha_m(\alpha_m \coth \alpha_m - 1)}$$
$$(d)$$

Taking a square plate, as an example, the magnitude of the bending moment at the middle of the built-in edge from expres-

---

[1] Only odd numbers must be taken for m in this symmetrical case.

sion (d) is found to be

$$(M_y)_{y=\frac{b}{2}, x=\frac{a}{2}} = -0.084qa^2.$$

This moment is numerically larger than the moment $-0.070qa^2$ which was found in the previous article for a square plate with two edges built in. Several values of the moment at the middle of the built-in side for various values of the ratio a/b are given in Table 24.

TABLE 24.—DEFLECTIONS AND BENDING MOMENTS IN A RECTANGULAR PLATE WITH ONE EDGE BUILT IN AND THE THREE OTHERS SIMPLY SUPPORTED

$$\nu = 0.3$$

b/a	$(w)_{x=a/2, y=0}$	$(M_y)_{x=a/2, y=b/2}$	$(M_x)_{x=a/2, y=0}$	$(M_y)_{x=a/2, y=0}$
∞	$0.142\ qa^4/Eh^3$	$-0.125qa^2$	$0.125qa^2$	$0.037qa^2$
2	$0.101\ qa^4/Eh^3$	$-0.122qa^2$	$0.094qa^2$	$0.047qa^2$
1.5	$0.070\ qa^4/Eh^3$	$-0.112qa^2$	$0.069qa^2$	$0.048qa^2$
1.4	$0.063\ qa^4/Eh^3$	$-0.109qa^2$	$0.063qa^2$	$0.047qa^2$
1.3	$0.055\ qa^4/Eh^3$	$-0.104qa^2$	$0.056qa^2$	$0.045qa^2$
1.2	$0.047\ qa^4/Eh^3$	$-0.098qa^2$	$0.049qa^2$	$0.044qa^2$
1.1	$0.038\ qa^4/Eh^3$	$-0.092qa^2$	$0.041qa^2$	$0.042qa^2$
1.0	$0.030\ qa^4/Eh^3$	$-0.084qa^2$	$0.034qa^2$	$0.039qa^2$
1/1.1	$0.035\ qb^4/Eh^3$	$-0.091qb^2$	$0.033qb^2$	$0.043qb^2$
1/1.2	$0.038\ qb^4/Eh^3$	$-0.098qb^2$	$0.032qb^2$	$0.047qb^2$
1/1.3	$0.041\ qb^4/Eh^3$	$-0.103qb^2$	$0.031qb^2$	$0.050qb^2$
1/1.4	$0.044\ qb^4/Eh^3$	$-0.108qb^2$	$0.030qb^2$	$0.052qb^2$
1/1.5	$0.046\ qb^4/Eh^3$	$-0.111qb^2$	$0.028qb^2$	$0.054qb^2$
0.5	$0.053\ qb^4/Eh^3$	$-0.122qb^2$	$0.023qb^2$	$0.060qb^2$
0	$0.057\ qb^4/Eh^3$	$-0.125qb^2$	$0.019qb^2$	$0.062qb^2$

Substituting the values (c) of the constants E_m into expression (154), we obtain the deflection surface produced by the moments of constraint, from which the deflection at the center of the plate is

$$(w_1)_{x=\frac{a}{2}, y=0} = \frac{a^2}{4\pi^2 D} \sum_{m=1,3,5,\cdots}^{\infty} \frac{(-1)^{\frac{m-1}{2}}}{m^2} \frac{E_m \alpha_m \tanh \alpha_m}{\cosh \alpha_m}. \quad (e)$$

For a square plate the first two terms of this series give

$$(w_1)_{x=\frac{a}{2}, y=0} = 0.0139 \frac{qa^4}{Eh^3}.$$

Subtracting this deflection from the deflection of the simply supported square plate (Table 5), we find that the deflection at the center of a uniformly loaded square plate with one edge built in is

$$(w)_{x=\frac{a}{2}, y=0} = 0.0304 \frac{qa^4}{Eh^3}.$$

Values of deflection and bending moment for several other values of the ratio a/b obtained in a similar way are given in Table 24.

Plates under Hydrostatic Pressure.—If the plate is under a hydrostatic pressure, as shown in Fig. 64, the slope along the edge $y = b/2$, in the case of simply supported edges, is (see page 209)

$$\left(\frac{\partial w}{\partial y}\right)_{y=\frac{b}{2}} = \frac{q_0 a^3}{\pi^4 D} \sum_{m=1}^{\infty} \frac{(-1)^{m+1}}{m^4} [\alpha_m - \tanh \alpha_m (1 + \alpha_m \tanh \alpha_m)]. \quad (f)$$

The slope produced by bending moments distributed along the edge $y = b/2$ is

$$\left(\frac{\partial w_1}{\partial y}\right)_{y=\frac{b}{2}} = \frac{a}{4\pi D} \sum_{m=1}^{\infty} \frac{1}{m} \sin \frac{m\pi x}{a} E_m (\alpha_m \tanh^2 \alpha_m - \tanh \alpha_m$$
$$+ \alpha_m \coth^2 \alpha_m - \coth \alpha_m - 2\alpha_m). \quad (g)$$

From the condition of constraint along this edge, we find by equating expression (g) to expression (f) with negative sign

$$E_m = -\frac{4q_0 a^2}{\pi^3} \cdot \frac{(-1)^{m+1}}{m^3}$$
$$\cdot \frac{\alpha_m - \tanh \alpha_m (1 + \alpha_m \tanh \alpha_m)}{\alpha_m \tanh^2 \alpha_m - \tanh \alpha_m + \alpha_m \coth^2 \alpha_m - \coth \alpha_m - 2\alpha_m}.$$

Hence the expression for the bending moment M_y along the edge $y = b/2$ is

$$(M_y)_{y=\frac{b}{2}} = \frac{4q_0 a^2}{\pi^3} \sum_{m=1}^{\infty} \frac{(-1)^{m+1}}{m^3} \sin \frac{m\pi x}{a}$$
$$\frac{\alpha_m - \tanh \alpha_m (1 + \alpha_m \tanh \alpha_m)}{\alpha_m - \tanh \alpha_m (\alpha_m \tanh \alpha_m - 1) + \alpha_m - \coth \alpha_m (\alpha_m \coth \alpha_m - 1)}. \quad (h)$$

This series converges rapidly, ·and we can readily calculate the value of the moment at any point of the built-in edge. Taking, for example, a square plate and putting $x = a/2$, we obtain for the moment at the middle of the built-in edge the value

$$(M_y)_{y=\frac{b}{2},x=\frac{a}{2}} = -0.042q_0a^2.$$

This is equal to one-half the value of the moment in Table 24 for a uniformly loaded square plate, as it should be. Values of the moment $(M_y)_{y=b/2}$ for several points of the built-in edge and for various values of the ratio b/a are given in Table 25. It is seen that as the ratio b/a decreases, the value of M_y along the built-in edge rapidly approaches the value $-q_0b^2x/8a$, which is the moment at the built-in end of a strip of length b uniformly loaded with a load of intensity q_0x/a.

TABLE 25.—VALUES OF THE MOMENT M_y ALONG THE BUILT-IN EDGE
$y = b/2$

b/a	$x = a/4$	$x = a/2$	$x = \frac{3}{4}a$
∞	$-0.039q_0a^2$	$-0.062q_0a^2$	$-0.055q_0a^2$
2	$-0.038q_0a^2$	$-0.061q_0a^2$	$-0.053q_0a^2$
$\frac{3}{2}$	$-0.034q_0a^2$	$-0.056q_0a^2$	$-0.050q_0a^2$
1	$-0.025q_0a^2$	$-0.042q_0a^2$	$-0.040q_0a^2$
$\frac{2}{3}$	$-0.030q_0b^2$	$-0.056q_0b^2$	$-0.060q_0b^2$
$\frac{1}{2}$	$-0.031q_0b^2$	$-0.061q_0b^2$	$-0.073q_0b^2$
0	$-0.031q_0b^2$	$-0.062q_0b^2$	$-0.094q_0b^2$

42. Rectangular Plates with Two Opposite Edges Simply Supported, the Third Edge Free and the Fourth Edge Built In or Simply Supported.—Assume that the edges $x = 0$ and $x = a$ are

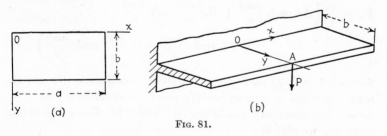

FIG. 81.

simply supported (Fig. 81a). The edge $y = b$ is free, and the edge $y = 0$ is built in. In such a case the boundary conditions are

$$w = 0, \qquad \frac{\partial^2 w}{\partial x^2} = 0 \text{ for } x = 0 \text{ and } x = a; \qquad (a)$$

$$w = 0, \qquad \frac{\partial w}{\partial y} = 0 \text{ for } y = 0; \qquad (b)$$

and along the free edge [see Eqs. (106), (107), page 90]

$$\left(\frac{\partial^2 w}{\partial y^2} + \nu \frac{\partial^2 w}{\partial x^2} \right)_{y=b} = 0; \qquad \left[\frac{\partial^3 w}{\partial y^3} + (2 - \nu) \frac{\partial^3 w}{\partial x^2\, \partial y} \right]_{y=b} = 0. \quad (c)$$

Let us consider the particular case of a uniformly distributed load. In such a case we proceed as in Art. 29 and assume that the total deflection consists of two parts, as follows:

$$w = w_1 + w_2,$$

where w_1 represents the deflection of a uniformly loaded and simply supported strip of length a which can be expressed by the series

$$w_1 = \frac{4qa^4}{\pi^5 D} \sum_{m=1,3,5,\cdots}^{\infty} \frac{1}{m^5} \sin \frac{m\pi x}{a}, \qquad (d)$$

and w_2 is represented by the series

$$w_2 = \sum_{m=1,3,5,\cdots}^{\infty} Y_m \sin \frac{m\pi x}{a}, \qquad (e)$$

where

$$Y_m = \frac{qa^4}{D}\left(A_m \cosh \frac{m\pi y}{a} + B_m \frac{m\pi y}{a} \sinh \frac{m\pi y}{a} \right.$$
$$\left. + C_m \sinh \frac{m\pi y}{a} + D_m \frac{m\pi y}{a} \cosh \frac{m\pi y}{a} \right). \quad (f)$$

Series (d) and (e) satisfy the boundary conditions (a), and the four constants in expression (f) must be determined so as to satisfy the boundary conditions (b) and (c). Using the conditions (b), we obtain

$$A_m = -\frac{4}{\pi^5 m^5}, \qquad C_m = -D_m. \qquad (g)$$

From the remaining two conditions (c) we find

$$\left.\begin{aligned}
B_m &= \frac{4}{\pi^5 m^5} \\
&\frac{(3+\nu)(1-\nu)\cosh^2\beta_m + 2\nu\cosh\beta_m}{(3+\nu)(1-\nu)\cosh^2\beta_m + (1-\nu)^2\beta_m^2 + (1+\nu)^2}, \\
C_m &= \frac{4}{\pi^5 m^5} \\
&\frac{(3+\nu)(1-\nu)\sinh\beta_m\cosh\beta_m + \nu(1+\nu)\sinh\beta_m}{(3+\nu)(1-\nu)\cosh^2\beta_m + (1-\nu)^2\beta_m^2 + (1+\nu)^2},
\end{aligned}\right\} \quad (h)$$

where $\beta_m = m\pi b/a$.

Substituting the constants (g) and (h) in Eq. (f) and using series (e) and (d), we obtain the expression for the deflection surface. The maximum deflection occurs in this case at the middle of the unsupported edge. If the length b is very large in comparison with a, *i.e.*, if the free edge is far away from the built-in edge, the deflection of the free edge is the same as that of a uniformly loaded and simply supported strip of length a multiplied by the constant factor $(3 - \nu)(1 + \nu)/(3 + \nu)$. Owing to the presence of this factor, the maximum deflection is larger than that of the strip by 6.4 per cent for $\nu = 0.3$. This fact can be readily explained if we observe that near the free edge the plate has an anticlastic deflection surface.

Taking another extreme case, when a is very large in comparison with b, the maximum deflection of the plate evidently is the same as for a uniformly loaded strip of length b built in at one end and free at the other. Several values of the maximum deflection calculated[1] for various values of the ratio b/a are given in Table 26. In the same table are given also the maximum values of bending moments which can be readily calculated from the expression for the deflection surface. The calculations show that $(M_x)_{\text{max.}}$ occurs at the middle of the unsupported edge. The numerical maximum of the moment M_y occurs at the middle of the built-in edge.

If the plate is bent by a load distributed along the free edge, instead of by a load distributed over the surface, the second of the boundary conditions (c) must be modified by putting the

---

[1] This table was calculated by Boobnov, *loc. cit.*, p. 3.

intensity of the load distributed along the free edge instead of zero on the right side of the equation.   The particular case of a concentrated force applied at the free edge of a very long plate was investigated (Fig. 81b).[1]   It was found that the deflection

TABLE 26.—DEFLECTIONS AND BENDING MOMENTS FOR A UNIFORMLY LOADED PLATE WITH TWO OPPOSITE EDGES SIMPLY SUPPORTED, THE THIRD EDGE FREE AND THE FOURTH BUILT IN

$$\nu = 0.3$$

b/a	$w_{max.}$	$x = a/2, y = b$	$x = a/2, y = 0$
		M_x	M_y
0	$1.37\ qb^4/Eh^3$	0	$-0.500qb^2$
$\frac{1}{3}$	$1.03\ qb^4/Eh^3$	$0.0078qa^2$	$-0.428qb^2$
$\frac{1}{2}$	$0.635\ qb^4/Eh^3$	$0.0293qa^2$	$-0.319qb^2$
$\frac{2}{3}$	$0.366\ qb^4/Eh^3$	$0.0558qa^2$	$-0.227qb^2$
1	$0.123\ qb^4/Eh^3$	$0.0972qa^2$	$-0.119qb^2$
$\frac{3}{2}$	$0.154\ qa^4/Eh^3$	$0.123qa^2$	$-0.124qa^2$
2	$0.164\ qa^4/Eh^3$	$0.131qa^2$	$-0.125qa^2$
3	$0.166\ qa^4/Eh^3$	$0.133qa^2$	$-0.125qa^2$
∞	$0.166\ qa^4/Eh^3$	$0.133qa^2$	$-0.125qa^2$

along the free edge can be represented by the formula

$$(w)_{y=b} = k\frac{Pb^2}{\pi D}.$$

The factor k rapidly diminishes as the distance from the point A of application of the load increases.   Several values of this factor are given in Table 27.

TABLE 27

x	0	$b/4$	$b/2$	b	$2b$
k	0.527	0.470	0.380	0.213	0.050

The bending moment M_y along the built-in edge is a maximum at 0 where its numerical value is $(M_y)_{x=0,y=0} = -0.508P$.

The case of a uniformly loaded rectangular plate simply supported along three edges and free along the edge $y = b$ (Fig.

[1] See C. W. MacGregor, *Mech. Engineering*, vol. 57, p. 225, 1935; also D. L. Holl, *J. Appl. Mech.*, vol. 4, p. 8, 1937.

81a) can be treated in the same manner as the previous case in which the edge $y = 0$ was built in. It is necessary only to replace the second of the boundary conditions (b) by the condition

$$\left[\left(\frac{\partial^2 w}{\partial y^2}\right) + \nu\left(\frac{\partial^2 w}{\partial x^2}\right)\right]_{y=0} = 0.$$

Omitting the derivations, we give here only the final numerical results obtained for this case. The maximum deflection occurs at the middle of the free edge. At the same point the maximum bending moment M_x takes place. These values of deflections $w_{max.}$ and $(M_x)_{max.}$ are given in the second and third columns of Table 28.[1] The last two columns give the bending moments at the center of the plate.

TABLE 28.—DEFLECTIONS AND BENDING MOMENTS IN UNIFORMLY LOADED RECTANGULAR PLATES WITH THREE EDGES SIMPLY SUPPORTED AND THE FOURTH EDGE FREE

$\nu = 0.3$

b/a	$x = a/2, y = b$		$x = a/2, y = b/2$	
	$w_{max.}$	$(M_x)_{max.}$	M_x	M_y
$\frac{1}{2}$	$0.0775\, qa^4/Eh^3$	$0.060qa^2$	$0.039qa^2$	$0.022qa^2$
$\frac{2}{3}$	$0.1057\, qa^4/Eh^3$	$0.083qa^2$	$0.055qa^2$	$0.030qa^2$
$1/1.4$	$0.1117\, qa^4/Eh^3$	$0.088qa^2$	$0.059qa^2$	$0.032qa^2$
$1/1.3$	$0.1192\, qa^4/Eh^3$	$0.094qa^2$	$0.064qa^2$	$0.034qa^2$
$1/1.2$	$0.1265\, qa^4/Eh^3$	$0.100qa^2$	$0.069qa^2$	$0.036qa^2$
$1/1.1$	$0.1345\, qa^4/Eh^3$	$0.107qa^2$	$0.074qa^2$	$0.037qa^2$
1	$0.1404\, qa^4/Eh^3$	$0.112qa^2$	$0.080qa^2$	$0.039qa^2$
1.1	$0.1464\, qa^4/Eh^3$	$0.117qa^2$	$0.085qa^2$	$0.040qa^2$
1.2	$0.1511\, qa^4/Eh^3$	$0.121qa^2$	$0.090qa^2$	$0.041qa^2$
1.3	$0.1547\, qa^4/Eh^3$	$0.124qa^2$	$0.094qa^2$	$0.042qa^2$
1.4	$0.1575\, qa^4/Eh^3$	$0.126qa^2$	$0.098qa^2$	$0.042qa^2$
1.5	$0.1596\, qa^4/Eh^3$	$0.128qa^2$	$0.101qa^2$	$0.042qa^2$
2	$0.1646\, qa^4/Eh^3$	$0.132qa^2$	$0.113qa^2$	$0.041qa^2$
3	$0.1660\, qa^4/Eh^3$	$0.133qa^2$	$0.122qa^2$	$0.039qa^2$
∞	$0.1662\, qa^4/Eh^3$	$0.133qa^2$	$0.125qa^2$	$0.037qa^2$

43. Rectangular Plates with Two Opposite Edges Simply Supported and the Other Two Edges Supported Elastically.—

[1] This table was calculated by B. G. Galerkin; see *Bull. Polytech. Inst.*, vol. 26, p. 124, St. Petersburg, 1915.

Let us consider the case where the edges $x = 0$ and $x = a$ (Fig. 80) are simply supported and the other two edges are supported by elastic beams. Assuming that the load is uniformly distributed and that the beams are identical, the deflection surface of the plate will be symmetrical with respect to the x-axis, and we have to consider only the conditions along the side $y = b/2$. Assuming that the beams resist bending in vertical planes only and do not resist torsion, the boundary conditions along the edge $y = b/2$, by using Eq. (108), are

$$\left(\frac{\partial^2 w}{\partial y^2} + \nu\frac{\partial^2 w}{\partial x^2}\right)_{y=\frac{b}{2}} = 0, \qquad D\left[\frac{\partial^3 w}{\partial y^3} + (2-\nu)\frac{\partial^3 w}{\partial x^2 \partial y}\right]_{y=\frac{b}{2}}$$

$$= \left(EI\frac{\partial^4 w}{\partial x^4}\right)_{y=\frac{b}{2}}, \quad (a)$$

where EI denotes the flexural rigidity of the supporting beams. Proceeding as in the previous article, we take the deflection surface in the form

$$w = w_1 + w_2, \tag{b}$$

where

$$w_1 = \frac{4qa^4}{\pi^5 D} \sum_{m=1,3,5,\cdots}^{\infty} \frac{1}{m^5} \sin\frac{m\pi x}{a} \tag{c}$$

and

$$w_2 = \sum_{m=1,3,5,\cdots}^{\infty} Y_m \sin\frac{m\pi x}{a}. \tag{d}$$

From symmetry it can be concluded that in expression (f) of the previous article we must put $C_m = D_m = 0$ and take

$$Y_m = \frac{qa^4}{D}\left(A_m \cosh\frac{m\pi y}{a} + B_m\frac{m\pi y}{a}\sinh\frac{m\pi y}{a}\right). \tag{e}$$

The remaining two constants A_m and B_m are found from the boundary conditions (a) from which, using the notations

$$\frac{m\pi b}{2a} = \alpha_m \qquad \frac{EI}{aD} = \lambda,$$

we obtain

$$A_m(1 - \nu)\cosh\,\alpha_m + B_m[2\cosh\,\alpha_m + (1 - \nu)\alpha_m\sinh\,\alpha_m] = \frac{4\nu}{m^5\pi^5},$$

$$-A_m[(1 - \nu)\sinh\,\alpha_m + m\pi\lambda\cosh\,\alpha_m] + B_m[(1 + \nu)\sinh\,\alpha_m$$

$$- (1 - \nu)\alpha_m\cosh\,\alpha_m - m\pi\lambda\alpha_m\sinh\,\alpha_m] = \frac{4\lambda}{m^4\pi^4}.$$

Solving these equations, we find

$$A_m = \frac{4}{m^5\pi^5}$$

$$\frac{\nu(1 + \nu)\sinh\,\alpha_m - \nu(1 - \nu)\alpha_m\cosh\,\alpha_m - m\pi\lambda(2\cosh\,\alpha_m + \alpha_m\sinh\,\alpha_m)}{(3 + \nu)(1 - \nu)\sinh\,\alpha_m\cosh\,\alpha_m - (1 - \nu)^2\alpha_m + 2m\pi\lambda\cosh^2\,\alpha_m}, \quad (f)$$

$$B_m = \frac{4}{m^5\pi^5}\frac{\nu(1 - \nu)\sinh\,\alpha_m + m\pi\lambda\cosh\,\alpha_m}{(3 + \nu)(1 - \nu)\sinh\,\alpha_m\cosh\,\alpha_m - (1 - \nu)^2\alpha_m + 2m\pi\lambda\cosh^2\,\alpha_m}. \quad (g)$$

The deflection surface of the plate is found by substituting these values of the constants in the expression

$$w = w_1 + w_2 = \frac{qa^4}{D}\sum_{m = 1,3,5,\,\cdots}^{\infty}\left(\frac{4}{\pi^5m^5} + A_m\cosh\frac{m\pi y}{a}\right.$$

$$\left. + B_m\frac{m\pi y}{a}\sinh\frac{m\pi y}{a}\right)\sin\frac{m\pi x}{a}. \quad (h)$$

If the supporting beams are absolutely rigid, $\lambda = \infty$ in expressions (f) and (g) and A_m and B_m assume the same value as in Art. 29 for a plate all four sides of which are supported on rigid supports.

Substituting $\lambda = 0$ in expressions (f) and (g), we obtain the values of the constants in series (h) for the case where two sides of the plate are simply supported and the other two are free.

The maximum deflection and the maximum bending moments are at the center of the plate. Several values of these quantities calculated for a square plate and for various values of λ are given in Table 29.[1]

[1] The table was calculated for the writer by K. A. Čališev, *Mem. Inst. Engineers of Ways of Communication*, St. Petersburg, 1914. More recently the problem was discussed by E. Müller, *Ingenieur-Archiv*, vol. 2, 1932, p. 606. The tables for non-symmetrical cases are calculated in this paper.

TABLE 29.—DEFLECTIONS AND BENDING MOMENTS AT THE CENTER OF A UNIFORMLY LOADED SQUARE PLATE WITH TWO EDGES SIMPLY SUPPORTED AND THE OTHER TWO SUPPORTED BY ELASTIC BEAMS
$$\nu = 0.3$$

$\lambda = EI/aD$	$w_{\max.}$	$(M_x)_{\max.}$	$(M_y)_{\max.}$
∞	$0.0443\ qa^4/Eh^3$	$0.0479qa^2$	$0.0479qa^2$
100	$0.0447\ qa^4/Eh^3$	$0.0481qa^2$	$0.0477qa^2$
30	$0.0454\ qa^4/Eh^3$	$0.0486qa^2$	$0.0473qa^2$
10	$0.0474\ qa^4/Eh^3$	$0.0500qa^2$	$0.0465qa^2$
6	$0.0495\ qa^4/Eh^3$	$0.0514qa^2$	$0.0455qa^2$
4	$0.0515\ qa^4/Eh^3$	$0.0528qa^2$	$0.0447qa^2$
2	$0.0578\ qa^4/Eh^3$	$0.0571qa^2$	$0.0419qa^2$
1	$0.0681\ qa^4/Eh^3$	$0.0643qa^2$	$0.0376qa^2$
0.5	$0.0826\ qa^4/Eh^3$	$0.0744qa^2$	$0.0315qa^2$
0	$0.1430\ qa^4/Eh^3$	$0.1160qa^2$	$0.0057qa^2$

44. Rectangular Plates with all Edges Built In.[1]—In discussing this problem, we use the same method as in the cases considered

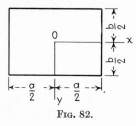

FIG. 82.

previously. We start with the solution of the problem for a simply supported rectangular plate and superpose on the deflection of such a plate the deflection of the plate by moments distributed along the edges (see Art. 39). These moments we adjust in such a manner as to satisfy the condition $\partial w/\partial n = 0$ at the boundary of the clamped plate. The method can be applied to any kind of lateral loading. To simplify our discussion we begin with the case of a uniformly distributed load. The deflections and the moments

[1] For the mathematical literature on this subject see "Encyklopädie der Mathematischen Wissenschaften," vol. 4, art. 25 (Tedone-Timpe), pp. 165 and 186. The recent references on the same subject are given in the paper by A. E. H. Love, *Proc. London Math. Soc.*, vol. 29, p. 189. The first numerical results for calculating stresses and deflections in clamped rectangular plates were obtained by B. M. Kojalovich in his doctor's dissertation, St. Petersburg, 1902. Further progress was made by J. G. Boobnov, who calculated the tables for deflections and moments in uniformly loaded rectangular plates with clamped edges; see Boobnov's "Theory of Structures of Ships," vol. 2, p. 465, St. Petersburg, 1914. The same problem was discussed also by H. Hencky in his dissertation "Der Spannungszustand in rechteckigen Platten," Münich, 1913. Hencky's method was recently used by I. A. Wojtaszak, *J. Appl. Mech.*, vol. 4, p. 173, 1937. The numerical

in this case will be symmetrical with respect to the coordinate axes shown in Fig. 82. The deflection of a simply supported plate, as given by Eq. (126) (page 128), is represented for the new coordinates in the following form:

$$w = \frac{4qa^4}{\pi^5 D} \sum_{m=1,3,5,\cdots}^{\infty} \frac{(-1)^{\frac{m-1}{2}}}{m^5} \cos \frac{m\pi x}{a} \left(1 - \frac{\alpha_m \tanh \alpha_m + 2}{2 \cosh \alpha_m} \cosh \frac{m\pi y}{a}\right.$$

$$\left. + \frac{1}{2 \cosh \alpha_m} \frac{m\pi y}{a} \sinh \frac{m\pi y}{a}\right), \quad (a)$$

where $\alpha_m = m\pi b/2a$. The rotation at the edge $y = b/2$ of the plate is

$$\left(\frac{\partial w}{\partial y}\right)_{y=\frac{b}{2}} = \frac{2qa^3}{\pi^4 D} \sum_{m=1,3,5,\cdots}^{\infty} \frac{(-1)^{\frac{m-1}{2}}}{m^4} \cos \frac{m\pi x}{a}$$

$$[\alpha_m - \tanh \alpha_m(1 + \alpha_m \tanh \alpha_m)]$$

$$= \frac{2qa^3}{\pi^4 D} \sum_{m=1,3,5,\cdots}^{\infty} \frac{(-1)^{\frac{m-1}{2}}}{m^4} \cos \frac{m\pi x}{a} \left(\frac{\alpha_m}{\cosh^2 \alpha_m} - \tanh \alpha_m\right). \quad (b)$$

Let us consider now the deflection of the plate by the moments distributed along the edges $y = \pm b/2$. From considerations of symmetry we conclude that the moments can be represented by the following series:

$$(M_y)_{y=\pm\frac{b}{2}} = \sum_{m=1,3,5,\cdots}^{\infty} (-1)^{\frac{m-1}{2}} E_m \cos \frac{m\pi x}{a}. \quad (c)$$

The corresponding deflection w_1 is obtained from expression (151) by substituting $x + a/2$ for x and taking $m = 1, 3, 5, \cdots$.

---

results obtained by Wojtaszak in this way for a uniformly loaded plate coincide with the values given in Boobnov's table. Our further discussion makes use of the method that was developed in the writer's paper, *Proc. 5th Intern. Cong. Appl. Mech.*, Cambridge, Mass., 1938; the method is more general than those previously mentioned; it can be applied to any kind of loading, including the case of a concentrated load.

Then

$$w_1 = -\frac{a^2}{2\pi^2 D} \sum_{m=1,3,5,\cdots}^{\infty} E_m \frac{(-1)^{\frac{m-1}{2}}}{m^2 \cosh \alpha_m} \cos \frac{m\pi x}{a} \left(\frac{m\pi y}{a} \sinh \frac{m\pi y}{a} \right.$$

$$\left. - \alpha_m \tanh \alpha_m \cosh \frac{m\pi y}{a} \right). \quad (d)$$

The rotation at the edge $y = b/2$, corresponding to this deflection, is

$$\left(\frac{\partial w_1}{\partial y} \right)_{y=\frac{b}{2}} = -\frac{a}{2\pi D} \sum_{m=1,3,5,\cdots}^{\infty} E_m \frac{(-1)^{\frac{m-1}{2}}}{m} \cos \frac{m\pi x}{a} \left(\tanh \alpha_m \right.$$

$$\left. + \frac{\alpha_m}{\cosh^2 \alpha_m} \right). \quad (e)$$

In our further discussion we shall need also the rotation at the edges parallel to the y-axis. Forming the derivative of the expression (d) with respect to x and putting $x = a/2$, we obtain

$$\left(\frac{\partial w_1}{\partial x} \right)_{x=\frac{a}{2}} = \frac{a}{2\pi D} \sum_{m=1,3,5,\cdots}^{\infty} E_m \frac{1}{m \cosh \alpha_m} \left(\frac{m\pi y}{a} \sinh \frac{m\pi y}{a} \right.$$

$$\left. - \alpha_m \tanh \alpha_m \cosh \frac{m\pi y}{a} \right) = -\frac{1}{4D} \sum_{m=1,3,5,\cdots}^{\infty} \frac{E_m}{\cosh^2 \alpha_m}$$

$$\left(b \sinh \alpha_m \cosh \frac{m\pi y}{a} - 2y \cosh \alpha_m \sinh \frac{m\pi y}{a} \right). \quad (f)$$

The expression in parentheses is an even function of y which vanishes at the edges $y = \pm b/2$. Such a function can be represented by the series

$$\sum_{i=1,3,5,\cdots}^{\infty} A_i \cos \frac{i\pi y}{b} \quad (g)$$

in which the coefficients A_i are calculated by using the formula

$$A_i = \frac{2}{b} \int_{-\frac{b}{2}}^{+\frac{b}{2}} \left(b \sinh \alpha_m \cosh \frac{m\pi y}{a} \right.$$

$$\left. - 2y \cosh \alpha_m \sinh \frac{m\pi y}{a} \right) \cos \frac{i\pi y}{b} dy,$$

from which it follows that

$$A_i = \frac{16ia(-1)^{\frac{i-1}{2}}}{m^3\pi^2}\frac{b^2}{a^2}\frac{1}{\left(\dfrac{b^2}{a^2} + \dfrac{i^2}{m^2}\right)^2}\cosh^2\alpha_m.$$

Substituting this in expressions (g) and (f), we obtain

$$\left(\frac{\partial w_1}{\partial x}\right)_{x=\frac{a}{2}} = -\frac{4b^2}{\pi^2 Da}\sum_{m=1,3,5,\cdots}^{\infty}\frac{E_m}{m^3}\sum_{i=1,3,5,\cdots}^{\infty}\frac{i(-1)^{\frac{i-1}{2}}}{\left(\dfrac{b^2}{a^2} + \dfrac{i^2}{m^2}\right)^2}\cos\frac{i\pi y}{b}. \quad (h)$$

In a similar manner expressions can be obtained for the deflections w_2 and for the rotation at edges for the case where moments M_x are distributed along the edges $x = \pm a/2$. Assuming a symmetrical distribution and taking

$$(M_x)_{x=\pm\frac{a}{2}} = \sum_{m=1,3,5,\cdots}^{\infty}(-1)^{\frac{m-1}{2}}F_m\cos\frac{m\pi y}{b}, \quad (i)$$

we find for this case, by using expressions (e) and (h), that

$$\left(\frac{\partial w_2}{\partial x}\right)_{x=\frac{a}{2}} = -\frac{b}{2\pi D}\sum_{m=1,3,5,\cdots}^{\infty}F_m\frac{(-1)^{\frac{m-1}{2}}}{m}\cos\frac{m\pi y}{b}\left(\tanh\beta_m\right.$$
$$\left. + \frac{\beta_m}{\cosh^2\beta_m}\right), \quad (j)$$

where $\beta_m = m\pi a/2b$, and that

$$\left(\frac{\partial w_2}{\partial y}\right)_{y=\frac{b}{2}} = -\frac{4a^2}{\pi^2 Db}\sum_{m=1,3,5,\cdots}^{\infty}\frac{F_m}{m^3}\sum_{i=1,3,5,\cdots}^{\infty}\frac{i(-1)^{\frac{i-1}{2}}}{\left(\dfrac{a^2}{b^2} + \dfrac{i^2}{m^2}\right)^2}\cos\frac{i\pi x}{a}. \quad (k)$$

When the moments (c) and (i) act simultaneously, the rotation at the edges of the plate is obtained by the method of superposition. Taking, for example, the edge $y = b/2$, we find

$$\left(\frac{\partial w_1}{\partial y} + \frac{\partial w_2}{\partial y}\right)_{y=\frac{b}{2}} = -\frac{a}{2\pi D} \sum_{m=1,3,5,\cdots}^{\infty} E_m \frac{(-1)^{\frac{m-1}{2}}}{m} \cos \frac{m\pi x}{a}$$

$$\left(\tanh \alpha_m + \frac{\alpha_m}{\cosh^2 \alpha_m}\right)$$

$$-\frac{4a^2}{\pi^2 Db} \sum_{m=1,3,5,\cdots}^{\infty} \frac{F_m}{m^3} \sum_{i=1,3,5,\cdots}^{\infty} \frac{i(-1)^{\frac{i-1}{2}}}{\left(\frac{a^2}{b^2} + \frac{i^2}{m^2}\right)^2} \cos \frac{i\pi x}{a}. \quad (l)$$

Having expressions (b) and (l), we can now derive the equations for calculating the constants E_m and F_m in series (c) and (i) which represent the moments acting along the edges of a clamped plate. In the case of a clamped plate the edges do not rotate. Hence, for the edges $y = \pm b/2$, we obtain

$$\left(\frac{\partial w}{\partial y}\right)_{y=\frac{b}{2}} + \left(\frac{\partial w_1}{\partial y} + \frac{\partial w_2}{\partial y}\right)_{y=\frac{b}{2}} = 0. \quad (m)$$

In a similar manner, for the edges $x = \pm a/2$, we find

$$\left(\frac{\partial w}{\partial x}\right)_{x=\frac{a}{2}} + \left(\frac{\partial w_1}{\partial x} + \frac{\partial w_2}{\partial x}\right)_{x=\frac{a}{2}} = 0. \quad (n)$$

If we substitute expressions (b) and (l) in Eq. (m) and group[1] together the terms that contain the same cos $(i\pi x/a)$ as a factor and then observe that Eq. (m) holds for any value of x, we can conclude that the coefficient by which cos $(i\pi x/a)$ is multiplied must be equal to zero for each value of i. In this manner we obtain a system that consists of an infinite number of linear equations for calculating the coefficients E_i and F_i as follows:

$$\frac{4qa^2}{\pi^3} \frac{1}{i^4}\left(\frac{\alpha_i}{\cosh^2 \alpha_i} - \tanh \alpha_i\right)$$

$$-\frac{E_i}{i}\left(\tanh \alpha_i + \frac{\alpha_i}{\cosh^2 \alpha_i}\right) - \frac{8ia}{\pi b} \sum_{m=1,3,5,\cdots}^{\infty} \frac{F_m}{m^3} \frac{1}{\left(\frac{a^2}{b^2} + \frac{i^2}{m^2}\right)^2} = 0. \quad (o)$$

A similar system of equations is obtained also from Eq. (n). The constants $E_1, E_3, \ldots, F_1, F_3, \ldots$ can be determined in

---

[1] It is assumed that the order of summation in expression (l) is interchangeable.

each particular case from these two systems of equations by the method of successive approximations.

To illustrate this method let us consider the case of a square plate. In such a case the distribution of the bending moments along all sides of the square is the same. Hence $E_i = F_i$, and the two systems of equations, mentioned above, are identical. The form of the equations is

$$\frac{E_i}{i}\left(\tanh \alpha_i + \frac{\alpha_i}{\cosh^2 \alpha_i}\right) + \frac{8i}{\pi} \sum_{m=1,3,5,\cdots}^{\infty} \frac{E_m}{m^3} \frac{1}{\left(1 + \frac{i^2}{m^2}\right)^2}$$

$$= \frac{4qa^2}{\pi^3} \frac{1}{i^4}\left(\frac{\alpha_i}{\cosh^2 \alpha_i} - \tanh \alpha_i\right).$$

Substituting the numerical values of the coefficients in these equations and considering only the first four coefficients, we obtain the following system of four equations with four unknown E_1, E_3, E_5 and E_7:

$$
\begin{aligned}
1.8033E_1 &+ 0.0764E_3 + 0.0188E_5 + 0.0071E_7 = 0.6677K \\
0.0764E_1 &+ 0.4045E_3 + 0.0330E_5 + 0.0159E_7 = 0.01232K \\
0.0188E_1 &+ 0.0330E_3 + 0.2255E_5 + 0.0163E_7 = 0.00160K \\
0.0071E_1 &+ 0.0159E_3 + 0.0163E_5 + 0.1558E_7 = 0.00042K,
\end{aligned}
$$
(p)

where $K = -4qa^2/\pi^3$. It may be seen that the terms along the diagonal have the largest coefficients. Hence we obtain the first approximations of the constants $E_1, \ldots, E_7$ by considering on the left sides of Eqs. (p) only the terms to the left of the heavy line. In such a way we obtain from the first of the equations $E_1 = 0.3700K$. Substituting this in the second equation, we obtain $E_3 = -0.0395K$. Substituting the values of E_1 and E_3 in the third equation, we find $E_5 = -0.0180K$. From the last equation we then obtain $E_7 = -0.0083K$. Substituting these first approximations in the terms to the right of the heavy line in Eqs. (p), we can calculate the second approximations, which are $E_1 = 0.3722K$, $E_3 = -0.0380K$, $E_5 = -0.0178K$, $E_7 = -0.0085K$. Repeating the calculations again, we shall obtain the third approximation, and so on.

Substituting the calculated values of the coefficients E_1, $E_3, \ldots$ in series (c), we obtain the bending moments along the clamped edges of the plate. The maximum of the absolute value of these moments is at the middle of the sides of the square. With the four Eqs. (p) taken, this value is

$$|M_y|_{y=\frac{b}{2},x=0} = |E_1 - E_3 + E_5 - E_7| = 0.0517qa^2.$$

The comparison of this result with Boobnov's table, calculated with a much larger number of equations similar to Eqs. (p), shows that the error in the maximum bending moment, by taking only four Eqs. (p), is less than 1 per cent. It may be seen that we obtain for the moment a series with alternating signs, and the magnitude of the error depends on the magnitude of the last of the calculated coefficients E_1, E_3, ...

Substituting the values of E_1, E_3, . . . in expression (d), we obtain the deflection of the plate produced by the moments distributed along the edges $y = \pm b/2$. For the center of the plate $(x = y = 0)$ this deflection is

$$(w_1)_{x=y=0} = \frac{a^2}{2\pi^2 D} \sum_{m=1,3,5,\cdots}^{\infty} E_m(-1)^{\frac{m-1}{2}} \frac{\alpha_m \tanh \alpha_m}{m^2 \cosh \alpha_m}$$

$$= -0.0153\frac{qa^4}{Eh^3}.$$

Doubling this result, to take into account the action of the moments distributed along the sides $x = \pm a/2$; and adding

TABLE 30.—DEFLECTIONS AND BENDING MOMENTS IN A UNIFORMLY LOADED RECTANGULAR PLATE WITH BUILT-IN EDGES
$\nu = 0.3$

b/a	$(w)_{x=0,y=0}$	$(M_x)_{x=a/2,y=0}$	$(M_y)_{x=0,y=b/2}$	$(M_x)_{x=0,y=0}$	$(M_y)_{x=0,y=0}$
1.0	$0.0138\ qa^4/Eh^3$	$-0.0513qa^2$	$-0.0513qa^2$		
1.1	$0.0164\ qa^4/Eh^3$	$-0.0581qa^2$	$-0.0538qa^2$	$0.0264qa^2$	$0.0231qa^2$
1.2	$0.0188\ qa^4/Eh^3$	$-0.0639qa^2$	$-0.0554qa^2$	$0.0299qa^2$	$0.0228qa^2$
1.3	$0.0209\ qa^4/Eh^3$	$-0.0687qa^2$	$-0.0563qa^2$	$0.0327qa^2$	$0.0222qa^2$
1.4	$0.0226\ qa^4/Eh^3$	$-0.0726qa^2$	$-0.0568qa^2$	$0.0349qa^2$	$0.0212qa^2$
1.5	$0.0240\ qa^4/Eh^3$	$-0.0757qa^2$			
1.6	$0.0251\ qa^4/Eh^3$	$-0.0780qa^2$	$-0.0571qa^2$	$0.0381qa^2$	$0.0193qa^2$
1.7	$0.0260\ qa^4/Eh^3$	$-0.0799qa^2$	$-0.0571qa^2$	$0.0392qa^2$	$0.0182qa^2$
1.8	$0.0267\ qa^4/Eh^3$	$-0.0812qa^2$	$-0.0571qa^2$	$0.0401qa^2$	$0.0174qa^2$
1.9	$0.0272\ qa^4/Eh^3$	$-0.0822qa^2$	$-0.0571qa^2$	$0.0407qa^2$	$0.0165qa^2$
2.0	$0.0277\ qa^4/Eh^3$	$-0.0829qa^2$	$-0.0571qa^2$		

to the deflection of the simply supported square plate (Table 5), we obtain for the deflection at the center of a uniformly loaded square plate with clamped edges

$$(w)_{\text{max.}} = (0.0443 - 0.0306)\frac{qa^4}{Eh^3} = 0.0137\frac{qa^4}{Eh^3}. \tag{q}$$

Similar calculations can be made for any ratio of the sides of a rectangular plate. The results of these calculations are given in Table 30.[1]

As a second example let us consider bending of a rectangular plate with clamped edges by a load P concentrated at the center. We begin again with the case of a simply supported rectangular plate. Using the results of Art. 32, we find from expression (f) (see page 148) for the unloaded portion of the plate and for $y > 0$

$$w = \sum_{m=1}^{\infty}\left(A'_m \cosh\frac{m\pi y}{a} + B'_m \sinh\frac{m\pi y}{a} + C'_m\frac{m\pi y}{a}\sinh\frac{m\pi y}{a}\right.$$

$$\left. + D'_m\frac{m\pi y}{a}\cosh\frac{m\pi y}{a}\right)\sin\frac{m\pi x}{a}. \tag{r}$$

When the plate is loaded along a narrow strip of the width b_1 extended along the x-axis, the constants A'_m, B'_m, . . . , calculated from the general expressions on page 150, are

$$A'_m = \frac{m\pi b_1 a_m}{4a \cosh \alpha_m}\left(\sinh \alpha_m - \frac{\alpha_m}{\cosh \alpha_m}\right),$$

$$B'_m = -\frac{m\pi b_1 a_m}{4a}, \qquad C'_m = -\frac{m\pi b_1 a_m}{4a}\tanh \alpha_m, \qquad D'_m = \frac{m\pi b_1 a_m}{4a},$$

where, for a concentrated load P at the center of the plate,

$$b_1 a_m = \frac{2Pa^3(-1)^{\frac{m-1}{2}}}{D\pi^4 m^4}.$$

Substituting into expression (r), we find

---

[1] The table was calculated by T. H. Evans; see *J. Appl. Mech.*, vol. 6, p. A-7, 1939.

$$w = \frac{Pa^2}{2\pi^3 D} \sum_{m=1,3,5,\cdots}^{\infty} \frac{(-1)^{\frac{m-1}{2}}}{m^3} \sin \frac{m\pi x}{a} \left[\frac{1}{\cosh \alpha_m} \left(\sinh \alpha_m \right. \right.$$

$$\left. \left. - \frac{\alpha_m}{\cosh \alpha_m} \right) \cosh \frac{m\pi y}{a} - \sinh \frac{m\pi y}{a} - \frac{m\pi y}{a} \tanh \alpha_m \sinh \frac{m\pi y}{a} \right.$$

$$\left. + \frac{m\pi y}{a} \cosh \frac{m\pi y}{a} \right]. \quad (s)$$

Taking the coordinate axis as shown in Fig. 82, we must substitute $x + a/2$ for x in expression (s), and we obtain

$$w = \frac{Pa^2}{2\pi^3 D} \sum_{m=1,3,5,\cdots}^{\infty} \frac{1}{m^3} \cos \frac{m\pi x}{a} \left[\left(\tanh \alpha_m \right. \right.$$

$$\left. - \frac{\alpha_m}{\cosh^2 \alpha_m} \right) \cosh \frac{m\pi y}{a} - \sinh \frac{m\pi y}{a}$$

$$\left. - \frac{m\pi y}{a} \tanh \alpha_m \sinh \frac{m\pi y}{a} + \frac{m\pi y}{a} \cosh \frac{m\pi y}{a} \right].$$

The angle of rotation along the edge $y = b/2$ is

$$\left(\frac{\partial w}{\partial y} \right)_{y=\frac{b}{2}} = -\frac{Pa}{2\pi^2 D} \sum_{m=1,3,5,\cdots}^{\infty} \frac{1}{m^2} \cos \frac{m\pi x}{a} \cdot \frac{\alpha_m \tanh \alpha_m}{\cosh \alpha_m}. \quad (t)$$

To calculate the bending moments along the clamped edges we proceed as in the previous case and obtain the same two systems of Eqs. (m) and (n). The expressions for w_1 and w_2 are the same as in the previous case, and it will be necessary to change only the first term of these equations by substituting expression (t), instead of $\left(\dfrac{\partial w}{\partial y} \right)_{y=b/2}$ in Eq. (m), and also a corresponding expression for $\left(\dfrac{\partial w}{\partial x} \right)_{x=a/2}$ in Eq. (n).

For the particular case of a square plate, limiting ourselves to four equations, we find that the left side of the equations will be the same as in Eq. (p). The right sides will be obtained from the expression (t), and we find

$1.8033E_1 + \lfloor 0.0764E_3 + 0.0188E_5 + 0.0071E_7 = -0.1828P,$
$0.0764E_1 + 0.4045E_3 + \lfloor 0.0330E_5 + 0.0159E_7 = +0.00299P,$
$0.0188E_1 + 0.0330E_3 + \overline{0.2255E_5 + \lfloor 0.0163E_7} = -0.000081P,$
$0.0071E_1 + 0.0159E_3 + 0.0163E_5 + 0.1558E_7 = +0.000005P.$

Solving this system of equations by successive approximations, as before, we find

$$E_1 = -0.1025P, \qquad E_3 = 0.0263P, \qquad E_5 = 0.0042P,$$
$$E_7 = 0.0015P.$$

Substituting these values in expression (c), the bending moment for the middle of the side $y = b/2$ can be obtained. A more accurate calculation[1] gives

$$(M_y)_{y=\frac{b}{2}, x=0} = -0.1257P.$$

Comparing this result with that for the uniformly loaded square plate, we conclude that the uniform load produces moments at the middle of the sides that are less than half of that which the same load produces if concentrated at the center.

Having the moments along the clamped edges, we can calculate the corresponding deflections by using Eq. (d). Superposing

TABLE 31.—BENDING MOMENTS AT THE MIDDLE OF LONGER SIDES AND DEFLECTIONS AT THE CENTER OF A RECTANGULAR PLATE LOADED AT THE CENTER
$\nu = 0.3$

$b/a =$	1	1.2	1.4	1.6	1.8	2
$M =$	$-0.1257P$	$-0.1490P$	$-0.1604P$	$-0.1651P$	$-0.1667P$	$-0.1674P$
$w =$	$0.0611\frac{Pa^2}{Eh^3}$	$0.0706\frac{Pa^2}{Eh^3}$	$0.0755\frac{Pa^2}{Eh^3}$	$0.0777\frac{Pa^2}{Eh^3}$	$0.0786\frac{Pa^2}{Eh^3}$	$0.0788\frac{Pa^2}{Eh^3}$

deflections produced by the moments on the deflections of a simply supported plate, we obtain the deflections of the plate with built-in edges. By the same method of superposition the other information regarding deflection of plates with built-in

[1] In this calculation seven equations, instead of four equations taken above, were used.

edges under a central concentrated load can be obtained. Some results of such calculations are given in Table 31.[1]

It is seen that the moment and the deflection approach rapidly constant values, corresponding to $b/a = \infty$, as the ratio b/a increases.

45. Continuous Rectangular Plates.—A rectangular plate of width b and length $= a_1 + a_2 + a_3$ supported along the edges and also along the intermediate lines ss and tt, as shown in Fig. 83, forms a simply supported continuous plate. The bending of each span of such a plate can be readily investigated by combining

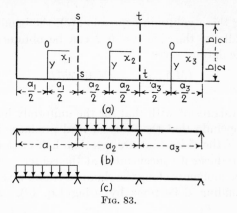

Fig. 83.

the known solutions for laterally loaded, simply supported rectangular plates with those for rectangular plates bent by moments distributed along the edges.

Let us begin with the symmetrical case in which

$$a_1 = a_2 = a_3 = a$$

and the middle span is uniformly loaded while the side spans are without load (Fig. 83b). Considering the middle span as a simply supported rectangular plate and using expression (b) of the previous article (see page 223), we conclude that the slope of the deflection surface along the edge $x_2 = a/2$ is

---

[1] The table was calculated by Dana Young, *J. Appl. Mech.*, vol. 6, p. A-114, 1939. To obtain the moments with the four correct figures it was necessary to use in this calculation seven coefficients E and seven coefficients F in Eqs. (m) and (n).

$$\left(\frac{\partial w}{\partial x_2}\right)_{x_2=\frac{a}{2}}$$

$$= \frac{2qb^3}{\pi^4 D} \sum_{m=1,3,5,\cdots}^{\infty} \frac{(-1)^{\frac{m-1}{2}}}{m^4} \cos\frac{m\pi y}{b}\left(\frac{\beta_m}{\cosh^2\beta_m} - \tanh\beta_m\right). \quad (a)$$

where $\beta_m = m\pi a/2b$. Owing to the continuity of the plate, bending moments M_x are distributed along the edges $x_2 = \pm a/2$. From symmetry it is seen that these moments can be represented by the following series:

$$(M_x)_{x_2=\pm\frac{a}{2}} = \sum_{m=1,3,5,\cdots}^{\infty} (-1)^{\frac{m-1}{2}} E_m \cos\frac{m\pi y}{b}. \quad (b)$$

The deflections w_1 produced by these moments can be obtained from Eq. (151), and the corresponding slope along the edge $x_2 = a/2$ [see Eq. (e), page 224] is

$$\left(\frac{\partial w_1}{\partial x_2}\right)_{x_2=\frac{a}{2}} = -\frac{b}{2\pi D} \sum_{m=1,3,5,\cdots}^{\infty} E_m \frac{(-1)^{\frac{m-1}{2}}}{m}$$

$$\cos\frac{m\pi y}{b}\left(\tanh\beta_m + \frac{\beta_m}{\cosh^2\beta_m}\right). \quad (c)$$

From the condition of continuity we conclude that the sum of expressions (a) and (c) representing the slope of the plate along the line $x_2 = a/2$ must be equal to the slope along the same line of the deflection surface of the plate in the adjacent span. Considering this latter span as a simply supported rectangular plate bent by the moments (b) distributed along the edge $x_3 = -a/2$, we find the corresponding deflection w_2 of the plate by using Eq. (154) (see page 204) from which follows

$$w_2 = \frac{b^2}{4\pi^2 D} \sum_{m=1,3,5,\cdots}^{\infty} E_m \cos\frac{m\pi y}{b}\frac{(-1)^{\frac{m-1}{2}}}{m^2}$$

$$\left[\frac{1}{\cosh\beta_m}\left(\beta_m\tanh\beta_m\cosh\frac{m\pi x_3}{b} - \frac{m\pi x_3}{b}\sinh\frac{m\pi x_3}{b}\right)\right.$$

$$\left. - \frac{1}{\sinh\beta_m}\left(\beta_m\coth\beta_m\sinh\frac{m\pi x_3}{b} - \frac{m\pi x_3}{b}\cosh\frac{m\pi x_3}{b}\right)\right]. \quad (d)$$

The corresponding slope along the edge $x_3 = -a/2$ is

$$\left(\frac{\partial w_2}{\partial x_3}\right)_{x_3 = -\frac{a}{2}} = \frac{b}{4\pi D} \sum_{m=1,3,5,\cdots}^{\infty} \frac{E_m}{m}(-1)^{\frac{m-1}{2}}$$

$$\cosh \frac{m\pi y}{b}\left(\tanh \beta_m + \coth \beta_m + \frac{\beta_m}{\cosh^2 \beta_m} - \frac{\beta_m}{\sinh^2 \beta_m}\right). \quad (e)$$

The equation for calculating the coefficients E_m is

$$\left(\frac{\partial w}{\partial x_2}\right)_{x_2 = \frac{a}{2}} + \left(\frac{\partial w_1}{\partial x_2}\right)_{x_2 = \frac{a}{2}} = \left(\frac{\partial w_2}{\partial x_3}\right)_{x_3 = -\frac{a}{2}}.$$

Since this equation holds for any value of y, we obtain for each value of m the following equation

$$\frac{2qb^3}{\pi^4 D} \frac{1}{m^4}\left(\frac{\beta_m}{\cosh^2 \beta_m} - \tanh \beta_m\right) - \frac{b}{2\pi D} \frac{E_m}{m}\left(\tanh \beta_m + \frac{\beta_m}{\cosh^2 \beta_m}\right)$$

$$= \frac{b}{4\pi D} \frac{E_m}{m}\left(\tanh \beta_m + \coth \beta_m + \frac{\beta_m}{\cosh^2 \beta_m} - \frac{\beta_m}{\sinh^2 \beta_m}\right), \quad (f)$$

from which

$$E_m = \frac{8qb^2}{\pi^3 m^3}$$

$$\cdot \frac{\beta_m - \tanh \beta_m \cosh^2 \beta_m}{3 \tanh \beta_m \cosh^2 \beta_m + \coth \beta_m \cosh^2 \beta_m + 3\beta_m - \beta_m \coth^2 \beta_m}. \quad (g)$$

It is seen that E_m decreases rapidly as m increases and approaches the value $-2qb^2/\pi^3 m^3$. Having the coefficients E_m calculated from (g), we obtain the values of the bending moments M_x along the line tt from expression (b). The value of this moment at $y = 0$, *i.e.*, at the middle of the width of the plate, is

$$(M_x)_{x_2 = \pm \frac{a}{2}, y = 0} = \sum_{m=1,3,5,\cdots}^{\infty} E_m(-1)^{\frac{m-1}{2}}.$$

Taking, as an example, $b = a$, we have $\beta_m = m\pi/2$, and the formula (g) gives

$$E_1 = -\frac{8qa^2}{\pi^3}0.1555, \qquad E_3 = -\frac{8qa^2}{\pi^3}0.0092,$$

$$E_5 = -\frac{8qa^2}{\pi^3}0.0020,$$

$$(M_x)_{x_2 = \pm \frac{a}{2}, y = 0} = -0.0381qa^2.$$

If a side span is uniformly loaded, as shown in Fig. 83c, the deflection surface is no longer symmetrical with respect to the vertical axis of symmetry of the plate, and the bending moment distributions along the lines ss and tt are not identical.   Let

$$\left.\begin{array}{l} (M_x)_{x_1=\frac{a_1}{2}} = \displaystyle\sum_{m=1,3,5,\,\cdots}^{\infty} (-1)^{\frac{m-1}{2}} E_m \cos \frac{m\pi y}{b}, \\[2em] (M_x)_{x_2=\frac{a_2}{2}} = \displaystyle\sum_{m=1,3,5,\,\cdots}^{\infty} (-1)^{\frac{m-1}{2}} F_m \cos \frac{m\pi y}{b}. \end{array}\right\} \quad (h)$$

To calculate the coefficients E_m and F_m we derive two systems of equations from the conditions of continuity of the deflection surface of the plate along the lines ss and tt.   Considering the loaded span and using expressions (a) and (e), we find that the slope of the deflection surface at the points of the support ss, for $a_1 = a_2 = a_3 = a$, is

$$\left(\frac{\partial w}{\partial x_1}\right)_{x_1=\frac{a}{2}} = \frac{2qb^3}{\pi^4 D} \sum_{m=1,3,5,\,\cdots}^{\infty} \frac{(-1)^{\frac{m-1}{2}}}{m^4} \cos \frac{m\pi y}{b} \left(\frac{\beta_m}{\cosh^2 \beta_m}\right.$$

$$- \tanh \beta_m\bigg) - \frac{b}{4\pi D} \sum_{m=1,3,5,\,\cdots}^{\infty} E_m \frac{(-1)^{\frac{m-1}{2}}}{m} \cosh \frac{m\pi y}{b}\bigg(\tanh \beta_m$$

$$+ \coth \beta_m + \frac{\beta_m}{\cosh^2 \beta_m} - \frac{\beta_m}{\sinh^2 \beta_m}\bigg). \quad (i)$$

Considering now the middle span as a rectangular plate bent by the moments M_x distributed along the lines ss and tt and given by the series (h), we find, by using Eq. (153) (see page 204),

$$\left(\frac{\partial w}{\partial x_2}\right)_{x_2=-\frac{a}{2}} = \frac{b}{4\pi D} \sum_{m=1,3,5,\,\cdots}^{\infty} \frac{(-1)^{\frac{m-1}{2}}}{m} \cos \frac{m\pi y}{b}\bigg[(E_m$$

$$+ F_m)\bigg(\frac{\beta_m}{\cosh^2 \beta_m} + \tanh \beta_m\bigg)$$

$$+ (E_m - F_m)\bigg(\coth \beta_m - \frac{\beta_m}{\sinh^2 \beta_m}\bigg)\bigg]. \quad (j)$$

From expressions (i) and (j) we obtain the following system of equations for calculating coefficients E_m and F_m:

$$A_m \frac{8qb^2}{\pi^3 m^3} + E_m(B_m + C_m) = -B_m(E_m + F_m) - C_m(E_m - F_m), \quad (k)$$

where the following notations are used:

$$A_m = \frac{\beta_m}{\cosh^2 \beta_m} - \tanh \beta_m, \qquad B_m = -\left(\frac{\beta_m}{\cosh^2 \beta_m} + \tanh \beta_m\right), \\ C_m = \frac{\beta_m}{\sinh^2 \beta_m} - \coth \beta_m. \qquad \qquad \qquad \qquad \quad \Bigg\} \quad (l)$$

The slope of the deflection surface of the middle span at the supporting line tt, by using expression (j), is

$$\left(\frac{\partial w}{\partial x_2}\right)_{x_2 = \frac{a}{2}} = -\frac{b}{4\pi D} \sum_{m = 1,3,5, \cdots}^{\infty} \frac{(-1)^{\frac{m-1}{2}}}{m} \cos \frac{m\pi y}{b}\bigg[(E_m \\ + F_m)\left(\frac{\beta_m}{\cosh^2 \beta_m} + \tanh \beta_m\right) + (F_m - E_m)\left(\coth \beta_m - \frac{\beta_m}{\sinh^2 \beta_m}\right)\bigg].$$

This slope must be equal to the slope in the adjacent unloaded span which is obtained from expression (c) by substituting F_m for E_m. In this way we find the second system of equations which, using notations (l), can be written in the following form:

$$B_m(E_m + F_m) + C_m(F_m - E_m) = -(B_m + C_m)F_m. \qquad (m)$$

From this equation we obtain

$$F_m = E_m \frac{C_m - B_m}{2(B_m + C_m)}. \qquad (n)$$

Substituting in Eqs. (k), we find

$$E_m = A_m \frac{8qa^2}{\pi^3 m^3} \frac{2(B_m + C_m)}{(C_m - B_m)^2 - 4(B_m + C_m)^2}. \qquad (o)$$

Substituting in each particular case for A_m, B_m and C_m their numerical values, obtained from Eqs. (l), we find the coefficients E_m and F_m; and then, from expressions (h), we obtain the bending moments along the lines ss and tt. Take, as an example, $b = a$. Then $\beta_m = m\pi/2$, and we find from Eqs. (l)

$$A_1 = -0.6677, \qquad B_1 = -1.1667, \qquad C_1 = -0.7936, \\ A_3 = -0.9983, \qquad B_3 = -1.0013, \qquad C_3 = -0.9987.$$

For m larger than 3 we can take with sufficient accuracy

$$A_m = B_m = C_m = -1.$$

Substituting these values in Eq. (o), we obtain

$$E_1 = -\frac{8qa^2}{\pi^3}0.1720, \qquad E_3 = -\frac{8qa^2}{\pi^3 3^3}0.2496, \qquad E_5 = -\frac{8qa^2}{\pi^3 5^3}0.2500.$$

The moment at the middle of the support ss is

$$(M_x)_{x_1=\frac{a}{2}, y=0} = (E_1 - E_3 + E_5 - \cdots) = -0.0424qa^2.$$

For the middle of the support tt we obtain

$$(M_x)_{x_2=\frac{a}{2}, y=0} = (F_1 - F_3 + F_5 - \cdots) = 0.0042qa^2.$$

Having the bending moments along the lines of support, the deflections of the plate in each span can readily be obtained by superposing on the deflections produced by the lateral load the deflections due to the moments at the supports.

The equations obtained for three spans can readily be generalized and expanded for the case of any number of spans. In this way an equation similar to the three moments equations of continuous beams will be obtained.[1] Let us consider two

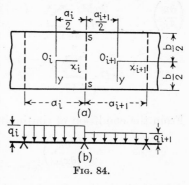

Fig. 84.

adjacent spans i and $i + 1$ of the length a_i and a_{i+1}, respectively (Fig. 84). The corresponding values of the functions (l) are denoted by A_m^i, B_m^i, C_m^i and A_m^{i+1}, B_m^{i+1}, C_m^{i+1}. The bending moments along the three consecutive lines of support can be represented by the series

$$M_x^{i-1} = \sum_{m=1,3,5,\cdots}^{\infty} (-1)^{\frac{m-1}{2}} E_m^{i-1} \cos \frac{m\pi y}{b},$$

$$M_x^{i} = \sum_{m=1,3,5,\cdots}^{\infty} (-1)^{\frac{m-1}{2}} E_m^{i} \cos \frac{m\pi y}{b},$$

$$M_x^{i+1} = \sum_{m=1,3,5,\cdots}^{\infty} (-1)^{\frac{m-1}{2}} E_m^{i+1} \cos \frac{m\pi y}{b}.$$

[1] This problem in a somewhat different way was discussed by B. G. Galerkin, "Elastic Thin Plates," Moscow, 1933. Continuous plates on elastic beams were considered by N. M. Newmark, *Bull. Univ. Ill.*, 84, 1938.

Considering the span $i + 1$ and using expressions (a) and (j), we find

$$\left(\frac{\partial w}{\partial x_{i+1}}\right)_{x_{i+1}=-\frac{a_{i+1}}{2}} = -\frac{2q_{i+1}b^3}{\pi^4 D} \sum_{m=1,3,5,\cdots}^{\infty} \frac{(-1)^{\frac{m-1}{2}}}{m^4} \cos\frac{m\pi y}{b} A_m^{i+1}$$

$$-\frac{b}{4\pi D} \sum_{m=1,3,5,\cdots}^{\infty} \frac{(-1)^{\frac{m-1}{2}}}{m} \cos\frac{m\pi y}{b}[(E_m^i + E_m^{i+1})B_m^{i+1}$$

$$- (E_m^{i+1} + E_m^i)C_m^{i+1}]. \quad (p)$$

In the same manner, considering the span i, we obtain

$$\left(\frac{\partial w}{\partial x_i}\right)_{x_i=\frac{a_i}{2}} = \frac{2q_i b^3}{\pi^4 D} \sum_{m=1,3,5,\cdots}^{\infty} \frac{(-1)^{\frac{m-1}{2}}}{m^4} \cos\frac{m\pi y}{b} A_m^i$$

$$+\frac{b}{4\pi D} \sum_{m=1,3,5,\cdots}^{\infty} \frac{(-1)^{\frac{m-1}{2}}}{m} \cos\frac{m\pi y}{b}[(E_m^{i-1} + E_m^i)B_m^i$$

$$+ (E_m^i - E_m^{i-1})C_m^i]. \quad (q)$$

From the condition of continuity we conclude that

$$\left(\frac{\partial w}{\partial x_{i+1}}\right)_{x_{i+1}=-\frac{a_{i+1}}{2}} = \left(\frac{\partial w}{\partial x_i}\right)_{x_i=\frac{a_i}{2}}.$$

Substituting expressions (p) and (q) in this equation and observing that it must be satisfied for any value of y, we obtain the following equation for calculating E_m^{i-1}, E_m^i and E_m^{i+1}:

$$E_m^{i-1}(B_m^i - C_m^i) + E_m^i(B_m^i + C_m^i + B_m^{i+1} + C_m^{i+1})$$

$$+ E_m^{i+1}(B_m^{i+1} - C_m^{i+1}) = -\frac{8b^2}{\pi^3 m^3}(q_{i+1}A_m^{i+1} + q_i A_m^i). \quad (155)$$

Equations (k) and (m), which we obtained previously, are particular cases of this equation. We can write as many Eqs. (155) as there are intermediate supports, and there is no difficulty in calculating the moments at the intermediate supports if the ends of the plate are simply supported. The left side of Eq. (155) holds not only for uniform load but also for any type of loading that is symmetrical in each span with respect to the x- and y-axes. The right side of Eq. (155), however, has a different value for each type of loading as in the three moments equation for beams.

46. Bending of Plates Supported by Rows of Equidistant Columns.—If the dimensions of the plate are large in comparison with the distances a and b between the columns (Fig. 85) and the lateral load is uniformly distributed, it can be concluded that the bending in all panels, which are not close to the boundary of the plate, may be assumed to be identical, so that we can limit the problem to the bending of one panel only. Taking the coordinate axes parallel to the rows of columns and the origin at the center of a panel, we may consider this panel as a uniformly loaded rectangular plate with sides a and b. From symmetry we con-

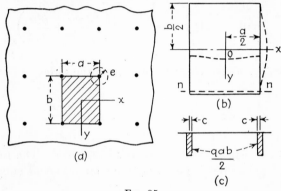

Fig. 85.

clude that the deflection surface of the plate is as shown by the dotted lines in Fig. 85*b*. The maximum deflection is at the center of the plate, and the deflection at the corners is zero. To simplify the problem we assume that the cross-sectional dimensions of the columns are small and can be neglected in so far as deflection and moments at the center of the plate are concerned.[1] We then have a uniformly loaded rectangular plate supported at the corners, and we conclude from symmetry that the slope of the deflection surface in the direction of the normal to the boundary and the shearing force are zero at all points along the edges of the plate except the corners.[2]

[1] In this simplified form the problem was discussed by several authors; see, for example, A. Nadai, "Uber die Biegung durchlaufender Platten," *Z. angew. Math. Mech.*, vol. 2, p. 1, 1922; and the book by B. G. Galerkin, "Thin Elastic Plates," Moscow, 1933.

[2] The equating to zero of the twisting moment M_{xy} along the boundary follows from the fact that the slope in the direction of the normal to the boundary is zero.

Proceeding as in the case of a simply supported plate (Art. 29), we take the total deflection w in the form

$$w = w_1 + w_2, \qquad (a)$$

where

$$w_1 = \frac{qb^4}{384D}\left(1 - \frac{4y^2}{b^2}\right)^2 \qquad (b)$$

represents the deflection of a uniformly loaded strip clamped at the ends $y = \pm b/2$ and satisfies the differential equation (101) of the plate as well as the boundary conditions

$$\left(\frac{\partial w_1}{\partial x}\right)_{x=\pm\frac{a}{2}} = 0, \qquad (Q_x)_{x=\pm\frac{a}{2}} = -D\frac{\partial}{\partial x}\left(\frac{\partial^2 w_1}{\partial x^2} + \frac{\partial^2 w_1}{\partial y^2}\right)_{x=\pm\frac{a}{2}} = 0.$$

$$(c)$$

The deflection w_2 is taken in the form of the series

$$w_2 = A_0 + \sum_{m=2,4,6,\cdots}^{\infty} Y_m \cos\frac{m\pi x}{a} \qquad (d)$$

each term of which satisfies the conditions (c). The functions Y_m must be chosen so as to satisfy the homogeneous equation

$$\Delta\Delta w_2 = 0 \qquad (e)$$

and so as to make w satisfy the boundary conditions at the edges $y = \pm b/2$. Equation (e) and the conditions of symmetry are satisfied by taking series (d) in the form

$$w_2 = A_0 + \sum_{m=2,4,6,\cdots}^{\infty}\left(A_m \cosh\frac{m\pi y}{a} + B_m\frac{m\pi y}{a}\sinh\frac{m\pi y}{a}\right)\cos\frac{m\pi x}{a},$$

$$(f)$$

where the constants A_0, A_m and B_m are to be determined from the boundary conditions along the edge $y = b/2$. From the condition concerning the slope, *viz.*, that

$$\left(\frac{\partial w}{\partial y}\right)_{y=\frac{b}{2}} = \left(\frac{\partial w_1}{\partial y} + \frac{\partial w_2}{\partial y}\right)_{y=\frac{b}{2}} = 0,$$

we readily find that

$$B_m = -A_m\frac{\tanh\alpha_m}{\alpha_m + \tanh\alpha_m} \qquad (g)$$

in which, as before,

$$\alpha_m = \frac{m\pi b}{2a}. \tag{h}$$

Considering now the boundary condition concerning the shearing force, we see that on a normal section nn (Fig. 85b) of the plate infinitely close to the boundary $y = b/2$, the shearing force Q_y is equal to zero at all points except those which are close to the column, and at these points Q_y must be infinitely large in order to transmit the finite load $\frac{1}{2}qab$ to the column (Fig. 85c) along an infinitely small distance between $x = a/2 - c$ and $x = a/2 + c$. Representing Q_y by a trigonometric series which, from symmetry, has the form

$$Q_y = C_0 + \sum_{m=2,4,6,\,\cdots}^{\infty} C_m \cos \frac{m\pi x}{a} \tag{i}$$

and observing that

$$Q_y = 0 \qquad \text{for} \qquad 0 < x < \frac{a}{2} - c, \qquad \text{and that}$$

$$\int_{\frac{a}{2}-c}^{\frac{a}{2}} Q_y \, dx = -\frac{qab}{4},$$

we find, by applying the usual method of calculation, that

$$C_0 = -\frac{qab}{2a} = -\frac{P}{2a}$$

and

$$C_m = \frac{4}{a} \int_0^{+\frac{a}{2}} Q_y \cos \frac{m\pi x}{a} dx = -\frac{P}{a}(-1)^{\frac{m}{2}},$$

where $P = qab$ is the total load on one panel of the plate. Substituting these values of the coefficients C_0 and C_m in series (i), the required boundary condition takes the following form:

$$(Q_y)_{y=\frac{b}{2}} = -D\left(\frac{\partial^3 w}{\partial y^3} + \frac{\partial^3 w}{\partial x^2 \, \partial y}\right)_{y=\frac{b}{2}}$$

$$= -\frac{P}{a} \sum_{m=2,4,6,\,\cdots}^{\infty} (-1)^{\frac{m}{2}} \cos \frac{m\pi x}{a} - \frac{P}{2a}.$$

Substituting expression (a) for w and observing that the second term in parentheses vanishes, on account of the boundary condition $\partial w / \partial y = 0$, we obtain

$$-D\left(\frac{\partial^3 w_2}{\partial y^3}\right)_{y=\frac{b}{2}} = -\frac{P}{a} \sum_{m=2,4,6,\cdots}^{\infty} (-1)^{\frac{m}{2}} \cos \frac{m\pi x}{a},$$

from which, by using expression (f), we find that

$$D\frac{m^3\pi^3}{a^3}[(A_m + 3B_m) \sinh \alpha_m + B_m \alpha_m \cosh \alpha_m] = \frac{P}{a}(-1)^{\frac{m}{2}}. \quad (j)$$

Solving Eqs. (g) and (j) for the constants A_m and B_m, we obtain:

$$A_m = -\frac{Pa^2}{2m^3\pi^3 D}(-1)^{\frac{m}{2}} \frac{\alpha_m + \tanh \alpha_m}{\sinh \alpha_m \tanh \alpha_m},$$

$$B_m = \frac{Pa^2}{2m^3\pi^3 D}(-1)^{\frac{m}{2}} \frac{1}{\sinh \alpha_m}. \quad (k)$$

The deflection of the plate takes the form

$$w = \frac{qb^4}{384D}\left(1 - \frac{4y^2}{b^2}\right)^2 + A_0 + \frac{qa^3 b}{2\pi^3 D} \sum_{m=2,4,6,\cdots}^{\infty} \frac{(-1)^{\frac{m}{2}} \cos \frac{m\pi x}{a}}{m^3 \sinh \alpha_m \tanh \alpha_m}$$

$$\left[\tanh \alpha_m \frac{m\pi y}{a} \sinh \frac{m\pi y}{a} - (\alpha_m + \tanh \alpha_m) \cosh \frac{m\pi y}{a}\right]. \quad (l)$$

The constant A_0 can now be determined from the condition that the deflection vanishes at the corners of the plate. Hence

$$(w)_{x=\frac{a}{2}, y=\frac{b}{2}} = 0,$$

and

$$A_0 = -\frac{qa^3 b}{2\pi^3 D} \sum_{m=2,4,6,\cdots}^{\infty} \frac{1}{m^3}\left(\alpha_m - \frac{\alpha_m + \tanh \alpha_m}{\tanh^2 \alpha_m}\right). \quad (m)$$

The deflection at any point of the plate can be calculated by using expressions (l) and (m). The maximum deflection is evidently at the center of the plate, at which point we have

$$(w)_{x=0,y=0} = \frac{qb^4}{384D} - \frac{qa^3b}{2\pi^3D} \sum_{m=2,4,6,\cdots}^{\infty} \frac{(-1)^{\frac{m}{2}}}{m^3} \frac{\alpha_m + \tanh \alpha_m}{\sinh \alpha_m \tanh \alpha_m}$$

$$- \frac{qa^3b}{2\pi^3D} \sum_{m=2,4,6,\cdots}^{\infty} \frac{1}{m^3}\left(\alpha_m - \frac{\alpha_m + \tanh \alpha_m}{\tanh^2 \alpha_m}\right). \quad (n)$$

Values of this deflection calculated for several values of the ratio b/a are given in Table 32. Values of the bending moments $(M_x)_{x=0,y=0}$ and $(M_y)_{x=0,y=0}$ calculated by using formulas (99) and expression (l) for deflection are also given. It is seen that for

TABLE 32.—DEFLECTIONS AND MOMENTS AT THE CENTER OF A PANEL
$\nu = 0.3$

$b/a =$		1	1.1	1.2	1.3	1.4	1.5	2.0	∞
$w = \alpha\dfrac{qb^4}{Eh^3}$	$\alpha =$	0.0634	0.0532	0.0467	0.0423	0.0391	0.0368	0.0319	0.0284
$M_x = \beta qb^2$	$\beta =$	0.0359	0.0292	0.0243	0.0210	0.0186	0.0169	0.0133	0.0125
$M_y = \beta_1 qb^2$	$\beta_1 =$	0.0359	0.0372	0.0377	0.0385	0.0392	0.0393	0.0412	0.0417

$b > a$ the maximum bending moment at the center of the plate does not differ much from the moment at the middle of a uniformly loaded strip of length b clamped at the ends.

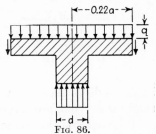

FIG. 86.

At the points of support of the plate there are concentrated reactions acting, and the moments calculated from expression (l) become infinitely large. To obtain the actual stresses in the portions of the plate near the columns, the cross-sectional dimensions of the columns should be considered. Let us begin with the case of a circular column. The calculation of the bending moments, using expression (l), shows[1] that in the case of a square panel ($a = b$) the bending moments in the radial direction practically vanish along a circle of radius $e = 0.22a$ (Fig. 85a) so that the portion of the plate around the column and inside such a

---

[1] Such calculations were made by A. Nadai; see his book "Elastische Platten," p. 155, Berlin, 1925.

circle is in the state of a simply supported plate. Hence the conditions of bending around a column are as shown in Fig. 86, and the maximum stress is readily obtained by using formulas

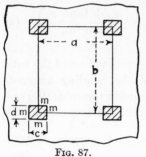

FIG. 87.

(75) previously derived for circular plates (see page 67) and combining cases 3 and 8 in Fig. 36.

The bending moments corresponding to the centers of columns of rectangular cross section can be calculated by assuming that the reactions are uniformly distributed over the rectangles, shown shaded in Fig. 87, that represent the cross sections of the columns.[1]   In the case of square panels and square columns we have $c/a = d/b = k$, and the moments at the centers of the columns and at the centers of the panels are given by the following formulas:

$$(M_x)_{x=y=\frac{a}{2}} = (M_y)_{x=y=\frac{a}{2}} = -\frac{(1+\nu)qa^2}{4}\left[\frac{(1-k)(2-k)}{12}\right.$$

$$\left. +\frac{1}{\pi^3 k^2}\sum_{m=1}^{\infty}\frac{2}{m^3 \sinh m\pi}\cdot\sinh\frac{m\pi k}{2}\cosh\frac{m\pi(2-k)}{2}\sin m\pi k\right]; \quad (o)$$

$$(M_x)_{x=y=0} = (M_y)_{x=y=0}$$

$$=\frac{(1+\nu)qa^2}{4}\left[\frac{1-k^2}{12}+\frac{1}{\pi^3 k^2}\sum_{m=1}^{\infty}(-1)^{m+1}\frac{\sinh m\pi k\sin m\pi k}{m^3\sinh m\pi}\right]. \quad (p)$$

The values of these moments, calculated for various values of k and for $\nu = 0.3$, are given in Table 33.

It is seen that the moments at the columns are much larger than the moments at the panel center and that their magnitude depends very much on the cross-sectional dimensions of the columns.   The moments at the panel center remain practically constant for ratios up to $k = 0.2$.   Hence the previous solution, obtained on the assumption that the reactions are concentrated

[1] This case was investigated by S. Woinowsky-Krieger, see *Z. angew. Math. Mech.*, vol. 14, p. 13, 1934; see also the papers by V. Lewe, *Bauingenieur*, vol. 1, p. 631, 1920; and by K. Frey, *Bauingenieur*, vol. 7, p. 21, 1926.

at the panel corners, is sufficiently accurate for the central portion of the panel.

TABLE 33.—MOMENTS AT THE CENTER AND AT THE CORNERS OF A SQUARE PANEL OF A UNIFORMLY LOADED PLATE
$\nu = 0.3$

$c/a = k$	$k =$	0	0.1	0.2	0.3	0.4	0.5
$(M)_{x=y=a/2} = \beta q a^2$	$\beta =$	$-\infty$	-0.206	-0.142	-0.101	-0.0735	-0.0528
$(M)_{x=y=0} = \beta_1 q a^2$	$\beta_1 =$	0.0359	0.0356	0.0348	0.0334	0.0313	0.0287
$Q_{\max.} = \gamma q a$	$\gamma =$	∞	2.73	....	0.842	....	0.419

The shearing forces have their maximum value at the middle of the sides of the columns, at points m in Fig. 87. This value,

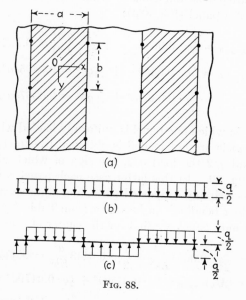

FIG. 88.

for the case of square panels, depends on the value of the ratio k and can be represented by the formula $Q = \gamma q a^2$. Several numerical values of the factor γ are given in Table 33. It is interesting to note that there is a difference of only about 10 per cent between these values and the average values obtained by dividing the total column load $q a^2 (1 - k^2)$ by the perimeter $4ka$ of the cross section of the column.

Uniform loading of the entire plate gives the most unfavorable condition at the columns.   To get the maximum bending moment at the center of a panel, the load must be distributed as shown by

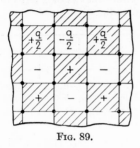

FIG. 89.

the shaded areas in Fig. 88a.   The solution for this case is readily obtained by combining the uniform load distribution of intensity $q/2$ shown in Fig. 88b with the load $q/2$ alternating in sign in consecutive spans shown in Fig. 88c.   The deflection surface for the latter case is evidently the same as that for a uniformly loaded strip of length a simply supported at the ends.[1]   Taking, as an example, the case of square panels and using the values in Table 32, we find for the center of a panel (Fig. 88a):

$$(w)_{x=y=0} = \frac{1}{2}q \cdot 0.0634\frac{a^4}{Eh^3} + \frac{5}{384}\frac{q}{2}\frac{a^4}{D} = 0.1028\frac{qa^4}{Eh^3},$$

$$(M_x)_{x=y=0} = \tfrac{1}{2}q \cdot 0.0359a^2 + \tfrac{1}{16}qa^2 = 0.0805qa^2,$$

$$(M_y)_{x=y=0} = \frac{1}{2}q \cdot 0.0359a^2 + \frac{\nu}{16}qa^2 = 0.0367qa^2.$$

The case in which one panel is uniformly loaded while the four adjacent panels are not loaded is obtained by superposing on a uniform load $q/2$ the load $q/2$, the sign of which alternates as shown in Fig. 89.   In this latter case each panel is in the same condition as a simply supported plate, and all necessary information regarding bending can be taken from Table 5.   Taking the case of a square panel, we find for the center of a panel that

$$(w)_{x=y=0} = \frac{1}{2}q \cdot 0.0634\frac{a^4}{Eh^3} + \frac{1}{2}q \cdot 0.0443\frac{a^4}{Eh^3} = 0.0539\frac{qa^4}{Eh^3},$$

$$(M_x)_{x=y=0} = (M_y)_{x=y=0} = \tfrac{1}{2}q \cdot 0.0359a^2 + \tfrac{1}{2}q \cdot 0.0479a^2 = 0.0419qa^2.$$

The case of bending of a long rectangular plate supported only by the two parallel rows of equidistant columns (Fig. 90) can also be solved without any difficulty for several types of loading.   We begin with the case in which the plate is bent by the moments M_y represented by the series

[1] It is assumed that the columns are not rigidly connected with the plate and can produce only vertical reactions.

$$(M_y)_{y=\pm\frac{b}{2}} = M_0 + \sum_{m=2,4,6,\cdots}^{\infty} E_m \cos \frac{m\pi x}{a}. \qquad (q)$$

Since there is no lateral load, the deflection surface of the plate can be taken in the form of the series

$$w = A_0 + A_1\left(y^2 - \frac{b^2}{4}\right)$$

$$+ \sum_{m=2,4,6,\cdots}^{\infty} \left(A_m \cosh \frac{m\pi y}{a} + B_m \frac{m\pi y}{a} \sinh \frac{m\pi y}{a}\right) \cos \frac{m\pi x}{a}, \qquad (r)$$

the coefficients of which are to be determined from the following boundary conditions:

$$\left.\begin{array}{r} -D\left(\dfrac{\partial^2 w}{\partial y^2} + \nu\dfrac{\partial^2 w}{\partial x^2}\right)_{y=\pm\frac{b}{2}} \\[2mm] = M_0 + \displaystyle\sum_{m=2,4,6,\cdots}^{\infty} E_m \cos \dfrac{m\pi x}{a}, \\[4mm] D\left[\dfrac{\partial^3 w}{\partial y^3} + (2-\nu)\dfrac{\partial^3 w}{\partial y\,\partial x^2}\right]_{y=\pm\frac{b}{2}} = 0, \end{array}\right\} \qquad (s)$$

and from the condition that the deflection vanishes at the columns. Substituting series (r) in Eqs. (s), we find that

$$\left.\begin{array}{l} A_1 = -\dfrac{M_0}{2D}, \\[3mm] A_m = -\dfrac{a^2 E_m}{\pi^2 m^2 D} \dfrac{(1+\nu)\sinh\alpha_m - (1-\nu)\alpha_m\cosh\alpha_m}{(3+\nu)(1-\nu)\sinh\alpha_m\cosh\alpha_m - \alpha_m(1-\nu)^2}, \\[3mm] B_m = -\dfrac{a^2 E_m}{\pi^2 m^2 D} \dfrac{\sinh\alpha_m}{(3+\nu)\sinh\alpha_m\cosh\alpha_m - \alpha_m(1-\nu)}. \end{array}\right\} \qquad (t)$$

Combining this solution with solution (l), we can investigate the bending of the plate shown in Fig. 90a under the action of a uniformly distributed load. For this purpose we calculate the bending moments M_y from expression (l) by using formula (99) and obtain

$$(M_y)_{y=\pm\frac{b}{2}} = -\frac{qb^2}{12} - \frac{qab}{2\pi} \sum_{m=2,4,6,\cdots}^{\infty} \frac{(-1)^{\frac{m}{2}}}{m} \left[\frac{1+\nu}{\tanh \alpha_m} \right.$$

$$\left. - \frac{\alpha_m(1-\nu)}{\sinh^2 \alpha_m} \right] \cos \frac{m\pi x}{a}. \quad (u)$$

Equating this moment to the moment (q) taken with the negative sign, we obtain the values of M_0 and E_m which are to be substituted in Eqs. (t) for the constants A_1, A_m and B_m in expression (r). Adding expression (r) with these values of the constants to expression (l), we obtain the desired solution for the uniformly loaded plate shown in Fig. 90a.

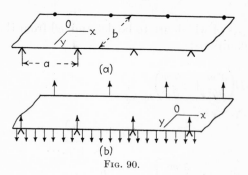

Fɪɢ. 90.

Combining this solution with that for a uniformly loaded and simply supported strip of length b which is given by the equation

$$w = -\frac{q}{24D}\left(\frac{b^2}{4} - y^2\right)\left(\frac{5}{4}b^2 - y^2\right),$$

we obtain the solution for the case in which the plate is bent by the load uniformly distributed along the edges of the plate as shown in Fig. 90b.

47. Bending of Plates on Elastic Foundation.—A laterally loaded plate may rest on an elastic foundation as in the case of a concrete road or foundation slab which is supported by the reactions of the subgrade. A plate resting on an elastic foundation may also be supported along its boundary. An example of this is shown in Fig. 91 where a beam of rectangular tubular cross section is pressed into an elastic foundation by the loads P. The bottom plate of the beam, loaded by the elastic reactions of the foundation, is supported by the vertical sides of the tube and by the vertical transverse diaphragms indicated in the figure by dotted lines. It is usually assumed in discussing bending of plates of this kind that the intensity of the reaction of the elastic foundation at any point is proportional to the deflection w at that point.[1] With this simplifying assumption the differential equation for the deflection of a plate on an elastic foundation becomes

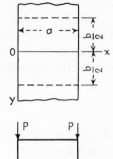

$$\frac{\partial^4 w}{\partial x^4} + 2\frac{\partial^4 w}{\partial x^2\,\partial y^2} + \frac{\partial^4 w}{\partial y^4} = \frac{q}{D} - \frac{kw}{D}, \qquad (a)$$

where q, as before, is the intensity of the lateral load, and kw is the reaction of the foundation, k being expressed usually in pounds per square inch per inch of deflection. Sometimes this quantity is called the *modulus of the foundation*.

Let us begin with the case shown in Fig. 91. If w_0 denotes the deflection of the edges of the bottom plate, and w the

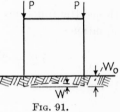

Fig. 91.

deflection of this plate with respect to the plane of its boundary, the intensity of the reaction of the foundation at any point is $k(w_0 - w)$, and Eq. (a) becomes

$$\Delta\Delta w = \frac{k}{D}(w_0 - w). \qquad (b)$$

Taking the coordinate axes as shown in the figure and assuming that the edges of the plate parallel to the y-axis are simply supported and the other two edges are clamped, the boundary conditions are

$$(w)_{x=0,x=a} = 0, \qquad \left(\frac{\partial^2 w}{\partial x^2}\right)_{x=0,x=a} = 0, \qquad (c)$$

$$(w)_{y=\pm\frac{b}{2}} = 0, \qquad \left(\frac{\partial w}{\partial y}\right)_{y=\pm\frac{b}{2}} = 0. \qquad (d)$$

[1] An example of a more rigorous treatment of the problem in which the foundation is considered as a semi-infinite elastic body and the general equations of elasticity are used to determine the reactions is given in a recent paper by A. H. A. Hogg, *Phil. Mag.*, vol. 25, p. 576, 1938.

The deflection w can be taken in the form of a series:

$$w = \frac{4kw_0}{D\pi} \sum_{m=1,3,5,\cdots}^{\infty} \frac{\sin \dfrac{m\pi x}{a}}{m\left(\dfrac{m^4\pi^4}{a^4} + \dfrac{k}{D}\right)} + \sum_{m=1,3,5,\cdots}^{\infty} Y_m \sin \frac{m\pi x}{a}. \qquad (e)$$

The first series on the right side is a particular solution of Eq. (b) representing the deflection of a simply supported strip resting on an elastic foundation. The second series is the solution of the homogeneous equation

$$\Delta\Delta w + \frac{k}{D}w = 0. \qquad (f)$$

Hence the functions Y_m have to satisfy the ordinary differential equation

$$Y_m^{IV} - 2\frac{m^2\pi^2}{a^2}Y_m'' + \left(\frac{m^4\pi^4}{a^4} + \frac{k}{D}\right)Y_m = 0. \qquad (g)$$

Using notations

$$\frac{m\pi}{a} = \mu_m, \qquad \frac{k}{D} = \lambda^4, \qquad (h)$$

$$2\beta_m^2 = \sqrt{\mu_m^4 + \lambda^4} + \mu_m^2, \qquad 2\gamma_m^2 = \sqrt{\mu_m^4 + \lambda^4} - \mu_m^2 \qquad (i)$$

and taking the solution of Eq. (g) in the form e^{ry}, we obtain for r the following four roots:

$$r = \beta + i\gamma, \qquad -\beta + i\gamma, \qquad \beta - i\gamma, \qquad -\beta - i\gamma.$$

The corresponding four independent particular solutions of Eq. (g) are

$$e^{\beta_m y} \cos \gamma_m y, \qquad e^{-\beta_m y} \cos \gamma_m y, \qquad e^{\beta_m y} \sin \gamma_m y, \qquad e^{-\beta_m y} \sin \gamma_m y, \qquad (j)$$

which can be taken also in the following form:

$$\cosh \beta_m y \cos \gamma_m y, \qquad \sinh \beta_m y \cos \gamma_m y, \qquad \cosh \beta_m y \sin \gamma_m y,$$
$$\sinh \beta_m y \sin \gamma_m y. \qquad (k)$$

From symmetry it can be concluded that Y_m in our case is an even function of y. Hence, by using integrals (k), we obtain

$$Y_m = A_m \cosh \beta_m y \cos \gamma_m y + B_m \sinh \beta_m y \sin \gamma_m y,$$

and the deflection of the plate is

$$
w = \sum_{m=1,3,5,\cdots}^{c} \sin \frac{m\pi x}{a} \left[\frac{4kw_0}{D\pi} \frac{1}{m\left(\dfrac{m^4\pi^4}{a^4} + \dfrac{k}{D}\right)} \right.
$$
$$
\left. + A_m \cosh \beta_m y \cos \gamma_m y + B_m \sinh \beta_m y \sin \gamma_m y \right]. \quad (l)
$$

This expression satisfies the boundary conditions (c). To satisfy the conditions (d) we must choose the constants A_m and B_m so as to satisfy the equations

$$
\left.
\begin{aligned}
\frac{4kw_0}{D\pi} \frac{1}{m\left(\dfrac{m^4\pi^4}{a^4} + \dfrac{k}{D}\right)} &+ A_m \cosh \frac{\beta_m b}{2} \cos \frac{\gamma_m b}{2} \\
&+ B_m \sinh \frac{\beta_m b}{2} \sin \frac{\gamma_m b}{2} = 0, \\
(A_m\beta_m + B_m\gamma_m) \sinh \frac{\beta_m b}{2} &\cos \frac{\gamma_m b}{2} \\
&- (A_m\gamma_m - B_m\beta_m) \cosh \frac{\beta_m b}{2} \sin \frac{\gamma_m b}{2} = 0.
\end{aligned}
\right\} \quad (m)
$$

Substituting these values of A_m and B_m in expression (l), we obtain the required deflection of the plate.

The problem of the plate with all four edges simply supported can be solved in a similar manner. The Navier solution can be used in this case also. Taking the coordinate axes as shown in Fig. 59 (page 113), the deflection of the plate is

$$
w = \sum_{m=1}^{\infty}\sum_{n=1}^{\infty} A_{mn} \sin \frac{m\pi x}{a} \sin \frac{n\pi y}{a}. \quad (n)
$$

As an example, let us consider the deflection of the plate by a force P concentrated at a point (ξ, η). Using the energy method (see Art. 28), the strain energy of bending of the plate from Eq. (124) is found to be

$$
V = \frac{\pi^4 ab}{8} D \sum_{m=1}^{\infty}\sum_{n=1}^{\infty} A_{mn}^2 \left(\frac{m^2}{a^2} + \frac{n^2}{b^2}\right)^2. \quad (o)
$$

The strain energy of the elastic foundation is

$$
V_1 = \int_0^a \int_0^b \frac{kw^2}{2} dx\, dy = \frac{kab}{8} A_{mn}^2. \quad (p)
$$

We use the principle of virtual displacements to determine the coefficients A_{mn} from which it follows that

$$P\delta A_{mn} \sin \frac{m\pi\xi}{a} \sin \frac{n\pi\eta}{b} = \frac{\partial}{\partial A_{mn}}(V + V_1)\partial A_{mn}$$

$$= \left[\frac{\pi^4 abD}{4}\left(\frac{m^2}{a^2} + \frac{n^2}{b^2}\right)^2 + \frac{kab}{4}\right]A_{mn} \; \delta A_{mn}.$$

Hence,

$$A_{mn} = \frac{4P \sin \dfrac{m\pi\xi}{a} \sin \dfrac{n\pi\eta}{b}}{ab\left[\pi^4 D\left(\dfrac{m^2}{a^2} + \dfrac{n^2}{b^2}\right)^2 + k\right]}.$$

Substituting these values of the coefficients in series (n), we obtain the deflection

$$w = \frac{4P}{ab}\sum_{m=1}^{\infty}\sum_{n=1}^{\infty} \frac{\sin \dfrac{m\pi\xi}{a} \sin \dfrac{n\pi\eta}{b}}{\pi^4 D\left(\dfrac{m^2}{a^2} + \dfrac{n^2}{b^2}\right)^2 + k} \cdot \sin \frac{m\pi x}{a} \sin \frac{n\pi y}{b}. \quad (q)$$

Having the deflection of the plate produced by a concentrated force, the deflection produced by any kind of lateral loading is obtained by the method of superposition. Take, as an example, the case of a uniformly distributed load of the intensity q. Substituting $qd\xi d\eta$ for P in expression (q) and integrating between the limits 0 and a and between 0 and b, we obtain

$$w = \frac{16q}{\pi^2}\sum_{m=1,3,5,\cdots}^{\infty}\sum_{n=1,3,5,\cdots}^{\infty} \frac{\sin \dfrac{m\pi x}{a} \sin \dfrac{n\pi y}{b}}{mn\left[\pi^4 D\left(\dfrac{m^2}{a^2} + \dfrac{n^2}{b^2}\right)^2 + k\right]}. \quad (r)$$

When k is equal to zero, this deflection reduces to that given in Navier solution (122) for the deflection of a uniformly loaded plate.

Let us consider now the case represented in Fig. 92. A large plate which rests on an elastic foundation is loaded at equidistant points along the x-axis by forces P.[1]   We shall take the coordinate

[1] This problem has been discussed by H. M. Westergaard; see *Ingeniøren*, vol. 32, p. 513, 1923.   Practical applications of the solution of this problem in concrete road design are discussed by H. M. Westergaard in the journal *Public Roads*, vol. 7, p. 25, 1926; vol. 10, p. 65, 1929; and vol. 14, p. 185, 1933.

axes as shown in the figure and use Eq. (*f*), since there is no distributed lateral load. Let us consider a solution of this equation in the form of the series

$$w = w_0 + \sum_{m=2,4,6,\,\cdots}^{\infty} Y_m \cos \frac{m\pi x}{a}, \qquad (s)$$

in which the first term

$$w_0 = \frac{P\lambda}{2\sqrt{2}\,ak} e^{\frac{-\lambda y}{\sqrt{2}}}\!\left(\cos \frac{\lambda y}{\sqrt{2}} + \sin \frac{\lambda y}{\sqrt{2}}\right) \qquad (t)$$

represents the deflection of an infinitely long strip of unit width parallel to the *y*-axis loaded at $y = 0$ by a load P/a.[1] The other terms of the series satisfy the requirement of symmetry that the

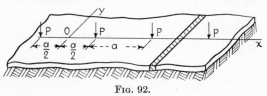

Fig. 92.

tangent to the deflection surface in the *x*-direction shall have a slope of zero at the loaded points and at the points midway between the loads. We take for functions Y_m the particular integrals (*j*) which vanish for infinite values of *y*. Hence,

$$Y_m = A_m e^{-\beta_m y} \cos \gamma_m y + B_m e^{-\beta_m y} \sin \gamma_m y.$$

To satisfy the symmetry condition $\left(\dfrac{\partial w}{\partial y}\right)_{y=0} = 0$ we must take in this expression

$$B_m = \frac{\beta_m A_m}{\gamma_m}.$$

Hence, by introducing the new constants $A'_m = A_m/\gamma_m$, we represent the deflections (*s*) in the following form:

$$w = w_0 + \sum_{m=2,4,6,\,\cdots}^{\infty} A'_m \cos \frac{m\pi x}{a} e^{-\beta_m y}(\gamma_m \cos \gamma_m y$$
$$+ \beta_m \sin \gamma_m y). \quad (u)$$

[1] See Eq. 237, p. 396.

In order to express the constants A'_m in terms of the magnitude of the loads P, we consider the shearing force Q_y acting along the normal section of the plate through the x-axis. From symmetry we conclude that this force vanishes at all points except the points of application of the loads P at which points the shearing forces must give resultants equal to $-P/2$. It was shown in the discussion of a similar distribution of shearing forces in the previous article (see page 241) that the shear forces can be represented by the series

$$Q_y = -\frac{P}{2a} - \frac{P}{a} \sum_{m=2,4,6,\cdots}^{\infty} (-1)^{\frac{m}{2}} \cos \frac{m\pi x}{a}.$$

The shearing force, as calculated from expression (u), is

$$Q_y = -D\frac{\partial}{\partial y}\left(\frac{\partial^2 w}{\partial x^2} + \frac{\partial^2 w}{\partial y^2}\right)_{y=0}$$

$$= -\frac{P}{2a} - 2D \sum_{m=2,4,6,\cdots}^{\infty} A'_m \beta_m \gamma_m (\beta_m^2 + \gamma_m^2) \cos \frac{m\pi x}{a}.$$

Comparing these two expressions for the shearing force, we find

$$A'_m = \frac{P(-1)^{\frac{m}{2}}}{2aD\beta_m\gamma_m(\beta_m^2 + \gamma_m^2)},$$

or, by using notations (i),

$$A'_m = \frac{P(-1)^{\frac{m}{2}}}{aD\lambda\sqrt{\lambda_m^4 + \mu_m^4}}.$$

Substituting this in expression (u), we finally obtain

$$w = w_0 + \frac{P\lambda^2}{ak} \sum_{m=2,4,6,\cdots}^{\infty} \frac{(-1)^{\frac{m}{2}}}{\sqrt{\lambda^4 + \mu_m^4}} \cos \frac{m\pi x}{a} e^{-\beta_m y}(\gamma_m \cos \gamma_m y$$

$$+ \beta_m \sin \gamma_m y). \quad (v)$$

The maximum deflection is evidently under the loads P and is obtained by substituting $x = a/2$, $y = 0$ in expression (v), which gives

$$w_{\text{max.}} = \frac{P\lambda}{2\sqrt{2}\,ak} + \frac{P\lambda^2}{ak} \sum_{m=2,4,6,\cdots}^{\infty} \frac{\gamma_m}{\sqrt{\lambda^4 + \mu_m^4}}. \qquad (156)$$

The deflection in the particular case of one isolated load P acting on an infinitely large plate[1] can also be obtained by setting $a = \infty$, in formula (156). In such a case the first term in the formula vanishes, and by using notations (i) we obtain

$$w_{\text{max.}} = \frac{P\lambda^2}{2\sqrt{2}\,\pi k} \sum_{m=2,4,6,\cdots}^{\infty} \frac{2\pi}{a} \sqrt{\frac{\sqrt{\lambda^4 + \mu_m^4} - \mu_m^2}{\lambda^4 + \mu_m^4}}$$

$$= \frac{P\lambda^2}{2\sqrt{2}\,\pi k} \int_0^\infty \sqrt{\frac{\sqrt{\lambda^4 + \mu^4} - \mu^2}{\lambda^4 + \mu^4}} \cdot d\mu.$$

Using the substitution

$$\frac{\mu^2}{\lambda^2} = \frac{1}{2u\sqrt{u^2 + 1}},$$

we find

$$w_{\text{max.}} = \frac{P\lambda^2}{2\sqrt{2}\,\pi k} \int_0^\infty \frac{1}{\sqrt{2}} \cdot \frac{du}{1 + u^2} = \frac{P\lambda^2}{8k}. \qquad (157)$$

With this magnitude of the deflection, the maximum pressure on the elastic foundation is

$$(p)_{\text{max.}} = kw_{\text{max.}} = \frac{P\lambda^2}{8} = \frac{P}{8}\sqrt{\frac{k}{D}}. \qquad (158)$$

The maximum tensile stress is at the bottom of the plate under the point of application of the load. The theory developed above gives an infinite value for the bending moment at this point, and recourse should be made to the theory of thick plates (see Art. 25). In the above-mentioned investigation by Westergaard the following formula for calculating maximum tensile stress at the bottom of the plate is established by using the thick-plate theory:

$$(\sigma_r)_{\text{max.}} = 0.275(1 + \nu)\frac{P}{h^2} \log_{10}\left(\frac{Eh^3}{kb^4}\right). \qquad (w)$$

Here h denotes the thickness of the plate, and

---

[1] This case was considered by H. Herz, *Wiedemann's Annalen der Physik und Chemie*, vol. 22, p. 449, 1884; see also his "Gesammelte Werke," vol. 1, p. 288, 1895.

$$b = \sqrt{1.6c^2 + h^2} - 0.675h, \quad \text{when} \quad c < 1.724h,$$
$$b = c, \quad \text{when} \quad c > 1.724h,$$

where c is the radius of the circle over the area of which the load P is assumed to be uniformly distributed. For $c = 0$ the case of the concentrated force is obtained.

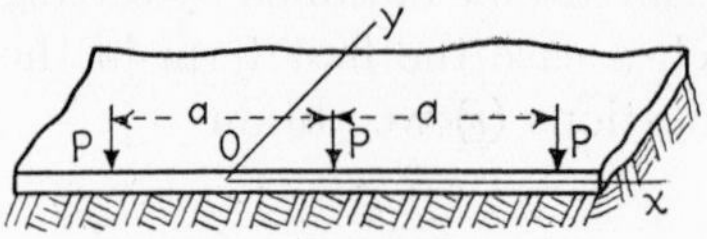

FIG. 93.

The case of equidistant loads P applied along the edge of a semi-infinite plate, as shown in Fig. 93, can also be treated in a similar way. The final formula for the maximum tensile stress at the bottom of the plate under the load when the distance a is large is

$$(\sigma_x)_{\text{max.}} = 0.529(1 + 0.54\nu)\frac{P}{h^2}\left[\log_{10}\left(\frac{Eh^3}{kb^4}\right) - 0.71\right], \quad (x)$$

where b is calculated as in the previous case, and c is the radius of the semicircle over the area of which the load P is assumed to be uniformly distributed. Formulas (w) and (x) have proved very useful in the design of concrete roads, in which case the circle of radius c represents the area of contact of the wheel tire with the road surface.

The case of a rectangular plate of finite dimensions resting on an elastic foundation and submitted to the action of a concentrated load has been discussed by H. Happel.[1] The Ritz method (see page 124) was used to determine the deflections of this plate, and it was shown in the particular example of a centrally loaded square plate that the series representing the deflection converges rapidly and that the deflection can be calculated with sufficient accuracy by taking only the few first terms of the series.[2] The case of an infinite plate supported by an elastic foundation and loaded by equidistant equal loads was discussed by V. Lewe.[3]

[1] HAPPEL, H., *Math. Z.*, vol. 6, p. 203, 1920.

[2] The problem of a square plate on an elastic foundation has also been investigated experimentally; see the paper by J. Vint and W. N. Elgood, *Phil. Mag.*, 7th Ser., vol. 19, p. 1, 1935; and that by G. Murphy, *Bull. Iowa Eng. Exper. Sta.* 135, 1937.

[3] LEWE, V., *Bauingenieur*, vol. 3, p. 453, 1923.

CHAPTER VII

PLATES OF VARIOUS SHAPES

48. Equations of Bending of Plates in Polar Coordinates.—
In the discussion of symmetrical bending of circular plates polar
coordinates were used (Chap. III). The same coordinates can
also be used to advantage in the general case of bending of circular plates.

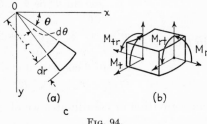

Fig. 94.

If the r and θ coordinates are taken, as shown in Fig. 94a,
the relation between the polar and Cartesian coordinates is
given by the equations

$$r^2 = x^2 + y^2, \qquad \theta = \text{arc tan } y/x, \qquad (a)$$

from which it follows that

$$\left.\begin{aligned}
\frac{\partial r}{\partial x} &= \frac{x}{r} = \cos\theta, & \frac{\partial r}{\partial y} &= \frac{y}{r} = \sin\theta, \\
\frac{\partial \theta}{\partial x} &= -\frac{y}{r^2} = -\frac{\sin\theta}{r}, & \frac{\partial \theta}{\partial y} &= \frac{x}{r^2} = \frac{\cos\theta}{r}.
\end{aligned}\right\} \qquad (b)$$

Using these expressions, we obtain the slope of the deflection
surface of a plate in the x-direction as

$$\frac{\partial w}{\partial x} = \frac{\partial w}{\partial r}\frac{\partial r}{\partial x} + \frac{\partial w}{\partial \theta}\frac{\partial \theta}{\partial x} = \frac{\partial w}{\partial r}\cos\theta - \frac{1}{r}\frac{\partial w}{\partial \theta}\sin\theta. \qquad (c)$$

A similar expression can be written for the slope in the y-direction.
To obtain the expression for curvature in polar coordinates the

257

second derivatives are required. Repeating twice the operation indicated in expression (c), we find

$$
\frac{\partial^2 w}{\partial x^2} = \left(\frac{\partial}{\partial r} \cos \theta - \frac{1}{r} \sin \theta \frac{\partial}{\partial \theta} \right) \left(\frac{\partial w}{\partial r} \cos \theta - \frac{1}{r} \frac{\partial w}{\partial \theta} \sin \theta \right)
$$

$$
= \frac{\partial^2 w}{\partial r^2} \cos^2 \theta - 2 \frac{\partial^2 w}{\partial \theta \, \partial r} \frac{\sin \theta \cos \theta}{r} + \frac{\partial w}{\partial r} \frac{\sin^2 \theta}{r}
$$

$$
+ 2 \frac{\partial w}{\partial \theta} \frac{\sin \theta \cos \theta}{r^2} + \frac{\partial^2 w}{\partial \theta^2} \frac{\sin^2 \theta}{r^2}. \quad (d)
$$

In a similar manner we obtain

$$
\frac{\partial^2 w}{\partial y^2} = \frac{\partial^2 w}{\partial r^2} \sin^2 \theta + 2 \frac{\partial^2 w}{\partial \theta \, \partial r} \frac{\sin \theta \cos \theta}{r} + \frac{\partial w}{\partial r} \frac{\cos^2 \theta}{r}
$$

$$
- 2 \frac{\partial w}{\partial \theta} \frac{\sin \theta \cos \theta}{r^2} + \frac{\partial^2 w}{\partial \theta^2} \frac{\cos^2 \theta}{r^2}, \quad (e)
$$

$$
\frac{\partial^2 w}{\partial x \, \partial y} = \frac{\partial^2 w}{\partial r^2} \sin \theta \cos \theta + \frac{\partial^2 w}{\partial r \, \partial \theta} \frac{\cos 2\theta}{r} - \frac{\partial w}{\partial \theta} \frac{\cos 2\theta}{r^2}
$$

$$
- \frac{\partial w}{\partial r} \frac{\sin \theta \cos \theta}{r} - \frac{\partial^2 w}{\partial \theta^2} \frac{\sin \theta \cos \theta}{r^2}. \quad (f)
$$

With this transformation of coordinates we obtain

$$
\Delta w = \frac{\partial^2 w}{\partial x^2} + \frac{\partial^2 w}{\partial y^2} = \frac{\partial^2 w}{\partial r^2} + \frac{1}{r} \frac{\partial w}{\partial r} + \frac{1}{r^2} \frac{\partial^2 w}{\partial \theta^2}. \quad (g)
$$

Repeating this operation twice, the differential equation (101) for the deflection surface of a laterally loaded plate transforms in polar coordinates to the following form:

$$
\Delta \Delta w = \left(\frac{\partial^2}{\partial r^2} + \frac{1}{r} \frac{\partial}{\partial r} + \frac{1}{r^2} \frac{\partial^2}{\partial \theta^2} \right) \left(\frac{\partial^2 w}{\partial r^2} + \frac{1}{r} \frac{\partial w}{\partial r} \right.
$$

$$
\left. + \frac{1}{r^2} \frac{\partial^2 w}{\partial \theta^2} \right) = \frac{q}{D}. \quad (159)
$$

When the load is symmetrically distributed with respect to the center of the plate, the deflection w is independent of θ, and Eq. (159) coincides with Eq. (58) (see page 58) which was obtained in the case of symmetrically loaded circular plates.

Let us consider an element cut out of the plate by two adjacent axial planes forming an angle $d\theta$ and by two cylindrical surfaces of radii r and $r + dr$, respectively (Fig. 94b). We denote the bending and twisting moments acting on the element per unit length by M_r, M_t and M_{rt} and take their positive directions as shown in the figure. To express these moments by the deflection w of the plate we assume that the x-axis coincides with the radius r. The moments M_r, M_t and M_{rt} then have the same values as the moments M_x, M_y and M_{xy} at the same point, and by substituting $\theta = 0$ in expressions (d), (e) and (f) we obtain

$$\left.\begin{aligned}
M_r &= -D\left(\frac{\partial^2 w}{\partial x^2} + \nu\frac{\partial^2 w}{\partial y^2}\right)_{\theta=0} \\
&= -D\left[\frac{\partial^2 w}{\partial r^2} + \nu\left(\frac{1}{r}\frac{\partial w}{\partial r} + \frac{1}{r^2}\frac{\partial^2 w}{\partial \theta^2}\right)\right], \\
M_t &= -D\left(\frac{\partial^2 w}{\partial y^2} + \nu\frac{\partial^2 w}{\partial x^2}\right)_{\theta=0} \\
&= -D\left(\frac{1}{r}\frac{\partial w}{\partial r} + \frac{1}{r^2}\frac{\partial^2 w}{\partial \theta^2} + \nu\frac{\partial^2 w}{\partial r^2}\right), \\
M_{rt} &= (1 - \nu)D\left(\frac{\partial^2 w}{\partial x\,\partial y}\right)_{\theta=0} \\
&= (1 - \nu)D\left(\frac{1}{r}\frac{\partial^2 w}{\partial r\,\partial \theta} - \frac{1}{r^2}\frac{\partial w}{\partial \theta}\right).
\end{aligned}\right\} \quad (160)$$

In a similar manner, from formulas (102) and (103), we obtain the expressions for the shearing forces

$$Q_r = -D\frac{\partial}{\partial r}(\Delta w) \quad \text{and} \quad Q_t = -D\frac{\partial(\Delta w)}{r\,\partial \theta}, \quad (161)$$

where Δw is given by expression (g).

In the case of a clamped edge the boundary conditions of a circular plate of radius a are

$$(w)_{r=a} = 0, \qquad \left(\frac{\partial w}{\partial r}\right)_{r=a} = 0. \qquad (h)$$

In the case of a simply supported edge

$$(w)_{r=a} = 0, \qquad (M_r)_{r=a} = 0. \qquad (i)$$

In the case of a free edge (see page 94)

$$(M_r)_{r=a} = 0, \qquad V = \left(Q_r - \frac{\partial M_{rt}}{r\,\partial \theta}\right)_{r=a} = 0. \qquad (j)$$

The general solution of Eq. (159) can be taken, as before, in the form of a sum

$$w = w_0 + w_1, \qquad (k)$$

in which w_0 is a particular solution of Eq. (159) and w_1 is the solution of the homogeneous equation

$$\left(\frac{\partial^2}{\partial r^2} + \frac{1}{r}\frac{\partial}{\partial r} + \frac{1}{r^2}\frac{\partial^2}{\partial \theta^2}\right)\left(\frac{\partial^2 w_1}{\partial r^2} + \frac{1}{r}\frac{\partial w_1}{\partial r} + \frac{1}{r^2}\frac{\partial^2 w_1}{\partial \theta^2}\right) = 0. \quad (162)$$

This latter solution we take in the form of the following series:[1]

$$w_1 = R_0 + \sum_{m=1}^{\infty} R_m \cos m\theta + \sum_{m=1}^{\infty} R'_m \sin m\theta, \quad (163)$$

in which R_0, R_1, . . . , R'_1, R'_2, . . . are functions of the radial distance r only. Substituting this series in Eq. (162), we obtain for each of these functions an ordinary differential equation of the following kind:

$$\left(\frac{d^2}{dr^2} + \frac{1}{r}\frac{d}{dr} - \frac{m^2}{r^2}\right)\left(\frac{d^2 R_m}{dr^2} + \frac{1}{r}\frac{dR_m}{dr} - \frac{m^2 R_m}{r^2}\right) = 0.$$

The general solution of this equation for $m > 1$ is

$$R_m = A_m r^m + B_m r^{-m} + C_m r^{m+2} + D_m r^{-m+2}. \quad (l)$$

For $m = 0$ and $m = 1$ the solutions are

and
$$\left.\begin{array}{l} R_0 = A_0 + B_0 r^2 + C_0 \log r + D_0 r^2 \log r \\[2mm] R_1 = A_1 r + B_1 r^3 + C_1 r^{-1} + D_1 r \log r. \end{array}\right\} \quad (m)$$

Similar expressions can be written for the functions R'_m. Substituting these expressions for the functions R_m and R'_m in series (163), we obtain the general solution of Eq. (162). The constants A_m, B_m, . . . , D_m in each particular case must be determined so as to satisfy the boundary conditions. The solution R_0, which is independent of the angle θ, represents symmetrical bending of circular plates. Several particular cases of this kind have already been discussed in Chap. III.

49. Circular Plates under a Linearly Varying Load.—If a circular plate is acted upon by a load distributed as shown in Fig. 95, this load can always be divided into two parts: (1) a uniformly distributed load of intensity $\frac{1}{2}(p_2 + p_1)$ and (2) a linearly varying load having zero intensity along the diameter

---

[1] This solution was given by A. Clebsch in his "Theorie der Elasticität fester Körper," 1862.

CD of the plate and the intensities $-p$ and $+p$ at the ends A and B of the diameter AB. The case of uniform load has already been discussed in Chap. III. We have to consider here only the non-uniform load represented in the figure by the two shaded triangles.[1]

The intensity of the load q at any point with coordinates r and θ is

$$q = \frac{pr \cos \theta}{a}. \qquad (a)$$

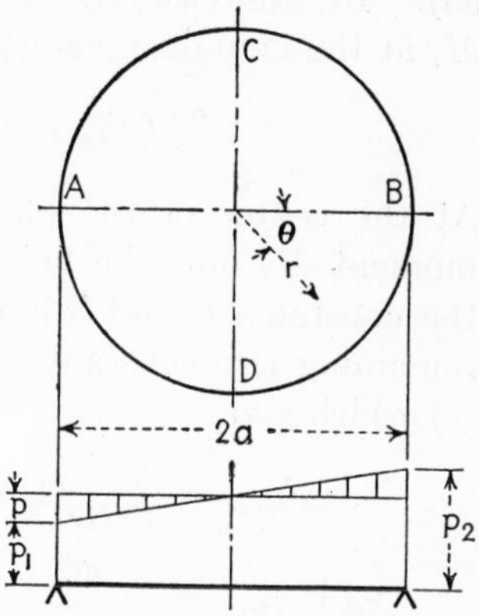

The particular solution of Eq. (159) can thus be taken in the following form:

$$w_0 = A\frac{pr^5 \cos \theta}{a}.$$

This, after substitution in Eq. (159), gives

$$A = \frac{1}{192D}.$$

Fig. 95.

Hence,

$$w_0 = \frac{pr^5 \cos \theta}{192aD}. \qquad (b)$$

As the solution of the homogeneous equation (162) we take only the term of series (163) that contains the function R_1 and assume

$$w_1 = (A_1r + B_1r^3 + C_1r^{-1} + D_1r \log r) \cos \theta. \qquad (c)$$

Since it is advantageous to work with dimensionless quantities, we introduce, in place of r, the ratio

$$\rho = \frac{r}{a}.$$

With this new notation the deflection of the plate becomes

$$w = w_0 + w_1 = \frac{pa^4}{192D}(\rho^5 + A\rho + B\rho^3 + C\rho^{-1}$$

$$+ D\rho \log \rho) \cos \theta, \qquad (d)$$

---

[1] This problem has been discussed by W. Flügge, *Bauingenieur*, vol. 10, p. 221, 1929.

where ρ varies from zero to unity.   The constants A, B, . . . in this expression must now be determined from the boundary conditions.

Let us begin with the case of a simply supported plate (Fig. 95).   In this case the deflection w and the bending moment M_r at the boundary vanish, and we obtain

$$(w)_{\rho=1} = 0, \qquad (M_r)_{\rho=1} = 0. \qquad (e)$$

At the center of the plate ($\rho = 0$) the deflection w and the moment M_r must be finite.   From this it follows at once that the constants C and D in expression (d) are equal to zero.   The remaining two constants A and B will now be found from Eqs. (e) which give

$$(w)_{\rho=1} = \frac{pa^4}{192D}(1 + A + B) \cos \theta = 0,$$

$$(M_r)_{\rho=1} = -\frac{pa^2}{192}[4(5 + \nu) + 2(3 + \nu)B] \cos \theta = 0.$$

Since these equations must be fulfilled for any value of θ, the factors before $\cos \theta$ must vanish.   This gives

$$1 + A + B = 0,$$
$$4(5 + \nu) + 2(3 + \nu)B = 0,$$

and we obtain

$$B = -\frac{2(5 + \nu)}{3 + \nu}, \qquad A = \frac{7 + \nu}{3 + \nu}.$$

Substituting these values in expression (d), we obtain the deflection w of the plate in the following form:

$$w = \frac{pa^4\rho(1 - \rho^2)}{192(3 + \nu)D}[7 + \nu - (3 + \nu)\rho^2] \cos \theta. \qquad (f)$$

For calculating the bending moments and the shearing forces we substitute expression (f) in Eqs. (160) and (161), from which

$$M_r = \frac{pa^2}{48}(5 + \nu)\rho(1 - \rho^2) \cos \theta,$$

$$\left. M_t = \frac{pa^2}{48(3 + \nu)}\rho[(5 + \nu)(1 + 3\nu) \right.$$
$$\left. - (1 + 5\nu)(3 + \nu)\rho^2] \cos \theta, \right\} \qquad (g)$$

$$Q_r = \frac{pa}{24(3 + \nu)}[2(5 + \nu) - 9(3 + \nu)\rho^2] \cos\theta,$$

$$Q_t = -\frac{pa}{24(3 + \nu)}\rho[2(5 + \nu) - 3(3 + \nu)\rho^2] \sin\theta.$$

$\qquad(h)$

It is seen that $(M_r)_{\text{max.}}$ occurs at $\rho = 1/\sqrt{3}$ and is equal to

$$(M_r)_{\text{max.}} = \frac{pa^2(5 + \nu)}{72\sqrt{3}}.$$

The maximum value of M_t occurs at

$$\rho = \sqrt{(5 + \nu)(1 + 3\nu)}/\sqrt{3(1 + 5\nu)(3 + \nu)}$$

and is equal to

$$(M_t)_{\text{max.}} = \frac{pa^2}{72} \cdot \frac{(5 + \nu)(1 + 3\nu)}{3 + \nu}.$$

The value of the intensity of the vertical reaction at the boundary is[1]

$$-V = -Q_r + \frac{\partial M_{rt}}{r \, \partial\theta} = \frac{pa}{4} \cos\theta.$$

The moment of this reaction with respect to the diameter CD of the plate (Fig. 95) is

$$4 \int_0^{\frac{\pi}{2}} \frac{pa}{4} \cos\theta \; a^2 \cos\theta \, d\theta = \frac{\pi a^3 p}{4}.$$

This moment balances the moment of the load distributed over the plate with respect to the same diameter.

As a second example let us consider the case of a circular plate with a free boundary. Such a condition is encountered in the case of a circular foundation slab supporting a chimney. As the result of wind pressure, a moment M will be transmitted to the slab (Fig. 96). Assuming that the reactions corresponding to this moment are distributed following a linear law as shown in the figure, we obtain the same kind of loading as in the previous case; and the general solution can be taken in the same form (d)

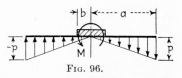

Fig. 96.

---

[1] The reaction in the upward direction is taken positive.

as before. The boundary conditions at the outer boundary of the plate, which is free from forces, are

$$(M_r)_{\rho=1} = 0, \qquad (V)_{\rho=1} = \left(Q_r - \frac{\partial M_{rt}}{r\,\partial\theta}\right)_{\rho=1} = 0. \qquad (i)$$

The inner portion of the plate of radius b is considered absolutely rigid. It is also assumed that the edge of the plate is clamped along the circle of radius b. Hence for $\rho = b/a = \beta$ the following boundary condition must be satisfied:

$$\left(\frac{\partial w}{\partial \rho}\right)_{\rho=\beta} = \left(\frac{w}{\rho}\right)_{\rho=\beta}. \qquad (j)$$

Substituting expression (d) in Eqs. (i) and (j), we obtain the following equations for the determination of the constants:

$$4(5 + \nu) + 2(3 + \nu)B + 2(1 - \nu)C + (1 + \nu)D = 0,$$
$$4(17 + \nu) + 2(3 + \nu)B + 2(1 - \nu)C - (3 - \nu)D = 0,$$
$$4\beta^4 + 2\beta^2 B - 2\beta^{-2}C + D = 0.$$

From these equations

$$B = -2\frac{4(2 + \nu) + (1 - \nu)\beta^2(3 + \beta^4)}{(3 + \nu) + (1 - \nu)\beta^4},$$
$$C = -2\frac{4(2 + \nu)\beta^4 - (3 + \nu)\beta^2(3 + \beta^4)}{(3 + \nu) + (1 - \nu)\beta^4}, \qquad D = 12.$$

Substituting these values in expression (d) and using Eqs. (160)

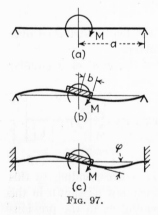

(a)

(b)

(c)

Fig. 97.

and (161), we can obtain the values of the moments and of the shearing forces. The constant A does not appear in these equations. The corresponding term in expression (d) represents the rotation of the plate as a rigid body with respect to the diameter perpendicular to the plane of Fig. 96. Provided the modulus of the foundation is known, the angle of rotation can be calculated from the condition of equilibrium of the given moment M and the reactions of the foundation.

Using expression (d), the case of a simply supported circular plate loaded by a moment M at the center (Fig. 97a) can be readily solved. In this case we have to omit the term containing ρ^5 which represents the distributed load. The constant C must be taken equal to zero to eliminate an infinitely large deflection at the center. Expression (d) thus reduces to

$$w = (A\rho + B\rho^3 + D\rho \log \rho) \cos \theta. \qquad (k)$$

The three constants A, B and D will now be determined from the following boundary conditions:

$$(w)_{\rho=1} = 0, \qquad (M_r)_{\rho=1} = 0,$$
$$-a\int_{-\pi}^{+\pi} (M_{rt})_{\rho=1} \sin \theta \, d\theta + a^2 \int_{-\pi}^{+\pi} (Q_r)_{\rho=1} \cos \theta \, d\theta + M = 0. \Bigg\} \quad (l)$$

The first two of these equations represent the conditions at a simply supported edge; the last states the condition of equilibrium of the forces and moments acting at the boundary of the plate and the external moment M. From Eqs. (l) we obtain

$$A = -\frac{1+\nu}{3+\nu}\frac{Ma}{8\pi D}, \qquad B = \frac{1+\nu}{3+\nu}\frac{Ma}{8\pi D}, \qquad D = -\frac{Ma}{4\pi D}.$$

Hence,

$$w = -\frac{Ma}{8\pi D(3+\nu)}\rho[(1+\nu)(1-\rho^2) + 2(3+\nu) \log \rho] \cos \theta. \quad (m)$$

Because of the presence of the logarithmic term in the brackets, the slope of the deflection surface as calculated from expression (m) becomes infinitely large. To eliminate this difficulty the central portion of radius b of the plate may be considered as absolutely rigid.[1] Assuming the plate to be clamped along this inner boundary, which rotates under the action of the moment M (Fig. 97b), we find

$$w = \frac{Ma}{8\pi D[(3+\nu) + (1-\nu)\beta^4]}\{-[(1+\nu) + (1-\nu)\beta^4]\rho^3$$
$$+ (1+\nu)(1-\beta^2)^2\rho + 2[(3+\nu) + (1-\nu)\beta^4]\rho \log \rho$$
$$- \beta^2[(1+\nu)\beta^2 - (3+\nu)]\rho^{-1}\} \cos \theta, \quad (n)$$

where $\beta = b/a$. When β is equal to zero, Eq. (n) reduces to Eq. (m) previously obtained. By substituting expression (n) in Eq. (160) the bending moments M_r and M_t can be calculated.

[1] Experiments with such plates were made by R. J. Roark, *Bull. Univ. Wis.* 74, 1932.

The case in which the outer boundary of the plate is clamped (Fig. 97c) can be discussed in a similar manner. This case is of practical interest in design of elastic couplings of shafts.[1] The maximum radial stresses at the inner and at the outer boundaries and the angle of rotation φ of the central rigid portion for this case are

$$(\sigma_r)_{r=b} = \alpha\frac{h}{a}E\varphi, \qquad (\sigma_r)_{r=a} = \alpha_1\frac{h}{a}E\varphi,$$

$$\varphi = \frac{M}{\alpha_2 Eh^3},$$

where the constants α, α_1 and α_2 have the values given in Table 34.

TABLE 34

$\beta = b/a$	α	α_1	α_2
0.5	14.17	7.10	12.40
0.6	19.54	12.85	28.48
0.7	36.25	25.65	77.90
0.8	82.26	66.50	314.00

50. Circular Plates under a Concentrated Load.—The case of a load applied at the center of the plate has already been discussed in Art. 19. Here we shall assume that the load P is applied at point A at distance b from the center O of the plate (Fig. 98).[2] Dividing the plate into two parts by the cylindrical section of radius b as shown in the figure by the dotted line, we can apply solution (163) for each of these portions of the plate. If the angle θ is measured from the radius OA, only the terms containing $\cos m\theta$ should be retained. Hence for the outer part of the plate we obtain

$$w = R_0 + \sum_{m=1}^{\infty} R_m \cos m\theta, \qquad (a)$$

---

[1] Reissner, H., *Ingenieur-Archiv*, vol. 1, p. 72, 1929.

[2] This problem was solved by Clebsch, *loc. cit.*, p. 260. See also A. Föppl, *Sitzungsb. bayer. Akad. Wiss.*, Jahrg., p. 155, 1912. The discussion of the same problem by using bipolar coordinates was given by E. Melan, *Eisenbau*, p. 190, 1920; and by W. Flügge, "Die Strenge Berechnung von Kreisplatten unter Einzellasten," Berlin, 1928. See also the paper by H. Schmidt, *Ingenieur-Archiv*, vol. 1, p. 147, 1930.

where

$$R_0 = A_0 + B_0 r^2 + C_0 \log r + D_0 r^2 \log r,$$
$$R_1 = A_1 r + B_1 r^3 + C_1 r^{-1} + D_1 r \log r,$$
$$\dots\dots\dots\dots\dots\dots\dots\dots\dots\dots\dots\dots\dots$$
$$R_m = A_m r^m + B_m r^{-m} + C_m r^{m+2} + D_m r^{-m+2}.$$
$$\left.\right\} \qquad (b)$$

Similar expressions can also be written for the functions R'_0, R'_1, R'_m corresponding to the inner portion of the plate. Using the symbols $A'_m, B'_m, \dots$ instead of $A_m, B_m, \dots$ for the constants of the latter portion of the plate, from the condition that the deflection, the slope and the moments must be finite at the center of the plate, we obtain

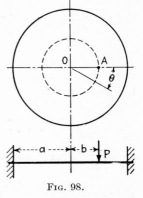

$$C'_0 = D'_0 = 0,$$
$$C'_1 = D'_1 = 0,$$
$$\dots\dots\dots\dots\dots$$
$$\dots\dots\dots\dots\dots$$
$$B'_m = D'_m = 0.$$

Hence for each term of series (a) we have to determine four constants for the outer portion of the plate and two for the inner portion.

Fig. 98.

The six equations necessary for this determination can be obtained from the boundary conditions at the edge of the plate and from the continuity conditions along the circle of radius b. If the outer edge of the plate is assumed to be clamped, the corresponding boundary conditions are

$$(w)_{r=a} = 0, \qquad \left(\frac{\partial w}{\partial r}\right)_{r=a} = 0. \qquad (c)$$

Denoting the deflection of the inner portion of the plate by w_1 and observing that there are no external moments applied along the circle of radius b, we write the continuity conditions along that circle as

$$w = w_1, \qquad \frac{\partial w}{\partial r} = \frac{\partial w_1}{\partial r}, \qquad \frac{\partial^2 w}{\partial r^2} = \frac{\partial^2 w_1}{\partial r^2}, \qquad \text{for} \qquad r = b. \qquad (d)$$

The last equation is obtained from a consideration of the shearing force Q_r along the dividing circle. This force is continuous at all points of the circle except point A, where it has a discontinuity due to concentrated force P. Using for this force the representation in form of the series[1]

$$\frac{P}{\pi b}\left(\frac{1}{2} + \sum_{m=1}^{\infty} \cos m\theta\right), \tag{e}$$

and for the shearing force the first of the expressions (161), we obtain

$$D\frac{\partial}{\partial r}(\Delta w)_{r=b} - D\frac{\partial}{\partial r}(\Delta w_1)_{r=b} = \frac{P}{\pi b}\left(\frac{1}{2} + \sum_{m=1}^{\infty} \cos m\theta\right). \tag{f}$$

From the six Eqs. (c), (d) and (f), the six constants can be calculated, and the functions R_m and R'_m can be represented in the following form:

$$R_0 = \frac{P}{8\pi D}\left[(r^2 + b^2)\log\frac{r}{a} + \frac{(a^2 + b^2)(a^2 - r^2)}{2a^2}\right],$$

$$R'_0 = \frac{P}{8\pi D}\left[(r^2 + b^2)\log\frac{b}{a} + \frac{(a^2 + r^2)(a^2 - b^2)}{2a^2}\right],$$

$$R_1 = -\frac{Pb^3}{16\pi D}\left[\frac{1}{r} + \frac{2(a^2 - b^2)r}{a^2 b^2} - \frac{(2a^2 - b^2)r^3}{a^4 b^2} - \frac{4r}{b^2}\log\frac{a}{r}\right],$$

$$R'_1 = -\frac{Pb^3}{16\pi D}\left[\frac{2(a^2 - b^2)r}{a^2 b^2} + \frac{(a^2 - b^2)^2 r^3}{a^4 b^4} - \frac{4r}{b^2}\log\frac{a}{r}\right],$$

$$R_m = \frac{Pb^m}{8m(m-1)\pi D}\left\{\frac{r^m}{a^{2m}}\left[(m-1)b^2 - ma^2 + (m-1)r^2\right.\right.$$
$$\left.\left. - \frac{m(m-1)}{m+1}\frac{b^2 r^2}{a^2}\right] + \frac{1}{r^m}\left(r^2 - \frac{m-1}{m+1}b^2\right)\right\},$$

$$R'_m = \frac{Pb^m}{8m(m-1)\pi D}\left\{\frac{r^m}{a^{2m}}\left[(m-1)b^2 - ma^2 + \frac{a^{2m}}{b^{2m-2}}\right]\right.$$
$$\left. + (m-1)\frac{r^{m+2}}{a^{2m}}\left[1 - \frac{m}{m+1}\frac{b^2}{a^2} - \frac{1}{m+1}\left(\frac{a}{b}\right)^{2m}\right]\right\}.$$

Using these functions, we obtain the deflection under the load as

$$(w)_{r=b,\,\theta=0} = \frac{P}{16\pi D}\frac{(a^2 - b^2)^2}{a^2}. \tag{164}$$

[1] This series is analogous to the series that was used in the case of rectangular plates, see p. 241.

For $b = 0$ this formula coincides with formula (92) for a centrally loaded plate. The case of the plate with simply supported edge can be treated in a similar manner.

The problem in which a circular ring plate is clamped along the inner edge $(r = b)$ and loaded by a concentrated force P at the outer boundary (Fig. 99) can also be solved by using series (a). In this case the boundary conditions for the clamped inner boundary are

$$(w)_{r=b} = 0, \qquad \left(\frac{\partial w}{\partial r}\right)_{r=b} = 0. \qquad (g)$$

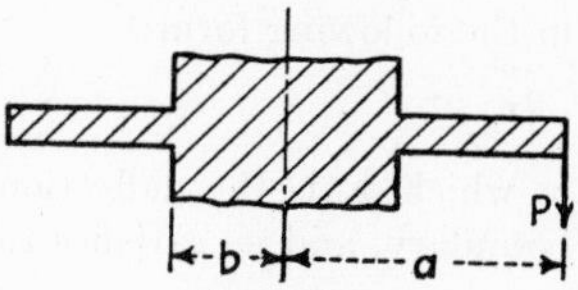

FIG. 99.

For the outer boundary, which is loaded only in one point, the conditions are

$$(M_r)_{r=a} = 0, \qquad (Q_r)_{r=a} = \frac{P}{\pi a}\left(\frac{1}{2} + \sum_{m=1}^{\infty} \cos m\theta\right). \qquad (h)$$

Calculations made for a particular case $b/a = \frac{2}{3}$ show[1] that the

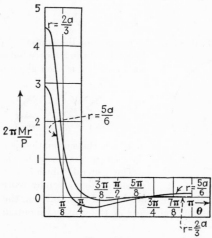

FIG. 100.

largest bending moment M_r at the inner boundary is

$$(M_r)_{r=b, \theta=0} = -4.45\frac{P}{2\pi}.$$

The variation of the moment along the inner edge and also along

[1] REISSNER, H., *loc. cit.*, p. 266.

a circle of radius $r = 5a/6$ is shown in Fig. 100. It can be seen that this moment diminishes rapidly as the angle θ, measured from the point of application of the load, increases.

51. Circular Plates Supported at Several Points along the Boundary.— Considering the case of a load symmetrically distributed with respect to the center of the plate, we take the general expression for the deflection surface in the following form:[1]

$$w = w_0 + w_1,\qquad\qquad (a)$$

in which w_0 is the deflection of a plate simply supported along the entire boundary, and w_1 satisfies the homogeneous differential equation

$$\Delta\Delta w_1 = 0.\qquad\qquad (b)$$

Denoting the concentrated reactions at the points of support $1, 2, 3, \ldots$ by $N_1, N_2, \ldots, N_i$ and using series (h) of the previous article for representation of concentrated forces, we have for each reaction N_i the expression

$$\frac{N_i}{\pi a}\left(\frac{1}{2} + \sum_{m=1}^{\infty} \cos m\theta_i\right),\qquad\qquad (c)$$

where

$$\theta_i = \theta - \gamma_i,$$

γ_i being the angle defining the position of the support i (Fig. 101). The intensity of the reactive forces at any point of the boundary is then given by the expression

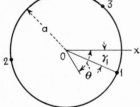

FIG. 101.

$$\sum_{1}^{i}\frac{N_i}{\pi a}\left(\frac{1}{2} + \sum_{m=1}^{\infty} \cos m\theta_i\right),\qquad (d)$$

in which the summation is extended over all the concentrated reactions (c).

The general solution of the homogeneous equation (b) is given by expression (163) (page 260). Assuming that the plate is solid and omitting the terms that give infinite deflections and moments at the center, we obtain from expression (163)

$$w_1 = A_0 + B_0 r^2 + \sum_{m=1}^{\infty}(A_m r^m + C_m r^{m+2})\cos m\theta$$

$$+ \sum_{m=1}^{\infty}(A'_m r^m + C'_m r^{m+2})\sin m\theta.\quad (e)$$

[1] Several problems of this kind were discussed by A. Nadai, *Z. Physik*, vol. 23, p. 366, 1922.

For determining the constants we have the following conditions at the boundary:

$$(M_r)_{r=a} = -D\left[\frac{\partial^2 w}{\partial r^2} + \nu\left(\frac{1}{r}\frac{\partial w}{\partial r} + \frac{1}{r^2}\frac{\partial^2 w}{\partial\theta^2}\right)\right]_{r=a} = 0,$$

$$(V)_{r=a} = \left(Q_r - \frac{\partial M_{rt}}{r\,\partial\theta}\right)_{r=a} = -\sum_1^i \frac{N_i}{\pi a}\left(\frac{1}{2} + \sum_{m=1}^\infty \cos m\theta_i\right), \quad (f)$$

in which M_{rt} and Q_r are given by Eqs. (160) and (161).

Let us consider a particular case in which the plate is supported at two points which are the ends of a diameter. We shall measure θ from this diameter. Then $\gamma_1 = 0$, $\gamma_2 = \pi$, and we obtain

$$w = w_0 + \frac{Pa^2}{2\pi(3+\nu)D}\left\{2\log 2 - 1 + \frac{1+\nu}{1-\nu}\left(2\log 2 - \frac{\pi^2}{12}\right)\right.$$
$$\left. - \sum_{m=2,4,6,\cdots}^\infty \left[\frac{1}{m(m-1)} + \frac{2(1+\nu)}{(1-\nu)(m-1)m^2} - \frac{\rho^2}{m(m+1)}\right]\rho^m \cos m\theta\right\}, \quad (g)$$

in which w_0 is the deflection of the simply supported and symmetrically loaded plate, P is the total load on the plate and $\rho = r/a$. When the load is applied at the center, we obtain from expression (g), by assuming $\nu = 0.25$,

$$(w)_{\rho=0} = 1.31\frac{Pa^2}{Eh^3},$$

$$(w)_{\rho=1,\theta=\frac{\pi}{2}} = 1.33\frac{Pa^2}{Eh^3}.$$

For a uniformly loaded plate we obtain

$$(w)_{\rho=0} = 0.269\frac{qa^4}{D},$$

$$(w)_{\rho=1,\theta=\frac{\pi}{2}} = 0.371\frac{qa^4}{D}.$$

By combining two solutions of the type (g), the case shown in Fig. 102 can also be obtained.

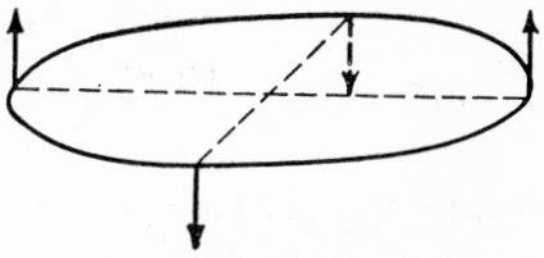

When a circular plate is supported at three points 120 deg. apart, the deflection produced at the center of the plate, when the load is applied at the center, is

$$(w)_{\rho=0} = 0.754\frac{Pa^2}{Eh^3}.$$

Fig. 102.

When the load is uniformly distributed, the deflection at the center is

$$(w)_{\rho=0} = 0.307\frac{Pa^2}{Eh^3},$$

where $P = \pi a^2 q$.

The case of a circular plate supported at three points was investigated by experiments with glass plates. These experiments showed a very satisfactory agreement with the theory.[1]

52. Plates in the Form of a Sector.—The general solution developed for circular plates (Art. 48) can also be adapted for a plate in the form of a sector, the straight edges of which are simply supported.[2] Take, as an example, a plate in the form of a semicircle simply supported along the

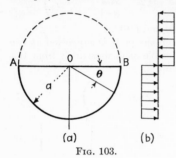

(a)   (b)

Fig. 103.

diameter AB and uniformly loaded (Fig. 103). The deflection of this plate is evidently the same as that of the circular plate indicated by the dotted line and loaded as shown in Fig. 103b. The distributed load is represented in such a case by the series

$$q = \sum_{m=1,3,5,\cdots}^{\infty} \frac{4q}{m\pi} \sin m\theta, \qquad (a)$$

and the differential equation of the deflection surface is

$$\Delta\Delta w = \frac{1}{D} \sum_{m=1,3,5,\cdots}^{\infty} \frac{4q}{m\pi} \sin m\theta. \qquad (b)$$

The particular solution of this equation that satisfies the boundary conditions along the diameter AB is

$$w_0 = \sum_{m=1,3,5,\cdots}^{\infty} \frac{4qr^4}{\pi m(16 - m^2)(4 - m^2)D} \sin m\theta. \qquad (c)$$

The solution of the homogeneous differential equation (162) that satisfies the conditions along the diameter AB is

$$w_1 = \sum_{m=1,3,5,\cdots}^{\infty} (A_m r^m + B_m r^{m+2}) \sin m\theta. \qquad (d)$$

Combining expressions (c) and (d), we obtain the complete expression for the deflection w of a semicircular plate. The constants A_m and B_m are determined in each particular case from the conditions along the circular boundary of the plate.

[1] These experiments were made by Nadai, *loc. cit.*, p. 270.

[2] Problems of this kind were discussed by A. Nadai, *Z. Ver. deut. Ing.*, vol. 59, p. 169, 1915. See also the book by Galerkin, *loc. cit.*, p. 237, in which numerical tables for such cases are given.

In the case of a simply supported plate we have

$$(w)_{r=a} = 0,$$

$$\left[\frac{\partial^2 w}{\partial r^2} + \nu\left(\frac{1}{r}\frac{\partial w}{\partial r} + \frac{1}{r^2}\frac{\partial^2 w}{\partial \theta^2}\right)\right]_{r=a} = 0. \qquad (e)$$

Substituting the sum of series (c) and (d) for w in these equations, we obtain the following equations for calculating A_m and B_m:

$$A_m a^m + B_m a^{m+2} = -\frac{4qa^2}{m\pi(16 - m^2)(4 - m^2)D},$$

$$A_m a^n[m(m-1) - \nu m(m-1)] + B_m a^{m+2}(m+1)[m + 2 + \nu(2 - m)]$$
$$= -\frac{4qa^2[12 + \nu(4 - m^2)]}{m\pi(16 - m^2)(4 - m^2)D}.$$

From these equations,

$$A_m = \frac{qa^4(m + 5 + \nu)}{a^m m\pi(16 - m^2)(2 + m)[m + \frac{1}{2}(1 + \nu)]D},$$

$$B_m = -\frac{qa^4(m + 3 + \nu)}{a^{m+2} m\pi(4 + m)(4 - m^2)[m + \frac{1}{2}(1 + \nu)]D}.$$

With these values of the constants the expression for deflection of the plate becomes

$$w = \frac{qa^4}{D}\sum_{m=1,3,5,\cdots}^{\infty}\left\{\frac{4r^4}{a^4}\frac{1}{m\pi(16 - m^2)(4 - m^2)}\right.$$

$$+ \frac{r^m}{a^m}\cdot\frac{m + 5 + \nu}{m\pi(16 - m^2)(2 + m)[m + \frac{1}{2}(1 + \nu)]}$$

$$\left. - \frac{r^{m+2}}{a^{m+2}}\frac{m + 3 + \nu}{m\pi(4 + m)(4 - m^2)[m + \frac{1}{2}(1 + \nu)]}\right\}\sin m\theta.$$

With this expression for the deflection, the bending moments are readily obtained from Eqs. (160).

In a similar manner we can obtain the solution for any sector with an angle π/k, k being a given integer. The final expressions for the deflections and bending moments at a given point can be represented in each particular case by the following formulas:

$$w = \alpha\frac{qa^4}{Eh^3}, \qquad M_r = \beta qa^2, \qquad M_t = \beta_1 qa^2, \qquad (f)$$

in which α, β and β_1 are numerical factors. Several values of these factors for points taken on the axis of symmetry of a sector are given in Table 35.

TABLE 35.—VALUES OF THE FACTORS α, β AND β_1 FOR VARIOUS ANGLES π/k OF A SECTOR SIMPLY SUPPORTED AT THE BOUNDARY
$\nu = 0.3$

π/k	$r/a = \frac{1}{4}$			$r/a = \frac{1}{2}$			$r/a = \frac{3}{4}$			$r/a = 1$		
	α	β	β_1	α	β	β_1	α	β	β_1	α	β	β_1
$\pi/4$	0.0006	−0.0015	0.0093	0.0036	0.0069	0.0183	0.0053	0.0161	0.0169	0	0	0.0025
$\pi/3$	0.0021	−0.0025	0.0177	0.0087	0.0149	0.0255	0.0101	0.0243	0.0213	0	0	0.0044
$\pi/2$	0.0101	0.0036	0.0319	0.0246	0.0353	0.0352	0.0222	0.0381	0.0286	0	0	0.0088
π	0.0643	0.0692	0.0357	0.0886	0.0868	0.0515	0.0612	0.0617	0.0468	0	0	0.0221

The case in which a plate in the form of a sector is clamped along the circular boundary and simply supported along the straight edges can be treated by the same method of solution as that used in the previous case. The values of the coefficients α and β for the points taken along the axis of symmetry of the sector are given in Table 36.

TABLE 36.—VALUES OF THE COEFFICIENTS α AND β FOR VARIOUS ANGLES π/k OF A SECTOR CLAMPED ALONG THE CIRCULAR BOUNDARY AND SIMPLY SUPPORTED ALONG THE STRAIGHT EDGES
$\nu = 0.3$

π/k	$r/a = \frac{1}{4}$		$r/a = \frac{1}{2}$		$r/a = \frac{3}{4}$		$r/a = 1$	
	α	β	α	β	α	β	α	β
$\pi/4$	0.0005	−0.0008	0.0028	0.0087	0.0031	0.0107	0	−0.0250
$\pi/3$	0.0019	−0.0006	0.0062	0.0143	0.0051	0.0123	0	−0.0340
$\pi/2$	0.0069	0.0068	0.0144	0.0272	0.0089	0.0113	0	−0.0488
π	0.0320	0.0473	0.0368	0.0446	0.0167	0.0016	0	−0.0756

It can be seen that in this case the maximum bending stress occurs at the mid-point of the circular edge of the sector.

If the circular edge of a uniformly loaded plate having the form of a sector is entirely free, the maximum deflection occurs at the mid-point of the unsupported circular edge. For the case when $\pi/k = \pi/2$ we obtain

$$w_{\text{max.}} = 0.691 \frac{qa^4}{Eh^3}.$$

The bending moment at the same point is

$$M_t = 0.1331 qa^2.$$

53. Bending of Circular Plates Resting on an Elastic Foundation.—We shall consider here only the case in which the load is symmetrically distributed with respect to the center of the plate. We shall also assume that the intensity of the reaction of the foundation at each point of the bottom surface of the plate is proportional to the deflection of the plate at that point. In such a case the deflection is independent of the angle θ (Fig. 94), and the differential equation (159) for the deflection of the plate reduces to the equation

$$\left(\frac{d^2}{dr^2} + \frac{1}{r}\frac{d}{dr}\right)\left(\frac{d^2w}{dr^2} + \frac{1}{r}\frac{dw}{dr}\right) = \frac{q - kw}{D}. \tag{165}$$

In this equation q is the intensity of lateral load, and k is the modulus of foundation. Thus kw represents the intensity of the reaction at each point on the bottom surface of the plate.

Let us first consider the particular case of a plate loaded at the center with a load P.[1] In this case q is equal to zero over the entire surface of the plate except at the center. By introducing the notation

$$\frac{k}{D} = \frac{1}{l^4}, \tag{a}$$

Eq. (165) becomes

$$l^4\left(\frac{d^2}{dr^2} + \frac{1}{r}\frac{d}{dr}\right)\left(\frac{d^2w}{dr^2} + \frac{1}{r}\frac{dw}{dr}\right) + w = 0. \tag{b}$$

Since k is measured in pounds per cubic inch and D in pound inches, the quantity l has the dimension of a length. To simplify our further discussion it is advantageous to introduce dimensionless quantities by using the following notations:

$$\frac{w}{l} = z, \qquad \frac{r}{l} = x. \tag{c}$$

Then Eq. (b) becomes

$$\left(\frac{d^2}{dx^2} + \frac{1}{x}\frac{d}{dx}\right)\left(\frac{d^2z}{dx^2} + \frac{1}{x}\frac{dz}{dx}\right) + z = 0. \tag{d}$$

Using the symbol

$$\Delta \text{ for } \frac{d^2}{dx^2} + \frac{1}{x}\frac{d}{dx},$$

---

[1] This problem was discussed by Hertz, *loc. cit.*, p. 255. See also A. Föppl, "Vorlesungen uber technische Mechanik," vol. 5, p. 103, 1922.

we then write

$$\Delta\Delta z + z = 0. \tag{e}$$

This is a linear differential equation of the fourth order, the general solution of which can be represented in the following form:

$$z = AX_1(x) + BX_2(x) + CX_3(x) + DX_4(x), \tag{f}$$

where $A, \ldots, D$ are constants of integration and the functions $X_1, \ldots, X_4$ are four independent solutions of Eq. (e).

We shall now try to find a solution of Eq. (e) in the form of a power series. Let $a_n x^n$ be a term of this series. Then by differentiation we find

$$\Delta(a_n x^n) = n(n-1)a_n x^{n-2} + na_n x^{n-2} = n^2 a_n x^{n-2}$$

and

$$\Delta\Delta(a_n x^n) = n^2(n-2)^2 a_n x^{n-4}.$$

To satisfy Eq. (e) it is necessary that to each term $a_n x^n$ in the series corresponds a term $a_{n-4} x^{n-4}$ such that

$$n^2(n-2)^2 a_n x^{n-4} + a_{n-4} x^{n-4} = 0. \tag{g}$$

Following this condition, all terms cancel when the series is substituted in Eq. (e); hence the series, if it is a convergent one, represents a particular solution of the equation. From Eq. (g) it follows that

$$a_n = -\frac{a_{n-4}}{n^2(n-2)^2}. \tag{h}$$

Observing also that

$$\Delta\Delta(a_0) = 0 \qquad \text{and} \qquad \Delta\Delta(a_2 x^2) = 0, \tag{i}$$

we can conclude that there are two series satisfying Eq. (e), viz.,

$$\left.\begin{array}{l}
X_1(x) = 1 - \dfrac{x^4}{2^2 \cdot 4^2} + \dfrac{x^8}{2^2 \cdot 4^2 \cdot 6^2 \cdot 8^2} \\[2ex]
\qquad\qquad - \dfrac{x^{12}}{2^2 \cdot 4^2 \cdot 6^2 \cdot 8^2 \cdot 10^2 \cdot 12^2} + \cdots \\[3ex]
\text{and} \\[1ex]
X_2(x) = x^2 - \dfrac{x^6}{4^2 \cdot 6^2} + \dfrac{x^{10}}{4^2 \cdot 6^2 \cdot 8^2 \cdot 10^2} \\[2ex]
\qquad\qquad - \dfrac{x^{14}}{4^2 \cdot 6^2 \cdot 8^2 \cdot 10^2 \cdot 12^2 \cdot 14^2} + \cdots
\end{array}\right\} \tag{j}$$

It may be seen from the notations (c) that for small values of the distance r, *i.e.*, for points that are close to the point of application of the load P, the quantity x is small and series (j) are rapidly convergent. It may be seen also that the consecutive derivatives of series (j) remain finite at the point of application of the load $(x = 0)$. This indicates that these series alone are not sufficient to represent the stress conditions at the point of application of the load where, as we know from previously discussed cases, the bending moments become infinitely large.

For this reason the particular solution X_3 of Eq. (e) will be taken in the following form:

$$X_3 = X_1 \log x + F_3(x), \qquad (k)$$

in which $F_3(x)$ is a function of x which can again be represented by a power series. By differentiation we find

$$\Delta\Delta X_3 = \frac{4}{x}\frac{d^3X_1}{dx^3} + \log x \, \Delta\Delta X_1 + \Delta\Delta F_3(x);$$

and substituting X_3 for z in Eq. (e), we obtain

$$\frac{4}{x}\frac{d^3X_1}{dx^3} + \log x(\Delta\Delta X_1 + X_1) + \Delta\Delta F_3(x) + F_3(x) = 0.$$

Since X_1 satisfies Eq. (e) and is represented by the first of the series (j), we obtain the following equation for determining $F_3(x)$:

$$\Delta\Delta F_3(x) + F_3(x) = -\frac{4}{x}\frac{d^3X_1}{dx^3} = -4\left(-\frac{2\cdot3\cdot4}{2^2\cdot4^2}\right.$$
$$\left. + \frac{6\cdot7\cdot8\cdot x^4}{2^2\cdot4^2\cdot6^2\cdot8^2} - \frac{10\cdot11\cdot12\cdot x^8}{2^2\cdot4^2\cdot6^2\cdot8^2\cdot10^2\cdot12^2} + \cdots \right). \qquad (l)$$

Taking $F_3(x)$ in the form of the series

$$F_3(x) = b_4x^4 + b_8x^8 + b_{12}x^{12} + \cdots \qquad (m)$$

and substituting this series in Eq. (l), we determine the coefficients b_4, b_8, b_{12}, ... so that the resulting equation will be satisfied. Observing that

$$\Delta\Delta(b_4x^4) = 4^2\cdot2^2\cdot b_4,$$

we find, by equating to zero the sum of the terms that do not contain x, that

$$4^2\cdot2^2\cdot b_4 = 4\cdot\frac{2\cdot3\cdot4}{2^2\cdot4^2},$$

or

$$b_4 = \frac{2 \cdot 3 \cdot 4^2}{2^4 \cdot 4^4} = \frac{3}{128}.$$

Equating to zero the sum of the terms containing x^4, we find

$$b_8 = -\frac{25}{1,769,472}.$$

In general, we find

$$b_n = (-1)^{\frac{n}{4}-1} \frac{1}{n^2(n-2)^2}\left[b_{n-4} + \frac{n(n-1)(n-2)}{2^2 \cdot 4^2 \cdot 6^2 \cdots n^2}\right].$$

Thus the third particular solution of Eq. (e) is

$$X_3 = X_1 \log x + \frac{3}{128}x^4 - \frac{25}{1,769,472}x^8 + \cdots. \qquad (n)$$

The fourth particular integral X_4 of Eq. (e) is obtained in a similar manner by taking

$$X_4 = X_2 \log x + F_4(x) = X_2 \log x + 4\frac{4 \cdot 5 \cdot 6}{4^4 \cdot 6^4}x^6$$

$$-\frac{1}{10^2 \cdot 8^2}\left(4 \cdot \frac{4 \cdot 5 \cdot 6}{4^4 \cdot 6^4} + \frac{10 \cdot 9 \cdot 8}{4^2 \cdot 6^2 \cdots 10^2}\right)x^{10} + \cdots. \qquad (o)$$

By substituting the particular solutions (j), (n) and (o) in expression (f) we obtain the general solution of Eq. (e) in the following form:

$$z = A\left(1 - \frac{x^4}{2^2 \cdot 4^2} + \frac{x^8}{2^2 \cdot 4^2 \cdot 6^2 \cdot 8^2} - \cdots\right)$$

$$+ B\left(x^2 - \frac{x^6}{4^2 \cdot 6^2} + \frac{x^{10}}{4^2 \cdot 6^2 \cdot 8^2 \cdot 10^2} - \cdots\right)$$

$$+ C\left[\left(1 - \frac{x^4}{2^2 \cdot 4^2} + \frac{x^8}{2^2 \cdot 4^2 \cdot 6^2 \cdot 8^2} - \cdots\right)\log x + \frac{3}{128}x^4 \right.$$

$$\left. - \frac{25}{1,769,472}x^8 + \cdots\right] + D\left[\left(x^2 - \frac{x^6}{4^2 \cdot 6^2} + \frac{x^{10}}{4^2 \cdot 6^2 \cdot 8^2 \cdot 10^2}\right.\right.$$

$$\left.\left. - \cdots\right)\log x + \frac{5}{3456}x^6 - \frac{1054 \cdot 10^{-4}}{442,368}x^{10} + \cdots\right]. \qquad (p)$$

It remains now to determine in each particular case the constants of integration $A, \ldots, D$ so as to satisfy the boundary conditions.

Let us consider the case in which the edge of the circular plate of radius a is entirely free, the boundary conditions for such a case being given by Eqs. (j), Art. 48 (see page 259). Using for the moments M_r and shearing forces Q_r the first of the equations (160) and the first of the equations (161), respectively, we write the boundary conditions as

$$\left.\begin{aligned}\left(\frac{d^2w}{dr^2} + \nu\frac{1}{r}\frac{dw}{dr}\right)_{r=a} &= 0, \\ \frac{d}{dr}\left(\frac{d^2w}{dr^2} + \frac{1}{r}\frac{dw}{dr}\right)_{r=a} &= 0. \end{aligned}\right\} \qquad (q)$$

In addition to these two conditions we have two more conditions that hold at the center of the plate; *viz.*, the deflection at the center of the plate must be finite, and the sum of the shearing forces distributed over the lateral surface of an infinitesimal circular cylinder cut out of the plate at its center must balance the concentrated force P. From the first of these two conditions it follows that the constant C in the general solution (p) vanishes. The second condition gives

$$\left(\int_0^{2\pi} Q_r r\, d\theta\right)_{r=\epsilon} + P = 0, \qquad (r)$$

or, by using notation (a),

$$-kl^4 \frac{d}{dr}\left(\frac{d^2w}{dr^2} + \frac{1}{r}\frac{dw}{dr}\right)_{r=\epsilon} 2\pi\epsilon + P = 0, \qquad (s)$$

where ϵ is the radius of the infinitesimal cylinder. Substituting lz for w in this equation and using for z expression (p), we find that for an infinitely small value of x equal to ϵ/l the equation reduces to

$$-kl^4 \cdot \frac{4D}{l\epsilon} \cdot 2\pi\epsilon + P = 0,$$

from which

$$D = \frac{P}{8\pi kl^3}. \qquad (t)$$

Having the values of the constants C and D, the remaining two constants A and B can be found from Eqs. (q). For given dimensions of the plate and given moduli of the plate and of the foundation these equations furnish two linear equations in A and B.

Let us take, as an example, a plate of radius $a = 5$ in. and of such rigidity that

$$l = \sqrt[4]{\frac{D}{k}} = 5 \text{ in.}$$

We apply at the center a load P such that

$$D = \frac{P}{8\pi k l^3} = 102 \cdot 10^{-5}.$$

Using this value of D and substituting lz for w, we find, by using expression (p) and taking $x = a/l = 1$, that Eqs. (q) give

$$0.500A + 0.250B = 4.062D = 4.062 \cdot 102 \cdot 10^{-5},$$
$$0.687A - 8.483B = 11.09D = 11.09 \cdot 102 \cdot 10^{-5}.$$

These equations give

$$A = 86 \cdot 10^{-4}, \qquad B = -64 \cdot 10^{-5}.$$

Substituting these values in expression (p) and retaining only the terms that contain x to a power not larger than the fourth, we obtain the following expression for the deflection:

$$w = lz = 5\left[86 \cdot 10^{-4}\left(1 - \frac{x^4}{2^2 \cdot 4^2} \right) - 64 \cdot 10^{-5}x^2 + 102 \cdot 10^{-5}x^2 \log x \right].$$

The deflection at the center $(x = 0)$ is then

$$(w)_{\text{max.}} = 43 \cdot 10^{-3} \text{ in.},$$

and the deflection at the boundary $(x = 1)$ is

$$(w)_{\text{min.}} = 39.1 \cdot 10^{-3} \text{ in.}$$

The difference of these deflections is comparatively small, and the pressure distribution over the foundation differs only slightly from a uniform distribution.

If we take the radius of the plate two times larger $(a = 10$ in.$)$ and retain the previous values for the rigidities of the plate, x becomes equal to 2 at the boundary, and Eqs. (q) reduce to

$$0.826A + 1.980B = 1.208D,$$
$$2.665A - 5.745B = 16.37D.$$

These equations give

$$A = 3.93D = 400 \cdot 10^{-5}, \qquad B = -1.03D = -105 \cdot 10^{-5}. \qquad (u)$$

The deflection is obtained from expression (p) as

$$w = lz = 5\left\{ 400 \cdot 10^{-5}\left(1 - \frac{x^4}{2^2 \cdot 4^2} \right) - 105 \cdot 10^{-5}\left(x^2 - \frac{x^6}{576} \right) \right.$$
$$\left. + 102 \cdot 10^{-5}\left[\log x \left(x^2 - \frac{x^6}{4^2 \cdot 6^2} \right) + \frac{5}{3,456}x^6 \right] \right\}.$$

The deflections at the center and at the boundary of the plate are, respectively,

$$w_{max.} = 2.10^{-2} \text{ in.} \quad \text{and} \quad w_{min.} = 0.88 \cdot 10^{-2} \text{ in.}$$

It is thus seen that, if the radius of the plate is twice as large as the quantity l, the distribution of pressure over the foundation is already very far from a uniform one.

If we take an infinitely large plate which was considered by H. Hertz (see page 255), the deflection under the load is, from Eq. (157),

$$w_{max.} = \frac{P}{8kl^2} = \pi l D = 3,14 \cdot 5 \cdot 102 \cdot 10^{-5} = 1.60 \cdot 10^{-2} \text{ in.}$$

Having an expression for the deflections w, the bending moments are obtained from Eqs. (160). At the point of application of the load these moments become infinitely large, and the results obtained by using the thick plate theory (see page 255) must be applied in calculating stresses at that point.

The general solution (f) of Eq. (e) can also be represented by Bessel functions for which there are numerical tables.[1] In this manner the discussion of various cases of bending of circular plates resting on an elastic foundation can be considerably simplified.[2]

The strain energy method also can be used for calculating the deflection of a circular plate resting on an elastic foundation. For example, to obtain a rough approximation for the case in which the deflection at the center does not differ much from the deflection at the boundary, we take for the deflection the expression

$$w = A + Br^2, \tag{v}$$

where A and B are two constants to be determined from the condition that the total energy of the system in stable equilibrium is a minimum (see Art. 28). From expression (v) we conclude that the deflection surface has a constant curvature equal to $2B$. Hence the strain energy of the plate of radius a, as given by Eq. (47) (page 50), is

$$V_1 = 4B^2 D\pi a^2 (1 + \nu).$$

The strain energy of the deformed elastic foundation is

$$V_2 = \int_0^{2\pi} \int_0^a \frac{kw^2}{2} r \, dr \, d\theta = \pi k \left(\frac{1}{2} A^2 a^2 + \frac{1}{2} A B a^4 + \frac{1}{6} B^2 a^6 \right).$$

The total potential energy of the system for the case of a load P applied at the center is

$$V = 4B^2 D\pi a^2 (1 + \nu) + \pi k (\tfrac{1}{2} A^2 a^2 + \tfrac{1}{2} A B a^4 + \tfrac{1}{6} B^2 a^6) - PA.$$

[1] See, for example, Jahnke-Emde, "Tables of Functions," Berlin, 1933.

[2] See paper by F. Schleicher, "Festschrift zur Hundertjahrfeier der Technischen Hochschule Karlsruhe," 1925; and J. J. Koch, *Ingenieur*, No. 6, 1925.

Taking the derivatives of this expression with respect to constants A and B and equating them to zero, we obtain

$$A + Ba^2 \left[\frac{2}{3} + \frac{16D(1 + \nu)}{ka^4} \right] = 0,$$

$$A + \frac{1}{2}Ba^2 = \frac{P}{\pi ka^2}.$$

Taking the previous numerical example (page 280) in which

$$l = a, \qquad \frac{D}{ka^4} = 1, \qquad \frac{P}{8\pi ka^3} = 102 \cdot 10^{-5},$$

we find

$$A = w_{\text{max.}} = 41.8 \cdot 10^{-3} \text{ in.}$$

This result is about 3 per cent less than the value $43 \cdot 10^{-3}$ in. previously obtained. To obtain a better accuracy more terms should be taken in expression (v).

When the deflection and the reactions of the foundation are found by the energy method, the calculation of stresses can be made by considering the given plate to be a circular one symmetrically loaded by the calculated reactions (see Chap. III). In this way a better accuracy will be obtained than if an approximate expression, such as expression (v), were used in calculating curvatures and bending moments.

If the foundations are assumed to be a semi-infinite elastic body instead of conforming with the simplifying assumption regarding reactions made in our previous discussion, the problem of bending of circular plates supported by an elastic foundation becomes more complicated. This problem has been discussed by D. L. Holl.[1]

54. Circular Plates of Non-uniform Thickness.—Circular plates of non-uniform thickness are sometimes encountered in the design of machine parts, such as diaphragms of steam turbines and pistons of reciprocating engines. The thickness of such plates is usually a function of the radial distance, and the acting load is symmetrical with respect to the center of the plate. We shall limit our further discussion to this symmetrical case.

Proceeding as was explained in Art. 15 and using the notations of that article, from the condition of equilibrium of an element as shown in Fig. 28 (page 56) we derive the following equation:

$$M_r + \frac{dM_r}{dr}r - M_t + Qr = 0, \tag{a}$$

in which, as before,

$$M_r = D\left(\frac{d\varphi}{dr} + \frac{\nu}{r}\varphi\right), \\ M_t = D\left(\frac{\varphi}{r} + \nu\frac{d\varphi}{dr}\right), \tag{b}$$

[1] *Proc. 5th Intern. Cong. Appl. Mech.*, Cambridge, Mass., **1938**.

where

$$\varphi = -\frac{dw}{dr} \tag{c}$$

and Q is the shearing force per unit length of a circular section of radius r. In the case of a solid plate, Q is given by the equation

$$Q = \frac{1}{2\pi r}\int_0^r q\, 2\pi r\, dr, \tag{d}$$

in which q is the intensity of the lateral load.

Substituting expressions (b), (c) and (d) in Eq. (a) and observing that the flexural rigidity D is no longer constant but varies with the radial distance r, we obtain the following equation:

$$D\frac{d}{dr}\left(\frac{d\varphi}{dr} + \frac{\varphi}{r}\right) + \frac{dD}{dr}\left(\frac{d\varphi}{dr} + \nu\frac{\varphi}{r}\right) = -\frac{1}{r}\int_0^r q\, r\, dr. \tag{e}$$

Thus the problem of bending of circular symmetrically loaded plates reduces to the solution of a differential equation (e) of the second order with variable coefficients. To represent the equation in dimensionless form we introduce the following notations:

a is the outer radius of the plate.

h is the thickness of the plate at any point.

h_0 is the thickness of the plate at the center.

$$\frac{r}{a} = x; \qquad \frac{h}{h_0} = y. \tag{f}$$

We also assume that the load is uniformly distributed. Using the notation

$$p = \frac{6(1 - \nu^2)a^3q}{Eh_0^3}, \tag{g}$$

Eq. (e) then becomes

$$\frac{d^2\varphi}{dx^2} + \left(\frac{1}{x} + \frac{d\log y^3}{dx}\right)\frac{d\varphi}{dx} - \left(\frac{1}{x^2} - \frac{\nu}{x}\frac{d\log y^3}{dx}\right)\varphi = -\frac{px}{y^3}. \tag{166}$$

In many cases the variation of the plate thickness can be represented with sufficient accuracy by the equation[1]

$$y = e^{-\frac{\beta x^2}{6}}, \tag{h}$$

[1] The first investigation of bending of circular plates of non-uniform thickness was made by H. Holzer, *Z. ges. Turbinenwesen*, vol. 15, p. 21, 1918. The results given in this article are taken from O. Pichler's doctor's dissertation, "Die Biegung kreissymmetrischer Platten von veräderlicher Dicke," Berlin, 1928. See also the paper by R. Gran Olsson, *Ingenieur-Archiv*, vol. 8, p. 81, 1937.

in which β is a constant that must be chosen in each particular case so as to approximate as closely as possible the actual proportions of the plate. The variation of thickness along a diameter of a plate corresponding to various

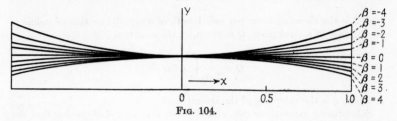

Fig. 104.

values of the constant β is shown in Fig. 104. Substituting expression (h) in Eq. (166), we find

$$\frac{d^2\varphi}{dx^2} + \left(\frac{1}{x} - \beta x\right)\frac{d\varphi}{dx} - \left(\frac{1}{x^2} + \nu\beta\right)\varphi = -pxe^{\frac{\beta x^2}{2}}. \qquad (i)$$

It can be readily verified that

$$\varphi_0 = -\frac{p}{(3-\nu)\beta}xe^{\frac{\beta x^2}{2}} \qquad (j)$$

is a particular solution of Eq. (i). One of the two solutions of the homogeneous equation corresponding to Eq. (i) can be taken in the form of a power series:

$$\varphi_1 = a_1\left[x + \sum_{n=1}^{\infty}\frac{\beta^n(1+\nu)(3+\nu)\cdots(2n-1+\nu)}{2\cdot 4\cdot 4\cdot 6\cdot 6\cdots 2n\cdot 2n(2n+2)}x^{2n+1}\right], \qquad (k)$$

in which a_1 is an arbitrary constant. The second solution of the same equation becomes infinitely large at the center of the plate, *i.e.*, for $x = 0$, and therefore should not be considered in the case of a plate without a hole at the center. If solutions (j) and (k) are combined, the general solution of Eq. (i) for a solid plate can be put in the following form:

$$\varphi = p\left(C\varphi_1 - \frac{x}{(3-\nu)\beta}e^{\frac{\beta x^2}{2}}\right). \qquad (l)$$

The constant C in each particular case must be determined from the condition at the boundary of the plate. Since series (k) is uniformly convergent, it can be differentiated, and the expressions for the bending moments can be obtained by substitution in Eqs. (b). The deflections can be obtained from Eq. (c).

In the case of a plate clamped at the edge, the boundary conditions are

$$(w)_{x=1} = 0, \qquad (\varphi)_{x=1} = 0, \qquad (m)$$

and the constant C in solution (l) is

$$C = \frac{e^{\frac{\beta}{2}}}{(3 - \nu)\beta(\varphi_1)_{x=1}}. \qquad (n)$$

To get the numerical value of C for a given value of β, which defines the shape of the diametrical section of the plate (see Fig. 104), the sum of series (k) must be calculated for $x = 1$. The results of such calculations are given in the above-mentioned paper by Pichler. This paper also gives the numerical values for the derivative and for the integral of series (k) by the use of which the moments and the deflections of a plate can be calculated.

The deflection of the plate at the center can be represented by the formula

$$w_{max.} = \alpha a p = \alpha \frac{6(1 - \nu^2)a^4 q}{E h_0^3}, \qquad (o)$$

in which α is a numerical factor depending on the value of the constant β. Several values of this factor, calculated for $\nu = 0.3$, are given in the second line of Table 37.

TABLE 37.—NUMERICAL FACTORS α AND α' FOR CALCULATING DEFLECTIONS AT THE CENTER OF CIRCULAR PLATES OF VARIABLE THICKNESS
$\nu = 0.3$

β	4	3	2	1	0	−1	−2	−3	−4
α	0.0801	0.0639	0.0505	0.0398	0.0313	0.0246	0.0192	0.0152	0.01195
α'	0.2233	0.1944	0.1692	0.1471	0.1273	0.1098	0.0937	0.0791	0.06605

The maximum bending stresses at various radial distances can be represented by the formulas

$$(\sigma_r)_{max.} = \pm\gamma\frac{3qa^2}{h_0^2}, \qquad (\sigma_t)_{max.} = \pm\gamma_1\frac{3qa^2}{h_0^2}. \qquad (p)$$

The values of the numerical factors γ and γ_1 for various proportions of the plate and for various values of $x = r/a$ are given by the curves in Figs. 105 and 106, respectively. For $\beta = 0$ these curves give the same values of stresses as were previously obtained for plates of uniform thickness (see Fig. 29, page 61).

In the case of a plate simply supported along the edge, the boundary conditions are

$$(w)_{x=1} = 0, \qquad (M_r)_{x=1} = 0. \qquad (q)$$

Investigation shows that the deflections and maximum stresses can be represented again by equations analogous to Eqs. (o) and (p). The notations α', γ' and γ_1' will be used for constants in this case, instead of α, γ and γ_1 as used for clamped plates. The values of α' are given in the last line of

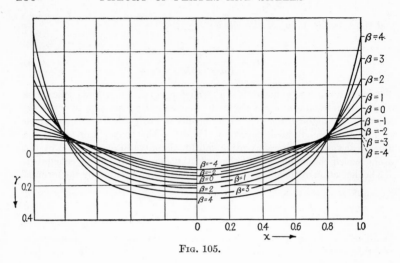

FIG. 105.

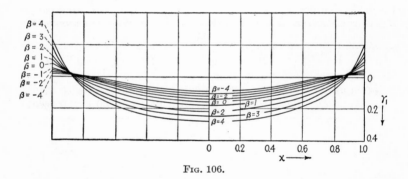

FIG. 106.

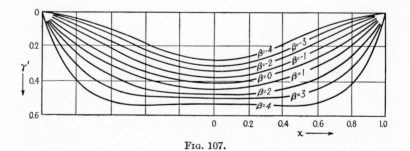

FIG. 107.

Table **37**, and the values of γ' and γ'_1 are represented graphically in Figs. 107 and 108, respectively.

To calculate the deflections and stresses in a given plate of variable thickness we begin by choosing the proper value for the constant β as given by the curves in Fig. 104. When the value of β has been determined and the conditions at the boundary are known, we can use the values of Table 37 to calculate the deflection at the center and the curves in Figs. 105, 106 or 107, 108 to calculate the maximum stress. If the shape of the diametrical section of the given plate cannot be represented with satisfactory accuracy by one of the curves in Fig. 104, an approximate method of solving the problem can always be used. This method consists of dividing the plate by concentric circles into several rings and using for each ring formulas

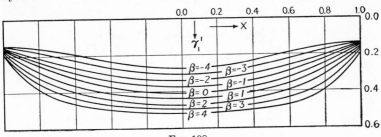

Fig. 108.

developed for a ring plate of constant thickness. The procedure of calculation is then similar to that proposed by R. Grammel for calculating stresses in rotating disks.[1]

55. Non-linear Problems in Bending of Circular Plates.—

From the theory of bending of bars it is known that, if the conditions at the supports of a bar or the loading conditions are changing with the deflection of the bar, this deflection will no longer be proportional to the load, and the principle of superposition cannot be applied.[2] Similar problems are also encountered in the case of bending of plates.[3] A simple example of this

---

[1] GRAMMEL, R., *Dinglers Polytech. J.*, vol. 338, p. 217, 1923. The analogy existing between the problem of a rotating disk and the problem of lateral bending of a circular plate of variable thickness was indicated by L. Föppl, *Z. angew. Math. Mech.*, vol. 2, p. 92, 1922. Non-symmetrical bending of circular plates of non-uniform thickness is discussed by G. Olsson, *Ingenieur-Archiv*, vol. 10, p. 14, 1939.

[2] An example of such problems is discussed in the author's "Strength of Materials," vol. 1, p. 157, 1930.

[3] See K. Girkman, *Der Stahlbau*, vol. 18, 1931. Several examples of such problems are discussed also in a paper by R. Hofmann, *Z. angew. Math. Mech.*, vol. 18, p. 226, 1938.

kind is shown in Fig. 109.   A circular plate of radius a is pressed
by a uniform load q against an absolutely rigid horizontal
foundation.   If moments of an intensity M_a are applied along
the edge of the plate, a ring-shaped portion of the plate may be
bent as shown in the figure, whereas a middle portion of radius b
may remain flat.   Such conditions prevail, for example, in the
bending of the bottom plate of a circular cylindrical container
filled with liquid.   The moments M_a represent in this case the
action of the cylindrical wall of the container, which undergoes
a local bending at the bottom.   Applying to the ring-shaped

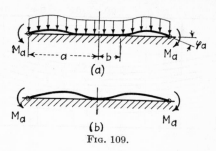

Fig. 109.

portion of the bottom plate the known solution for a uniformly
loaded circular plate [see expression (m) in Art. 48], we obtain
the deflection

$$w = C_1 + C_2 \log r + C_3 r^2 + C_4 r^2 \log r + \frac{qr^4}{64D}. \qquad (a)$$

For determining the constants of integration $C_1, \ldots, C_4$ we
have the following boundary conditions at the outer edge:

$$(w)_{r=a} = 0, \qquad (M_r)_{r=a} = -M_a. \qquad (b)$$

Along the circle of radius b the deflection and the slope are zero.
The bending moment M_r also must be zero along this circle,
since the inner portion of the plate remains flat.   Hence the conditions at the circle of radius b are

$$(w)_{r=b} = 0, \qquad \left(\frac{dw}{dr}\right)_{r=b} = 0, \qquad (M_r)_{r=b} = 0. \qquad (c)$$

By applying conditions (b) and (c) to expression (a) we obtain
the five following equations:

$$C_1 + C_2 \log a + C_3 a^2 + C_4 a^2 \log a = -\frac{qa^4}{64D},$$

$$C_1 + C_2 \log b + C_3 b^2 + C_4 b^2 \log b = -\frac{qb^4}{64D},$$

$$C_2 \frac{\nu - 1}{a^2} + C_3 2(\nu + 1)$$

$$+ C_4 (3 + 2 \log a + 2\nu \log a + \nu) = -\frac{qa^2}{16D}(3 + \nu) + \frac{M_a}{D},$$

$$C_2 \frac{\nu - 1}{b^2} + C_3 2(\nu + 1)$$

$$+ C_4 (3 + 2 \log b + 2\nu \log b + \nu) = -\frac{qb^2}{16D}(3 + \nu),$$

$$C_2 \frac{1}{b} + C_3 2b + C_4 b(2 \log b + 1) = -\frac{qb^3}{16D}. \qquad (d)$$

By eliminating the constants $C_1, \ldots, C_4$ from these equations we obtain an equation connecting M_a and the ratio b/a, from which the radius b of the flat portion of the plate can be calculated for each given value of M_a. With this value of b the constants of integration can be evaluated, and the expression for the deflection of the plate can be obtained from Eq. (a). Representing the moment M_a and the angle of rotation φ_a of the edge of the plate by the equations

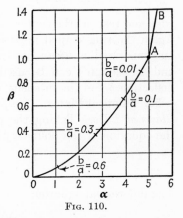

FIG. 110.

$$M_a = \alpha \frac{qa^2}{32} \quad \text{and} \quad \varphi_a = \beta \frac{qa^3}{32D} \qquad (e)$$

and repeating the above-mentioned calculations for several values of the moment M_a, we can represent the relation between the constant factors α and β graphically, as shown in Fig. 110, for the particular case[1] $\nu = 0$. It is seen from this figure that β does not vary in proportion to α and that the resistance to rotation of the edge of the plate decreases as the ratio b/a decreases. This condition holds up to the value $\alpha = 5$ at which value $\beta = 1$, $b/a = 0$, and the plate touches the foundation only at the

---

[1] This case is discussed in the paper by Hofmann, *loc. cit.*, p. 287.

center, as shown in Fig. 109b. For larger values of α, $i.e.$, for moments larger than $M_a = 5qa^2/32$, the plate does not touch the foundation, and the relation between α and β is represented by the straight line AB. The value $M_a = 5qa^2/32$ is that value at which the deflection at the center of the plate produced by the moments M_a is numerically equal to the deflection of a uniformly loaded plate simply supported along the edge [see Eq. (68)].

Another example of the same kind is shown in Fig. 111. A uniformly loaded circular plate is simply supported along the

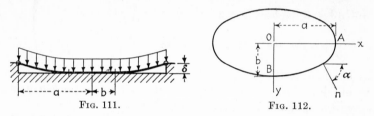

FIG. 111.   FIG. 112.

edge and rests at the center upon an absolutely rigid foundation. Again the ring-shaped portion of the plate with outer radius a and inner radius b can be treated as a uniformly loaded plate, and solution (a) can be used. The ratio b/a depends on the deflection δ and the intensity of the load q.

56. Elliptical Plates. *Uniformly Loaded Elliptical Plate with a Clamped Edge.*—Taking the coordinates as shown in Fig. 112, the equation of the boundary of the plate is

$$\frac{x^2}{a^2} + \frac{y^2}{b^2} - 1 = 0. \tag{a}$$

The differential equation

$$\Delta \Delta w = \frac{q}{D} \tag{b}$$

and the boundary conditions for the clamped edges, $i.e.$,

$$w = 0 \quad \text{and} \quad \frac{\partial w}{\partial n} = 0, \tag{c}$$

are satisfied by taking for the deflection w the expression[1]

---

[1] This solution and the solution for a uniformly varying load q are obtained by G. H. Bryan; see A. E. H. Love's book, "Theory of Elasticity," 4th ed. p. 484. The case of an elliptical plate of variable thickness is discussed by G. Olsson, *Ingenieur-Archiv*, vol. 9, p. 108, 1938.

$$w = w_0\left(1 - \frac{x^2}{a^2} - \frac{y^2}{b^2}\right)^2. \qquad (d)$$

It is noted that this expression and its first derivatives with respect to x and y vanish at the boundary by virtue of Eq. (a). Substituting expression (d) in Eq. (b), we see that the equation is also satisfied provided

$$w_0 = \frac{q}{D\left(\dfrac{24}{a^4} + \dfrac{24}{b^4} + \dfrac{16}{a^2b^2}\right)}. \qquad (167)$$

Thus, since expression (d) satisfies Eq. (b) and the boundary conditions, it represents the rigorous solution for a uniformly loaded elliptical plate with a clamped edge. Substituting $x = y = 0$ in expression (d), we find that w_0, as given by Eq. (167), is the deflection of the plate at the center. If $a = b$, we obtain for the deflection the value previously derived for a clamped circular plate [Eq. (62), page 60]. If $a = \infty$, the deflection w_0 becomes equal to the deflection of a uniformly loaded strip with clamped ends and having the span $2b$.

The bending and twisting moments are obtained by substituting expression (d) in Eqs. (99) and (100). In this way we find

$$M_x = -D\left(\frac{\partial^2 w}{\partial x^2} + \nu\frac{\partial^2 w}{\partial y^2}\right) = -4w_0 D\left[\frac{3x^2}{a^4} + \frac{y^2}{a^2b^2} - \frac{1}{a^2}\right.$$
$$\left. + \nu\left(\frac{x^2}{a^2b^2} + \frac{3y^2}{b^4} - \frac{1}{b^2}\right)\right]. \quad (e)$$

For the center of the plate and for the ends of the horizontal axis we obtain, respectively,

$$(M_x)_{x=0,y=0} = 4w_0 D\left(\frac{1}{a^2} + \frac{\nu}{b^2}\right) \quad \text{and} \quad (M_x)_{x=a,y=0} = -\frac{8w_0 D}{a^2}. \qquad (f)$$

Similarly, for the moments M_y at the center and at the ends of the vertical axis we find, respectively,

$$(M_y)_{x=0,y=0} = 4w_0 D\left(\frac{1}{b^2} + \frac{\nu}{a^2}\right) \quad \text{and} \quad (M_y)_{x=0,y=b} = -\frac{8w_0 D}{b^2} \qquad (g)$$

It is seen that the maximum bending stress is obtained at the ends of the shorter principal axis of the ellipse. Having the moments M_x, M_y and M_{xy}, the values of the bending moment M_n and the twisting moment M_{nt} at any point on the boundary are obtained from Eqs. (c) (Art. 22, page 94) by substituting in these equations

$$\cos \alpha = \frac{dy}{ds} = \frac{b^2 x}{\sqrt{a^4 y^2 + b^4 x^2}}, \qquad \sin \alpha = -\frac{dx}{ds} = \frac{a^2 y}{\sqrt{a^4 y^2 + b^4 x^2}}$$

$$(h)$$

The shearing forces Q_x and Q_y at any point are obtained by substituting expression (d) in Eqs. (102) and (103). At the boundary the shearing force Q_n is obtained from Eq. (d) (Art. 22, page 94), and the reaction V_n from Eq. (g) of the same article. In this manner we find that the intensity of the reaction is a maximum at the ends of the minor axis of the ellipse and that its absolute value is

$$(V_n)_{\text{max.}} = \frac{a^2 b (3a^2 + b^2) q}{3a^4 + 3b^4 + 2a^2 b^2} \qquad \text{for} \qquad a > b. \qquad (i)$$

The smallest absolute value of V_n is at the ends of the major axis of the ellipse where

$$(V_n)_{\text{min.}} = \frac{ab^2(a^2 + 3b^2)q}{3a^4 + 3b^4 + 2a^2 b^2}. \qquad (j)$$

For a circle, $a = b$, and we find $(V_n)_{\text{max.}} = (V_n)_{\text{min.}} = qa/2$.

Elliptical Plate with a Clamped Edge and Bent by a Uniformly Varying Pressure.—Assuming that $q = q_0 x$, we find that Eq. (b) and the boundary conditions (c) are satisfied by taking

$$w = \frac{q_0 x}{24D} \frac{\left(1 - \dfrac{x^2}{a^2} - \dfrac{y^2}{b^2}\right)^2}{\dfrac{5}{a^4} + \dfrac{1}{b^4} + \dfrac{2}{a^2 b^2}}. \qquad (168)$$

From this expression the bending moments and the reactions at the boundary can be calculated as in the previous case.

Uniformly Loaded Elliptical Plate with Simply Supported Edge.—The solution for this case is more complicated than in the case of clamped edges;[1] therefore we give here only some final numerical results. Assuming that $a/b > 1$, we represent the deflection and the bending moments at the center by the formulas

$$(w)_{x=y=0} = \alpha \frac{qb^4}{Eh^3}, \qquad M_x = \beta q b^2, \qquad M_y = \beta_1 q b^2. \qquad (k)$$

[1] See B. G. Galerkin, *Z. angew. Math. Mech.*, vol. 3, p. 113, 1923.

The values of the constant factors α, β and β_1 for various values of the ratio a/b and for $\nu = 0.3$ are given in Table 38.

TABLE 38.—FACTORS α, β, β_1 IN FORMULAS (k) FOR UNIFORMLY LOADED AND SIMPLY SUPPORTED ELLIPTICAL PLATES
$$\nu = 0.3$$

a/b	1	1.1	1.2	1.3	1.4	1.5	2	3	4	5	∞
$\alpha =$	0.70	0.83	0.96	1.07	1.17	1.26	1.58	1.88	2.02	2.10	2.28
$\beta =$	0.206	0.215	0.219	0.223	0.223	0.222	0.210	0.188	0.184	0.170	0.150
$\beta_1 =$	0.206	0.235	0.261	0.282	0.303	0.321	0.379	0.433	0.465	0.480	0.500

Comparison of these numerical values with those previously obtained for rectangular plates (Table 5, page 133) shows that for equal values of the ratio of the sides of rectangular plates and the ratio a/b of the semi-axes of elliptical plates the values of the deflections and the moments at the center in the two kinds of plate do not differ appreciably. The case of a plate having the form of half an ellipse bounded by the transverse axis has also been discussed.[1]

57. Triangular Plates. *Equilateral Triangular Plate Simply Supported at the Edges.*—The bending of such a triangular plate by moments M_n uniformly distributed along the boundary has already been discussed (see page 102). It was

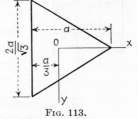

FIG. 113.

shown that in such a case the deflection surface of the plate is the same as that of a uniformly stretched and uniformly loaded membrane and is represented by the equation

$$w = \frac{M_n}{4aD}\left[x^3 - 3y^2x - a(x^2 + y^2) + \frac{4}{27}a^3 \right], \qquad (a)$$

in which a denotes the height of the triangle, and the coordinate axes are taken as shown in Fig. 113.

In the case of a uniformly loaded plate the deflection surface is[2]

$$w = \frac{q}{64aD}\left[x^3 - 3y^2x - a(x^2 + y^2) + \frac{4}{27}a^3 \right]\left(\frac{4}{9}a^2 - x^2 - y^2 \right). \tag{169}$$

[1] GALERKIN, B. G., *Messenger Math.*, vol. 52, p. 99, 1923.

[2] The problem of bending of a plate having the form of an equilateral triangle was solved by S. Woinowsky-Krieger, *Ingenieur-Archiv.* vol. 4, p. 254, 1933.

By differentiation we find

$$\Delta w = -\frac{q}{4aD}\left[x^3 - 3y^2x - a(x^2 + y^2) + \frac{4}{27}a^3\right]. \quad (b)$$

It may be seen from (169) and (b) that the deflection and the bending moment at the boundary vanish, since the expression in the brackets is zero at the boundary. Further differentiation gives

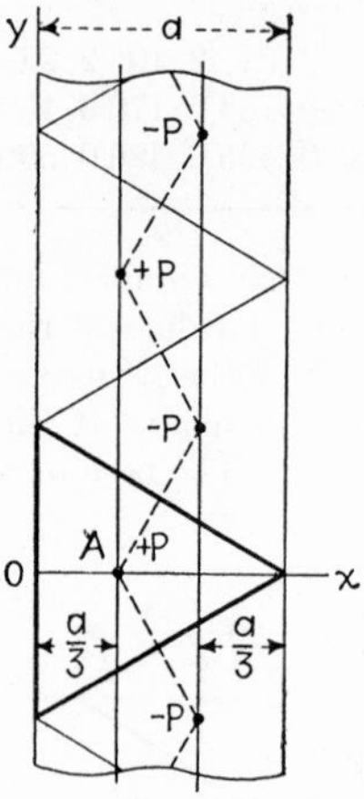

$$\Delta\Delta w = \frac{q}{D}. \quad (c)$$

Hence the differential equation of the deflection surface is also satisfied, and expression (169) represents the solution of the problem. Having the expression for deflections, the expressions for the bending moments and the shearing forces can be readily obtained. The maximum bending moment occurs on the lines bisecting the angles of the triangle. Considering the points along the x-axis and taking $\nu = 0.3$, we find

Fig. 114.

$$(M_x)_{\text{max.}} = 0.0248qa^2, \quad \text{at} \quad x = -0.062a; \atop (M_y)_{\text{max.}} = 0.0259qa^2, \quad \text{at} \quad x = 0.129a. \qquad (170)$$

At the center of the plate

$$M_x = M_y = (1 + \nu)\frac{qa^2}{54}. \quad (171)$$

The case of a concentrated force acting on the plate can be solved by using the *method of images* (see page 174). Let us take a case in which the point of application of the load is at the center A of the plate (Fig. 114). Considering the plate, shown in the figure by the heavy lines, as a portion of an infinitely long rectangular plate of width a, we apply the fictitious loads P with alternating signs as shown in the figure. The nodal lines of the deflection surface, produced by such loading, evidently divide the infinitely long plate into equilateral triangles each of which is in exactly the same condition as the given plate. Thus our problem is reduced to that of bending of an infinitely long rectangular plate loaded by the two rows of equidistant loads $+P$ and $-P$. Knowing the solution for one concentrated force (see Art. 31) and using the method of superposition, the deflection at point A and the stresses near that point can be readily calculated, since the effect of the fictitious forces on bending decreases rapidly as their distance from point A increases. In this manner we find the deflection at A

$$w_0 = 0.00571 \frac{Pa^2}{D}. \tag{172}$$

The bending moments at a small distance c from A are given by the expressions

$$\left.\begin{aligned}
M_x &= \frac{(1+\nu)P}{4\pi}\left(\log\frac{a\sqrt{3}}{\pi c} - 0.379\right) - \frac{(1-\nu)P}{8\pi}, \\
M_y &= \frac{(1+\nu)P}{4\pi}\left(\log\frac{a\sqrt{3}}{\pi c} - 0.379\right) + \frac{(1-\nu)P}{8\pi}.
\end{aligned}\right\} \tag{173}$$

Since for a simply supported and centrally loaded circular plate of radius a_0 the radial and the tangential moments at a distance c from the center are, respectively (see page 74),

$$M_r = \frac{(1+\nu)P}{4\pi}\log\frac{a_0}{c} \quad \text{and} \quad M_t = \frac{(1+\nu)P}{4\pi}\log\frac{a_0}{c} + \frac{(1-\nu)P}{4\pi}, \quad (d)$$

it can be concluded that the first terms on the right side of Eqs. (173) are identical with the logarithmical terms for a circular plate with a radius

$$a_0 = \frac{a\sqrt{3}}{\pi}e^{-0.379}. \tag{e}$$

Hence the local stresses near the point of application of the load can be calculated by using the thick-plate theory developed for circular plates (see Art. 19).

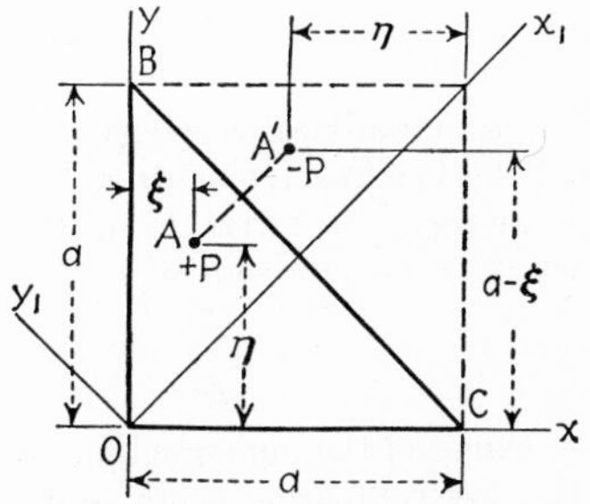

FIG. 115.

Plate in the Form of an Isosceles Right Triangle with Simply Supported Edges.—Such a plate may be considered as one-half of a square plate, as indicated in Fig. 115 by dotted lines, and the methods previously developed for rectangular plates can be applied.[1] If a load P is applied at a point A with coordinates ξ, η (Fig. 115), we assume a fictitious load $-P$ applied at A' which is the image of the point A with respect to the line BC. These two loads evidently produce a deflection of the square plate such that the diagonal BC becomes a nodal line. Thus the portion OBC of the square plate is in exactly the same condition as a simply supported triangular plate OBC. Considering the load $+P$ and using the Navier solution for a square plate (page 122), we obtain the deflection

$$w_1 = \frac{4Pa^2}{\pi^4 D} \sum_{m=1}^{\infty} \sum_{n=1}^{\infty} \frac{\sin \dfrac{m\pi\xi}{a} \sin \dfrac{n\pi\eta}{a}}{(m^2 + n^2)^2} \sin \frac{m\pi x}{a} \sin \frac{n\pi y}{a}. \tag{f}$$

In the same manner, considering the load $-P$ and taking $a - \eta$ instead of ξ and $a - \xi$ instead of η, we obtain

$$w_2 = -\frac{4Pa^2}{\pi^4 D} \sum_{m=1}^{\infty} \sum_{n=1}^{\infty} (-1)^{m+n} \frac{\sin \dfrac{m\pi\eta}{a} \sin \dfrac{n\pi\xi}{a}}{(m^2 + n^2)^2} \sin \frac{m\pi x}{a} \sin \frac{n\pi y}{a}. \tag{g}$$

The complete deflection of the triangular plate is obtained by summing up expressions (f) and (g); i.e.,

$$w = w_1 + w_2. \tag{h}$$

To obtain the deflection of the triangular plate produced by a uniformly distributed load of intensity q, we substitute $q\, d\xi\, d\eta$ for P and integrate expression (h) over the area of the triangle OBC. In this manner we obtain

$$w = \frac{16qa^4}{\pi^6 D}\left[\sum_{m=1,3,5,\cdots} \sum_{n=2,4,6,\cdots}^{\infty} \frac{n \sin \dfrac{m\pi x}{a} \sin \dfrac{n\pi y}{a}}{m(n^2 - m^2)(m^2 + n^2)^2} \right.$$
$$\left. + \sum_{m=2,4,6,\cdots} \sum_{n=1,3,5,\cdots}^{\infty} \frac{m \sin \dfrac{m\pi x}{a} \sin \dfrac{n\pi y}{a}}{n(m^2 - n^2)(m^2 + n^2)^2} \right]. \tag{i}$$

This is a rapidly converging series and can be used to calculate the deflection and the bending moments at any point in the plate. Taking the axis of symmetry of the triangle in Fig. 115 as the x_1-axis and representing the deflections and the moments M_{x_1} and M_{y_1} along this axis by the formulas

$$w = \alpha \frac{qa^4}{Eh^3}, \qquad M_{x_1} = \beta qa^2, \qquad M_{y_1} = \beta_1 qa^2, \tag{j}$$

the values of the numerical factors α, β and β_1 are as given in Figs. 116 and 117 By comparing these results with those given in Table 5 for a uni-

---

[1] This method of solution was given by A. Nadai, "Elastische Platten," p. 178, 1925. Another way of handling the same problem was given by B. G. Galerkin, *Bull. acad. sci. de Russie*, p. 223, 1919; and *Bull. Polytech. Inst.*, vol. 28, p. 1, St. Petersburg, 1919.

formly loaded square plate, it can be concluded that for the same value of a the maximum bending moment for a triangular plate is somewhat less than half the maximum bending moment for a square plate.

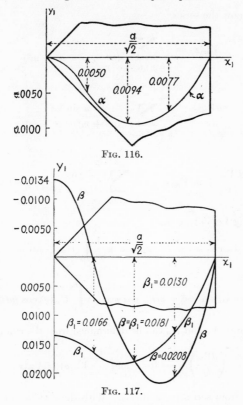

Fɪɢ. 116.

Fɪɢ. 117.

To simplify the calculation of the deflections and moments the double series (i) can be transformed to simple series.[1]   For this purpose we use the known series

$$U_m(x) = \sum_{n=2,4,6,\cdots}^{\infty} \frac{\cos nx}{(n^2 + m^2)^2} = -\frac{2}{m^4} + \frac{\pi}{2m^3} \frac{\cosh m\left(\frac{\pi}{2} - x\right)}{\sinh \frac{\pi m}{2}}$$

$$+ \frac{\pi^2}{4m^2} \frac{\cosh mx}{\sinh^2 \frac{\pi m}{2}} + \frac{\pi x}{2m^2} \frac{\sinh m\left(\frac{\pi}{2} - x\right)}{\sinh \frac{m\pi}{2}}, \quad (k)$$

[1] This transformation was communicated to the writer by J. V. Uspensky.

which can be represented in the following form

$$U_m(x) = (\alpha_m + \beta_m x) \cosh mx + (\gamma_m + \delta_m) \sinh mx - \frac{2}{m^4}. \qquad (l)$$

Considering now the series

$$V_m(x) = \sum_{n=2,4,6,\cdots}^{\infty} \frac{\cos nx}{(n^2 + m^2)^2 (n^2 - m^2)}, \qquad (m)$$

we obtain

$$\frac{dV_m}{dx} = -\sum_{n=2,4,6,\cdots}^{\infty} \frac{n \sin nx}{(n^2 + m^2)^2 (n^2 - m^2)}, \qquad (n)$$

and

$$\frac{d^2V_m}{dx^2} + m^2 V_m = -\sum_{n=2,4,6,\cdots}^{\infty} \frac{\cos nx}{(n^2 + m^2)^2} = -U_m. \qquad (o)$$

By integrating Eq. (o) we find

$$V_m = A_m \cos mx + B_m \sin mx + \frac{1}{m} \int_0^x U_m(\xi) \sin m(\xi - x) d\xi, \qquad (p)$$

and

$$\frac{dV_m}{dx} = -mA_m \sin mx + mB_m \cos mx - \int_0^x U_m(\xi) \cos m(\xi - x) d\xi. \qquad (q)$$

The constants A_m and B_m can be determined from the conditions

$$\left(\frac{dV_m}{dx}\right)_{x=0} = 0 \qquad \text{and} \qquad V_m(o) = V_m(\pi) \qquad (r)$$

which follow from series (n) and (m). With these values of the constants expression (q) gives the sum of series (n) which reduces the double series in expression (i) to a simple series.

CHAPTER VIII

BENDING OF PLATES UNDER THE COMBINED ACTION OF LATERAL LOADS AND FORCES IN THE MIDDLE PLANE OF THE PLATE

58. Differential Equation of the Deflection Surface.—In our previous discussion it has always been assumed that the plate is bent by lateral loads only. If in addition to lateral loads there are forces acting in the middle plane of the plate, these latter forces may have a considerable effect on the bending of the plate and must be considered in deriving the corresponding differential equation of the deflection surface. Proceeding as in the case of lateral loading (see Art. 21, page 85), we consider the equilibrium of a small element cut from the plate by two pairs of planes parallel to the xz- and yz-coordinate planes (Fig. 118). In addition to the forces discussed in Art. 21 we now have forces acting in the middle plane of the plate. We denote the magnitude of these forces per unit length by N_x, N_y and $N_{xy} = N_{yx}$, as shown in

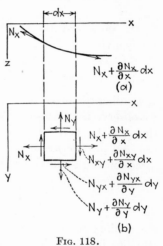

Fig. 118.

the figure. Projecting these forces on the x- and y-axes and assuming that there are no body forces or tangential forces acting in those directions at the faces of the plate, we obtain the following equations of equilibrium:

$$\left. \begin{array}{l} \dfrac{\partial N_x}{\partial x} + \dfrac{\partial N_{xy}}{\partial y} = 0, \\[3mm] \dfrac{\partial N_{xy}}{\partial x} + \dfrac{\partial N_y}{\partial y} = 0. \end{array} \right\} \qquad (174)$$

These equations are entirely independent of the three equations

299

of equilibrium considered in Art. 21 and can be treated separately, as will be shown in Art. 60.

In considering the projection of the forces shown in Fig. 118 on the z-axis, we must take into account the bending of the plate and the resulting small angles between the forces N_x and N_y that act on the opposite sides of the element. As a result of this bending the projection of the normal forces N_x on the z-axis gives

$$-N_x\,dy\frac{\partial w}{\partial x} + \left(N_x + \frac{\partial N_x}{\partial x}dx\right)\left(\frac{\partial w}{\partial x} + \frac{\partial^2 w}{\partial x^2}dx\right)dy.$$

After simplification, if the small quantities of higher than the second order are neglected, this projection becomes

$$N_x\frac{\partial^2 w}{\partial x^2}dx\,dy + \frac{\partial N_x}{\partial x}\frac{\partial w}{\partial x}dx\,dy. \qquad (a)$$

In the same way the projection of the normal forces N_y on the z-axis gives

$$N_y\frac{\partial^2 w}{\partial y^2}dx\,dy + \frac{\partial N_y}{\partial y}\frac{\partial w}{\partial y}dx\,dy. \qquad (b)$$

Regarding the projection of the shearing forces N_{xy} on the z-axis, we observe that the slope of the deflection surface in the y-direction on the two opposite sides of the element is $\partial w/\partial y$ and $(\partial w/\partial y) + (\partial^2 w/\partial x\partial y)dx$. Hence the projection of the shearing forces on the z-axis is equal to

$$N_{xy}\frac{\partial^2 w}{\partial x\partial y}dxdy + \frac{\partial N_{xy}}{\partial x}\frac{\partial w}{\partial y}dxdy.$$

An analogous expression can be obtained for the projection of the shearing forces $N_{yx} = N_{xy}$ on the z-axis. The final expression for the projection of all the shearing forces on the z-axis then can be written as

$$2N_{xy}\frac{\partial^2 w}{\partial x\partial y}dx\,dy + \frac{\partial N_{xy}}{\partial x}\frac{\partial w}{\partial y}dx\,dy + \frac{\partial N_{xy}}{\partial y}\frac{\partial w}{\partial x}dx\,dy. \qquad (c)$$

Adding expressions (a), (b) and (c) to the load $q\,dx\,dy$ acting on the element and using Eqs. (174), we obtain, instead of Eq. (g) (page 87), the following equation of equilibrium:

$$\frac{\partial^2 M_x}{\partial x^2} - 2\frac{\partial^2 M_{xy}}{\partial x\,\partial y} + \frac{\partial^2 M_y}{\partial y^2} = -\left(q + N_x\frac{\partial^2 w}{\partial x^2} + N_y\frac{\partial^2 w}{\partial y^2} + 2N_{xy}\frac{\partial^2 w}{\partial x\,\partial y}\right).$$

Substituting expressions (99) and (100) for M_x, M_y and M_{xy}, we obtain

$$\frac{\partial^4 w}{\partial x^4} + 2\frac{\partial^4 w}{\partial x^2\,\partial y^2} + \frac{\partial^4 w}{\partial y^4} = \frac{1}{D}\left(q + N_x\frac{\partial^2 w}{\partial x^2} + N_y\frac{\partial^2 w}{\partial y^2} \right.$$
$$\left. + 2N_{xy}\frac{\partial^2 w}{\partial x\,\partial y} \right). \quad (175)$$

This equation should be used instead of Eq. (101) in determining the deflection of a plate if in addition to lateral loads there are forces in the middle plane of the plate.

If there are body forces[1] acting in the middle plane of the plate or tangential forces distributed over the surfaces of the plate, the differential equations of equilibrium of the element shown in Fig. 118 become

$$\left. \begin{array}{l} \dfrac{\partial N_x}{\partial x} + \dfrac{\partial N_{xy}}{\partial y} + X = 0, \\[2mm] \dfrac{\partial N_{xy}}{\partial x} + \dfrac{\partial N_y}{\partial y} + Y = 0. \end{array} \right\} \quad (176)$$

Here X and Y denote the two components of the body forces or of the tangential forces per unit area of the middle plane of the plate.

Using Eqs. (176), instead of Eqs. (174), we obtain the following differential equation[2] for the deflection surface:

$$\frac{\partial^4 w}{\partial x^4} + 2\frac{\partial^4 w}{\partial x^2\,\partial y^2} + \frac{\partial^4 w}{\partial y^4} = \frac{1}{D}\left(q + N_x\frac{\partial^2 w}{\partial x^2} + N_y\frac{\partial^2 w}{\partial y^2} + 2N_{xy}\frac{\partial^2 w}{\partial x\,\partial y} \right.$$
$$\left. - X\frac{\partial w}{\partial x} - Y\frac{\partial w}{\partial y} \right). \quad (177)$$

Equation (175) or Eq. (177) together with the conditions at the boundary (see Art. 22, page 89) defines the deflection of a plate loaded laterally and submitted to the action of forces in the middle plane of the plate.

59. Rectangular Plate with Simply Supported Edges under the Combined Action of Uniform Lateral Load and Uniform Tension.

—Assume that the plate is under uniform tension in the x-direction, as shown in Fig. 119. The uniform lateral load q can be represented by the trigonometric series (see page 118)

---

[1] An example of a body force acting in the middle plane of the plate is the gravity force in the case of a vertical position of a plate.

[2] This differential equation has been derived by Saint Venant (see final note 73) in his translation of Clebsch, "Théorie de l'élasticité des corps solides," p. 704, 1883.

$$q = \frac{16q}{\pi^2} \sum_{m=1,3,5,\cdots}^{\infty} \sum_{n=1,3,5,\cdots}^{\infty} \frac{1}{mn} \sin \frac{m\pi x}{a} \sin \frac{n\pi y}{b}, \qquad (a)$$

Equation (175) thus becomes

$$\frac{\partial^4 w}{\partial x^4} + 2\frac{\partial^4 w}{\partial x^2 \, \partial y^2} + \frac{\partial^4 w}{\partial y^4} - \frac{N_x}{D}\frac{\partial^2 w}{\partial x^2}$$

$$= \frac{16q}{D\pi^2} \sum_{m=1,3,5,\cdots}^{\infty} \sum_{n=1,3,5,\cdots}^{\infty} \frac{1}{mn} \sin \frac{m\pi x}{a} \sin \frac{n\pi y}{b}. \qquad (b)$$

This equation and the boundary conditions at the simply supported edges will be satisfied if we take the deflection w in the form of the series

$$w = \sum \sum a_{mn} \sin \frac{m\pi x}{a} \sin \frac{n\pi y}{b}. \qquad (c)$$

Substituting this series in Eq. (b), we find the following values for the coefficients a_{mn}:

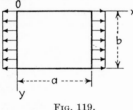

FIG. 119.

$$a_{mn} = \frac{16q}{D\pi^6 mn\left[\left(\dfrac{m^2}{a^2} + \dfrac{n^2}{b^2}\right)^2 + \dfrac{N_x m^2}{\pi^2 Da^2}\right]}, \qquad (d)$$

in which m and n are odd numbers 1, 3, 5, . . . , and $a_{mn} = 0$ if m or n or both are even numbers.   Hence the deflection surface of the plate is

$$w = \frac{16q}{\pi^6 D} \sum_{m=1,3,5,\cdots}^{\infty} \sum_{n=1,3,5,\cdots}^{\infty} \frac{1}{mn\left[\left(\dfrac{m^2}{a^2} + \dfrac{n^2}{b^2}\right)^2 + \dfrac{N_x m^2}{\pi^2 \, Da^2}\right]} \sin \frac{m\pi x}{a} \sin \frac{n\pi y}{b}. \qquad (e)$$

Comparing this result with solution (122) (page 118), we conclude from the presence of the term $N_x m^2/\pi^2 Da^2$ in the brackets of the denominator that the deflection of the plate is somewhat diminished by the action of the tensile forces N_x. This is as would be expected.

If, instead of tension, we have compression, the force N_x becomes negative, and the deflections (e) become larger than those of the plate bent by lateral load only. It may also be seen in this case that at certain values of the compressive force N_x the denominator of one of the terms in series (e) may vanish. This indicates that at such values of N_x the plate may buckle laterally without any lateral loading. This phenomenon of elastic instability will be discussed later.

60. Application of the Energy Method.—The energy method, which was previously used in discussing bending of plates by lateral loading (see Art. 28, page 120), can also be applied to the cases in which the lateral load is combined with forces acting in the middle plane of the plate. To establish the expression for the strain energy corresponding to the latter forces let us assume that these forces are applied first to the unbent plate. In this way we obtain a two-dimensional problem which can be treated by the methods of the theory of elasticity.[1] Assuming that this problem is solved and that the forces N_x, N_y and N_{xy} are known at each point of the plate, the components of strain of the middle plane of the plate are obtained from the known formulas representing Hooke's law, *viz.*,

$$\left. \begin{aligned} \epsilon_x &= \frac{1}{hE}(N_x - \nu N_y), \qquad \epsilon_y = \frac{1}{hE}(N_y - \nu N_x), \\ \gamma_{xy} &= \frac{N_{xy}}{hG}. \end{aligned} \right\} \qquad (a)$$

The strain energy, due to stretching of the middle plane of the plate, is then

$$\begin{aligned} V_1 &= \tfrac{1}{2}\iint (N_x\epsilon_x + N_y\epsilon_y + N_{xy}\gamma_{xy})dx\,dy \\ &= \frac{1}{2hE}\int\int [N_x^2 + N_y^2 - 2\nu N_x N_y + 2(1 + \nu)N_{xy}^2]dx\,dy, \quad (178) \end{aligned}$$

where the integration is extended over the entire plate.

Let us now apply the lateral load. This load will bend the plate and produce additional strain of the middle plane. In our previous discussion of bending of plates, this latter strain was always neglected. Here, however, we have to take it into consideration, since this small strain in combination with the finite forces N_x, N_y, N_{xy} may add to the expression for strain energy some

---

[1] See, for example, author's "Theory of Elasticity," p. 12.

terms of the same order as the strain energy of bending.   The
x-, y- and z-components of the small displacement that a point in
the middle plane of the plate experiences during bending will be
denoted by u, v and w, respectively.   Considering a linear ele-

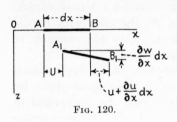

FIG. 120.

ment AB of that plane in the
x-direction, it may be seen from Fig.
120 that the elongation of the element due to the displacement u is
equal to $(\partial u / \partial x)dx$.   The elongation of the same element due to the
displacement w is $\frac{1}{2}(\partial w / \partial x)^2 \, dx$, as
may be seen from the comparison of
the length of the element $A_1 B_1$ in Fig. 120 with the length of its
projection on the x-axis.   Thus the total unit elongation in the
x-direction of an element taken in the middle plane of the plate is

$$\epsilon_x' = \frac{\partial u}{\partial x} + \frac{1}{2}\left(\frac{\partial w}{\partial x}\right)^2. \tag{179}$$

Similarly the strain in the y-direction is

$$\epsilon_y' = \frac{\partial v}{\partial y} + \frac{1}{2}\left(\frac{\partial w}{\partial y}\right)^2. \tag{180}$$

Considering now the shearing strain in the middle plane due
to bending, we conclude as before (see Fig. 23) that the shearing

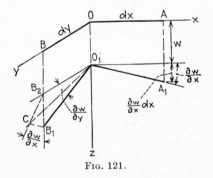

FIG. 121.

strain due to the displacements u and v is $(\partial u / \partial y) + (\partial v / \partial x)$.
To determine the shearing strain due to the displacement w we
take two infinitely small linear elements OA and OB in the x-
and y-directions, as shown in Fig. 121.   Because of displacements

in the z-direction these elements come to the positions O_1A_1 and O_1B_1. The difference between the angle $\pi/2$ and the angle $A_1O_1B_1$ is the shearing strain corresponding to the displacement w. To determine this difference we consider the right angle $B_2O_1A_1$, in which B_2O_1 is parallel to BO. Rotating the plane $B_2O_1A_1$ with respect to O_1A_1 by the angle $\partial w/\partial y$, we bring the plane $B_2O_1A_1$ into coincidence with the plane $B_1O_1A_1$[1] and the point B_2 to position C. The displacement B_2C is equal to $(\partial w/\partial y)dy$ and is inclined to the vertical B_2B_1 by the angle $\partial w/\partial x$. Hence B_1C is equal to $(\partial w/\partial x)(\partial w/\partial y)dy$, and the angle CO_1B_1, which represents the shearing strain corresponding to the displacement w, is $(\partial w/\partial x)(\partial w/\partial y)$. Adding this shearing strain to the strain produced by the displacements u and v, we obtain

$$\gamma'_{xy} = \frac{\partial u}{\partial y} + \frac{\partial v}{\partial x} + \frac{\partial w}{\partial x}\frac{\partial w}{\partial y}. \tag{181}$$

Formulas (179), (180) and (181) represent the components of the additional strain in the middle plane of the plate due to small deflections. Considering them as very small in comparison with the components ϵ_x, ϵ_y and γ_{xy} used in the derivation of expression (178), we can assume that the forces N_x, N_y, N_{xy} remain unchanged during bending. With this assumption the additional strain energy of the plate, due to the strain produced in the middle plane by bending, is

$$V_2 = \iint(N_x\epsilon'_x + N_y\epsilon'_y + N_{xy}\gamma'_{xy})dx\,dy.$$

Substituting expressions (179), (180) and (181) for ϵ'_x, ϵ'_y and γ'_{xy}, we finally obtain

$$V_2 = \iint\left[N_x\frac{\partial u}{\partial x} + N_y\frac{\partial v}{\partial y} + N_{xy}\left(\frac{\partial u}{\partial y} + \frac{\partial v}{\partial x}\right)\right]dx\,dy$$
$$+ \frac{1}{2}\iint\left[N_x\left(\frac{\partial w}{\partial x}\right)^2 + N_y\left(\frac{\partial w}{\partial y}\right)^2 + 2N_{xy}\frac{\partial w}{\partial x}\frac{\partial w}{\partial y}\right]dx\,dy. \tag{182}$$

It can be shown, by integration by parts, that the first integral on the right-hand side of expression (182) is equal to the work done during bending by the forces acting in the middle plane of the plate. Taking, for example, a rectangular plate with

---

[1] The angles $\partial w/\partial y$ and $\partial w/\partial x$ correspond to small deflections of the plate and are regarded as small quantities.

the coordinate axes directed, as shown in Fig. 119, we obtain for the first term of the integral

$$\int_0^b \int_0^a N_x \frac{\partial u}{\partial x} dx\, dy = \int_0^b \left| N_x u \right|_0^a dy - \int_0^b \int_0^a u \frac{\partial N_x}{\partial x} dx\, dy.$$

Proceeding in the same manner with the other terms of the first integral in expression (182), we finally find

$$\int_0^b \int_0^a \left[N_x \frac{\partial u}{\partial x} + N_y \frac{\partial v}{\partial y} + N_{xy} \left(\frac{\partial u}{\partial y} + \frac{\partial v}{\partial x} \right) \right] dx\, dy$$

$$= \int_0^b \left(\left| N_x u \right|_0^a + \left| N_{xy} v \right|_0^a \right) dy + \int_0^a \left(\left| N_y v \right|_0^b + \left| N_{xy} u \right|_0^b \right) dx$$

$$- \int_0^b \int_0^a u \left(\frac{\partial N_x}{\partial x} + \frac{\partial N_{xy}}{\partial y} \right) dx\, dy - \int_0^b \int_0^a v \left(\frac{\partial N_{xy}}{\partial x} + \frac{\partial N_y}{\partial y} \right) dx\, dy.$$

The first integral on the right-hand side of this expression is evidently equal to the work done during bending by the forces applied at the edges $x = 0$ and $x = a$ of the plate. Similarly the second integral is equal to the work done by the forces applied at the edges $y = 0$ and $y = b$. The last two integrals, by virtue of Eqs. (176), are equal to the work done during bending by the body forces acting in the middle plane. These integrals each vanish in the absence of such corresponding forces.

Adding expressions (178) and (182) to the energy of bending [see Eq. (111), page 95], we obtain the total strain energy of a bent plate under the combined action of lateral loads and forces acting in the middle plane of the plate. This strain energy is equal to the work T_v done by the lateral load during bending of the plate plus the work T_h done by the forces acting in the middle plane of the plate. Observing that this latter work is equal to the strain energy V_1 plus the strain energy represented by the first integral of expression (182), we conclude that the work produced by the lateral forces is

$$T_v = \frac{1}{2} \int \int \left[N_x \left(\frac{\partial w}{\partial x} \right)^2 + N_y \left(\frac{\partial w}{\partial y} \right)^2 + 2 N_{xy} \frac{\partial w}{\partial x} \frac{\partial w}{\partial y} \right] dx\, dy$$

$$+ \frac{D}{2} \int \int \left\{ \left(\frac{\partial^2 w}{\partial x^2} + \frac{\partial^2 w}{\partial y^2} \right)^2 - 2(1 - \nu) \left[\frac{\partial^2 w}{\partial x^2} \frac{\partial^2 w}{\partial y^2} - \left(\frac{\partial^2 w}{\partial x\, \partial y} \right)^2 \right] \right\} dx\, dy.$$

$$(183)$$

Applying the principle of virtual displacement, we now give a variation δw to the deflection w and obtain, from Eq. (183),

$$\delta T_v = \frac{1}{2}\delta \int \int \left[N_x\left(\frac{\partial w}{\partial x}\right)^2 + N_y\left(\frac{\partial w}{\partial y}\right)^2 + 2N_{xy}\frac{\partial w}{\partial x}\frac{\partial w}{\partial y} \right] dx\, dy$$

$$+ \frac{D}{2}\delta \int \int \left\{ \left(\frac{\partial^2 w}{\partial x^2} + \frac{\partial^2 w}{\partial y^2}\right)^2 - 2(1-\nu)\left[\frac{\partial^2 w}{\partial x^2}\frac{\partial^2 w}{\partial y^2} - \left(\frac{\partial^2 w}{\partial x\, \partial y}\right)^2\right] \right\}$$

$$dx\, dy. \quad (184)$$

The left side in this equation represents the work done during the virtual displacement by the lateral load, and the right side is the corresponding change in the strain energy of the plate. The application of this equation will be illustrated by several examples in the next article.

61. Simply Supported Rectangular Plates under the Combined Action of Lateral Loads and of Forces in the Middle Plane of the Plate.—Let us begin with the case of a rectangular plate uniformly stretched in the x-direction (Fig. 119) and carrying a concentrated load P at a point with coordinates ξ and η. The general expression for the deflection that satisfies the boundary conditions is

$$w = \sum_{m=1,2,3,\cdots}^{\infty} \sum_{n=1,2,3,\cdots}^{\infty} a_{mn} \sin\frac{m\pi x}{a} \sin\frac{n\pi y}{b}. \quad (a)$$

To obtain the coefficients a_{mn} in this series we use the general equation (184). Since $N_y = N_{xy} = 0$ in our case, the first integral on the right side of Eq. (183), after substitution of series (a) for w, is

$$\frac{1}{2}\int_0^a \int_0^b N_x\left(\frac{\partial w}{\partial x}\right)^2 dx\, dy = \frac{ab}{8}N_x \sum_{m=1}^{\infty}\sum_{n=1}^{\infty} a_{mn}^2 \frac{m^2\pi^2}{a^2}. \quad (b)$$

The strain energy of bending representing the second integral in Eq. (183) is [see Eq. (124), page 121]

$$V = \frac{\pi^4 ab}{8}D \sum_{m=1}^{\infty}\sum_{n=1}^{\infty} a_{mn}^2 \left(\frac{m^2}{a^2} + \frac{n^2}{b^2}\right)^2. \quad (c)$$

To obtain a virtual deflection δw we give to a coefficient $a_{m_1 n_1}$ an increase $\delta a_{m_1 n_1}$. The corresponding deflection of the plate is

$$\delta w = \delta a_{m_1 n_1} \sin\frac{m_1\pi x}{a} \sin\frac{n_1\pi y}{b}.$$

The work done during this virtual displacement by the lateral load P is

$$P\delta a_{m_1 n_1} \sin \frac{m_1 \pi \xi}{a} \sin \frac{n_1 \pi \eta}{b}. \qquad (d)$$

The corresponding change in the strain energy consists of the two terms which are

$$\left.\begin{aligned}
\frac{1}{2}\delta \int_0^a \int_0^b N_x \left(\frac{\partial w}{\partial x}\right)^2 dx\, dy \\
= \frac{ab}{8} N_x \frac{\partial}{\partial a_{m_1 n_1}} \left(\sum_{m=1}^{\infty} \sum_{n=1}^{\infty} a_{mn}^2 \frac{m^2 \pi^2}{a^2}\right) \delta a_{m_1 n_1} = \frac{ab}{4} N_x a_{m_1 n_1} \frac{m_1^2 \pi^2}{a^2} \delta a_{m_1 n_1}
\end{aligned}\right\} \quad (e)$$

and

$$\delta V = \frac{\partial V}{\partial a_{m_1 n_1}} \delta a_{m_1 n_1} = \frac{\pi^4 ab}{4} D a_{m_1 n_1} \left(\frac{m_1^2}{a^2} + \frac{n_1^2}{b^2}\right)^2 \delta a_{m_1 n_1}.$$

Substituting expressions (d) and (e) in Eq. (184), we obtain

$$P\delta a_{m_1 n_1} \sin \frac{m_1 \pi \xi}{a} \sin \frac{n_1 \pi \eta}{b} = \frac{ab}{4} N_x a_{m_1 n_1} \frac{m_1^2 \pi^2}{a^2} \delta a_{m_1 n_1}$$
$$+ \frac{\pi^4 ab}{4} D a_{m_1 n_1} \left(\frac{m_1^2}{a^2} + \frac{n_1^2}{b^2}\right)^2 \delta a_{m_1 n_1},$$

from which

$$a_{m_1 n_1} = \frac{4P \sin \dfrac{m_1 \pi \xi}{a} \sin \dfrac{n_1 \pi \eta}{b}}{ab\pi^4 D\left[\left(\dfrac{m_1^2}{a^2} + \dfrac{n_1^2}{b^2}\right)^2 + \dfrac{m_1^2 N_x}{\pi^2 a^2 D}\right]}. \qquad (f)$$

Substituting these values of the coefficients $a_{m_1 n_1}$ in expression (a), we find the deflection of the plate to be

$$w = \frac{4P}{ab\pi^4 D} \sum_{m=1}^{\infty} \sum_{n=1}^{\infty} \frac{\sin \dfrac{m\pi \xi}{a} \sin \dfrac{n\pi \eta}{b}}{\left(\dfrac{m^2}{a^2} + \dfrac{n^2}{b^2}\right)^2 + \dfrac{m^2 N_x}{\pi^2 a^2 D}} \sin \frac{m\pi x}{a} \sin \frac{n\pi y}{b}. \qquad (g)$$

If, instead of the tensile forces N_x, there are compressive forces of the same magnitude, the deflection of the plate is obtained by substituting $-N_x$ in place of N_x in expression (g). This substitution gives

$$w = \frac{4P}{ab\pi^4 D} \sum_{m=1}^{\infty} \sum_{n=1}^{\infty} \frac{\sin \dfrac{m\pi\xi}{a} \sin \dfrac{n\pi\eta}{b}}{\left(\dfrac{m^2}{a^2} + \dfrac{n^2}{b^2}\right)^2 - \dfrac{m^2 N_x}{\pi^2 a^2 D}} \sin \frac{m\pi x}{a} \sin \frac{n\pi y}{b}. \quad (h)$$

The smallest value of N_x at which the denominator of one of the terms in expression (h) becomes equal to zero is the *critical value* of the compressive force N_x. It is evident that this critical value is obtained by taking $n = 1$. Hence

$$(N_x)_{cr} = \frac{\pi^2 a^2 D}{m^2}\left(\frac{m^2}{a^2} + \frac{1}{b^2}\right)^2 = \frac{\pi^2 D}{b^2}\left(\frac{mb}{a} + \frac{a}{mb}\right)^2, \quad (185)$$

where m must be chosen so as to make expression (185) a minimum. Plotting the factor

$$k = \left(\frac{mb}{a} + \frac{a}{mb}\right)^2$$

against the ratio a/b, for various integral values of m, we obtain a system of curves shown in Fig. 122. The portions of the

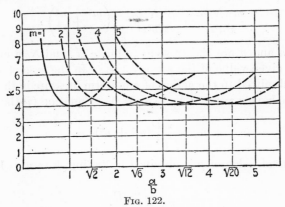

Fig. 122.

curves that must be used in determining k are indicated by heavy lines. It is seen that the factor k is equal to 4 for a square plate as well as for any plate that can be subdivided into an integral number of squares with the side b. It can also be seen that for long plates k remains practically constant at a value of 4.[1]

---

[1] A more detailed discussion of this problem is given in the author's "Theory of Elastic Stability," p. 327.

By using the deflection (g) produced by one concentrated load, the deflection produced by any lateral load can be obtained by superposition. Assuming, for example, that the plate is uniformly loaded by a load of intensity q, we substitute $q\, d\xi\, d\eta$ for P in expression (g) and integrate the expression over the entire area of the plate. In this way we obtain the same expression for the deflection of the plate under uniform load as has already been derived in another manner (see page 302).

If the plate laterally loaded by the force P is compressed in the middle plane by uniformly distributed forces N_x and N_y, proceeding as before we obtain

$$w = \frac{4P}{ab\pi^4 D}\sum_{m=1}^{\infty}\sum_{n=1}^{\infty}\frac{\sin\dfrac{m\pi\xi}{a}\sin\dfrac{n\pi\eta}{b}}{\left(\dfrac{m^2}{a^2}+\dfrac{n^2}{b^2}\right)^2 - \dfrac{m^2 N_x}{\pi^2 a^2 D} - \dfrac{n^2 N_y}{\pi^2 b^2 D}}\sin\frac{m\pi x}{a}\sin\frac{n\pi y}{b}.$$

$$(i)$$

The critical value of the forces N_x and N_y is obtained from the condition[1]

$$\frac{m^2 (N_x)_{cr}}{\pi^2 a^2 D} + \frac{n^2 (N_y)_{cr}}{\pi^2 b^2 D} = \left(\frac{m^2}{a^2}+\frac{n^2}{b^2}\right)^2,$$

$$(j)$$

where m and n are chosen so as to make N_x and N_y a minimum for any given value of the ratio $N_x : N_y$. In the case of a square plate submitted to the action of a uniform pressure in the middle plane we have $a = b$ and $N_x = N_y = p$. Equation (j) then gives

$$p_{cr} = \frac{\pi^2 D}{a^2}(m^2 + n^2)_{min}.$$

$$(k)$$

The critical value of p is obtained by taking $m = n = 1$, which gives

$$p_{cr} = \frac{2\pi^2 D}{a^2}.$$

$$(186)$$

In the case of a plate in the form of an isosceles right triangle with simply supported edges (Fig. 115) the deflection surface of the buckled plate which satisfies all the boundary conditions is[2]

[1] A complete discussion of this problem is given in the author's "Theory of Elastic Stability," p. 333.

[2] This is the form of natural vibration of a square plate having a diagonal as a nodal line.

$$w = a\left(\sin\frac{\pi x}{a}\cdot\sin\frac{2\pi y}{a} + \sin\frac{2\pi x}{a}\sin\frac{\pi y}{a}\right).$$

Thus the critical value of the compressive stress is obtained by substituting $m = 1$, $n = 2$ or $m = 2$, $n = 1$ into expression (k). This gives

$$p_{cr} = \frac{5\pi^2 D}{a^2}. \tag{187}$$

62. Methods of Calculation of Critical Forces.—It was indicated in the previous article that at certain values of the forces acting in the middle plane of a plate a lateral buckling of the plate may occur. A knowledge of such critical values of the forces is of a great practical importance in the design of thin-walled structures. For this reason various methods of calculating these values will now be discussed.

We can proceed, as was done in the previous article, by finding a general expression for the deflection produced by the combined action of the lateral load and the forces acting in the middle plane of the plate and then determining the values of the forces acting in the middle plane at which the deflection increases indefinitely. The smallest of these values is then the critical force.

Another method of calculating the critical forces is to assume that the plate buckles slightly under the action of the forces applied in its middle plane and then to calculate the magnitudes that the forces must have in order to keep the plate in such a slightly buckled form. The differential equation of the deflection surface in this case is obtained from Eq. (175) or (177) by putting $q = 0$, *i.e.*, by assuming that there is no lateral load. If there are no body forces acting in the middle plane, the equation for the buckled plate then becomes

$$\frac{\partial^4 w}{\partial x^4} + 2\frac{\partial^4 w}{\partial x^2\,\partial y^2} + \frac{\partial^4 w}{\partial y^4} = \frac{1}{D}\left(N_x\frac{\partial^2 w}{\partial x^2} + N_y\frac{\partial^2 w}{\partial y^2}\right.$$
$$\left. + 2N_{xy}\frac{\partial^2 w}{\partial x\,\partial y}\right) \cdots \tag{188}$$

The simplest case is obtained when the forces N_x, N_y and N_{xy} are constant throughout the plate. If we assume that there are given ratios between these forces as expressed by

$$N_y = \alpha N_x \quad \text{and} \quad N_{xy} = \beta N_x$$

and solve Eq. (188) for the given boundary conditions, we shall find that the assumed buckling of the plate is possible only for certain definite values of N_x. The smallest of these values is the desired critical value.

If the forces N_x, N_y and N_{xy} are not constant, the problem becomes more complicated, since Eq. (188) then has variable coefficients. The general conclusion remains the same, however. In such cases we can assume that the expressions for the forces N_x, N_y and N_{xy} have a common factor γ, such that a gradual increase of loading is obtained by an increase of this factor. From the discussion of Eq. (188) together with the given boundary conditions, it will be concluded that curved forms of equilibrium are possible only for certain values of the factor γ and that the smallest of these values defines the critical loading.

The energy method also can be used in investigating the buckling of plates.[1] This method is especially useful in those cases where a rigorous solution of Eq. (188) is unknown and where it is required to find an approximate value of the critical load. In applying this method we assume that the plate, which is stressed only by forces acting in its middle plane, undergoes some small lateral deflection w consistent with the given boundary conditions. Then, using Eq. (183) and observing that there is no lateral load in this case, we obtain

$$\frac{1}{2}\int\int\left[N_x\left(\frac{\partial w}{\partial x}\right)^2 + N_y\left(\frac{\partial w}{\partial y}\right)^2 + 2N_{xy}\frac{\partial w}{\partial x}\frac{\partial w}{\partial y}\right]dx\,dy$$
$$+ \frac{D}{2}\int\int\left\{\left(\frac{\partial^2 w}{\partial x^2} + \frac{\partial^2 w}{\partial y^2}\right)^2 - 2(1 - \nu)\left[\frac{\partial^2 w}{\partial x^2}\frac{\partial^2 w}{\partial y^2}\right.\right.$$
$$\left.\left.- \left(\frac{\partial^2 w}{\partial x\,\partial y}\right)^2\right]\right\}dx\,dy = 0. \quad (189)$$

The critical value of the forces acting in the middle plane of the plate is the smallest of the values at which Eq. (189) is satisfied. In determining this critical value we assume that, in general, the forces N_x, N_y and N_{xy} are represented by certain functions of x and y having a common factor γ so that

$$N_x = \gamma N_x', \qquad N_y = \gamma N_y', \qquad N_{xy} = \gamma N_{xy}'. \quad (a)$$

[1] This method was first used by G. H. Bryan, *Proc. London Math. Soc.*, vol. 22, p. 54; see also author's book "Theory of Elastic Stability," 1936; and H. Reissner's paper *Z. angew. Math. Mech.*, vol. 5, p. 475, 1925.

A simultaneous increase of these forces is obtained by making γ increase. From Eq. (189) we then obtain

$$\gamma = -\frac{D\iint\left\{\left(\frac{\partial^2 w}{\partial x^2} + \frac{\partial^2 w}{\partial y^2}\right)^2 - 2(1-\nu)\left[\frac{\partial^2 w}{\partial x^2}\frac{\partial^2 w}{\partial y^2} - \left(\frac{\partial^2 w}{\partial x\,\partial y}\right)^2\right]\right\}dx\,dy}{\iint\left[N_x'\left(\frac{\partial w}{\partial x}\right)^2 + N_y'\left(\frac{\partial w}{\partial y}\right)^2 + 2N_{xy}'\frac{\partial w}{\partial x}\frac{\partial w}{\partial y}\right]dx\,dy}. \qquad (190)$$

To determine the critical value of γ it is necessary to find, in each particular case, an expression for w that satisfies the given boundary conditions and makes expression (190) a minimum. This requires that the first variation of the fraction (190) vanish. If the numerator of expression (190) is denoted by I_1, the denominator by I_2, the first variation of this expression is

$$\delta\gamma = -\frac{I_2\,\delta I_1 - I_1\,\delta I_2}{I_2^2}.$$

Observing that $\gamma = I_1/I_2$, this variation, when equated to zero, gives

$$\frac{1}{I_2}(\delta I_1 - \gamma\,\delta I_2) = 0. \qquad (b)$$

By calculating the indicated variations and assuming that there are no body forces in the middle plane of the plate, *i.e.*, that Eqs. (174) hold, we again obtain Eq. (188). Thus the energy method brings us in this way to the integration of the same equation, as has already been discussed.

For an approximate calculation of the critical values of the forces N_x, N_y and N_{xy} we assume the deflection w to be in the form of a series

$$w = a_1 f_1(x,y) + a_2 f_2(x,y) + \cdots,$$

in which the functions $f_1(x,y)$, $f_2(x,y)$, . . . satisfy the boundary conditions and are chosen so as to be suitable for the representation of the buckled surface of the plate. In each particular case we shall be guided in choosing these functions by experimental data regarding the shape of a buckled plate. The coefficients a_1, a_2, a_3, . . . of the series must now be chosen so as to make expression (190) a minimum. Using this condition and proceeding as in the derivation of Eq. (*b*) above, we obtain the following equations:

$$\left.\begin{aligned}\frac{\partial I_1}{\partial a_1} - \gamma\frac{\partial I_2}{\partial a_1} = 0;\\[2mm]\frac{\partial I_1}{\partial a_2} - \gamma\frac{\partial I_2}{\partial a_2} = 0;\end{aligned}\right\}\qquad(191)$$

. . . .

It can be seen from expression (190) that the expressions for I_1 and I_2 are homogeneous functions of the second degree in terms of a_1, a_2, ...   Hence Eqs. (191) represent a system of homogeneous linear equations in a_1, a_2, ...   Such equations may yield for a_1, a_2, . . . solutions different from zero only if the determinant of these equations is zero.   Putting this determinant equal to zero, an equation for determining the critical value of γ will be obtained.   This method of approximate calculation of the critical values of the forces acting in the middle plane of a plate will be illustrated by examples in Art. 64.

63. Buckling of Uniformly Compressed Rectangular Plates Simply Supported along Two Opposite Sides Perpendicular to the Direction of Compression and Having Various Edge Conditions along the Other Two Sides.—In the discussion of this problem both the energy method and the method of integration of the differential equation for the deflected plate can be used.[1]   In applying the method of integration we use Eq. (188).   For the case of uniform compression along the x-axis (see Fig. 123), if N_x is

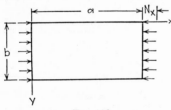

Fig. 123.

considered as positive for compression, this equation becomes

$$\frac{\partial^4 w}{\partial x^4} + 2\frac{\partial^4 w}{\partial x^2\,\partial y^2} + \frac{\partial^4 w}{\partial y^4} = -\frac{N_x}{D}\frac{\partial^2 w}{\partial x^2}. \qquad(a)$$

Assuming that under the action of the compressive forces the plate buckles in m sinusoidal waves, we take the solution of Eq. (*a*) in the form

[1] The method of integration was used by the writer in the paper published in the *Bull. Polytech. Inst.*, Kiev, 1907; see also *Z. Math. Physik*, vol. 58, p. 343, 1910.   The use of the energy method was shown in the paper published in *Ann. ponts chaussées*, vol. 4, p. 372, 1913.

$$w = Y \sin \frac{m\pi x}{a}, \qquad (b)$$

in which Y is a function $f(y)$ which is to be determined later. Expression (b) satisfies the boundary conditions along the supported sides $x = 0$ and $x = a$ of the plate, since

$$w = 0 \qquad \text{and} \qquad \frac{\partial^2 w}{\partial x^2} + \nu \frac{\partial^2 w}{\partial y^2} = 0$$

for $x = 0$ and $x = a$. Substituting (b) into Eq. (a), we obtain the following ordinary differential equation for determining the function $Y = f(y)$:

$$Y^{\mathrm{IV}} - \frac{2m^2\pi^2}{a^2} Y'' + \left(\frac{m^4\pi^4}{a^4} - \frac{N_x}{D} \frac{m^2\pi^2}{a^2} \right) Y = 0. \qquad (c)$$

Noting that because of some constraints along the sides $y = 0$ and $y = b$ we always have

$$\frac{N_x}{D} > \frac{m^2\pi^2}{a^2},$$

and introducing the notations

$$\alpha = \sqrt{\frac{m^2\pi^2}{a^2} + \sqrt{\frac{N_x}{D} \frac{m^2\pi^2}{a^2}}} \qquad \text{and} \qquad \beta = \sqrt{-\frac{m^2\pi^2}{a^2} + \sqrt{\frac{N_x}{D} \frac{m^2\pi^2}{a^2}}}, \qquad (d)$$

the general solution of Eq. (c) can be represented in the following form:

$$Y = C_1 e^{-\alpha y} + C_2 e^{\alpha y} + C_3 \cos \beta y + C_4 \sin \beta y. \qquad (e)$$

The constants of integration in this solution must be determined in each particular case from the conditions of constraint along the sides $y = 0$ and $y = b$. Several particular cases of constraint along these sides will now be discussed.

Side $y = 0$ Is Simply Supported; Side $y = b$ Is Free.—From these conditions it follows [see Eqs. (107), (108)] that

$$w = 0, \qquad \frac{\partial^2 w}{\partial y^2} + \nu \frac{\partial^2 w}{\partial x^2} = 0 \qquad \text{for} \qquad y = 0, \qquad (f)$$

$$\frac{\partial^2 w}{\partial y^2} + \nu \frac{\partial^2 w}{\partial x^2} = 0, \qquad \frac{\partial^3 w}{\partial y^3} + (2 - \nu) \frac{\partial^3 w}{\partial x^2 \partial y} = 0 \qquad \text{for} \qquad y = b. \qquad (g)$$

The boundary conditions (f) will be satisfied if, in the general solution (e), we take

$$C_1 = -C_2 \quad \text{and} \quad C_3 = 0.$$

The function Y can then be written in the form

$$Y = A \sinh \alpha y + B \sin \beta y,$$

in which A and B are constants. From the boundary conditions (g), it then follows that

$$\left.\begin{aligned}
A\left(\alpha^2 - \nu\frac{m^2\pi^2}{a^2}\right)\sinh \alpha b - B\left(\beta^2 + \nu\frac{m^2\pi^2}{a^2}\right)\sin \beta b &= 0, \\
A\alpha\left[\alpha^2 - (2 - \nu)\frac{m^2\pi^2}{a^2}\right]\cosh \alpha b & \\
- \beta B\left[\beta^2 + (2 - \nu)\frac{m^2\pi^2}{a^2}\right]\cos \beta b &= 0.
\end{aligned}\right\} \quad (h)$$

These equations can be satisfied by taking $A = B = 0$. With these values the deflection at each point of the plate is zero, and we obtain the flat form of equilibrium of the plate. The buckled form of equilibrium of the plate becomes possible only if Eqs. (h) have a solution for A and B different from zero. This requires that the determinant of these equations should be zero; i.e.,

$$\beta\left(\alpha^2 - \nu\frac{m^2\pi^2}{a^2}\right)^2 \tanh \alpha b = \alpha\left(\beta^2 + \nu\frac{m^2\pi^2}{a^2}\right)^2 \tan \beta b. \quad (i)$$

Since α and β contain N_x [see notations (d)], Eq. (i) can be used for the calculation of the critical value of N_x if the dimensions of the plate and the elastic constants of the material are known. These calculations show that the smallest value of N_x is obtained by taking $m = 1$, i.e., by assuming that the buckled plate has only one half wave. The magnitude of the corresponding critical compressive stress can be represented by the formula

$$(\sigma_x)_{cr} = \frac{(N_x)_{cr}}{h} = k\frac{\pi^2 D}{b^2 h}, \quad (j)$$

in which k is a numerical factor depending upon the magnitude of the ratio a/b. Several values of this factor, calculated from Eq. (i) for $\nu = 0.25$, are given in the second line of Table 39 below. For long plates it can be assumed with sufficient accuracy that

$$k = \left(0.456 + \frac{b^2}{a^2}\right).$$

In the third line of Table 39 the critical stresses are given as calculated on the assumption that $E = 30.10^6$ lb. per square inch, $\nu = 0.25$ and $h/b = 0.01$. For any other material with a modulus E_1 and any other value of the ratio h/b the critical stress is obtained by multiplying the numbers of the table by the factor

$$\frac{E_1}{30 \cdot 10^2}\left(\frac{h}{b}\right)^2.$$

TABLE 39.—NUMERICAL VALUES OF k IN EQ. (j) WHEN SIDE $y = 0$ IS
SIMPLY SUPPORTED AND SIDE $y = b$ IS FREE (FIG. 123)

a/b	0.50	1.0	1.2	1.4	1.6	1.8	2.0	2.5	3.0	4.0	5.0
k	4.40	1.440	1.135	0.952	0.835	0.755	0.698	0.610	0.564	0.516	0.506
$(\sigma_x)_{cr}$, lb./sq. in.	11,600	3,790	2,990	2,500	2,200	1,990	1,840	1,600	1,480	1,360	1,330

Edge conditions similar to those assumed above are realized in the case of compression of an angle as shown in Fig. 124. When the compressive stresses, uniformly distributed over the width of the sides of the angle, become equal to the critical stress as given by formula (j), the free longitudinal edges of the angle buckle, as shown in the figure, but the line AB remains straight. The edge conditions along the line AB are the same as along a simply supported edge. Experiments made with angles in compression[1] are in good agreement with the theory. In the case of comparatively short angles buckling occurs, as shown in Fig. 124. For a long strut with such an angular cross section Euler's critical compressive stress may become smaller than that given by formula (j), in which case the strut buckles like a compressed column.

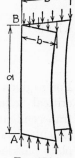

FIG. 124.

[1] See paper by F. J. Bridget, C. C. Jerome and A. B. Vosseller, *Trans. Am. Soc. Mech. Eng.*, p. 569, 1934. See also paper by C. F. Kollbrunner, Zürich, 1935.

Side $y = 0$ *Is Built In, Side* $y = b$ *Is Free (Fig.* 123).—In this case the edge conditions for determining the constants in the general solution (e) are

$$w = 0, \qquad \frac{\partial w}{\partial y} = 0 \qquad \text{for} \qquad y = 0; \qquad (k)$$

$$\frac{\partial^2 w}{\partial y^2} + \nu \frac{\partial^2 w}{\partial x^2} = 0, \qquad \frac{\partial^3 w}{\partial y^3} + (2 - \nu)\frac{\partial^3 w}{\partial x^2 \partial y} = 0 \qquad \text{for} \qquad y = b. \tag{l}$$

From the conditions (k) it follows that

$$C_1 = -\frac{\alpha C_3 - \beta C_4}{2\alpha} \qquad \text{and} \qquad C_2 = -\frac{\alpha C_3 + \beta C_4}{2\alpha}.$$

The function Y can then be represented in the form

$$Y = A(\cos \beta y - \cosh \alpha y) + B\left(\sin \beta y - \frac{\beta}{\alpha} \sinh \alpha y\right).$$

Substituting this expression in equations (l), we obtain two homogeneous equations linear in A and B. The critical value of the compressive stress is now determined by equating the determinant of these equations to zero. This gives

$$2ts + (s^2 + t^2) \cos \beta b \cosh \alpha b$$
$$= \frac{1}{\alpha\beta}(\alpha^2 t^2 - \beta^2 s^2) \sin \beta b \sinh \alpha b, \quad (m)$$

where

$$t = \beta^2 + \nu\frac{m^2\pi^2}{a^2}, \qquad s = \alpha^2 - \nu\frac{m^2\pi^2}{a^2}.$$

For a given value of the ratio a/b and a given value of ν the critical value of compressive stress can be calculated from the transcendental equation (m) and can be represented by Eq. (j). Calculations show that, for a comparatively short length a, the plate buckles in one half wave, and we must take $m = 1$ in our calculations. Several values of the numerical factor k in Eq. (j) corresponding to various values of the ratio a/b are given in Table 40 (p. 319). The same values are also represented in Fig. 125 by the curve $m = 1$. It is seen that at the beginning the values of k decrease with an increase in the ratio a/b, the minimum value of k ($k = 1.328$) being obtained for $a/b = 1.635$.

Beginning from this value, k increases with the ratio a/b. Having the curve for $m = 1$, the curves for $m = 2$, $m = 3$, $\cdots$ can be constructed. By using such curves the number of half waves in any particular case can readily be determined. In the case of a comparatively long plate we can, with sufficient accuracy, take $k = 1.328$ in Eq. (j).

TABLE 40.—NUMERICAL VALUES OF k IN EQ. (j) WHEN SIDE $y = 0$ IS BUILT IN AND SIDE $y = b$ IS FREE (FIG. 123)
$$(\nu = 0.25)$$

a/b	1.0	1.1	1.2	1.3	1.4	1.5	1.6	1.7	1.8	1.9	2.0	2.2	2.4
k	1.70	1.56	1.47	1.41	1.36	1.34	1.33	1.33	1.34	1.36	1.38	1.45	1.47
$(\sigma_x)_{cr}$, lb./sq. in.	4,470	4,110	3,870	3,710	3,580	3,520	3,500	3,500	3,520	3,580	3,630	3,820	3,870

In the third row of Table 40 the values of the critical stresses are given as calculated from Eq. (j), assuming $E = 30 \cdot 10^6$ lb.

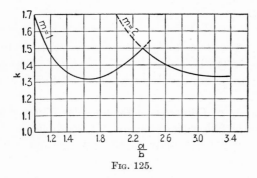

FIG. 125.

per square inch, $\nu = 0.25$ and $h/b = 0.01$. By using these figures the critical stresses for plates of any other proportions and any value of the modulus can easily be calculated.

Sides $y = 0$ and $y = b$ Are Both Built In.—In this case the boundary conditions are

$$w = 0 \qquad \frac{\partial w}{\partial y} = 0, \qquad \text{for} \qquad y = 0 \qquad \text{and} \qquad y = b.$$

Proceeding as in the previous cases, we obtain the following transcendental equation for the calculation of the critical value of the compression forces:

$$(\cos \beta b - \cosh \alpha b)^2 = -\left(\sin \beta b - \frac{\beta}{\alpha}\sinh \alpha b\right)\left(\sin \beta b + \frac{\alpha}{\beta}\sinh \alpha b\right).$$

The critical values of the compressive stress are again given by Eq. (j). Several values of the numerical factor k as calculated for various values of the ratio a/b are given in Table 41.

TABLE 41.—NUMERICAL VALUES OF k IN EQ. (j) WHEN BOTH SIDES $y = 0$
AND $y = b$ ARE BUILT IN
($\nu = 0.25$)

a/b	0.4	0.5	0.6	0.7	0.8	0.9	1.0
k	9.44	7.69	7.05	7.00	7.29	7.83	7.69

It is seen that the smallest value of k is obtained when

$$0.6 < \frac{a}{b} < 0.7.$$

This indicates that in this case a long compressed plate buckles in comparatively short waves. The number of waves can be determined as before by plotting curves similar to those shown in Fig. 125.

64. Buckling of Compressed Rectangular Plates with Built-in Edges.—In the following discussion of the problem of buckling of a clamped rectangular plate the energy method will be used.[1] The coordinate axes are taken as shown in Fig. 123, and it is assumed that the shape of the plate does not differ appreciably from a square and that the forces N_x and N_y are uniformly distributed.[2] We can then expect that the deflection surface of the buckled plate is represented satisfactorily by the equation

$$w = \frac{w_0}{4}\left(1 - \cos\frac{2\pi x}{a}\right)\left(1 - \cos\frac{2\pi y}{b}\right), \tag{a}$$

[1] Another method of treating the same problem was given by G. I. Taylor, *Z. angew. Math. Mech.*, vol. 13, p. 147, 1933; see also K. Sezawa and W. Watanabe, *Rept. Aeronautical Research Inst.* Tokyo Imp. Univ., vol. 11, p. 409, 1936.

[2] The compressive forces here are taken as positive, and the sign of expression (183) is changed accordingly.

which is seen to satisfy the boundary conditions. With this expression for deflections, the strain energy of bending represented by the second integral of Eq. (189) is

$$V = \frac{\pi^4 w_0^2 D}{8} ab\left(\frac{3}{a^4} + \frac{3}{b^4} + \frac{2}{a^2 b^2}\right). \tag{b}$$

The first integral of the same equation is

$$\frac{N_x}{2}\int_0^a \int_0^b \left(\frac{\partial w}{\partial x}\right)^2 dx\, dy + \frac{N_y}{2}\int_0^a \int_0^b \left(\frac{\partial w}{\partial y}\right)^2 dx\, dy$$
$$= \frac{3\pi^2}{32} w_0^2 \frac{b}{a}\left(N_x + \frac{a^2}{b^2} N_y\right). \tag{c}$$

Substituting expressions (b) and (c) in Eq. (189), we obtain the following equation for calculating the critical values of the compressive forces N_x and N_y:

$$\left(N_x + \frac{a^2}{b^2} N_y\right)_{cr} = \frac{4\pi^2}{3} Da^2\left(\frac{3}{a^4} + \frac{3}{b^4} + \frac{2}{a^2 b^2}\right). \tag{d}$$

In the particular case of a square plate submitted to the action of equal compression in two perpendicular directions $a = b$ and $N_x = N_y$, we then obtain from Eq. (d)

$$(N_x)_{cr} = 5.33\pi^2 \frac{D}{a^2}. \tag{e}$$

The solution by G. I. Taylor, mentioned above, gives for this case

$$(N_x)_{cr} = 5.30\pi^2 \frac{D}{a^2}. \tag{f}$$

If the plate is compressed in the x-direction only, we obtain, by putting $N_y = 0$ in Eq. (d), $(N_x)_{cr} = 105(D/a^2)$.

It was shown in Art. 62 that to determine the true value of the critical forces it is necessary to find for w a form that makes expression (190) a minimum. By assuming for w an arbitrary form such as that of Eq. (a), we usually obtain from expression (190) a value that is larger than the minimum value of the same expression. Hence formulas (e) will give too large a value for $(N_x)_{cr}$. At the same time it can be shown[1] that the Taylor method gives too small a value for the critical load. The true value of the critical load is thus somewhere between the values (e) and (f).

[1] See A. Weinstein, *J. London Math. Soc.*, vol. 10, p. 184, 1935; and E. Trefftz, *Z. angew. Math. Mech.*, vol. 15, p. 339, 1935.

To get a better approximation for the critical force by using the energy method, it is necessary to take for w an expression with several parameters and determine these parameters so as to make expression (190) a minimum. Such calculations have been made[1] for the case of a plate uniformly compressed in the direction of the x-axis (Fig. 123). The deflection surface was taken in the form

$$w = a_{11}\psi_1(x)\varphi_1(y) + a_{31}\psi_3(x)\varphi_1(y) + a_{51}\psi_5(x)\varphi_1(y) \qquad (g)$$

for buckling in an odd number of waves and in the form

$$w = a_{21}\psi_2(x)\varphi_1(y) + a_{41}\psi_4(x)\varphi_1(y) + a_{61}\psi_6(x)\varphi_1(y) \qquad (h)$$

for buckling in an even number of waves. The functions $\psi(x)$ and $\varphi(y)$ in these expressions are functions representing, respectively, the normal modes of vibration of a bar of length a and b clamped at both ends. For the function $\varphi(y)$ the form corresponding to the fundamental mode of vibration is used in all cases. For the function $\psi(x)$ higher modes of vibration are also considered. Substituting expression (g) or expression (h) in Eq. (190), we obtain the system of linear equations (191) and calculate the critical values of N_x for various values of a/b by setting the determinant of these equations equal to zero. In this way we obtain

$$(N_x)_{cr} = k\frac{D}{b^2}, \qquad (i)$$

where k is a numerical factor depending on the ratio a/b of the sides of the plate. Several values of this factor are given in Table 42.[2]

TABLE 42.—VALUES OF k IN Eq. (i) FOR A RECTANGULAR PLATE WITH BUILT-IN EDGES

a/b	0.5	0.75	1.0	1.25	1.50	1.75	2.0	2.25	2.50	2.75	3.0	3.50	3.75	4.0
k	195.5	126.0	103.5_3	92.6	83.4	80.7	79.6_3	78.6	78.9	76.6	75.2_3	72.8_3	73.0	73.5

The results of calculation are also represented graphically in Fig. 126. From this figure we can determine, in each particular case, the number of waves into which the buckled plate is subdivided. For comparison, curves calculated by Taylor's method are also given. Knowing the upper and the lower limits for k, we can arrive at a conclusion in each particular case regarding the accuracy of the values given in Table 42.

65. Buckling of Circular and Elliptical Plates. *Uniformly Compressed Circular Plate.*—Let us begin with the case of a plate with a clamped edge.

---

[1] See paper by J. L. Maulbetsch, *J. Appl. Mech.*, vol. 4, p. 59, 1937.

[2] A subscript 3 after values of k indicates that three terms in expressions (g) or (h) were used in the calculations. The other values of k are calculated by using only two terms in the same expressions.

To obtain an approximate value of the critical compressive force N_r in the radial direction, we assume that the shape of the buckled plate is the same as that of a plate bent by uniform load (see page 62). Then

$$w = w_0\left(1 - \frac{r^2}{a^2}\right)^2, \qquad (a)$$

where a is the radius of the plate and w_0 its deflection at the center. If polar coordinates are used in Eq. (189), the first integral of that equation becomes

$$-\frac{1}{2}\int_0^{2\pi}\int_0^a N_r\left(\frac{\partial w}{\partial r}\right)^2 r\, dr\, d\theta = -\frac{2\pi N_r w_0^2}{3}. \qquad (b)$$

The second integral of the same equation, which represents the strain energy

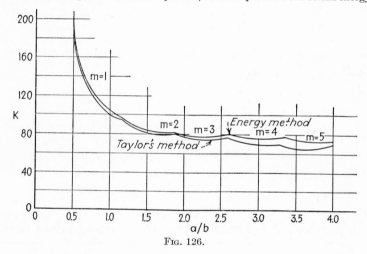

FIG. 126.

of bending, is calculated by substituting the values $\partial^2 w/\partial r^2$ and $(1/r)(\partial w/\partial r)$ for the principal curvatures in expression (47). Then

$$V = \frac{D}{2}\int_0^{2\pi}\int_0^a\left[\left(\frac{\partial^2 w}{\partial r^2}\right)^2 + \frac{1}{r^2}\left(\frac{\partial w}{\partial r}\right)^2 + \frac{2\nu}{r}\frac{\partial w}{\partial r}\frac{\partial^2 w}{\partial r^2}\right]r\, dr\, d\theta = 2\pi\frac{16}{3}D\frac{w_0^2}{a^2}. \qquad (c)$$

Substituting (b) and (c) in Eq. (189), we find

$$N_{cr} = \frac{16D}{a^2}. \qquad (d)$$

The exact value of the critical force which can be obtained in this case by integration of Eq. (188) is[1]

[1] BRYAN, G. H., *Proc. London Math. Soc.*, vol. 22, p. 54, 1891; see also A. Nadai, *Z. Ver. deut. Ing.*, vol. 59, p. 169, 1915.

$$N_{cr} = \frac{14.68D}{a^2}.$$ (192)

Thus the error of the approximate solution is about 9 per cent.

In the case of a simply supported plate the solution of Eq. (188) gives

$$N_{cr} = \frac{4.20D}{a^2}.$$ (193)

This indicates that the critical compressive stress for this type of support is about three and a half times smaller than in the case of a plate with a clamped edge.

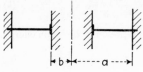
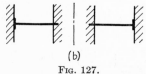

(b)

Fig. 127.

Circular Plate with a Hole at the Center.—If a uniformly compressed plate with a hole at the center is built in along the outer edge while the inner edge is free to deflect but cannot rotate (Fig. 127a), the critical value of the compressive force N again can be obtained by integrating Eq. (188).[1] Such a calculation gives

$$N_{cr} = \frac{kD}{a^2},$$ (e)

where k is a numerical factor depending upon the ratio a/b of the outer and the inner radii of the plate. Several values of this factor are given in Table 43.

TABLE 43.—NUMERICAL VALUES OF FACTOR k IN EQ. (e)

a/b	1.5	2	3	4	5	8	10	∞
k	89.93	40.88	24.06	19.76	17.94	16.00	15.54	14.68

The same table can also be used if the inner edge of the plate is built in and the outer can deflect freely but cannot rotate (Fig. 127b).

If the plate is submitted to the action of compressive forces distributed along only the inner boundary (Fig. 128), the forces N_r are no longer constant, and the integration of Eq. (188) becomes more complicated.[2] An approximate solution can be obtained by using the energy method.[3] Assuming that the

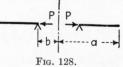

Fig. 128.

[1] OLSSON, R. G., *Ingenieur-Archiv*, vol. 8, p. 449, 1937.

[2] The case of compressive forces distributed along the outer boundary of the plate has been discussed by E. Meissner, *Schweiz. Bauzeitung*, vol. 101, p. 87, 1933.

[3] The result obtained in this manner was communicated to the author by Stewart Way.

plate is simply supported along the inner edge and free along the outer edge, we take for the deflection the expression

$$w = C_1(r - b) + C_2(r - b)^2 + C_3(r - b)^3 + C_4(r - b)^4, \qquad (f)$$

which satisfies the condition $w = 0$ for $r = b$. The remaining boundary conditions are

$$(M_r)_{r=b} = -D\left(\frac{\partial^2 w}{\partial r^2} + \nu\frac{1}{r}\frac{\partial w}{\partial r}\right)_{r=b} = 0,$$

$$(M_r)_{r=a} = -D\left(\frac{\partial^2 w}{\partial r^2} + \nu\frac{1}{r}\frac{\partial w}{\partial r}\right)_{r=a} = 0,$$

$$(Q_r)_{r=a} = -D\frac{\partial}{\partial r}\left(\frac{\partial^2 w}{\partial r^2} + \frac{1}{r}\frac{\partial w}{\partial r}\right)_{r=a} = 0.$$

From these three equations three of the four constants in expression (f) can be eliminated, so that w will finally contain only one constant. Substituting this expression in the integrals (b) and (c) and using for N_r the known value of Lame's formula,

$$N_r = \frac{pb^2h}{a^2 - b^2}\left(\frac{a^2}{r^2} - 1\right),$$

in which p is the magnitude of the internal pressure, we obtain for the critical value of the pressure p the formula

$$p_{cr} = \frac{kD}{ha^2}, \qquad (g)$$

in which k is a numerical factor depending on the magnitude of the ratio a/b. Taking, for example, $a = 2b$ and $\nu = 0.3$, we find

$$p_{cr} = 5.62\frac{D}{ha^2}.$$

Uniformly Compressed Elliptical Plate.—The case of a uniformly compressed elliptical plate with a clamped edge has been discussed by S. Woinovsky-Krieger.[1] The critical value of the compressive force N is given by the equation

$$N_{cr} = \frac{kD}{b^2}, \qquad (h)$$

in which k is a numerical factor the value of which depends on the ratio a/b of the semi-axes of the ellipse. Several values of this factor as calculated by the energy method are given in Table 44.

[1] *J. App. Mech.*, vol. 4, p. 177, 1937.

TABLE 44.—NUMERICAL VALUES OF k IN EQ. (h)

a/b	1.0	1.1	1.2	1.3	1.4	1.5	2.0	3.0	4.0
k	14.79	13.57	12.76	12.20	11.81	11.54	11.02	11.01	11.15

If the value of k for $a = b$ in this table is compared with the value of k in Eq. (192), it can be seen that the error of the approximate solution is only 0.7 per cent. Better accuracy is obtained with this solution than with solution (d), because the expression for w was taken with two parameters, and two equations of the type (191) were used in calculating the critical force, whereas only one parameter was used in obtaining Eq. (d).

66. Bending of Plates with a Small Initial Curvature.[1]— Assume that a plate has some initial warp of the middle surface so that at any point there is an initial deflection w_0 which is small in comparison with the thickness of the plate. If such a plate is submitted to the action of transverse loading, additional deflection w_1 will be produced, and the total deflection at any point of the middle surface of the plate will be $w_0 + w_1$. In calculating the deflection w_1 we use Eq. (101) derived for flat plates. This procedure is justifiable if the initial deflection w_0 is small, since we may consider the initial deflection as produced by a fictitious load and apply the principle of superposition.[2] If in addition to lateral loads there are forces acting in the middle plane of the plate, the effect of these forces on bending depends not only on w_1 but also on w_0. To take this into account, in applying Eq. (175) we use the total deflection $w = w_0 + w_1$ on the right-hand side of the equation. It will be remembered that the left-hand side of the same equation was obtained from expressions for the bending moments in the plate. Since these moments depend not on the total curvature but only on the change in curvature of the plate, the deflection w_1 should be used instead of w in applying that side of the equation to this problem. Hence, for the case of an initially curved plate, Eq. (175) becomes

---

[1] See author's paper in *Mem. Inst. of Ways of Communication*, vol. 89, St. Petersburg, 1915 (Russian).

[2] In the case of large deflections the magnitude of the deflection is no longer proportional to the load, and the principle of superposition is not applicable.

$$\frac{\partial^4 w_1}{\partial x^4} + 2\frac{\partial^4 w_1}{\partial x^2\,\partial y^2} + \frac{\partial^4 w_1}{\partial y^4} = \frac{1}{D}\bigg[q + N_x\frac{\partial^2(w_0 + w_1)}{\partial x^2}$$
$$+ N_y\frac{\partial^2(w_0 + w_1)}{\partial y^2} + 2N_{xy}\frac{\partial^2(w_0 + w_1)}{\partial x\,\partial y}\bigg]. \quad (194)$$

It is seen that the effect of an initial curvature on the deflection is equivalent to the effect of a fictitious lateral load of an intensity

$$N_x\frac{\partial^2 w_0}{\partial x^2} + N_y\frac{\partial^2 w_0}{\partial y^2} + 2N_{xy}\frac{\partial^2 w_0}{\partial x\,\partial y}.$$

Thus a plate will experience bending under the action of forces in the xy-plane alone provided there is an initial curvature.

Take as an example the case of a rectangular plate (Fig. 119), and assume that the initial deflection of the plate is defined by the equation

$$w_0 = a_{11} \sin \frac{\pi x}{a} \sin \frac{\pi y}{b}. \quad (a)$$

If uniformly distributed compressive forces N_x are acting on the edges of this plate, Eq. (194) becomes

$$\frac{\partial^4 w_1}{\partial x^4} + 2\frac{\partial^4 w_1}{\partial x^2\,\partial y^2} + \frac{\partial^4 w_1}{\partial y^4} = \frac{1}{D}\bigg(N_x\frac{a_{11}\pi^2}{a^2} \sin \frac{\pi x}{a} \sin \frac{\pi y}{b}$$
$$- N_x\frac{\partial^2 w_1}{\partial x^2}\bigg). \quad (b)$$

Let us take the solution of this equation in the form

$$w_1 = A \sin \frac{\pi x}{a} \sin \frac{\pi y}{b}. \quad (c)$$

Substituting this value of w_1 into Eq. (b), we obtain

$$A = \frac{a_{11}N_x}{\dfrac{\pi^2 D}{a^2}\bigg(1 + \dfrac{a^2}{b^2}\bigg)^2 - N_x}.$$

With this value of A expression (c) gives the deflection of the plate produced by the compressive forces N_x. Adding this deflection to the initial deflection (a), we obtain for the total deflection of the plate the following expression:

$$w = w_0 + w_1 = \frac{a_{11}}{1 - \alpha} \sin \frac{\pi x}{a} \sin \frac{\pi y}{b}, \quad (d)$$

in which

$$\alpha = \frac{N_x}{\dfrac{\pi^2 D}{a^2}\left(1 + \dfrac{a^2}{b^2}\right)^2}. \qquad (e)$$

The maximum deflection will be at the center and will be

$$w_{\text{max.}} = \frac{a_{11}}{1 - \alpha}. \qquad (f)$$

This formula is analogous to that used for a bar with initial curvature.[1]

In a more general case we can take the initial deflection surface of the rectangular plate in the form of the following series:

$$w_0 = \sum_{m=1}^{\infty}\sum_{n=1}^{\infty} a_{mn} \sin \frac{m\pi x}{a} \sin \frac{n\pi y}{b}. \qquad (g)$$

Substituting this series in Eq. (194), we find that the additional deflection at any point of the plate is

$$w_1 = \sum_{m=1}^{\infty}\sum_{n=1}^{\infty} b_{mn} \sin \frac{m\pi x}{a} \sin \frac{n\pi y}{b}, \qquad (h)$$

in which

$$b_{mn} = \frac{a_{mn}N_x}{\dfrac{\pi^2 D}{a^2}\left(m + \dfrac{n^2}{m}\dfrac{a^2}{b^2}\right)^2 - N_x}. \qquad (i)$$

It is seen that all the coefficients b_{mn} increase with an increase of N_x. Thus when N_x approaches the critical value, the term in series (h) that corresponds to the laterally buckled shape of the plate [see Eq. (185)] becomes the predominating one. We have here a complete analogy with the case of bending of initially curved bars under compression.

The problem can be handled in the same manner if, instead of compression, we have tension in the middle plane of the plate. In such a case it is necessary only to change the sign of N_x in the previous equations. Without any difficulty we can also obtain the deflection in the case when there are not only forces N_x but also forces N_y and N_{xy} uniformly distributed along the edges of the plate.

[1] See author's "Strength of Materials," vol. 2, p. 422, 1930.

CHAPTER IX

LARGE DEFLECTIONS OF PLATES

67. Bending of Circular Plates by Moments Uniformly Distributed along the Edge.—In the previous discussion of pure bending of circular plates it was shown (see page 51) that the strain of the middle plane of the plate can be neglected in cases in which the deflections are small as compared with the thickness of the plate. In cases in which the deflections are no longer small in comparison with the thickness of the plate but are still small as compared with the other dimensions, the analysis of the problem must be extended to include the strain of the middle plane of the plate.[1]

We shall assume that a circular plate is bent by the moment M_0 uniformly distributed along the edge of the plate (Fig. 129a). Since the deflection surface in such a case is symmetrical with respect to the center O, the displacement of a point in the middle plane of the plate can be resolved into two components: a component u in the radial direction and a component w perpendicular to the plane of the plate. Proceeding as previously indicated in Fig. 120 (page 304), we conclude that the strain in the radial direction is

$$\epsilon_r = \frac{du}{dr} + \frac{1}{2}\left(\frac{dw}{dr}\right)^2. \tag{a}$$

The strain in the tangential direction is evidently

$$\epsilon_t = \frac{u}{r}. \tag{b}$$

Denoting the corresponding tensile forces per unit length by N_r and N_t and applying Hooke's law, we obtain

$$\left.\begin{aligned}
N_r &= \frac{Eh}{1-\nu^2}(\epsilon_r + \nu\epsilon_t) = \frac{Eh}{1-\nu^2}\left[\frac{du}{dr} + \frac{1}{2}\left(\frac{dw}{dr}\right)^2 + \nu\frac{u}{r}\right], \\
N_t &= \frac{Eh}{1-\nu^2}(\epsilon_t + \nu\epsilon_r) = \frac{Eh}{1-\nu^2}\left[\frac{u}{r} + \nu\frac{du}{dr} + \frac{\nu}{2}\left(\frac{dw}{dr}\right)^2\right].
\end{aligned}\right\} \tag{c}$$

---

[1] This problem has been discussed by the writer, see *Mem. Inst. of Ways of Communication*, vol. 89, 1915.

These forces must be taken into consideration in deriving equations of equilibrium for an element of the plate such as that shown in Figs. 129b and 129c. Taking the sum of the projections in the

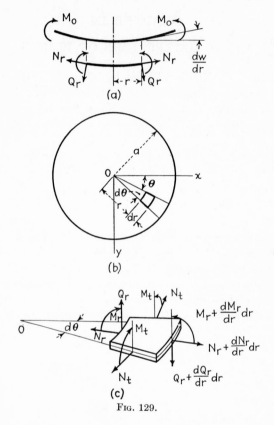

Fig. 129.

radial direction of all the forces acting on the element, we obtain

$$r\frac{dN_r}{dr}dr\ d\theta + N_r\ dr\ d\theta - N_t\ dr\ d\theta = 0,$$

from which

$$N_r - N_t + r\frac{dN_r}{dr} = 0. \qquad (d)$$

The second equation of equilibrium of the element is obtained by taking moments of all the forces with respect to an axis perpendicular to the radius in the same manner as in the derivation of Eq. (55) (page 57). In this way we obtain[1]

$$Q_r = -D\left(\frac{d^3w}{dr^3} + \frac{1}{r}\frac{d^2w}{dr^2} - \frac{1}{r^2}\frac{dw}{dr}\right). \tag{e}$$

The magnitude of the shearing force Q_r is obtained by considering the equilibrium of the inner circular portion of the plate of radius r (Fig. 129a). Such a consideration gives the relation

$$Q_r = -N_r\frac{dw}{dr}, \tag{f}$$

Substituting this expression for shearing force in Eq. (e) and using expressions (c) for N_r and N_t, we can represent the equations of equilibrium (d) and (e) in the following form:

$$\left.\begin{aligned}
\frac{d^2u}{dr^2} &= -\frac{1}{r}\frac{du}{dr} + \frac{u}{r^2} - \frac{1-\nu}{2r}\left(\frac{dw}{dr}\right)^2 - \frac{dw}{dr}\frac{d^2w}{dr^2}, \\
\frac{d^3w}{dr^3} &= -\frac{1}{r}\frac{d^2w}{dr^2} + \frac{1}{r^2}\frac{dw}{dr} + \frac{12}{h^2}\frac{dw}{dr}\left[\frac{du}{dr} + \nu\frac{u}{r} + \frac{1}{2}\left(\frac{dw}{dr}\right)^2\right].
\end{aligned}\right\} \tag{195}$$

These two non-linear equations can be integrated numerically by starting from the center of the plate and advancing by small increments in the radial direction. For a circular element of a small radius c at the center, we assume a certain radial strain

$$\epsilon_0 = \left(\frac{du}{dr}\right)_{r=0}$$

and a certain uniform curvature

$$\frac{1}{\rho_0} = -\left(\frac{d^2w}{dr^2}\right)_{r=0}.$$

With these values of radial strain and curvature at the center, the values of the radial displacement u and the slope dw/dr for $r = c$ can be calculated. Thus all the quantities on the right-hand side of Eq. (195) are known, and the values of d^2u/dr^2 and of d^3w/dr^3 for $r = c$ can be calculated. As soon as these values are known, another radial step of length c can be made, and all the quantities entering in the right-hand side of Eqs. (195)

---

[1] The direction for Q_r is opposite to that used in Fig. 28. This explains the minus sign in Eq. (e).

can be calculated for $r = 2c$[1] and so on. The numerical values of u and w and their derivatives at the end of any interval being known, the values of the forces N_r and N_t can then be calculated from Eqs. (c) and the bending moments M_r and M_t from Eqs. (52) and (53) (see page 56). By such repeated calculations

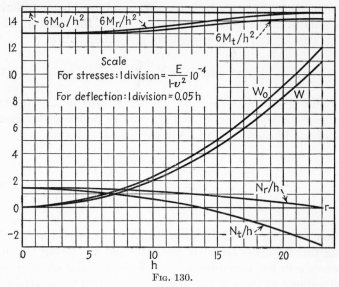

Fig. 130.

we proceed up to the radial distance $r = a$ at which the radial force N_r vanishes. In this way we obtain a circular plate of radius a bent by moments M_0 uniformly distributed along the edge. By changing the numerical values of ϵ_0 and $1/\rho_0$ at the center we obtain plates with various values of the outer radius and various values of the moment along the edge.

Figure (130) shows graphically the results obtained for a plate with

$$a \approx 23h \quad \text{and} \quad (M_r)_{r=a} = M_0 = 2.93 \cdot 10^{-3}\frac{D}{h}.$$

[1] If the intervals into which the radius is divided are sufficiently small, a simple procedure, such as that used in the author's "Vibration Problems in Engineering," p. 126, can be applied. The numerical results represented in Fig. 130 are obtained in this manner. A higher accuracy can be obtained by using the methods of Adams or Störmer. For an account of the Adams method see Francis Bashforth's book on forms of fluid drops, Cambridge University Press, 1883. Störmer's method is discussed very completely in A. N. Krilov's book. "Approximate Calculations," published by the Russian Academy of Sciences. Moscow, 1935.

It will be noted that the maximum deflection of the plate is 0.55h, which is about 9 per cent less than the deflection w_0 given by the elementary theory which neglects the strain in the middle plane of the plate. The forces N_r and N_t are both positive in the central portion of the plate. In the outer portion of the plate the forces N_t become negative; *i.e.*, compression exists in the tangential direction. The maximum tangential compressive stress at the edge amounts to about 18 per cent of the maximum bending stress $6M_0/h^2$. The bending stresses produced by the moments M_r and M_t are somewhat smaller than the stress $6M_0/h^2$ given by the elementary theory and become smallest at the center, at which point the error of the elementary theory amounts to about 12 per cent. From this numerical example it may be concluded that for deflections of the order of 0.5h the errors in maximum deflection and maximum stress as given by the elementary theory become considerable and that the strain of the middle plane must be taken into account to obtain more accurate results.

68. Approximate Formulas for Uniformly Loaded Circular Plate with Large Deflections.—The method used in the previous article can also be applied in the case of lateral loading of a plate. It is not, however, of practical use, since a considerable amount of numerical calculation is required to obtain the deflections and stresses in each particular case. A more useful formula for an approximate calculation of the deflections can be obtained by applying the energy method.[1] Let a circular plate of radius a be clamped at the edge and be subject to a uniformly distributed load of intensity q. Assuming that the shape of the deflected surface can be represented by the same equation as in the case of small deflections, we take

$$w = w_0\left(1 - \frac{r^2}{a^2}\right)^2.$$ (a)

The corresponding strain energy of bending from Eq. (c) (page 323) is

$$V = \frac{32\pi}{3}\frac{w_0^2}{a^2}.$$ (b)

For the radial displacements we take the expression

$$u = r(a - r)(C_1 + C_2 r + C_3 r^2 + \cdots),$$ (c)

---

[1] See "Vibration Problems in Engineering," p. 431, 1937.

each term of which satisfies the boundary conditions that u must vanish at the center and at the edge of the plate. From expressions (a) and (c) for the displacements, we calculate the strain components ϵ_r and ϵ_t of the middle plane as shown in the previous article and obtain the strain energy due to stretching of the middle plane by using the expression

$$V_1 = 2\pi \int_0^a \left(\frac{N_r \epsilon_r}{2} + \frac{N_t \epsilon_t}{2} \right) r\, dr$$

$$= \frac{\pi E h}{1 - \nu^2} \int_0^a (\epsilon_r^2 + \epsilon_t^2 + 2\nu \epsilon_r \epsilon_t) r\, dr. \quad (d)$$

Taking only the first two terms in series (c), we obtain

$$V_1 = \frac{\pi E h a^2}{1 - \nu^2} \Big(0.250 C_1^2 a^2 + 0.1167 C_2^2 a^4 + 0.300 C_1 C_2 a^3$$

$$- 0.00846 C_1 a \frac{8 w_0^2}{a^2} + 0.00682 C_2 a^2 \frac{8 w_0^2}{a^2} + 0.00477 \frac{64 w_0^4}{a^4} \Big). \quad (e)$$

The constants C_1 and C_2 are now determined from the condition that the total energy of the plate for a position of equilibrium is a minimum. Hence

$$\frac{\partial V_1}{\partial C_1} = 0, \quad \text{and} \quad \frac{\partial V_1}{\partial C_2} = 0. \quad (f)$$

Substituting expression (e) for V_1, we obtain two linear equations for C_1 and C_2. From these we find that

$$C_1 = 1.185 \frac{w_0^2}{a^3} \quad \text{and} \quad C_2 = -1.75 \frac{w_0^2}{a^4}.$$

Then, from Eq. (e) we obtain[1]

$$V_1 = 2.59 \pi D \frac{w_0^4}{a^2 h^2}. \quad (g)$$

Adding this energy, which results from stretching of the middle plane, to the energy of bending (b), we obtain the total strain energy

$$V + V_1 = \frac{32}{3} \pi D \frac{w_0^2}{a^2} \Big(1 + 0.244 \frac{w_0^2}{h^2} \Big). \quad (h)$$

The second term in the parenthesis represents the correction due

[1] It is assumed that $\nu = 0.3$ in this calculation.

to strain in the middle surface of the plate. It is readily seen that this correction is small and can be neglected if the deflection w_0 at the center of the plate is small in comparison with the thickness h of the plate.

The strain energy being known from expression (h), the deflection of the plate is obtained by applying the principle of virtual displacements. From this principle it follows that

$$\frac{d(V_1 + V_1)}{dw_0} \delta w_0 = 2\pi \int_0^a q \; \delta w \; r \; dr = 2\pi q \; \delta w_0 \int_0^a \left(1 - \frac{r^2}{a^2}\right)^2 r \; dr.$$

Substituting expression (h) in this equation, we obtain a cubic equation for w_0. This equation can be put in the form

$$w_0 = \frac{qa^4}{64D} \cdot \frac{1}{1 + 0.488\dfrac{w_0^2}{h^2}}. \tag{196}$$

The last factor on the right-hand side represents the effect of the stretching of the middle surface on the deflection. Because of this effect the deflection w_0 is no longer proportional to the intensity q of the load, and the rigidity of the plate increases with the deflection. For example, taking $w_0 = \frac{1}{2}h$, we obtain, from Eq. (196),

$$w_0 = 0.89\frac{qa^4}{64D}.$$

This indicates that the deflection in this case is 11 per cent less than that obtained by neglecting the stretching of the middle surface.

Another method for the approximate solution of the problem has been developed by A. Nadai.[1] He begins with equations of equilibrium similar to Eqs. (195). To derive them we have only to change Eq. (f), of the previous article, to fit the case of lateral load of intensity q. After such a change the expression for the shearing force evidently becomes

$$Q_r = -N_r\frac{dw}{dr} - \frac{1}{r}\int_0^r qr \; dr. \tag{i}$$

Using this expression in the same manner in which expression (f) was used in the previous article, we obtain the following system of equations in place of Eqs. (195):

[1] See his book "Elastische Platten," p. 288, 1925.

$$\left.\begin{aligned}
\frac{d^2u}{dr^2} + \frac{1}{r}\frac{du}{dr} - \frac{u}{r^2} &= -\frac{1-\nu}{2r}\left(\frac{dw}{dr}\right)^2 - \frac{dw}{dr}\frac{d^2w}{dr^2}, \\
\frac{d^3w}{dr^3} + \frac{1}{r}\frac{d^2w}{dr^2} - \frac{1}{r^2}\frac{dw}{dr} &= \frac{12}{h^2}\frac{dw}{dr}\left[\frac{du}{dr} + \nu\frac{u}{r} + \frac{1}{2}\left(\frac{dw}{dr}\right)^2\right] \\
&\qquad + \frac{1}{Dr}\int_0^r qr\,dr.
\end{aligned}\right\} \quad (197)$$

To obtain an approximate solution of the problem a suitable expression for the deflection w should be taken as a first approximation. Substituting it in the right-hand side of the first of the equations (197), we obtain a linear equation for u which can be integrated, to give a first approximation for u. Substituting the first approximations for u and w in the right-hand side of the second of the equations (197), we obtain a linear differential equation for w which can be integrated to give a second approximation for w. This second approximation can then be used to obtain further approximations for u and w by repeating the same sequence of calculations.

In discussing bending of a uniformly loaded circular plate with a clamped edge, Nadai begins with the derivative dw/dr and takes as first approximation the expression

$$\frac{dw}{dr} = C\left[\frac{r}{a} - \left(\frac{r}{a}\right)^n\right], \qquad (j)$$

which vanishes for $r = 0$ and $r = a$ in compliance with the condition at the built-in edge. The first of the equations (197) then gives the first approximation for u. Substituting these first approximations for u and dw/dr in the second of the equations (197) and solving it for q, we determine the constants C and n in expression (j) so as to make q as nearly a constant as possible. In this manner the following equation[1] for calculating the deflection at the center is obtained when $\nu = 0.25$:

$$\frac{w_0}{h} + 0.583\left(\frac{w_0}{h}\right)^3 = 0.176\frac{q}{E}\left(\frac{a}{h}\right)^4. \qquad (198)$$

[1] Another method for the approximate solution of Eqs. (197) was developed by K. Federhoffer, *Eisenbau*, vol. 9, p. 152, 1918; see also *Forschungsarbeiten*, vol. 7, p. 148, 1936. His equation for w_0 differs from Eq. (198) only by the numerical value of the coefficient on the left-hand side; *viz.*, 0.523 must be used instead of 0.583 for $\nu = 0.25$.

In the case of very thin plates the deflection w_0 may become very large in comparison with h. In such cases the resistance of the plate to bending can be neglected, and it can be treated as a flexible membrane. The general equations for such a membrane are obtained from Eqs. (197) by putting zero in place of the left side of the second of the equations. An approximate solution of the resulting equations is obtained by neglecting the first term on the left side of Eq. (198) as being small in comparison with the second term. Hence

$$0.583\left(\frac{w_0}{h}\right)^3 \approx 0.176\frac{q}{E}\left(\frac{a}{h}\right)^4 \quad \text{and} \quad w_0 = 0.665a\sqrt[3]{\frac{qa}{Eh}}.$$

A more complete investigation of the same problem[1] gives

$$w_0 = 0.662a\sqrt[3]{\frac{qa}{Eh}}. \tag{199}$$

This formula, which is in very satisfactory agreement with experiments,[2] shows that the deflections are not proportional to the intensity of the load but vary as the cube root of that intensity. For the tensile stresses at the center of the membrane and at the boundary the same solution gives, respectively,

$$(\sigma_r)_{r=0} = 0.423\sqrt[3]{\frac{Eq^2a^2}{h^2}} \quad \text{and} \quad (\sigma_r)_{r=a} = 0.328\sqrt{\frac{Eq^2a^2}{h^2}}.$$

To obtain deflections that are proportional to the pressure, as is often required in various measuring instruments, recourse should be had to corrugated membranes[3] such as that shown in Fig. 131. As a

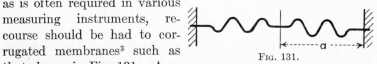

Fig. 131.

result of the corrugations the deformation consists primarily of bending and thus increases in proportion to the pressure.[4]

---

[1] The solution of this problem was given by H. Hencky, *Z. Math. Physik*, vol. 63, p. 311, 1915.

[2] See Bruno Eck, *Z. angew. Math. Mech.*, vol. 7, p. 498, 1927.

[3] The theory of deflection of such membranes is discussed by K. Stange, *Ingenieur-Archiv*, vol. 2, p. 47, 1931.

[4] For a bibliography on diaphragms used in measuring instruments see the M. D. Hersey paper, *Rept. Nat. Advisory Comm. Aeronautics*, 165, 1923.

69. Exact Solution for a Uniformly Loaded Circular Plate with a Clamped Edge.[1]—To obtain a more satisfactory solution of the problem of large deflections of a uniformly loaded circular plate with a clamped edge, it is necessary to solve Eqs. (197). To do this we first write the equations in a somewhat different form. As may be seen from its derivation in Art. 67, the first of these equations is equivalent to the equation

$$N_r - N_t + r\frac{dN_r}{dr} = 0. \tag{a}$$

Also, as is seen from Eq. (e) of Art. 67 and Eq. (i) of Art. (68), the second of the same equations can be put in the following form:

$$D\left(\frac{d^3w}{dr^3} + \frac{1}{r}\frac{d^2w}{dr^2} - \frac{1}{r^2}\frac{dw}{dr}\right) = N_r\frac{dw}{dr} + \frac{qr}{2}. \tag{b}$$

From the general expressions for the radial and tangential strain (page 329) we obtain

$$\epsilon_r = \epsilon_t + r\frac{d\epsilon_t}{dr} + \frac{1}{2}\left(\frac{dw}{dr}\right)^2.$$

Substituting

$$\epsilon_r = \frac{1}{hE}(N_r - \nu N_t), \qquad \text{and} \qquad \epsilon_t = \frac{1}{hE}(N_t - \nu N_r)$$

in this equation and using Eq. (a), we obtain

$$r\frac{d}{dr}(N_r + N_t) + \frac{hE}{2}\left(\frac{dw}{dr}\right)^2 = 0. \tag{c}$$

The three Eqs. (a), (b) and (c) containing the three unknown functions N_r, N_t and w will now be used in solving the problem. We begin by transforming these equations to a dimensionless form by introducing the following notations

$$p = \frac{q}{E}, \qquad \xi = \frac{r}{h}, \qquad S_r = \frac{N_r}{hE}, \qquad S_t = \frac{N_t}{hE}. \tag{d}$$

With this notation, Eqs. (a), (b) and (c) become, respectively,

[1] This solution is due to S. Way, *Trans. Am. Soc. Mech. Eng.*, vol. 56, p. 627, 1934.

$$\frac{d}{d\xi}(\xi S_r) - S_t = 0, \tag{e}$$

$$\frac{1}{12(1 - \nu^2)}\frac{d}{d\xi}\left[\frac{1}{\xi}\frac{d}{d\xi}\left(\xi\frac{dw}{dr}\right)\right] = \frac{p\xi}{2} + S_r\frac{dw}{dr}, \tag{f}$$

$$\xi\frac{d}{d\xi}(S_r + S_t) + \frac{1}{2}\left(\frac{dw}{dr}\right)^2 = 0. \tag{g}$$

The boundary conditions in this case require that the radial displacement u and the slope dw/dr vanish at the boundary. Using Eq. (b) (Art. 67) for the displacements u and applying Hooke's law, these conditions become

$$(u)_{r=a} = r(S_t - \nu S_r)_{r=a} = 0, \tag{h}$$

$$\left(\frac{dw}{dr}\right)_{r=a} = 0. \tag{i}$$

Assuming that S_r is a symmetrical function and dw/dr an antisymmetrical function of ξ, we represent these functions by the following power series:

$$S_r = B_0 + B_2\xi^2 + B_4\xi^4 + \cdots, \tag{j}$$

$$\frac{dw}{dr} = \sqrt{8}(C_1\xi + C_3\xi^3 + C_5\xi^5 + \cdots). \tag{k}$$

in which B_0, B_2, ... and C_1, C_3, ... are constants to be determined later. Substituting the first of these series in Eq. (e), we find

$$S_t = B_0 + 3B_2\xi^2 + 5B_4\xi^4 + \cdots. \tag{l}$$

By integrating and differentiating Eq. (k), we obtain, respectively.

$$\frac{w}{h} = \sqrt{8}\left(C_1\frac{\xi^2}{2} + C_3\frac{\xi^4}{4} + C_5\frac{\xi^6}{6} + \cdots\right), \tag{m}$$

$$\frac{d}{d\xi}\left(\frac{dw}{dr}\right) = \sqrt{8}(C_1 + 3C_3\xi^2 + 5C_5\xi^4 + \cdots). \tag{n}$$

It is seen that all the quantities in which we are interested can be found if we know the constants B_0, B_2, ..., C_1, C_3, ... Substituting series (j), (k) and (l) in Eqs. (f) and (g) and observing that these equations must be satisfied for any value of ξ, we find the following relations between the constants B and C:

$$B_k = -\frac{4}{k(k+2)} \sum_{m=1,3,5,\cdots}^{k-1} C_m C_{k-m}; \ k = 2, 4, 6, \cdots, $$

$$C_k = \frac{12(1-\nu^2)}{k^2-1} \sum_{m=0,2,4,\cdots}^{k-3} B_m C_{k-2-m}; \ k = 5, 7, 9, \cdots, $$

$$C_3 = \frac{3}{2}(1-\nu^2)\left(\frac{p}{2\sqrt{8}} + B_0 C_1\right). $$

(o)

It can be seen that when the two constants B_0 and C_1 are assigned, all the other constants are determined by relations (o). The

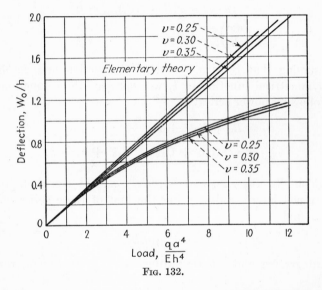

Fig. 132.

quantities S_r, S_t and dw/dr are then determined by series (j), (l) and (k) for all points in the plate. As may be seen from series (j) and (n), fixing B_0 and C_1 is equivalent to selecting the values of S_r and the curvature at the center of the plate.[1]

To obtain the curves for calculating deflections and stresses in particular cases, the following procedure was used. For given values of ν and $p = q/E$ and for selected values of B_0 and C_1, a

[1] The selection of these same quantities has already been encountered in the case of bending of circular plates by moments uniformly distributed along the edge (see page 331).

considerable number of numerical cases were calculated,[1] and the radii of the plates were determined so as to satisfy the boundary condition (i). For all these plates the values of S_r and S_t at the boundary were calculated, and the values of the radial displacements $(u)_{r=a}$ at the boundary were determined. Since all calculations were made with arbitrarily assumed values of B_0 and

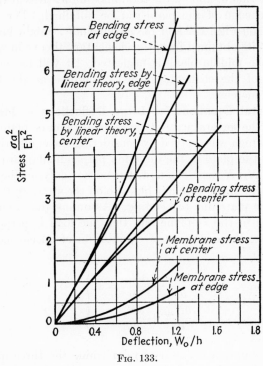

FIG. 133.

C_1, the boundary condition (h) was not satisfied. However, by interpolation it was possible to obtain all the necessary data for plates for which both conditions (h) and (i) are satisfied. The result of these calculations are represented graphically in Fig. 132. If the deflection of the plate is found from this figure, the corresponding stress can be obtained by using the curves of Fig. 133. In this figure, curves are given for the membrane stresses

$$\sigma_r = \frac{N_r}{h}$$

[1] Nineteen particular cases have been calculated by Way, *loc. cit.*, p. 338.

and for the bending stresses

$$\sigma_r' = \frac{6M_r}{h^2},$$

as calculated for the center and for the edge of the plate.[1]   By adding together σ_r and σ_r', the total maximum stress at the center and at the edge of the plate can be obtained.   For purposes of comparison Figs. 132 and 133 also include straight lines showing the results obtained from the elementary theory in which the strain of the middle plane is neglected.   It will be noted that the errors of the elementary theory increase as the load and deflections increase.

70. General Equations for Large Deflections of Plates.—In discussing the general case of large deflections of plates we use Eq. (177) which was derived by considering the equilibrium of an element of the plate in the direction perpendicular to the plate. The forces N_x, N_y and N_{xy} now depend not only on the external forces applied in the xy-plane but also on the strain of the middle plane of the plate due to bending.   Assuming that there are no body forces in the xy-plane and that the load is perpendicular to the plate, the equations of equilibrium of an element in the xy-plane are

$$\left.\begin{aligned} \frac{\partial N_x}{\partial x} + \frac{\partial N_{xy}}{\partial y} &= 0, \\ \frac{\partial N_{xy}}{\partial x} + \frac{\partial N_y}{\partial y} &= 0. \end{aligned}\right\} \qquad (a)$$

The third equation necessary to determine the three quantities N_x, N_y, and N_{xy} is obtained from a consideration of the strain in the middle surface of the plate during bending.   The corresponding strain components [see Eqs. (179), (180) and (181)] are

$$\left.\begin{aligned} \epsilon_x &= \frac{\partial u}{\partial x} + \frac{1}{2}\left(\frac{\partial w}{\partial x}\right)^2, \\ \epsilon_y &= \frac{\partial v}{\partial y} + \frac{1}{2}\left(\frac{\partial w}{\partial y}\right)^2, \\ \gamma_{xy} &= \frac{\partial u}{\partial y} + \frac{\partial v}{\partial x} + \frac{\partial w}{\partial x}\frac{\partial w}{\partial y}. \end{aligned}\right\} \qquad (b)$$

---

[1] The stresses are given in dimensionless form.

By taking the second derivatives of these expressions and combining the resulting expressions, it can be shown that

$$\frac{\partial^2 \epsilon_x}{\partial y^2} + \frac{\partial^2 \epsilon_y}{\partial x^2} - \frac{\partial^2 \gamma_{xy}}{\partial x\,\partial y} = \left(\frac{\partial^2 w}{\partial x\,\partial y}\right)^2 - \frac{\partial^2 w}{\partial x^2}\frac{\partial^2 w}{\partial y^2}. \tag{c}$$

By replacing the strain components by the equivalent expressions

$$\left.\begin{aligned}
\epsilon_x &= \frac{1}{hE}(N_x - \nu N_y),\\[2mm]
\epsilon_y &= \frac{1}{hE}(N_y - \nu N_x),\\[2mm]
\gamma_{xy} &= \frac{1}{hG}N_{xy},
\end{aligned}\right\} \tag{d}$$

the third equation in terms of N_x, N_y and N_{xy} is obtained.

The solution of these three equations is greatly simplified by the introduction of a *stress function*.[1] It may be seen that Eqs. (a) are identically satisfied by taking

$$N_x = h\frac{\partial^2 F}{\partial y^2}, \qquad N_y = h\frac{\partial^2 F}{\partial x^2}, \qquad N_{xy} = -h\frac{\partial^2 F}{\partial x\,\partial y}, \tag{e}$$

where F is a function of x and y. If these expressions for the forces are substituted in Eqs. (d), the strain components become

$$\epsilon_x = \frac{1}{E}\left(\frac{\partial^2 F}{\partial y^2} - \nu\frac{\partial^2 F}{\partial x^2}\right),$$

$$\epsilon_y = \frac{1}{E}\left(\frac{\partial^2 F}{\partial x^2} - \nu\frac{\partial^2 F}{\partial y^2}\right),$$

$$\gamma_{xy} = -\frac{2(1+\nu)}{E}\frac{\partial^2 F}{\partial x\,\partial y}.$$

Substituting these expressions in Eq. (c), we obtain

$$\frac{\partial^4 F}{\partial x^4} + 2\frac{\partial^4 F}{\partial x^2\,\partial y^2} + \frac{\partial^4 F}{\partial y^4} = E\left[\left(\frac{\partial^2 w}{\partial x\,\partial y}\right)^2 - \frac{\partial^2 w}{\partial x^2}\frac{\partial^2 w}{\partial y^2}\right]. \tag{200}$$

The second equation necessary to determine F and w is obtained by substituting expressions (e) in Eq. (175) which gives

$$\frac{\partial^4 w}{\partial x^4} + 2\frac{\partial^4 w}{\partial x^2\,\partial y^2} + \frac{\partial^4 w}{\partial y^4} = \frac{h}{D}\left(\frac{q}{h} + \frac{\partial^2 F}{\partial y^2}\frac{\partial^2 w}{\partial x^2}\right.$$
$$\left. + \frac{\partial^2 F}{\partial x^2}\frac{\partial^2 w}{\partial y^2} - 2\frac{\partial^2 F}{\partial x\,\partial y}\frac{\partial^2 w}{\partial x\,\partial y}\right). \tag{201}$$

---

[1] See author's "Theory of Elasticity," p. 24, 1934.

Equations (200) and (201), together with the boundary conditions, determine the two functions F and w.[1] Having the stress function F, we can determine the stresses in the middle surface of a plate by applying Eqs. (e). From the function w, which defines the deflection surface of the plate, the bending and the shearing stresses can be obtained by using the same formulas as in the case of plates with small deflection [see Eqs. (99) and (100)]. Thus the investigation of large deflections of plates reduces to the solution of the two non-linear differential equations (200) and (201). The solution of these equations in the general case is unknown. Some approximate solutions of the problem are known, however, and will be discussed in the next article.

In the particular case of bending of a plate to a cylindrical surface whose axis is parallel to the y-axis, Eqs. (200) and (201) are simplified by observing that in this case w is a function of x only and that $\partial^2 F / \partial x^2$ amd $\partial^2 F / \partial y^2$ are constants. Equation (200) is then satisfied identically, and Eq. (201) reduces to

$$\frac{\partial^4 w}{\partial x^4} = \frac{q}{D} + \frac{N_x}{D} \frac{\partial^2 w}{\partial x^2}.$$

Problems of this kind have already been discussed fully in Chap. I.

In the case of very thin plates which may have deflections many times larger than their thickness, the resistance of the plate to bending can be neglected; i.e., the flexural rigidity D can be taken equal to zero, and the problem reduced to that of finding the deflection of a flexible membrane. Equations (200) and (201) then become[2]

$$\left.\begin{aligned}
\frac{\partial^4 F}{\partial x^4} + 2\frac{\partial^4 F}{\partial x^2 \, \partial y^2} + \frac{\partial^4 F}{\partial y^4} &= E\left[\left(\frac{\partial^2 w}{\partial x \, \partial y}\right)^2 - \frac{\partial^2 w}{\partial x^2} \frac{\partial^2 w}{\partial y^2}\right], \\
\frac{q}{h} + \frac{\partial^2 F}{\partial y^2} \frac{\partial^2 w}{\partial x^2} + \frac{\partial^2 F}{\partial x^2} \frac{\partial^2 w}{\partial y^2} &- 2\frac{\partial^2 F}{\partial x \, \partial y} \frac{\partial^2 w}{\partial x \, \partial y} = 0.
\end{aligned}\right\} \quad (202)$$

A numerical solution of this system of equations by the use of finite differences has been discussed by H. Hencky.[3]

---

[1] These two equations were derived by Th. von Kármán, See "Encyklopädie der Mathematischen Wissenschaften," vol. IV$_4$, p. 349, 1910.

[2] These equations were obtained by A. Föppl, "Vorlesungen über Technische Mechanik," vol. 5, p. 132, 1907.

[3] HENCKY, H., Z. angew. Math. Mech., vol. 1, pp. 81 and 423, 1921; see also KAISER, R., Z. angew. Math. Mech., vol. 16, p. 73, 1936.

The energy method affords another means of obtaining an approximate solution for the deflection of a membrane. The strain energy of a membrane, which is due solely to stretching of its middle surface, is given by the expression

$$V = \tfrac{1}{2}\int\int(N_x\epsilon_x + N_y\epsilon_y + N_{xy}\gamma_{xy})dx\,dy$$

$$= \frac{Eh}{2(1-\nu^2)}\int\int[\epsilon_x^2 + \epsilon_y^2 + 2\nu\epsilon_x\epsilon_y + \tfrac{1}{2}(1-\nu)\gamma_{xy}^2]dx\,dy.$$

Substituting expressions (179), (180) and (181) for the strain components ϵ_x, ϵ_y, γ_{xy}, we obtain

$$V = \frac{Eh}{2(1-\nu^2)}\int\int\left\{\left(\frac{\partial u}{\partial x}\right)^2 + \frac{\partial u}{\partial x}\left(\frac{\partial w}{\partial x}\right)^2 + \left(\frac{\partial v}{\partial y}\right)^2 + \frac{\partial v}{\partial y}\left(\frac{\partial w}{\partial y}\right)^2\right.$$

$$+ \tfrac{1}{4}\left[\left(\frac{\partial w}{\partial x}\right)^2 + \left(\frac{\partial w}{\partial y}\right)^2\right]^2 + 2\nu\left[\frac{\partial u}{\partial x}\frac{\partial v}{\partial y} + \tfrac{1}{2}\frac{\partial v}{\partial y}\left(\frac{\partial w}{\partial x}\right)^2 + \tfrac{1}{2}\frac{\partial u}{\partial x}\left(\frac{\partial w}{\partial y}\right)^2\right]$$

$$+ \frac{1-\nu}{2}\left[\left(\frac{\partial u}{\partial y}\right)^2 + 2\frac{\partial u}{\partial y}\frac{\partial v}{\partial x} + \left(\frac{\partial v}{\partial x}\right)^2 + 2\frac{\partial u}{\partial y}\frac{\partial w}{\partial x}\frac{\partial w}{\partial y}\right.$$

$$\left.\left. + 2\frac{\partial v}{\partial x}\frac{\partial w}{\partial x}\frac{\partial w}{\partial y}\right]\right\}dx\,dy. \quad (203)$$

In applying the energy method we must assume in each particular case suitable expressions for the displacements u, v and w. These expressions must, of course, satisfy the boundary conditions and will contain several arbitrary parameters the magnitudes of which have to be determined by the use of the principle of virtual displacements. To illustrate the method, let us consider a uniformly loaded square membrane[1] with sides of length $2a$ (Fig. 134). The displacements u, v and w in this case must vanish at the boundary. Moreover,

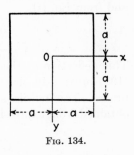

FIG. 134.

from symmetry, it can be concluded that w is an even function of x and y, whereas u and v are odd functions of x and of y, respectively. All these requirements are satisfied by taking the following expressions for the displacements:

[1] Calculations for this case are given in the book "Drang und Zwang" by August and Ludwig Föppl, vol. 1, p. 226, 1924; see also Hencky, *loc cit.*, p. 344.

$$w = w_0 \cos \frac{\pi x}{2a} \cos \frac{\pi y}{2a},$$

$$u = c \sin \frac{\pi x}{a} \cos \frac{\pi y}{2a}, \qquad (f)$$

$$v = c \sin \frac{\pi y}{a} \cos \frac{\pi x}{2a},$$

which contain two parameters w_0 and c. Substituting these expressions in Eq. (203), we obtain, for $\nu = 0.25$,

$$V = \frac{Eh}{7.5}\left\{ \frac{5\pi^4}{64} \frac{w_0^4}{a^2} - \frac{17\pi^2}{6} \frac{cw_0^2}{a} + c^2\left(\frac{35\pi^2}{4} + \frac{80}{9}\right)\right\}. \qquad (g)$$

The principle of virtual displacements gives the two following equations:[1]

$$\frac{\partial V}{\partial c} = 0, \qquad (h)$$

$$\frac{\partial V}{\partial w_0}\delta w_0 = \int_{-a}^{+a}\int_{-a}^{+a} q\, \delta w_0 \cos \frac{\pi x}{2a} \cos \frac{\pi y}{2a} dx\, dy. \qquad (i)$$

Substituting expression (g) in place of V, we obtain from Eq. (h)

$$c = 0.147\frac{w_0^2}{a}$$

and from Eq. (i)

$$w_0 = 0.802a\sqrt[3]{\frac{qa}{Eh}}. \qquad (204)$$

This deflection at the center is somewhat larger than the value (199) previously obtained for a uniformly loaded circular membrane. The tensile strain at the center of the membrane as obtained from expressions (f) is

$$\epsilon_x = \epsilon_y = \frac{\pi c}{a} = 0.462\frac{w_0^2}{a^2},$$

and the corresponding tensile stress is

$$\sigma = \frac{E}{1 - \nu} \cdot 0.462\frac{w_0^2}{a^2} = 0.616\frac{Ew_0^2}{a^2} = 0.396\sqrt[3]{\frac{q^2Ea^2}{h^2}}. \qquad (205)$$

[1] The right side of Eq. (h) is zero, since the variation of the parameter c produces only horizontal displacements and the vertical load does not produce work.

Some application of these results to the investigation of large deflections of thin plates will be shown in the next article.

71. Large Deflections of Uniformly Loaded Rectangular Plates.—We begin with the case of a plate with clamped edges. To obtain an approximate solution of the problem the energy method will be used.[1] The total strain energy V of the plate is obtained by adding to the energy of bending [expression (111), page 95] the energy due to strain of the middle surface [expression (203), page 345]. The principle of virtual displacements then gives the equation

$$\delta V - \delta \int\int qw \, dx \, dy = 0 \qquad (a)$$

which holds for any variation of the displacements u, v and w. By deriving the variation of V we can obtain from Eq. (a) the system of Eqs. (200) and (201), the exact solution of which is unknown. To find an approximate solution of our problem we assume for u, v and w three functions satisfying the boundary conditions imposed by the clamped edges and containing several parameters which will be determined by using Eq. (a). For a rectangular plate with sides $2a$ and $2b$ and coordinate axes, as shown in Fig. 134, we shall take the displacements in the following form:

$$\left.\begin{aligned}
u &= (a^2 - x^2)(b^2 - y^2)x(b_{00} + b_{02}y^2 + b_{20}x^2 + b_{22}x^2y^2), \\
v &= (a^2 - x^2)(b^2 - y^2)y(c_{00} + c_{02}y^2 + c_{20}x^2 + c_{22}x^2y^2), \\
w &= (a^2 - x^2)^2(b^2 - y^2)^2(a_{00} + a_{02}y^2 + a_{20}x^2).
\end{aligned}\right\} \qquad (b)$$

The first two of these expressions, which represent the displacements u and v in the middle plane of the plate, are odd functions in x and y, respectively, and vanish at the boundary. The expression for w, which is an even function in x and y, vanishes at the boundary as do also its first derivatives. Thus all the boundary conditions imposed by the clamped edges are satisfied.

Expressions (b) contain 11 parameters b_{00}, . . . , a_{20}, which will now be determined from Eq. (a), which must be satisfied for any variation of each of these parameters. In such a way we obtain 11 equations, 3 of the form

$$\frac{\partial}{\partial a_{mn}}\left(V - \int\int qw \, dx \, dy\right) = 0 \qquad (c)$$

and 8 equations of the form[2]

$$\frac{\partial V}{\partial b_{mn}} = 0, \qquad \text{or} \qquad \frac{\partial V}{\partial c_{mn}} = 0. \qquad (d)$$

---

[1] Such a solution has been given by S. Way, see *Proc. 5th Intern. Cong. Appl. Mech.*, Cambridge, Mass., 1938.

[2] The zeros on the right sides of these equations result from the fact that the lateral load does not do work when u or v varies.

These equations are not linear in the parameters a_{mn}, b_{mn} and c_{mn} as was true in the case of small deflections (see page 124). The three equations of the form (c) will contain terms of the third degree in the parameters a_{mn}. Equations of the form (d) will be linear in the parameters b_{mn} and c_{mn} and quadratic in the parameters a_{mn}. A solution is obtained by solving Eqs. (d) for the b_{mn}'s and c_{mn}'s in terms of the a_{mn}'s and then substituting these expressions in Eqs. (c). In this way we obtain three equations of the third degree involving the parameters a_{mn} alone. These equations can then be solved numerically in each particular case by successive approximations.

Numerical values of all the parameters have been computed for various intensities of the load q and for three different shapes of the plate $b/a = 1$, $b/a = \frac{2}{3}$ and $b/a = \frac{1}{2}$ by assuming $\nu = 0.3$.

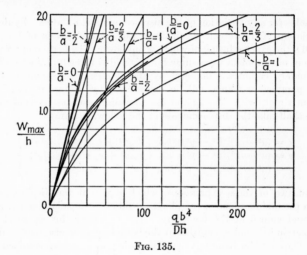

Fig. 135.

It can be seen from the expression for w that, if we know the constant a_{00}, we can at once obtain the deflection of the plate at the center. These deflections are graphically represented in Fig. 135 in which $w_{max.}/h$ is plotted against qb^4/Dh. For comparison the figure also includes the straight lines that represent the deflections calculated by using the theory of small deflections. Also included is the curve for $b/a = 0$ which represents deflections of an infinitely long plate calculated as explained in Art. 3 (see page 10). It can be seen that the deflections of finite plates with $b/a < \frac{2}{3}$ are very close to those obtained for an infinitely long plate.

Knowing the displacements as given by expressions (b), we can calculate the strain of the middle plane and the corresponding membrane stresses from Eqs. (b) of the previous article. The bending stresses can then be found from Eqs. (99) and (100) for the bending and twisting moments. By adding the membrane and the bending stresses, we obtain the total stress. The maximum values of this stress are at the middle of the long sides of plates. They are given in graphical form in Fig. 136. For comparison, the figure also includes straight lines representing the stresses obtained by the theory of small deflections and a curve $b/a = 0$ representing the stresses for an infinitely long plate. It would seem reasonable to expect the total stress to be greater for $b/a = 0$ than for $b/a = \frac{1}{2}$ for any value of load. We see that the curve for $b/a = 0$ falls below the curves for $b/a = \frac{1}{2}$ and $b/a = \frac{2}{3}$. This is probably a result of approximations in the energy solution which arise out of the use of a finite number of constants. It indicates

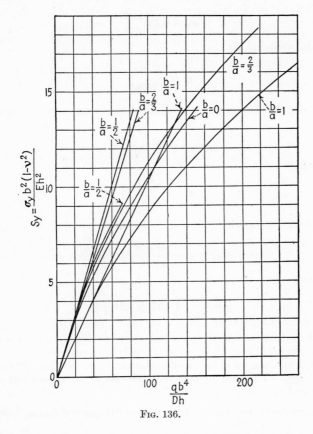

Fig. 136.

that the calculated stresses are in error on the safe side, *i.e.*, that they are too large. The error for $b/a = \frac{1}{2}$ appears to be about 10 per cent.

The energy method can also be applied in the case of large deflections of simply supported rectangular plates. However, as may be seen from the foregoing discussion of the case of clamped edges, the application of this method requires a considerable amount of computation. To get an approximate solution for a simply supported rectangular plate a simple method consisting of a combination of the known solutions given by the theory of small deflections and the membrane theory can be used.[1]   This method will now be illustrated on a simple example of a square plate.   We assume that the load q can be resolved into two parts q_1 and q_2 in such a manner that the part q_1 is balanced by the bending and shearing stresses calculated by the theory of small deflections, the part q_2 being balanced by the membrane stresses.   The deflection at the center as calculated for a square plate with the sides $2a$ by the theory of small deflections is[2]

$$w_0 = 0.730 \frac{q_1 a^4}{Eh^3}.$$

From this we determine

$$q_1 = \frac{w_0 Eh^3}{0.730 a^4}. \tag{e}$$

Considering the plate as a membrane and using formula (204), we obtain

$$w_0 = 0.802 a \sqrt[3]{\frac{q_2 a}{Eh}},$$

from which

$$q_2 = \frac{w_0^3 Eh}{0.516 a^4}. \tag{f}$$

The deflection w_0 is now obtained from the equation

$$q = q_1 + q_2 = \frac{w_0 Eh^3}{0.730 a^4} + \frac{w_0^3 Eh}{0.516 a^4},$$

which gives

$$q = \frac{w_0 Eh^3}{a^4} \left(1.37 + 1.94 \frac{w_0^2}{h^2} \right). \tag{206}$$

After the deflection w_0 has been calculated from this equation, the loads q_1 and q_2 are found from Eqs. (e) and (f), and the corresponding stresses are calculated by using for q_1 the small deflection theory (see Art. 29) and for q_2, Eq. (205).   The total stress is then the sum of the stresses due to the loads q_1 and q_2.

[1] This method is recommended in the book "Drang und Zwang," loc. cit., p. 345.

[2] The factor 0.730 is obtained by multiplying the number 0.0443, given in Table 5, by 16 and by 1.03.   The factor 1.03 arises from the change of the value of Poisson's ratio $\nu = 0.3$, used in the table to the value $\nu = 0.25$ used in this example.

CHAPTER X

DEFORMATION OF SHELLS WITHOUT BENDING

72. Definitions and Notation.—In the following discussion of the deformations and stresses in shells the system of notation is the same as that used in the discussion of plates. We denote the

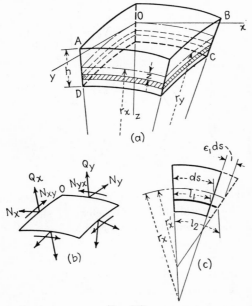

Fig. 137.

thickness of the shell by h, this quantity always being considered small in comparison with the other dimensions of the shell and with its radii of curvature. The surface that bisects the thickness of the plate is called the *middle surface*. By specifying the form of the middle surface and the thickness of the shell at each point, a shell is entirely defined geometrically.

To analyze the internal forces we cut from the shell an infinitely small element formed by two pairs of adjacent planes which are normal to the middle surface of the shell and which contain its principal curvatures (Fig. 137a). We take the coordinate axes x and y tangent at O to the lines of principal curvature and the axis z normal to the middle surface, as shown in the figure. The principal radii of curvature which lie in the xz- and yz-planes are denoted by r_x and r_y, respectively. The stresses acting on the plane faces of the element are resolved in the directions of the coordinate axes, and the stress components are denoted by our previous symbols σ_x, σ_y, $\tau_{xy} = \tau_{yx}$, τ_{zz}. With this notation[1] the resultant forces per unit length of the normal sections shown in Fig. 137b are

$$N_x = \int_{-\frac{h}{2}}^{+\frac{h}{2}} \sigma_x \left(1 - \frac{z}{r_y}\right) dz, \qquad N_y = \int_{-\frac{h}{2}}^{+\frac{h}{2}} \sigma_y \left(1 - \frac{z}{r_x}\right) dz; \quad (a)$$

$$N_{xy} = \int_{-\frac{h}{2}}^{+\frac{h}{2}} \tau_{xy} \left(1 - \frac{z}{r_y}\right) dz, \qquad N_{yx} = \int_{-\frac{h}{2}}^{+\frac{h}{2}} \tau_{yx} \left(1 - \frac{z}{r_x}\right) dz, \quad (b)$$

$$Q_x = \int_{-\frac{h}{2}}^{+\frac{h}{2}} \tau_{xz} \left(1 - \frac{z}{r_y}\right) dz, \qquad Q_y = \int_{-\frac{h}{2}}^{+\frac{h}{2}} \tau_{yz} \left(1 - \frac{z}{r_x}\right) dz. \quad (c)$$

The small quantities z/r_x and z/r_y appear in expressions (a), (b), (c), because the lateral sides of the element shown in Fig. 137a have a trapezoidal form due to the curvature of the shell. As a result of this, the shearing forces N_{xy} and N_{yx} are generally not equal to each other, although it still holds that $\tau_{xy} = \tau_{yx}$. In our further discussion we shall always assume that the thickness h is very small in comparison with the radii r_x, r_y and omit the terms z/r_x and z/r_y in expressions (a), (b), (c). Then $N_{xy} = N_{yx}$ and the resultant forces are given by the same expressions as in the case of plates (see Art. 21).

The bending and twisting moments per unit length of the normal sections are given by the expressions

---

[1] In the cases of surfaces of revolution in which the position of the element is defined by the angles θ and φ (see Fig. 138) the subscripts θ and φ are used instead of x and y in notation for stresses, resultant forces and resultant moments.

$$M_x = \int_{-\frac{h}{2}}^{+\frac{h}{2}} \sigma_x z \left(1 - \frac{z}{r_y}\right) dz, \qquad M_y = \int_{-\frac{h}{2}}^{+\frac{h}{2}} \sigma_y z \left(1 - \frac{z}{r_x}\right) dz, \quad (d)$$

$$M_{xy} = -\int_{-\frac{h}{2}}^{+\frac{h}{2}} \tau_{xy} z \left(1 - \frac{z}{r_y}\right) dz, \qquad M_{yx} = \int_{-\frac{h}{2}}^{+\frac{h}{2}} \tau_{yx} z \left(1 - \frac{z}{r_x}\right) dz. \quad (e)$$

in which the rule used in determining the directions of the moments is the same as in the case of plates. In our further discussion we again neglect the small quantities z/r_x and z/r_y, due to the curvature of the shell, and use for the moments the same expressions as in the discussion of plates.

In considering bending of the shell, we assume that linear elements, such as AD and BC (Fig. 137a), which are normal to the middle surface of the shell, remain straight and become normal to the deformed middle surface of the shell. Let us begin with a simple case in which, during bending, the lateral faces of the element $ABCD$ rotate only with respect to their lines of intersection with the middle surface. If r'_x and r'_y are the values of the radii of curvature after deformation, the unit elongations of a thin lamina at a distance z from the middle surface (Fig. 137a) are

$$\epsilon_x = -\frac{z}{1 - \dfrac{z}{r_x}}\left(\frac{1}{r'_x} - \frac{1}{r_x}\right), \qquad \epsilon_y = -\frac{z}{1 - \dfrac{z}{r_y}}\left(\frac{1}{r'_y} - \frac{1}{r_y}\right). \quad (f)$$

If, in addition to rotation, the lateral sides of the element are displaced parallel to themselves, owing to stretching of the middle surface; and if the corresponding unit elongations of the middle surface in the x- and y-directions are denoted by ϵ_1 and ϵ_2, respectively, the elongation ϵ_x of the lamina considered above, as seen from Fig. 137c, is

$$\epsilon_x = \frac{l_2 - l_1}{l_1}.$$

Substituting

$$l_1 = ds\left(1 - \frac{z}{r_x}\right), \qquad l_2 = ds(1 + \epsilon_1)\left(1 - \frac{z}{r'_x}\right),$$

we obtain

$$\epsilon_x = \frac{\epsilon_1}{1 - \dfrac{z}{r_x}} - \frac{z}{1 - \dfrac{z}{r_x}}\left[\frac{1}{(1 - \epsilon_1)r_x'} - \frac{1}{r_x}\right]. \qquad (g)$$

A similar expression can be obtained for the elongation ϵ_y. In our further discussion the thickness h of the shell will be always assumed small in comparison with the radii of curvature. In such a case the quantities z/r_x and z/r_y can be neglected in comparison with unity. We shall neglect also the effect of the elongations ϵ_1 and ϵ_2 on the curvature.[1] Then, instead of such expressions as expression (g), we obtain

$$\epsilon_x = \epsilon_1 - z\left(\frac{1}{r_x'} - \frac{1}{r_x}\right) = \epsilon_1 - \chi_x z,$$

$$\epsilon_y = \epsilon_2 - z\left(\frac{1}{r_y'} - \frac{1}{r_y}\right) = \epsilon_2 - \chi_y z,$$

where χ_x and χ_y denote the changes of curvature. Using these expressions for the components of strain of a lamina and assuming that there are no normal stresses between laminae ($\sigma_z = 0$), the following expressions for the components of stress are obtained:

$$\sigma_x = \frac{E}{1 - \nu^2}[\epsilon_1 + \nu\epsilon_2 - z(\chi_x + \nu\chi_y)],$$

$$\sigma_y = \frac{E}{1 - \nu^2}[\epsilon_2 + \nu\epsilon_1 - z(\chi_y + \nu\chi_x)].$$

Substituting these expressions in Eqs. (a) and (d) and neglecting the small quantities z/r_x and z/r_y in comparison with unity, we obtain

$$\left.\begin{array}{ll} N_x = \dfrac{Eh}{1 - \nu^2}(\epsilon_1 + \nu\epsilon_2), & N_y = \dfrac{Eh}{1 - \nu^2}(\epsilon_2 + \nu\epsilon_1), \\[2mm] M_x = -D(\chi_x + \nu\chi_y), & M_y = -D(\chi_y + \nu\chi_x), \end{array}\right\} \qquad (207)$$

where D has the same meaning as in the case of plates [see Eq. (3)] and denotes the flexural rigidity of the shell.

---

[1] Similar simplifications are usually made in the theory of bending of thin curved bars. It can be shown in this case that the procedure is justifiable if the depth of the cross section h, is small in comparison with the radius r, say $h/r < 0.1$; see author's "Strength of Materials" vol. 2, p. 429, 1930.

A more general case of deformation of the element in Fig. 137 is obtained if we assume that, in addition to normal stresses, shearing stresses also are acting on the lateral sides of the element. Denoting by γ the shearing strain in the middle surface of the shell and by $\chi_{xy}\, dx$ the rotation of the edge BC relative to Oz with respect to the x-axis (Fig. 137a) and proceeding as in the case of plates [see Eq. (42)], we find

$$\tau_{xy} = (\gamma - 2z\chi_{xy})G.$$

Substituting this in Eqs. (b) and (e) and using our previous simplifications, we obtain

$$\left.\begin{array}{l} N_{xy} = N_{yx} = \dfrac{\gamma hE}{2(1 + \nu)}, \\[2mm] M_{xy} = -M_{yx} = D(1 - \nu)\chi_{xy}. \end{array}\right\} \tag{208}$$

Thus assuming that during bending of a shell the linear elements normal to the middle surface remain straight and become normal to the deformed middle surface, we can express the resultant forces per unit length N_x, N_y and N_{xy} and the moments M_x, M_y and M_{xy} in terms of six quantities: the three components of strain ϵ_1, ϵ_2 and γ of the middle surface of the shell and the three quantities χ_x, χ_y and χ_{xy} representing the changes of curvature and the twist of the middle surface.

In many problems of deformation of shells the bending stresses can be neglected, and only the stresses due to strain in the middle surface of the shell need be considered. Take, as an example, a thin spherical container submitted to the action of a uniformly distributed internal pressure normal to the surface of the shell. Under this action the middle surface of the shell undergoes a uniform strain; and since the thickness of the shell is small, the tensile stresses can be assumed as uniformly distributed across the thickness. A similar example is afforded by a thin circular cylindrical container in which a gas or a liquid is compressed by means of pistons which move freely along the axis of the cylinder. Under the action of a uniform internal pressure the hoop stresses that are produced in the cylindrical shell are uniformly distributed over the thickness of the shell. If the ends of the cylinder are built in along the edges, the shell is no longer free to expand laterally, and some bending must occur near the built-in edges when internal pressure is applied. A more complete investigation shows, however (see Art. 81), that this bending is of a local character and that the portion of the shell at some distance from the ends continues to remain cylindrical and undergoes only strain in the middle surface without appreciable bending.

If the conditions of a shell are such that bending can be neglected, the problem of stress analysis is greatly simplified, since the resultant moments (d) and (e) and the resultant shearing forces (c) vanish. Thus the only unknowns are the three quantities N_x, N_y and $N_{xy} = N_{yx}$, which can be determined from the conditions of equilibrium of an element, such as shown in Fig. 137. Hence the problem becomes statically determined if all the forces acting on the shell are known. The forces N_x, N_y and N_{xy} obtained in this manner are sometimes called *membrane forces*, and the theory of shells based on the omission of bending stresses is called *membrane theory*. The application of this theory to various particular cases will be discussed in the remainder of this chapter.

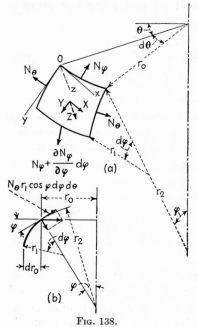

Fig. 138.

73. Shells in the Form of a Surface of Revolution and Loaded Symmetrically with Respect to Their Axis.—Shells that have the form of surfaces of revolution find extensive application in various kinds of containers, tanks and domes. A surface of revolution is obtained by rotation of a plane curve about an axis lying in the plane of the curve. This curve is called the *meridian*, and its plane is a *meridian plane*. An element of a shell is cut out by two adjacent meridians and two parallel circles, as shown in Fig. 138a. The position of a meridian is defined by an angle θ, measured from some datum meridian plane; and the position of a parallel circle is defined by the angle φ, made by the normal to the surface and the axis of rotation. The meridian plane and the plane perpendicular to the meridian are the planes of principal curvature at a point of a surface of revolution, and the corresponding radii of curvature are denoted by r_1 and r_2, respectively. The radius of the parallel circle is denoted by r_0 so that the length of the sides of the element meeting at O, as shown in the figure, are $r_1 \, d\varphi$ and $r_0 \, d\theta = r_2 \sin \varphi \, d\theta$. The surface area of the element is then $r_1 r_2 \sin \varphi \, d\varphi \, d\theta$.

From the assumed symmetry of loading and deformation it can be concluded that there will be no shearing forces acting on the sides of the element. The magnitudes of the normal forces per unit length are denoted by N_φ and N_θ as shown in the figure. The intensity of the external load, which acts in the meridian plane, in the case of symmetry, is resolved in two components Y and Z parallel to the coordinate axes. Multiplying these components with the area $r_1 r_2 \sin \varphi \, d\varphi \, d\theta$, we obtain the components of the external load acting on the element.

In writing the equations of equilibrium of the element, let us begin with the forces in the direction of the tangent to the meridian. On the upper side of the element the force

$$N_\varphi r_0 \, d\theta = N_\varphi r_2 \sin \varphi \, d\theta \qquad (a)$$

is acting.

The corresponding force on the lower side of the element is

$$\left(N_\varphi + \frac{dN_\varphi}{d\varphi} d\varphi \right)\left(r_0 + \frac{dr_0}{d\varphi} d\varphi \right) d\theta. \qquad (b)$$

From expressions (a) and (b), by neglecting a small quantity of second order, we find the resultant in the y-direction to be equal to

$$N_\varphi \frac{dr_0}{d\varphi} d\varphi \, d\theta + \frac{dN_\varphi}{d\varphi} r_0 \, d\varphi \, d\theta = \frac{d}{d\varphi}(N_\varphi r_0) d\varphi \, d\theta. \qquad (c)$$

The component of the external force in the same direction is

$$Y r_1 r_0 \, d\varphi \, d\theta. \qquad (d)$$

The forces acting on the lateral sides of the element are equal to $N_\theta r_1 \, d\varphi$ and have a resultant in the direction of the radius of the parallel circle equal to $N_\theta r_1 \, d\varphi \, d\theta$. The component of this force in the y-direction (Fig. 138b) is

$$-N_\theta r_1 \cos \varphi \, d\varphi \, d\theta. \qquad (e)$$

Summing up the forces (c), (d) and (e), the equation of equilibrium in the direction of the tangent to the meridian becomes

$$\frac{d}{d\varphi}(N_\varphi r_0) - N_\theta r_1 \cos \varphi + Y r_1 r_0 = 0. \qquad (f)$$

The second equation of equilibrium is obtained by summing up the projections of the forces in the z-direction. The forces acting on the upper and lower sides of the element have a resultant in the z-direction equal to

$$N_\varphi r_0 \, d\theta \, d\varphi. \qquad (g)$$

The forces acting on the lateral sides of the element and having the resultant $N_\theta r_1 \, d\varphi \, d\theta$ in the radial direction of the parallel circle give a component in the z-direction of the magnitude

$$N_\theta r_1 \sin \varphi \, d\varphi \, d\theta. \qquad (h)$$

The external load acting on the element has in the same direction a component

$$Z r_1 r_0 \, d\theta \, d\varphi. \qquad (i)$$

Summing up the forces (g), (h) and (i), we obtain the second equation of equilibrium

$$N_\varphi r_0 + N_\theta r_1 \sin \varphi + Z r_1 r_0 = 0. \qquad (j)$$

From the two Eqs. (f) and (j) the forces N_θ and N_φ can be calculated in each particular case if the radii r_0 and r_1 and the components Y and Z of the intensity of the external load are given.

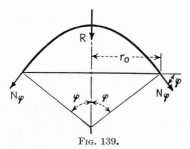

Fig. 139.

Instead of the equilibrium of an element, the equilibrium of the portion of the shell above the parallel circle defined by the angle φ may be considered (Fig. 139). If the resultant of the total load on that portion of the shell is denoted by R, the equation of equilibrium is

$$2\pi r_0 N_\varphi \sin \varphi + R = 0. \qquad (209)$$

This equation can be used instead of the differential equation (f), from which it can be obtained by integration. If Eq. (j) is divided by $r_1 r_0$, it can be written in the form

$$\frac{N_\varphi}{r_1} + \frac{N_\theta}{r_2} = -Z. \quad (210)$$

It is seen that when N_φ is obtained from Eq. (209), the force N_θ can be calculated from Eq. (210). Hence the problem of membrane stresses can be readily solved in each particular case. Some applications of these equations will be discussed in the next article.

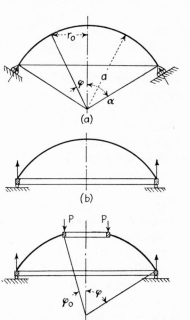

(a)

(b)

(c)

Fig. 140.

74. Particular Cases of Shells in the Form of Surfaces of Revolution.[1] *Spherical Dome.*— Assume that a spherical shell (Fig. 140a) is submitted to the action of its own weight, the magnitude of which per unit area is constant and equal to q. Denoting the radius of the sphere by a, we have $r_0 = a \sin \varphi$ and

$$R = 2\pi \int_0^\varphi a^2 q \sin \varphi \, d\varphi = 2\pi a^2 q (1 - \cos \varphi).$$

Equations (209) and (210) then give

$$\left.\begin{aligned} N_\varphi &= -\frac{aq(1 - \cos \varphi)}{\sin^2 \varphi} = -\frac{aq}{1 + \cos \varphi}, \\ N_\theta &= aq\left(\frac{1}{1 + \cos \varphi} - \cos \varphi\right). \end{aligned}\right\} \quad (211)$$

It is seen that the forces N_φ are always negative. There is thus a compression along the meridians that increases as the angle φ increases. For $\varphi = 0$ we have $N_\varphi = -aq/2$; and for $\varphi = \pi/2$,

[1] Examples of this kind can be found in the book by P. Forchheimer, "Die Berechung ebener und gekrümmter Behälterböden," 3d ed., Berlin, 1931; see also J. W. Geckeler's article in "Handbuch der Physik," vol. 6, Berlin, 1928.

$N_\varphi = -aq$. The forces N_θ are also negative for small angles φ. When

$$\frac{1}{1 + \cos \varphi} - \cos \varphi = 0,$$

i.e., for $\varphi = 51° 50'$, N_θ becomes equal to zero and, with further increase of φ, becomes positive. This indicates that for φ greater than 51° 50′ there are tensile stresses in the direction perpendicular to the meridians.

The stresses as calculated from (211) will represent the actual stresses in the shell with great accuracy[1] if the supports are of such a type that the reactions are tangent to meridians (Fig. 140a). Usually the arrangement is such that only vertical reactions are imposed on the dome by the supports, whereas the horizontal components of the forces N_φ are taken by a supporting ring (Fig. 140b) which undergoes a uniform circumferential extension. Since this extension is usually different from the strain along the parallel circle of the shell, as calculated from expressions (211), some bending of the shell will occur near the supporting ring. An investigation of this bending[2] shows that in the case of a thin shell it is of a very localized character and that at a certain distance from the supporting ring Eqs. (211) continue to represent the stress conditions in the shell with satisfactory accuracy.

Very often the upper portion of a spherical dome is removed, as shown in Fig. 140c, and an upper reinforcing ring is used to support the upper structure. If $2\varphi_0$ is the angle corresponding to the opening and P is the vertical load per unit length of the upper reinforcing ring, the resultant R corresponding to an angle φ is

$$R = 2\pi \int_{\varphi_0}^{\varphi} a^2 q \sin \varphi \, d\varphi + 2\pi P a \sin \varphi_0.$$

From Eqs. (209) and (210) we then find

$$\left.\begin{aligned}
N_\varphi &= -aq \frac{\cos \varphi_0 - \cos \varphi}{\sin^2 \varphi} - P \frac{\sin \varphi_0}{\sin^2 \varphi}, \\
N_\theta &= aq \left(\frac{\cos \varphi_0 - \cos \varphi}{\sin^2 \varphi} - \cos \varphi \right) + P \frac{\sin \varphi_0}{\sin^2 \varphi}.
\end{aligned}\right\} \quad (212)$$

[1] Small bending stresses due to strain of the middle surface will be discussed in Chap. XII.

[2] See Chap. XII.

As another example of a spherical shell let us consider a spherical tank supported along a parallel circle AA (Fig. 141) and filled with liquid of a specific weight γ. The inner pressure for

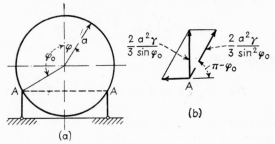

Fɪɢ. 141.

any angle φ is given by the expression[1]

$$p = -Z = \gamma a(1 - \cos \varphi).$$

The resultant R of this pressure for the portion of the shell defined by an angle φ is

$$R = -2\pi a^2 \int_0^{\varphi} \gamma a(1 - \cos \varphi) \sin \varphi \cos \varphi \, d\varphi$$
$$= -2\pi a^3 \gamma [\tfrac{1}{6} - \tfrac{1}{2} \cos^2 \varphi(1 - \tfrac{2}{3} \cos \varphi)].$$

Substituting in Eq. (209), we obtain

$$N_{\varphi} = \frac{\gamma a^2}{6 \sin^2 \varphi}[1 - \cos^2 \varphi(3 - 2 \cos \varphi)]$$
$$= \frac{\gamma a^2}{6}\left(1 - \frac{2 \cos^2 \varphi}{1 + \cos \varphi}\right); \quad (213)$$

and from Eq. (210) we find that

$$N_{\theta} = \frac{\gamma a^2}{6}\left(5 - 6 \cos \varphi + \frac{2 \cos^2 \varphi}{1 + \cos \varphi}\right). \quad (214)$$

Equations (213) and (214) hold for $\varphi < \varphi_0$. In calculating the resultant R for larger values of φ, *i.e.*, for the lower portion of the tank, we must take into account not only the internal pressure but also the sum of the vertical reactions along the ring AA. This sum is evidently equal to the total weight of the liquid

---

[1] A uniform pressure producing a uniform tension in the spherical shell can be superposed without any complication on this pressure.

$4\pi a^3 \gamma/3$.   Hence,

$$R = -\tfrac{4}{3}\pi a^3 \gamma - 2\pi a^3 \gamma[\tfrac{1}{6} - \tfrac{1}{2}\cos^2 \varphi(1 - \tfrac{2}{3}\cos \varphi)].$$

Substituting in Eq. (209), we obtain

$$N_\varphi = \frac{\gamma a^2}{6}\left(5 + \frac{2\cos^2 \varphi}{1 - \cos \varphi}\right); \tag{215}$$

and from Eq. (210),

$$N_\theta = \frac{\gamma a^2}{6}\left(1 - 6\cos \varphi - \frac{2\cos^2 \varphi}{1 - \cos \varphi}\right). \tag{216}$$

Comparing expressions (213) and (215), we see that along the supporting ring AA the forces N_φ change abruptly by an amount equal to $2\gamma a^2/3 \sin^2 \varphi_0$. The same quantity is also obtained if we consider the vertical reaction per unit length of the ring AA and resolve it into two components (Fig. 141b): one in the direction of the tangent to the meridian and the other in the horizontal direction. The first of these components is equal to the abrupt change in the magnitude of N_φ mentioned above; the horizontal component represents the reaction on the supporting ring which produces in it a uniform compression. This compression can be eliminated if we use members in the direction of tangents to the meridians instead of vertical supporting members, as shown in Fig. 141a. As may be seen from expressions (214) and (216), the forces N_θ also experience an abrupt change at the circle AA. This indicates that there is an abrupt change in the circumferential expansion on the two sides of the parallel circle AA. Thus the membrane theory does not satisfy the condition of continuity at the circle AA, and we may expect some local bending to take place near the supporting ring.

Conical Shell.—In this case certain membrane stresses can be produced by a force applied at the top of the cone. If a force P is applied in the direction of the axis of the cone, the stress distribution is symmetrical, and from Fig. 142a we obtain

$$N_\varphi = -\frac{P}{2\pi r_0 \cos \alpha}. \tag{a}$$

Equation (210) then gives $N_\theta = 0$. If a force S is acting in the direction of a generator (Fig. 142b), the stress distribution is no longer symmetrical. The stress distribution can be found by developing the shell into the circular sector loaded as shown in Fig. 142c. The angle of this sector is $2\beta = 2\pi \sin \alpha$. The forces N_φ are found by considering a purely radial stress distribution[1]:

$$N_\varphi = -\frac{S \cos \psi}{a(\beta + \tfrac{1}{2} \sin 2\beta)}. \qquad (b)$$

If the force applied at the top of the cone has any arbitrary

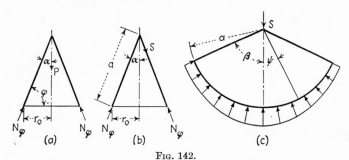

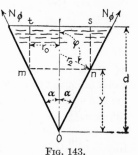

$$\text{Fig. 142.}$$

direction, it can always be resolved into two components: one in the direction of the axis of the cone and the other in the direction of the generatrix, and the membrane stresses can be obtained by combining the stresses given by expressions (a) and (b).

If lateral forces are symmetrically distributed over the conical surface, the membrane stresses can be calculated by using Eqs. (209) and (210). Since the curvature of the meridian in the case of a cone is zero, $r_1 = \infty$; we can write these equations in the following form:

$$\left. \begin{aligned} N_\varphi &= -\frac{R}{2\pi r_0 \sin \varphi}, \\ N_\theta &= -Z r_2 = -\frac{Z r_0}{\sin \varphi}. \end{aligned} \right\} \qquad (c)$$

$$\text{Fig. 143.}$$

Each of the resultant forces N_φ and N_θ can be calculated independently provided the load distribution is known. As an example, we take the case of the conical tank filled with a liquid of specific weight γ as shown in Fig. 143. Measuring the distances y from the bottom of the tank and denoting by d the total depth of the liquid in the tank,

---

[1] See author's "The Theory of Elasticity," p. 93, 1934.

the pressure at any parallel circle mn is

$$p = -Z = \gamma(d - y).$$

Also, for such a tank $\varphi = (\pi/2) + \alpha$ and $r_0 = y \tan \alpha$. Substituting in the second of the equations (c), we obtain

$$N_\theta = \frac{\gamma(d - y)y \tan \alpha}{\cos \alpha}. \tag{d}$$

This force is evidently a maximum when $y = d/2$, and we find

$$(N_\theta)_{\text{max.}} = \frac{\gamma d^2 \tan \alpha}{4 \cos \alpha}.$$

In calculating the force N_φ we observe that the load R in the first of the equations (c) is numerically equal to the weight of the liquid in the conical part mno together with the weight of the liquid in the cylindrical part $mnst$. Hence

$$R = -\pi\gamma y^2(d - y + \tfrac{1}{3}y) \tan^2 \alpha,$$

and we obtain

$$N_\varphi = \frac{\gamma y(d - \tfrac{2}{3}y) \tan \alpha}{2 \cos \alpha}. \tag{e}$$

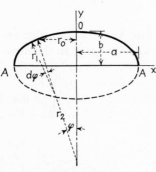

This force becomes a maximum when $y = \tfrac{3}{4}d$, at which point

$$(N_\varphi)_{\text{max.}} = \frac{3}{16} \frac{d^2\gamma \tan \alpha}{\cos \alpha}.$$

Fig. 144.

If the forces supporting the tank are in the direction of generatrices, as shown in Fig. 143, expressions (d) and (e) represent the stress conditions in the shell with great accuracy. Usually there will be a reinforcing ring along the upper edge of the tank. This ring takes the horizontal components of the forces N_φ; the vertical components of the same forces constitute the reactions supporting the tank. In such a case it will be found that a local bending of the shell takes place at the reinforcing ring.

Shell in the Form of an Ellipsoid of Revolution.—Such a shell is used very often for the ends of a cylindrical boiler. In such a case a half of the ellipsoid is used, as shown in Fig. 144. The principal radii of curvature in the case of an ellipse with semi-axes a and b are given by the formulas

$$r_1 = \frac{a^2 b^2}{(a^2 \sin^2 \varphi + b^2 \cos^2 \varphi)^{\frac{3}{2}}}, \qquad r_2 = \frac{a^2}{(a^2 \sin^2 \varphi + b^2 \cos^2 \varphi)^{\frac{1}{2}}}, \quad (f)$$

or, by using the orthogonal coordinates x and y shown in the figure,

$$r_1 = r_2^3 \frac{b^2}{a^4}, \qquad r_2 = \frac{(a^4 y^2 + b^4 x^2)^{\frac{1}{2}}}{b^2}. \qquad (g)$$

If the principal curvatures are determined from Eq. (f) or (g), the forces N_φ and N_θ are readily found from Eqs. (209) and (210). Let p be the uniform steam pressure in the boiler. Then for a parallel circle of a radius r_0 we have $R = -\pi p r_0^2$, and Eq. (209) gives

$$N_\varphi = \frac{p r_0}{2 \sin \varphi} = \frac{p r_2}{2}. \qquad (217)$$

Substituting in Eq. (210), we find

$$N_\theta = r_2 p - \frac{r_2}{r_1} N_\varphi = p\left(r_2 - \frac{r_2^2}{2 r_1}\right). \qquad (218)$$

At the top of the shell, point O, we have $r_1 = r_2 = a^2/b$, and Eqs. (217) and (218) give

$$N_\varphi = N_\theta = \frac{p a^2}{2b}. \qquad (h)$$

At the equator AA we have $r_1 = b^2/a$ and $r_2 = a$; hence

$$N_\varphi = \frac{pa}{2}, \qquad N_\theta = pa\left(1 - \frac{a^2}{2b^2}\right). \qquad (i)$$

It is seen that the forces N_φ are always positive, whereas the forces N_θ become negative at the equator if

$$a^2 > 2b^2. \qquad (j)$$

In the particular case of a sphere, $a = b$; and we find in all points $N_\varphi = N_\theta = pa/2$.

Shell in Form of a Torus.—If a torus is obtained by rotation of a circle of radius a about a vertical axis (Fig. 145), the forces N_φ are obtained by considering the equilibrium of the ring-shaped portion of the shell represented in the figure by the heavy line AB. Since the forces N_φ along the parallel circle BB are horizontal, we need consider only the forces N_φ along the circle AA and the external forces acting on the ring when discussing equilibrium in the vertical direction. Assuming that the shell is submitted

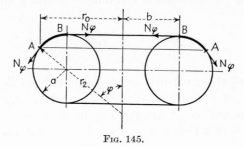

to the action of uniform internal pressure p, we obtain the equation of equilibrium

$$2\pi r_0 N_\varphi \sin \varphi = \pi p(r_0^2 - b^2),$$

from which

$$N_\varphi = \frac{p(r_0^2 - b^2)}{2r_0 \sin \varphi} = \frac{pa(r_0 + b)}{2r_0}. \tag{219}$$

Substituting this expression in Eq. (210), we find

$$N_\theta = \frac{pr_2(r_0 - b)}{2r_0} = \frac{pa}{2}. \tag{220}$$

A torus of an elliptical cross section may be treated in a similar manner.

75. Shells of Constant Strength.—As a first example of a shell of constant strength, let us consider a dome of non-uniform thickness supporting its own weight. The weight of the shell per unit area of the middle surface is γh, and the two components of this weight along the coordinate axes are

$$Y = \gamma h \sin \varphi, \qquad Z = \gamma h \cos \varphi. \tag{a}$$

In the case of a shell of constant strength the form of the meridians is determined in such a way that the compressive stress is constant and equal to σ in all the directions in the middle surface, i.e., so that

$$N_\varphi = N_\theta = -\sigma h.$$

Substituting in Eq. (210), we find

$$\sigma h \left(\frac{1}{r_1} + \frac{1}{r_2} \right) = \gamma h \cos \varphi, \tag{b}$$

or, by substituting $r_2 = r_0 \sin \varphi$ and solving for r_1,

$$r_1 = \frac{r_0}{\dfrac{\gamma}{\sigma} r_0 \cos \varphi - \sin \varphi}. \qquad (c)$$

From Fig. 138b, we have

$$r_1 \, d\varphi = \frac{dr_0}{\cos \varphi}.$$

Thus Eq. (c) can be represented in the form

$$\frac{dr_0}{d\varphi} = \frac{r_0 \cos \varphi}{\dfrac{\gamma}{\sigma} r_0 \cos \varphi - \sin \varphi}. \qquad (d)$$

At the top of the dome where $\varphi = 0$, the right side of the equation becomes indefinite. To remove this difficulty we use Eq. (b). Because of the conditions of symmetry at the top, $r_1 = r_2$, and we conclude that

$$r_1 = r_2 = \frac{2\sigma}{\gamma} \qquad \text{and} \qquad dr_0 = r_1 \, d\varphi = \frac{2\sigma}{\gamma} d\varphi.$$

Hence, for the top of the dome we have

$$\frac{dr_0}{d\varphi} = \frac{2\sigma}{\gamma}. \qquad (e)$$

Using Eqs. (e) and (d), we can obtain the shape of the meridian by numerical integration starting from the top of the dome and calculating for each increment $\Delta\varphi$ of the angle φ the corresponding increment Δr_0 of the radius r_0. To find the variation of the thickness of the shell, Eq. (f), Art. 73, must be used. Substituting $N_\varphi = N_\theta = -\sigma h$ in this equation and observing that σ is constant, we obtain

$$-\frac{d}{d\varphi}(hr_0) + hr_1 \cos \varphi + \frac{\gamma}{\sigma} r_1 r_0 h \sin \varphi = 0. \qquad (f)$$

Substituting expression (c) for r_1, the following equation is obtained:

$$\frac{d}{d\varphi}(hr_0) = hr_0 \frac{\cos \varphi + \dfrac{\gamma}{\sigma} r_0 \sin \varphi}{\dfrac{\gamma}{\sigma} r_0 \cos \varphi - \sin \varphi}. \qquad (g)$$

For $\varphi = 0$, we obtain from Eq. (f)

$$\frac{d}{d\varphi}(hr_0) \approx hr_1 = h \frac{dr_0}{d\varphi}.$$

It is seen that for the first increment $\Delta\varphi$ of the angle φ any constant value for h can be taken.   Then for the other points of the meridian the thickness is found by the numerical integration of Eq. (g).   In Fig. 146 the result of such a calculation is represented.[1]   It is seen that the condition

$$N_\theta = N_\varphi = -\sigma h$$

brings us not only to a definite form of the middle surface of the dome but also to a definite law of variation of the thickness of the dome along the meridian.

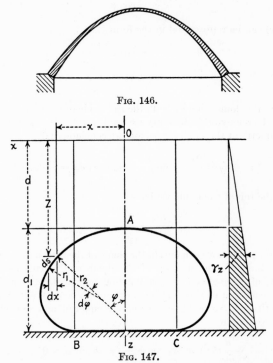

FIG. 146.

FIG. 147.

In the case of a tank of equal strength that contains a liquid with a pressure γd at the upper point A (Fig. 147) we must find a shape of the meridian such that an internal pressure equal to γz will give rise at all points of the shell to forces[2]

$$N_\varphi = N_\theta = \text{const.}$$

[1] This example has been calculated by W. Flügge; see his "Statik und Dynamik der Schalen," p. 33, Berlin, 1934.

[2] A mathematical discussion of this problem is given in the book by C. Runge and H. König, "Vorlesungen über Numerisches Rechnen," p. 320, Berlin, 1924.

A similar problem is encountered in finding the shape of a drop of liquid resting on a horizontal plane. Because of the capillary forces a thin surface film of uniform tension is formed which envelops the liquid and prevents it from spreading over the supporting surface. Both problems are mathematically identical.

In such cases, Eq. (210) gives

$$N_\varphi \left(\frac{1}{r_1} + \frac{1}{r_2} \right) = \gamma z. \qquad (h)$$

Taking the orthogonal coordinates as shown in the figure, we have

$$r_2 = \frac{x}{\sin \varphi}, \qquad r_1 \, d\varphi = ds = \frac{dx}{\cos \varphi}.$$

Hence,

$$\frac{1}{r_2} = \frac{\sin \varphi}{x}, \qquad \frac{1}{r_1} = \frac{\cos \varphi \, d\varphi}{dx} = \frac{d \sin \varphi}{dx},$$

and Eq. (h) gives

$$\frac{d \sin \varphi}{dx} + \frac{\sin \varphi}{x} = \frac{\gamma z}{N_\varphi}. \qquad (i)$$

Observing that

$$\tan \varphi = \frac{dz}{dx} \qquad \text{and} \qquad \sin \varphi = \frac{\tan \varphi}{\sqrt{1 + \tan^2 \varphi}}, \qquad (j)$$

it is possible to eliminate $\sin \varphi$ from Eq. (i) and obtain in this way a differential equation for z as a function of x. The equation obtained in this manner is very complicated, and a simpler means of solving the problem is to introduce a new variable $u = \sin \varphi$. Making this substitution in Eq. (i) and (j), we obtain

$$\frac{du}{dx} + \frac{u}{x} = \frac{\gamma z}{N_\varphi}, \qquad (k)$$

$$\frac{dz}{dx} = \frac{u}{\sqrt{1 - u^2}}. \qquad (l)$$

These equations can be integrated numerically starting from the upper point A of the tank. At this point, from symmetry, $r_1 = r_2$, and we find from Eq. (h) that

$$r_1 = \frac{2N_\varphi}{\gamma d}.$$

By introducing the notation

$$\frac{N_\varphi}{\gamma} = a^2,$$

we write

$$r_1 = \frac{2a^2}{d}. \qquad (m)$$

With this radius we make the first element of the meridian curve $r_1 \Delta \varphi = \Delta x$, corresponding to the small angle $\Delta \varphi$. At the end of this arc we have, as for a small arc of a circle,

$$\left. \begin{aligned} z &\approx d + r_1 \frac{(\Delta \varphi)^2}{2} = d + \frac{(\Delta x)^2}{2r_1} = d\left(1 + \frac{(\Delta x)^2}{4a^2}\right) \\ u &\approx \frac{\Delta x}{r_1} = d\frac{\Delta x}{2a^2}. \end{aligned} \right\} \qquad (n)$$

When the values u and z have been found from Eqs. (n), the values of du/dx and dz/dx for the same point are found from Eqs. (k) and (l). With these values of the derivatives we can calculate the values of z and u at the end of the next interval, and so on. Such calculations can be continued without difficulty up to an angle φ equal, say, to 50 deg., at which the value of u becomes approximately 0.75. From this point on and up to $\varphi = 140$ deg. the increments of z are much longer than the corresponding increments of x, and it is advantageous to take z as the independent variable instead of x. For $\varphi > 140$ deg., x must again be taken as the independent variable, and the calculation is continued up to the point B where the meridian curve has the horizontal tangent BC. Over the circular area BC the tank has a horizontal surface of contact with the foundation, and the pressure $\gamma(d + d_1)$ is balanced by the reaction of the foundation.

A tank designed in this manner[1] is a tank of constant strength only if the pressure at A is such as assumed in the calculations. For any other value of this pressure the forces N_θ and N_φ will no longer be constant but will vary along the meridian. Their magnitude can then be calculated by using the general equations (209) and (210). It will also be found that the equilibrium of the tank requires that vertical shearing forces act along the parallel circle BC. This indicates that close to this circle a local bending of the wall of the tank must take place.

76. Displacements in Symmetrically Loaded Shells Having the Form of a Surface of Revolution.

—In the case of symmetrical deformation of a shell, a small displacement of a point can be resolved into two components: v in the direction of the tangent to the meridian and w in the direction of the normal to the middle surface. Considering an element AB of the meridian (Fig. 148), we see that the increase of the length of the element due to tangential displacements v and $v + (dv/d\varphi)d\varphi$ of its ends is equal

---

[1] A tank of this kind was constructed by the Chicago Bridge and Iron Works; see C. L. Day, *Eng. News Rec.*, vol. 103, p. 416, 1929.

to $(dv/d\varphi)d\varphi$. Because of the radial displacements w of the points A and B the length of the element decreases by an amount $w\,d\varphi$. The change in the length of the element due to the difference in the radial displacements of the points A and B can be neglected as a small quantity of higher order. Thus the total change in length of the element AB due to deformation is

$$\frac{dv}{d\varphi}d\varphi - w\,d\varphi.$$

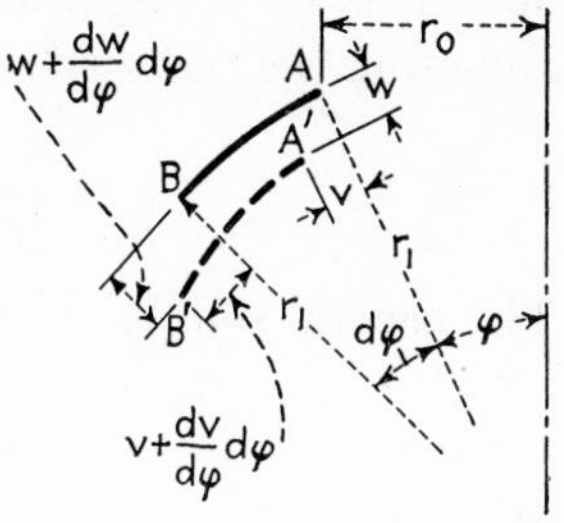

Dividing this by the initial length $r_1\,d\varphi$ of the element, we find the strain of the shell in the meridional direction to be

$$\epsilon_\varphi = \frac{1}{r_1}\frac{dv}{d\varphi} - \frac{w}{r_1}. \qquad (a)$$

FIG. 148.

Considering an element of a parallel circle it may be seen (Fig. 148) that owing to displacements v and w the radius r_0 of the circle increases by the amount

$$v\cos\varphi - w\sin\varphi.$$

The circumference of the parallel circle increases in the same proportion as its radius; hence,

$$\epsilon_\theta = \frac{1}{r_0}(v\cos\varphi - w\sin\varphi),$$

or, substituting $r_0 = r_2\sin\varphi$,

$$\epsilon_\theta = \frac{v}{r_2}\cot\varphi - \frac{w}{r_2}. \qquad (b)$$

Eliminating w from Eqs. (a) and (b), we obtain for v the differential equation

$$\frac{dv}{d\varphi} - v\cot\varphi = r_1\epsilon_\varphi - r_2\epsilon_\theta. \qquad (c)$$

The strain components ϵ_φ and ϵ_θ can be expressed in terms of the forces N_φ and N_θ by applying Hooke's law. This gives

$$\left.\begin{array}{l}\epsilon_\varphi = \dfrac{1}{Eh}(N_\varphi - \nu N_\theta),\\[2mm] \epsilon_\theta = \dfrac{1}{Eh}(N_\theta - \nu N_\varphi).\end{array}\right\} \qquad (d)$$

Substituting in Eq. (c), we obtain

$$\frac{dv}{d\varphi} - v \cot \varphi = \frac{1}{Eh}[N_\varphi(r_1 + \nu r_2) - N_\theta(r_2 + \nu r_1)]. \quad (221)$$

In each particular case the forces N_φ and N_θ can be found from the loading conditions, and the displacement v will then be obtained by integration of the differential equation (221). Denoting the right side of this equation by $f(\varphi)$, we write

$$\frac{dv}{d\varphi} - v \cot \varphi = f(\varphi).$$

The general solution of this equation is

$$v = \sin \varphi \left(\int \frac{f(\varphi)}{\sin \varphi} d\varphi + C \right), \quad (e)$$

in which C is a constant of integration to be determined from the condition at the support.

Take, as an example, a spherical shell of constant thickness loaded by its own weight (Fig. 140a). In such a case $r_1 = r_2 = a$, N_φ and N_θ are given by expressions (211), and Eq. (221) becomes

$$\frac{dv}{d\varphi} - v \cot \varphi = \frac{a^2 q(1 + \nu)}{Eh} \left(\cos \varphi - \frac{2}{1 + \cos \varphi} \right).$$

The general solution (e) is then

$$v = \frac{a^2 q(1 + \nu)}{Eh} \left[\sin \varphi \log (1 + \cos \varphi) - \frac{\sin \varphi}{1 + \cos \varphi} \right] + C \sin \varphi. \quad (f)$$

The constant C will now be determined from the condition that for $\varphi = \alpha$ the displacement v is zero (Fig. 140a). From this condition

$$C = \frac{a^2 q(1 + \nu)}{Eh} \left[\frac{1}{1 + \cos \alpha} - \log (1 + \cos \alpha) \right]. \quad (g)$$

The displacement v is obtained by substitution in expression (f). The displacement w is readily found from Eq. (b). At the support, where $v = 0$, the displacement w can be calculated directly from Eq. (b) without using solution (f) by substituting for ϵ_θ its value from the second of the equations (d).

77. Shells in the Form of a Surface of Revolution under Unsymmetrical Loading.—Considering again an element cut from a shell by two adjacent meridians and two parallel circles (Fig. 149), in the general case not only normal forces N_φ and N_θ but also shearing forces $N_{\varphi\theta} = N_{\theta\varphi}$ will act on the sides of the element. Taking the sum of the projections in the y-direction

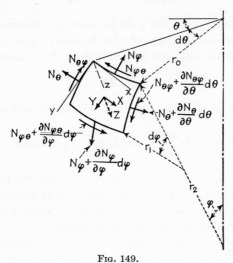

Fig. 149.

of all forces acting on the element, we must add to the forces considered in Art. 73 the force

$$\frac{\partial N_{\theta\varphi}}{\partial \theta} r_1 \, d\theta \, d\varphi \qquad (a)$$

representing the difference in the shearing forces acting on the lateral sides of the element. Hence, instead of Eq. (f) (Art. 73), we obtain the equation

$$\frac{\partial}{\partial \varphi}(N_\varphi r_0) + \frac{\partial N_{\theta\varphi}}{\partial \theta} r_1 - N_\theta r_1 \cos \varphi + Y r_1 r_0 = 0. \qquad (222)$$

Considering the forces in the x-direction, we must include the difference of the shearing forces acting on the top and bottom of the element as given by the expression

$$N_{\varphi\theta}\frac{dr_0}{d\varphi}d\varphi \, d\theta + \frac{\partial N_{\varphi\theta}}{\partial \varphi}r_0 \, d\varphi \, d\theta = \frac{\partial}{\partial \varphi}(r_0 N_{\varphi\theta})d\varphi \, d\theta, \qquad (b)$$

the force

$$\frac{\partial N_\theta}{\partial \theta} r_1 \, d\theta \, d\varphi \qquad (c)$$

due to variation of the force N_θ and the force

$$N_{\theta\varphi} r_1 \cos \varphi \, d\theta \, d\varphi \qquad (d)$$

due to the small angle $\cos \varphi \, d\theta$ between the shearing forces $N_{\theta\varphi}$ acting on the lateral sides of the element. The component in x-direction of the external load acting on the element is

$$X r_0 r_1 \, d\theta \, d\varphi. \qquad (e)$$

Summing up all these forces, we obtain the equation

$$\frac{\partial}{\partial \varphi}(r_0 N_{\varphi\theta}) + \frac{\partial N_\theta}{\partial \theta} r_1 + N_{\theta\varphi} r_1 \cos \varphi + X r_0 r_1 = 0. \qquad (223)$$

The third equation of equilibrium is obtained by projecting the forces on the z-axis. Since the projection of shearing forces on this axis vanishes, the third equation conforms with Eq. (210) which was derived for symmetrical loading.

The problem of determining membrane stresses under unsymmetrical loading reduces to the solution of the three Eqs. (222), (223) and (210) for given values of the components X, Y and Z of the intensity of the external load. The application of these equations to the case of shells subjected to wind pressure will be discussed in the next article.

78. Stresses Produced by Wind Pressure.[1]—As a particular example of the application of the general equations of equilibrium derived in the previous article, let us consider the action of wind pressure on a shell. Assuming that the direction of the wind is in the meridian plane $\theta = 0$ and that the pressure is normal to the surface, we take

$$X = Y = 0, \qquad Z = p \sin \varphi \cos \theta. \qquad (a)$$

---

[1] The first investigation of this kind was made by H. Reissner, "Müller-Breslau-Festschrift," p. 181, Leipzig, 1912; see also F. Dischinger in F. von Emperger's "Handbuch für Eisenbetonbau," 4th ed., vol. 6, Berlin, 1928; E. Wiedemann, *Schweiz. Bauzeitung*, vol. 108, p. 249, 1936; and K. Girkmann, *Der Stahlbau*, vol. 6, 1933.

The equations of equilibrium then become

$$\left.\begin{array}{l}
\dfrac{\partial}{\partial \varphi}(r_0 N_\varphi) + \dfrac{\partial N_{\theta\varphi}}{\partial \theta} r_1 - N_\theta r_1 \cos \varphi = 0, \\[2ex]
\dfrac{\partial}{\partial \varphi}(r_0 N_{\varphi\theta}) + \dfrac{\partial N_\theta}{\partial \theta} r_1 + N_{\theta\varphi} r_1 \cos \varphi = 0, \\[2ex]
N_\varphi r_0 + N_\theta r_1 \sin \varphi = -p r_0 r_1 \sin \varphi \cos \theta.
\end{array}\right\} \quad (b)$$

By using the last of these equations we eliminate the force N_θ and obtain the following two differential equations[1] of the first order for determining N_φ and $N_{\theta\varphi} = N_{\varphi\theta}$:

$$\left.\begin{array}{l}
\dfrac{\partial N_\varphi}{\partial \varphi} + \left(\dfrac{1}{r_0}\dfrac{dr_0}{d\varphi} + \cot \varphi\right) N_\varphi + \dfrac{r_1}{r_0}\dfrac{\partial N_{\theta\varphi}}{\partial \theta} = -p r_1 \cos \varphi \cos \theta; \\[2ex]
\dfrac{\partial N_{\theta\varphi}}{\partial \varphi} + \left(\dfrac{1}{r_0}\dfrac{dr_0}{d\varphi} + \dfrac{r_1}{r_2}\cot \varphi\right) N_{\theta\varphi} - \dfrac{1}{\sin \varphi}\dfrac{\partial N_\varphi}{\partial \theta} = -p r_1 \sin \theta.
\end{array}\right\} \quad (c)$$

Let us consider the particular problem of a spherical shell, in which case $r_1 = r_2 = a$. We take the solution of Eqs. (c) in the form

$$N_\varphi = S_\varphi \cos \theta, \qquad N_{\theta\varphi} = S_{\theta\varphi} \sin \theta, \qquad (d)$$

in which S_φ and $S_{\theta\varphi}$ are functions of φ only. Substituting in Eqs. (c), we obtain the following ordinary differential equations for the determination of these functions:

$$\left.\begin{array}{l}
\dfrac{dS_\varphi}{d\varphi} + 2 \cot\varphi\, S_\varphi + \dfrac{1}{\sin\varphi} S_{\theta\varphi} = -pa \cos \varphi, \\[2ex]
\dfrac{dS_{\theta\varphi}}{d\varphi} + 2 \cot\varphi\, S_{\theta\varphi} + \dfrac{1}{\sin\varphi} S_\varphi = -pa.
\end{array}\right\} \quad (e)$$

By adding and subtracting these equations and introducing the notation

$$U_1 = S_\varphi + S_{\theta\varphi}, \qquad U_2 = S_\varphi - S_{\theta\varphi}, \qquad (f)$$

the following two ordinary differential equations, each containing only one unknown, are obtained:

$$\left.\begin{array}{l}
\dfrac{dU_1}{d\varphi} + \left(2 \cot \varphi + \dfrac{1}{\sin \varphi}\right) U_1 = -pa(1 + \cos \varphi); \\[2ex]
\dfrac{dU_2}{d\varphi} + \left(2 \cot \varphi - \dfrac{1}{\sin \varphi}\right) U_2 = pa(1 - \cos \varphi).
\end{array}\right\} \quad (g)$$

---

[1] The application of the stress function in investigating wind stresses was used by A. Pucher. *Pub. Intern. Assoc. Bridge and Structural Eng.* vol. 5, p. 275, 1938.

Applying the general rule for integrating differential equations of the first order, we obtain

$$U_1 = \frac{1 + \cos \varphi}{\sin^3 \varphi} \left[C_1 + pa \left(\cos \varphi - \frac{1}{3} \cos^3 \varphi \right) \right], \left. \atop \right\} \quad (h)$$
$$U_2 = \frac{1 - \cos \varphi}{\sin^3 \varphi} \left[C_2 - pa \left(\cos \varphi - \frac{1}{3} \cos^3 \varphi \right) \right],$$

where C_1 and C_2 are constants of integration. Substituting in Eqs. (f) and using Eqs. (d), we finally obtain

$$N_\varphi = \frac{\cos \theta}{\sin^3 \varphi} \left[\frac{C_1 + C_2}{2} + \frac{C_1 - C_2}{2} \cos \varphi \right.$$
$$\left. + pa \left(\cos^2 \varphi - \frac{1}{3} \cos^4 \varphi \right) \right], \left. \atop \right\} \quad (i)$$
$$N_{\theta\varphi} = \frac{\sin \theta}{\sin^3 \varphi} \left[\frac{C_1 - C_2}{2} + \frac{C_1 + C_2}{2} \cos \varphi \right.$$
$$\left. + pa \left(\cos \varphi - \frac{1}{3} \cos^3 \varphi \right) \right].$$

To determine the constants of integration C_1 and C_2 let us consider a shell in the form of a hemisphere and put $\varphi = \pi/2$ in expressions (i). Then the forces along the equator of the shell are

$$N_\varphi = \frac{C_1 + C_2}{2} \cos \theta, \qquad N_{\theta\varphi} = \frac{C_1 - C_2}{2} \sin \theta. \qquad (j)$$

Since the pressure at each point of the sphere is in a radial direction, the moment of the wind forces with respect to the diameter of the sphere perpendicular to the plane $\theta = 0$ is zero. Using this fact and applying the first of the equations (j), we obtain

$$\int_0^{2\pi} N_\varphi a^2 \cos \theta \, d\theta = a^2 \frac{C_1 + C_2}{2} \int_0^{2\pi} \cos^2 \theta \, d\theta = 0,$$

which gives

$$C_1 = -C_2. \qquad (k)$$

The second necessary equation is obtained by taking the sum of the components of all forces acting on the half sphere in the direction of the horizontal diameter in the plane $\theta = 0$. This gives

$$\int_0^{2\pi} N_{\theta\varphi} a \sin\theta \, d\theta$$

$$= -\int_0^{\frac{\pi}{2}} \int_0^{2\pi} p \sin\varphi \cos\theta \cdot a \sin\varphi \sin\varphi \cos\theta \, d\varphi \, d\theta,$$

or

$$a\pi\frac{C_1 - C_2}{2} = -pa^2\frac{2}{3}\pi. \tag{l}$$

From (k) and (l) we obtain

$$C_1 = -\tfrac{2}{3}ap, \qquad C_2 = \tfrac{2}{3}ap.$$

Substituting these values for the constants in expressions (i) and using the third of the equations (b), we obtain

$$\left.\begin{aligned}
N_\varphi &= -\frac{pa}{3}\frac{\cos\theta\cos\varphi}{\sin^3\varphi}(2 - 3\cos\varphi + \cos^3\varphi), \\[4pt]
N_\theta &= \frac{pa}{3}\frac{\cos\theta}{\sin^3\varphi}(2\cos\varphi - 3\sin^2\varphi - 2\cos^4\varphi), \\[4pt]
N_{\theta\varphi} &= -\frac{pa}{3}\frac{\sin\theta}{\sin^3\varphi}(2 - 3\cos\varphi + \cos^3\varphi).
\end{aligned}\right\} \tag{m}$$

By using these expressions the wind stresses at any point of the shell can be readily calculated. If the shell is in the form of a hemisphere, there will be no normal forces acting along the edge of the shell, since $(N_\varphi)_{\varphi=\pi/2} = 0$. The shearing forces $N_{\theta\varphi}$ along the edge are different from zero and are equal and opposite to the horizontal resultant of the wind pressure. The maximum numerical value of these forces is found at the ends of the diameter perpendic-

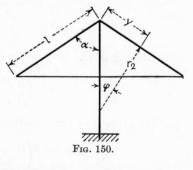

Fig. 150.

ular to the plane $\theta = 0$, at which point they are equal to $\pm 2pa/3$.

As a second application of Eqs. (c) let us consider the case of a shell having the shape of a circular cone and supported by a column at the vertex (Fig. 150). In this case the radius r_1 is infinitely large. For an element dy of a meridian we can write $dy = r_1 \, d\varphi$. Hence

$$\frac{d}{d\varphi} = r_1\frac{d}{dy}.$$

In addition we have

$$r_0 = y \sin \alpha, \qquad \frac{dr_0}{dy} = \sin \alpha, \qquad r_2 = y \tan \alpha.$$

Substituting in Eqs. (c), we obtain for a conical shell submitted to a wind pressure $Z = p \sin \varphi \cos \theta$ the equations

$$\left. \begin{aligned} \frac{\partial N_\varphi}{\partial y} + \frac{N_\varphi}{y} + \frac{1}{y \sin \alpha} \frac{\partial N_{\theta\varphi}}{\partial \theta} &= -p \sin \alpha \cos \theta, \\ \frac{\partial N_{\theta\varphi}}{\partial y} + \frac{2N_{\theta\varphi}}{y} &= -p \sin \theta. \end{aligned} \right\} \qquad (n)$$

The second equation can be readily integrated to obtain

$$N_{\theta\varphi} = -\frac{1}{y^2}\left(\frac{py^3}{3} + C\right) \sin \theta. \qquad (o)$$

The edge of the shell $y = l$ is free from forces; hence the constant of integration in expression (o) is

$$C = -\frac{pl^3}{3},$$

and we finally obtain

$$N_{\theta\varphi} = \frac{p}{3} \frac{l^3 - y^3}{y^2} \sin \theta. \qquad (p)$$

Substituting in the first of the equations (n), we find

$$\frac{\partial N_\varphi}{\partial y} + \frac{N_\varphi}{y} = -\left(\frac{p}{3} \frac{l^3 - y^3}{y^3 \sin \alpha} + p \sin \alpha\right) \cos \theta.$$

The integration of this equation gives

$$N_\varphi = \frac{p \cos \theta}{\sin \alpha}\left(\frac{l^3 - y^3}{3y^2} - \frac{l^2 - y^2}{2y} \cos^2 \alpha\right) \qquad (q)$$

which vanishes at the edge $y = l$ as it should. The forces N_θ are obtained from the third of the equations (b), which gives

$$N_\theta = -py \sin \alpha \cos \theta. \qquad (r)$$

The expressions (p), (q) and (r) give the complete solution for the stresses due to wind pressure on the conical shell represented in Fig. 150. At the top $y = 0$ the forces N_φ and $N_{\theta\varphi}$ become infinitely large. To remove this difficulty we must assume a parallel circle corresponding to a certain finite value of y along which the conical shell is fastened to the column. The forces N_φ $N_{\theta\varphi}$ distributed along this circle balance the wind pressure acting on the cone. It can be seen that, if the radius of the circle is not sufficient, these forces may become very large.

79. Spherical Shell Supported at Isolated Points.[1]—We begin with the general case of a shell having the form of a surface of revolution and consider the case when the forces are acting only along the edge of the shell so that $X = Y = Z = 0$. The general equations (b) of the previous article then become

$$
\left.
\begin{aligned}
&\frac{\partial}{\partial \varphi}(r_0 N_\varphi) + \frac{\partial N_{\theta\varphi}}{\partial \theta} r_1 - N_\theta r_1 \cos\,\varphi = 0, \\
&\frac{\partial}{\partial \varphi}(r_0 N_{\theta\varphi}) + \frac{\partial N_\theta}{\partial \theta} r_1 + N_{\theta\varphi} r_1 \cos\,\varphi = 0, \\
&N_\varphi r_0 + N_\theta r_1 \sin\,\varphi = 0.
\end{aligned}
\right\} \quad (a)
$$

Let us take the solution of these equations in the form

$$
\left.
\begin{aligned}
N_\varphi &= S_{\varphi n} \cos n\theta, \\
N_\theta &= S_{\theta n} \cos n\theta, \\
N_{\theta\varphi} &= S_{\theta\varphi n} \sin n\theta,
\end{aligned}
\right\} \quad (b)
$$

where $S_{\varphi n}$, $S_{\theta n}$ and $S_{\theta\varphi n}$ are functions of φ only and n is an integer. Substituting expressions (b) in Eqs. (a), we obtain

$$
\left.
\begin{aligned}
&\frac{d}{d\varphi}(r_0 S_{\varphi n}) + n r_1 S_{\theta\varphi n} - r_1 S_{\theta n} \cos\,\varphi = 0, \\
&\frac{d}{d\varphi}(r_0 S_{\theta\varphi n}) - n r_1 S_{\theta n} + r_1 S_{\theta\varphi n} \cos\,\varphi = 0, \\
&S_{\varphi n} + \frac{r_1}{r_2} S_{\theta n} = 0.
\end{aligned}
\right\} \quad (c)
$$

Using the third of these equations, we can eliminate the function $S_{\theta n}$ and thus obtain

$$
\left.
\begin{aligned}
&\frac{dS_{\varphi n}}{d\varphi} + \left(\frac{1}{r_0}\frac{dr_0}{d\varphi} + \cot\,\varphi\right) S_{\varphi n} + n\frac{r_1}{r_2}\frac{S_{\theta\varphi n}}{\sin\,\varphi} = 0, \\
&\frac{dS_{\theta\varphi n}}{d\varphi} + \left(\frac{1}{r_0}\frac{dr_0}{d\varphi} + \frac{r_1}{r_2}\cot\,\varphi\right) S_{\theta\varphi n} + \frac{nS_{\varphi n}}{\sin\,\varphi} = 0.
\end{aligned}
\right\} \quad (d)
$$

[1] FLÜGGE, W., *loc. cit.*, p. 43. For the application of the stress function in solution of such problems, see paper by Pucher, *loc. cit.*, p. 375.

In the particular case of a spherical shell $r_1 = r_2 = a$, $r_0 = a \sin \varphi$; and Eqs. (d) reduce to the following simple form:

$$\left. \begin{aligned} \frac{dS_{\varphi n}}{d\varphi} + 2 \cot\varphi S_{\varphi n} + \frac{n}{\sin\varphi} S_{\theta\varphi n} &= 0; \\ \frac{dS_{\theta\varphi n}}{d\varphi} + 2 \cot\varphi S_{\theta\varphi n} + \frac{n}{\sin\varphi} S_{\varphi n} &= 0. \end{aligned} \right\} \quad (e)$$

Proceeding as in the previous article, by taking the sum and the difference of Eqs. (e) and introducing the notation

$$U_{1n} = S_{\varphi n} + S_{\theta\varphi n}, \qquad U_{2n} = S_{\varphi n} - S_{\theta\varphi n}, \qquad (f)$$

we obtain

$$\left. \begin{aligned} \frac{dU_{1n}}{d\varphi} + \left(2 \cot \varphi + \frac{n}{\sin \varphi} \right) U_{1n} &= 0, \\ \frac{dU_{2n}}{d\varphi} + \left(2 \cot \varphi - \frac{n}{\sin \varphi} \right) U_{2n} &= 0. \end{aligned} \right\} \quad (g)$$

The solution of these equations is

$$U_{1n} = C_{1n} \frac{\left(\cot \dfrac{\varphi}{2} \right)^n}{\sin^2 \varphi}, \qquad U_{2n} = C_{2n} \frac{\left(\tan \dfrac{\varphi}{2} \right)^n}{\sin^2 \varphi}. \qquad (h)$$

From Eqs. (f) we then obtain

$$\left. \begin{aligned} S_{\varphi n} &= \frac{U_{1n} + U_{2n}}{2} = \frac{1}{2 \sin^2 \varphi} \left[C_{1n} \left(\cot \frac{\varphi}{2} \right)^n + C_{2n} \left(\tan \frac{\varphi}{2} \right)^n \right], \\ S_{\theta\varphi n} &= \frac{U_{1n} - U_{2n}}{2} = \frac{1}{2 \sin^2 \varphi} \left[C_{1n} \left(\cot \frac{\varphi}{2} \right)^n - C_{2n} \left(\tan \frac{\varphi}{2} \right)^n \right]. \end{aligned} \right\} \quad (i)$$

If we have a shell without an opening at the top, expressions (i) must be finite for $\varphi = 0$. This requires that the constant of integration $C_{1n} = 0$. Substituting this in Eq. (i) and using Eqs. (b), we find

$$\left. \begin{aligned} N_\varphi &= -N_\theta = \frac{C_{2n}}{2 \sin^2 \varphi} \left(\tan \frac{\varphi}{2} \right)^n \cos n\theta, \\ N_{\theta\varphi} &= -\frac{C_{2n}}{2 \sin^2 \varphi} \left(\tan \frac{\varphi}{2} \right)^n \sin n\theta. \end{aligned} \right\} \quad (j)$$

Substituting for φ the angle φ_0 corresponding to the edge of the spherical shell, we shall obtain the normal and the shearing forces which must be distributed along the edge of the shell to produce in this shell the forces (j). Taking, as an example, the case when $\varphi_0 = \pi/2$, i.e., the shell is a hemisphere, we obtain, from expressions (j),

$$(N_\varphi)_{\varphi=\frac{\pi}{2}} = \frac{C_{2n}}{2} \cos n\theta, \quad\left.\right\}$$

$$(N_{\theta\varphi})_{\varphi=\frac{\pi}{2}} = -\frac{C_{2n}}{2} \sin n\theta. \quad\left.\right\} \qquad (k)$$

Knowing the stresses produced in a spherical shell by normal and shearing forces applied to the edge and proportional to $\cos n\theta$ and $\sin n\theta$, respectively, we can treat the problem of any distribution of normal forces along the edge by representing this distribution by a trigonometric series in which each term of the series is a solution similar to the solution (j).[1] Take, as an

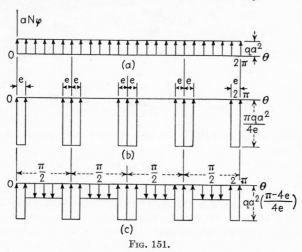

Fig. 151.

example, the case of a hemispherical dome of radius a, carrying only its own weight of q lb. per square foot and supported by four symmetrically located columns. If the dome is resting on a continuous foundation, the forces N_φ are uniformly distributed along the edge as shown in Fig. 151a, in which the intensity of force aN_φ per unit angle is plotted against the angle θ. In the case of four equidistant columns the distribution of reactions will be as shown in Fig. 151b, in which $2e$ denotes the angle corresponding to the circumferential distance supported by each column. Subtracting the force distribution of Fig. 151a from the force distribution of Fig. 151b, we obtain

[1] In using a series $N_\varphi = \frac{1}{2} \sum\limits_{n=1,2,3,\,\cdots}^{\infty} C_{2n} \cos n\theta$ for normal forces we obtain a distribution of these forces symmetrical with respect to the diameter $\theta = 0$. In the general case the series will contain not only cosine terms but also sine terms. The solutions for sine terms can be obtained in exactly the same manner as in our discussion of the cosine terms. It is only necessary to exchange the places of $\cos n\theta$ and $\sin n\theta$ in Eqs. (b).

the distribution of Fig. 151c, representing a system of forces in equilibrium. This distribution can be represented in form of a series

$$(aN_\varphi)_{\varphi = \frac{\pi}{2}} = \sum_{n = 4,8,12, \cdots}^{\infty} A_n \cos n\theta, \tag{l}$$

in which only the terms $n = 4, 8, 12, \cdots$ must be considered, since the diagram 151c repeats itself after each interval of $\pi/2$ and has four complete periods in the angle 2π. Applying the usual method for calculating the coefficients of series (l), we find

$$A_n = \frac{2qa^2}{ne} \sin (ne).$$

Hence the distribution shown by diagram 151c is represented by the series

$$(aN_\varphi)_{\varphi = \frac{\pi}{2}} = \frac{2qa^2}{e} \sum_{n = 4,8,12, \cdots}^{\infty} \frac{\sin ne}{n} \cos n\theta. \tag{m}$$

Comparing each term of this series with the first of the equations (k)   we conclude that

$$C_{2n} = \frac{4qa}{e} \frac{\sin ne}{n}.$$

The stresses produced in the shell by the forces (m) are now obtained by taking a solution of the form (j) corresponding to each term of series (m) and then superposing these solutions.   In such a manner we obtain

$$\left. \begin{aligned} N_\varphi = -N_\theta &= \frac{2qa}{e \sin^2 \varphi} \sum_{n = 4,8,12, \cdots}^{\infty} \frac{\sin ne}{n} \left(\tan \frac{\varphi}{2} \right)^n \cos n\theta, \\ N_{\theta\varphi} &= -\frac{2qa}{e \sin^2 \varphi} \sum_{n = 4,8,12, \cdots}^{\infty} \frac{\sin ne}{n} \left(\tan \frac{\varphi}{2} \right)^n \sin n\theta. \end{aligned} \right\} \tag{n}$$

Superposing this solution on solution (211), which was previously obtained for a dome supported by forces uniformly distributed along the edge (Fig. 140a), we obtain formulas for calculating the stresses in a dome resting on four columns.   It must be noted, however, that, whereas the above-mentioned superposition gives the necessary distribution of the reactive forces N_φ as shown in Fig. 151b, it also introduces shearing forces $N_{\theta\varphi}$ which do not vanish at the edge of the dome. Thus our solution does not satisfy all the conditions of the problem.   In fact, so long as we limit ourselves to membrane theory, we shall not have enough constants to satisfy all the conditions and to obtain the complete solution of the problem.   In actual constructions a reinforcing ring is usually put along the edge of the shell to carry the shearing forces $N_{\theta\varphi}$. In such cases the solution obtained by the combination of solutions (211) and (n) will be a sufficiently accurate representation of the internal forces produced in a spherical dome resting on four columns. For a more satisfactory solution of this problem the bending theory of shells must be used.[1]

The method discussed in this article can also be used in the case of a non-spherical dome. In such cases it is necessary to have recourse to Eqs. (d) which can be solved with sufficient accuracy by using numerical integration.[2]

80. Membrane Theory of Cylindrical Shells.—In discussing a cylindrical shell (Fig. 152a) we assume that the generator of the

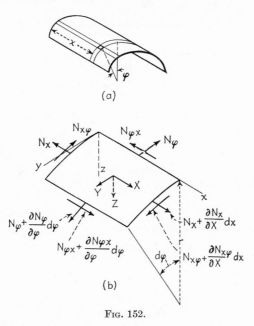

(a)

(b)

Fig. 152.

shell is horizontal and parallel to the x-axis. An element is cut from the shell by two adjacent generators and two cross sections perpendicular to the x-axis, and its position is defined by the coordinate x and the angle φ. The forces acting on the sides of the element are shown in Fig. 152b. In addition a load will be distributed over the surface of the element, the components of the

---

[1] An example of such a solution is given in A. Aas Jacobsen's paper, *Ingenieur-Archiv*, vol. 8, p. 275, 1937.

[2] An example of such integration is given in Flügge's book, *loc. cit.*, p. 47.

intensity of this load being denoted, as before, by X, Y and Z. Considering the equilibrium of the element and summing up the forces in the x-direction, we obtain

$$\frac{\partial N_x}{\partial x} r d\varphi \, dx + \frac{\partial N_{\varphi x}}{\partial \varphi} d\varphi \, dx + X r d\varphi \, dx = 0. \qquad (a)$$

Similarly the forces in the direction of the tangent to the normal cross section, *i.e.*, in the y-direction, give as a corresponding equation of equilibrium

$$\frac{\partial N_{x\varphi}}{\partial x} r d\varphi \, dx + \frac{\partial N_\varphi}{\partial \varphi} d\varphi \, dx + Y r d\varphi \, dx = 0. \qquad (b)$$

The forces acting in the direction of the normal to the shell, *i.e.*,

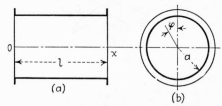

(a)

(b)

Fig. 153.

in the z-direction, give the equation

$$N_\varphi \, d\varphi \, dx + Z r d\varphi \, dx = 0. \qquad (c)$$

After simplification, the three equations of equilibrium can be represented in the following form:

$$\left.\begin{array}{c} \dfrac{\partial N_x}{\partial x} + \dfrac{1}{r} \dfrac{\partial N_{x\varphi}}{\partial \varphi} = -X, \\[2mm] \dfrac{\partial N_{x\varphi}}{\partial x} + \dfrac{1}{r} \dfrac{\partial N_\varphi}{\partial \varphi} = -Y, \\[2mm] N_\varphi = -Zr. \end{array}\right\} \qquad (224)$$

In each particular case we readily find the value of N_φ. Substituting this value in the second of the equations, we then obtain $N_{x\varphi}$ by integration. Using the value of $N_{x\varphi}$ thus obtained we find N_x by integrating the first equation.

As an example of the application of Eqs. (224) let us consider a horizontal circular tube filled with liquid and supported at the ends.[1] Measuring the angle φ as shown in Fig. 153b and denoting

---

[1] This problem was discussed by D. Thoma, *Z. ges. Turbinenwesen*, vol. 17, p. 49, 1920.

by p_0 the pressure at the axis of the tube, the pressure at any point is $p_0 - \gamma a \cos \varphi$. We thus obtain

$$X = Y = 0. \qquad Z = -p_0 + \gamma a \cos \varphi. \tag{d}$$

Substituting in Eqs. (224), we find

$$N_\varphi = p_0 a - \gamma a^2 \cos \varphi, \tag{e}$$

$$N_{x\varphi} = -\int \gamma a \sin \varphi \, dx + C_1(\varphi) = -\gamma a x \sin \varphi + C_1(\varphi), \tag{f}$$

$$N_x = \int \gamma \cos \varphi \, x \, dx - \frac{1}{a} \int \frac{dC_1(\varphi)}{d\varphi} dx + C_2(\varphi)$$

$$= \gamma \frac{x^2}{2} \cos \varphi - \frac{x}{a} \frac{dC_1(\varphi)}{d\varphi} + C_2(\varphi). \tag{g}$$

The functions $C_1(\varphi)$ and $C_2(\varphi)$ must now be determined from the conditions at the edges.

Let us first assume that there are no forces N_x at the ends of the tube. Then

$$(N_x)_{x=0} = 0 \qquad (N_x)_{x=l} = 0.$$

We shall satisfy these conditions by taking

$$C_2(\varphi) = 0, \qquad C_1(\varphi) = \frac{a\gamma l}{2} \sin \varphi + C.$$

It is seen from expression (f) that the constant C represents forces $N_{x\varphi}$ uniformly distributed around the edge of the tube, as is the case when the tube is subjected to torsion. If there is no torque applied, we must take $C = 0$. Then the solution of Eqs. (224) in our particular case is

$$\left.\begin{aligned} N_\varphi &= p_0 a - \gamma a^2 \cos \varphi, \\ N_{x\varphi} &= \gamma a\left(\frac{l}{2} - x\right) \sin \varphi, \\ N_x &= -\frac{\gamma}{2} x(l - x) \cos \varphi. \end{aligned}\right\} \tag{225}$$

It is seen that $N_{x\varphi}$ and N_x are proportional, respectively, to the shearing force and to the bending moment of a uniformly loaded beam of span l and can be obtained by applying beam formulas to the tube carrying a uniformly distributed load of the magnitude[1] $\pi a^2 \gamma$ per unit length of the tube.

---

[1] The weight of the tube is neglected in this discussion.

By a proper selection of the function $C_2(\varphi)$ we can also obtain a solution of the problem for a cylindrical shell with built-in edges. In such a case the length of the generator remains unchanged, and we have the condition

$$\int_0^l (N_x - \nu N_\varphi) dx = 0.$$

Substituting

$$N_x = -\frac{\gamma}{2}x(l - x) \cos \varphi + C_2(\varphi), \qquad N_\varphi = p_0 a - \gamma a^2 \cos \varphi,$$

we obtain

$$C_2(\varphi) = \nu p_0 a + \left(\frac{l^2}{12} - \nu a^2\right)\gamma \cos \varphi$$

and

$$N_x = -\frac{\gamma x}{2}(l - x) \cos \varphi + \nu p_0 a + \left(\frac{l^2}{12} - \nu a^2\right)\gamma \cos \varphi. \quad (226)$$

Owing to the action of the forces N_φ and N_x there will be a certain amount of strain in the circumferential direction at the end of

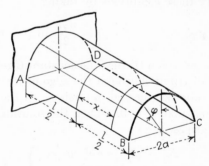

Fig. 154.

the tube in contradiction to our assumption of built-in edges. This indicates that at the ends of the tube there will be some local bending, which is disregarded in the membrane theory. A more complete solution of the problem can be obtained only by considering membrane stresses together with bending stresses, as will be discussed in the next chapter.

Sections of cylindrical shells, such as shown in Fig. 154, are sometimes used as coverings of various kinds of structure. These shells are usually supported only at the ends while the edges AB

and CD are free. In calculating the membrane stresses for such shells the previous Eqs. (224) can again be used. Take, for example, a shell of a semicircular cross section supporting its own weight which is assumed to be uniformly distributed over the surface of the shell. In such a case we have

$$X = 0, \qquad Y = p \sin \varphi, \qquad Z = p \cos \varphi.$$

The third of the equations (224) gives

$$N_\varphi = -pa \cos \varphi \qquad (h)$$

which vanishes along the edges AB and CD as it should. It is seen that this condition will also be satisfied if some other curve is taken instead of a semicircle provided only that $\varphi = \pm \pi/2$ at the edges. Substituting expression (h) in the second of the equations (224), we find

$$N_{x\varphi} = -2px \sin \varphi + C_1(\varphi). \qquad (i)$$

By putting the origin of the coordinates at the middle of the span and assuming the same end conditions at both ends, $x = \pm l/2$ of the tube, it can be concluded from symmetry that $C_1(\varphi) = 0$. Hence,

$$N_{x\varphi} = -2px \sin \varphi. \qquad (j)$$

It is seen that this solution does not vanish along the edges AB and CD as it should for free edges. In structural applications, however, the edges are usually reinforced by longitudinal members strong enough to resist the tension produced by shearing force (j). Substituting expression (j) in the first of the equations (224), we obtain

$$N_x = \frac{px^2}{a} \cos \varphi + C_2(\varphi). \qquad (k)$$

If the ends of the shell are supported in such a manner that the reactions act in the planes of the end cross sections, the forces N_x must vanish at the ends. Hence $C_2(\varphi) = -pl^2 \cos \varphi/4a$, and we obtain

$$N_x = -\frac{p \cos \varphi}{4a}(l^2 - 4x^2). \qquad (l)$$

Expressions (h), (j) and (l) represent the solution of Eqs. (224) for our particular case (Fig. 154) satisfying the conditions at the ends and also one of the conditions along the edges AB and CD. The second condition, which concerns the shearing forces $N_{x\varphi}$, cannot be satisfied by using the membrane stresses alone. In practical applications it is assumed that the forces $N_{x\varphi}$ will be taken by the longitudinal members that reinforce the edges. It can be expected that this assumption will be satisfactory in those cases in which the length of the shell is not large, say $l \lessgtr 2a$, and that the membrane theory will give an approximate picture of the stress distribution in such cases. For longer shells a satisfactory solution can be obtained only by considering bending as well as membrane stresses. This problem will be discussed in the next chapter (see Art. 91).

CHAPTER XI

GENERAL THEORY OF CYLINDRICAL SHELLS

81. A Circular Cylindrical Shell Loaded Symmetrically with Respect to Its Axis.—In practical applications we frequently encounter problems in which a circular cylindrical shell is submitted to the action of forces distributed symmetrically with

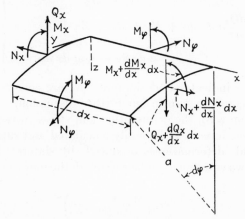

Fig. 155.

respect to the axis of the cylinder. The stress distribution in cylindrical boilers submitted to the action of steam pressure, stresses in cylindrical containers having a vertical axis and submitted to internal liquid pressure and stresses in circular pipes under uniform internal pressure are examples of such problems.

To establish the equations required for the solution of these problems we consider an element, as shown in Figs. 152a and 155, and consider the equations of equilibrium. It can be concluded from symmetry that the membrane shearing forces $N_{x\varphi} = N_{\varphi x}$ vanish in this case and that forces N_φ are constant along the circumference. Regarding the transverse shearing forces, it can also be concluded from symmetry that only the forces Q_x do not vanish. Considering the moments acting on the element in

389

Fig. 155, we also conclude from symmetry that the twisting moments $M_{x\varphi} = M_{\varphi x}$ vanish and that the bending moments M_φ are constant along the circumference.   Under such conditions of symmetry three of the six equations of equilibrium of the element are identically satisfied, and we have to consider only the remaining three equations, *viz.*, those obtained by projecting the forces on the x- and z-axes, and by taking the moment of the forces about the y-axis.   Assuming that the external forces consist only of a pressure normal to the surface, these three equations of equilibrium are

$$\left.\begin{aligned}
\frac{dN_x}{dx}a \; dx \; d\varphi &= 0, \\
\frac{dQ_x}{dx}a \; dx \; d\varphi + N_\varphi \; dx \; d\varphi + Za \; dx \; d\varphi &= 0, \\
\frac{dM_x}{dx}a \; dx \; d\varphi - Q_x a \; dx \; d\varphi &= 0.
\end{aligned}\right\} \qquad (a)$$

The first one indicates that the forces N_x are constant,[1] and we take them equal to zero in our further discussion.   If they are different from zero, the deformation and stress corresponding to such constant forces can be easily calculated and superposed on stresses and deformations produced by lateral load.   The remaining two equations can be written in the following simplified form:

$$\left.\begin{aligned}
\frac{dQ_x}{dx} + \frac{1}{a}N_\varphi &= -Z; \\
\frac{dM_x}{dx} - Q_x &= 0.
\end{aligned}\right\} \qquad (b)$$

These two equations contain three unknown quantities N_φ, Q_x and M_x.   To solve the problem we must therefore consider the displacements of points in the middle surface of the shell.

From symmetry we conclude that the component v of the displacement in the circumferential direction vanishes.   We thus have to consider only the components u and w in the x- and z-directions, respectively.   The expressions for the strain components then become

$$\epsilon_x = \frac{du}{dx}, \qquad \epsilon_\varphi = -\frac{w}{a}. \qquad (c)$$

---

[1] The effect of these forces on bending is neglected in this discussion.

Hence, by applying Hooke's law, we obtain

$$N_x = \frac{Eh}{1 - \nu^2}(\epsilon_x + \nu\epsilon_\varphi) = \frac{Eh}{1 - \nu^2}\left(\frac{du}{dx} - \nu\frac{w}{a}\right) = 0,$$

$$N_\varphi = \frac{Eh}{1 - \nu^2}(\epsilon_\varphi + \nu\epsilon_x) = \frac{Eh}{1 - \nu^2}\left(-\frac{w}{a} + \nu\frac{du}{dx}\right). \qquad (d)$$

From the first of these equations it follows that

$$\frac{du}{dx} = \nu\frac{w}{a},$$

and the second equation gives

$$N_\varphi = -\frac{Ehw}{a}. \qquad (e)$$

Considering the bending moments, we conclude from symmetry that there is no change in curvature in the circumferential direction. The curvature in the x-direction is equal to $-d^2w/dx^2$. Using the same equations as for plates, we then obtain

$$M_\varphi = \nu M_x,$$

$$M_x = -D\frac{d^2w}{dx^2}, \qquad (f)$$

where

$$D = \frac{Eh^3}{12(1 - \nu^2)}$$

is the flexural rigidity of the shell.

Returning now to Eqs. (b) and eliminating Q_x from these equations, we obtain

$$\frac{d^2M_x}{dx^2} + \frac{1}{a}N_\varphi = -Z,$$

from which, by using Eqs. (e) and (f), we obtain

$$\frac{d^2}{dx^2}\left(D\frac{d^2w}{dx^2}\right) + \frac{Eh}{a^2}w = Z. \qquad (227)$$

All problems of symmetrical deformation of circular cylindrical shells thus reduce to the integration of Eq. (227).

The simplest application of this equation is obtained when the thickness of the shell is constant. Under such conditions Eq.

(227) becomes

$$D\frac{d^4w}{dx^4} + \frac{Eh}{a^2}w = Z. \tag{228}$$

Using the notation

$$\beta^4 = \frac{Eh}{4a^2D} = \frac{3(1 - \nu^2)}{a^2h^2}, \tag{229}$$

Eq. (228) can be represented in the simplified form

$$\frac{d^4w}{dx^4} + 4\beta^4w = \frac{Z}{D}. \tag{230}$$

This is the same equation as is obtained for a prismatical bar with a flexural rigidity D, supported by a continuous elastic foundation and submitted to the action of a load of intensity Z.[1] The general solution of this equation is

$$w = e^{\beta x}(C_1 \cos \beta x + C_2 \sin \beta x)$$
$$+ e^{-\beta x}(C_3 \cos \beta x + C_4 \sin \beta x) + f(x), \tag{231}$$

in which $f(x)$ is a particular solution of Eq. (230) and $C_1, \ldots, C_4$ are the constants of integration which must be determined in each particular case from the conditions at the ends of the cylinder.

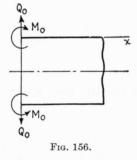

Take, as an example, a long circular pipe submitted to the action of bending moments M_0 and shearing forces Q_0 both uniformly distributed along the edge $x = 0$ (Fig. 156). In this case there is no pressure Z distributed over the surface of the shell, and $f(x) = 0$ in the general solution (231). Since the forces applied at the end $x = 0$ produce a local bending which dies out rapidly as the distance x from the loaded end increases, we conclude that the first term on the right side of Eq. (231) must vanish. Hence, $C_1 = C_2 = 0$, and we obtain

Fig. 156.

$$w = e^{-\beta x}(C_3 \cos \beta x + C_4 \sin \beta x). \tag{g}$$

The two constants C_3 and C_4 can now be determined from the conditions at the loaded end which may be written

[1] See author's "Strength of Materials," vol. 2, p. 401, 1930.

$$(M_x)_{x=0} = -D\left(\frac{d^2w}{dx^2}\right)_{x=0} = M_0,$$

$$(Q_x)_{x=0} = \left(\frac{dM_x}{dx}\right)_{x=0} = -D\left(\frac{d^3w}{dx^3}\right)_{x=0} = Q_0. \quad\quad (h)$$

Substituting expression (g) for w, we obtain from these end conditions

$$C_3 = -\frac{1}{2\beta^3 D}(Q_0 + \beta M_0), \qquad C_4 = \frac{M_0}{2\beta^2 D}. \quad\quad (i)$$

The final expression for w is thus

$$w = \frac{e^{-\beta x}}{2\beta^3 D}[\beta M_0(\sin\beta x - \cos\beta x) - Q_0\cos\beta x]. \quad (232)$$

The maximum deflection is obtained at the loaded end where

$$(w)_{x=0} = -\frac{1}{2\beta^3 D}(\beta M_0 + Q_0). \quad\quad (233)$$

The negative sign for this deflection results from the fact that w is taken positive toward the axis of the cylinder. The slope at the loaded end is obtained by differentiating expression (232). This gives

$$\left(\frac{dw}{dx}\right)_{x=0} = \frac{e^{-\beta x}}{2\beta^2 D}[2\beta M_0\cos\beta x + Q_0(\cos\beta x + \sin\beta x)]_{x=0}$$

$$= \frac{1}{2\beta^2 D}(2\beta M_0 + Q_0). \quad (234)$$

By introducing the notation

$$\varphi(\beta x) = e^{-\beta x}(\cos\beta x + \sin\beta x),$$
$$\psi(\beta x) = e^{-\beta x}(\cos\beta x - \sin\beta x),$$
$$\theta(\beta x) = e^{-\beta x}\cos\beta x, \qquad \zeta(\beta x) = e^{-\beta x}\sin\beta x, \quad (235)$$

the expressions for deflection and its consecutive derivatives can be represented in the following simplified form:

$$w = -\frac{1}{2\beta^3 D}[\beta M_0\psi(\beta x) + Q_0\theta(\beta x)],$$

$$\frac{dw}{dx} = \frac{1}{2\beta^2 D}[2\beta M_0\theta(\beta x) + Q_0\varphi(\beta x)],$$

$$\frac{d^2w}{dx^2} = -\frac{1}{2\beta D}[2\beta M_0\varphi(\beta x) + 2Q_0\zeta(\beta x)],$$

$$\frac{d^3w}{dx^3} = \frac{1}{D}[2\beta M_0\zeta(\beta x) - Q_0\psi(\beta x)].$$

$$\quad (236)$$

TABLE 45.—TABLE OF FUNCTIONS ϕ, ψ, θ AND ζ

βx	ϕ	ψ	θ	ζ
0	1.0000	1.0000	1.0000	0
0.1	0.9907	0.8100	0.9003	0.0903
0.2	0.9651	0.6398	0.8024	0.1627
0.3	0.9267	0.4888	0.7077	0.2189
0.4	0.8784	0.3564	0.6174	0.2610
0.5	0.8231	0.2415	0.5323	0.2908
0.6	0.7628	0.1431	0.4530	0.3099
0.7	0.6997	0.0599	0.3798	0.3199
0.8	0.6354	−0.0093	0.3131	0.3223
0.9	0.5712	−0.0657	0.2527	0.3185
1.0	0.5083	−0.1108	0.1988	0.3096
1.1	0.4476	−0.1457	0.1510	0.2967
1.2	0.3899	−0.1716	0.1091	0.2807
1.3	0.3355	−0.1897	0.0729	0.2626
1.4	0.2849	−0.2011	0.0419	0.2430
1.5	0.2384	−0.2068	0.0158	0.2226
1.6	0.1959	−0.2077	−0.0059	0.2018
1.7	0.1576	−0.2047	−0.0235	0.1812
1.8	0.1234	−0.1985	−0.0376	0.1610
1.9	0.0932	−0.1899	−0.0484	0.1415
2.0	0.0667	−0.1794	−0.0563	0.1230
2.1	0.0439	−0.1675	−0.0618	0.1057
2.2	0.0244	−0.1548	−0.0652	0.0895
2.3	0.0080	−0.1416	−0.0668	0.0748
2.4	−0.0056	−0.1282	−0.0669	0.0613
2.5	−0.0166	−0.1149	−0.0658	0.0492
2.6	−0.0254	−0.1019	−0.0636	0.0383
2.7	−0.0320	−0.0895	−0.0608	0.0287
2.8	−0.0369	−0.0777	−0.0573	0.0204
2.9	−0.0403	−0.0666	−0.0534	0.0132
3.0	−0.0423	−0.0563	−0.0493	0.0071
3.1	−0.0431	−0.0469	−0.0450	0.0019
3.2	−0.0431	−0.0383	−0.0407	−0.0024
3.3	−0.0422	−0.0306	−0.0364	−0.0058
3.4	−0.0408	−0.0237	−0.0323	−0.0085
3.5	−0.0389	−0.0177	−0.0283	−0.0106
3.6	−0.0366	−0.0124	−0.0245	−0.0121
3.7	−0.0341	−0.0079	−0.0210	−0.0131
3.8	−0.0314	−0.0040	−0.0177	−0.0137
3.9	−0.0286	−0.0008	−0.0147	−0.0140
4.0	−0.0258	0.0019	−0.0120	−0.0139
4.1	−0.0231	0.0040	−0.0095	−0.0136
4.2	−0.0204	0.0057	−0.0074	−0.0131
4.3	−0.0179	0.0070	−0.0054	−0.0125
4.4	−0.0155	0.0079	−0.0038	−0.0117
4.5	−0.0132	0.0085	−0.0023	−0.0108
4.6	−0.0111	0.0089	−0.0011	−0.0100
4.7	−0.0092	0.0090	0.0001	−0.0091
4.8	−0.0075	0.0089	0.0007	−0.0082
4.9	−0.0059	0.0087	0.0014	−0.0073
5.0	−0.0046	0.0084	0.0019	−0.0065
5.1	−0.0033	0.0080	0.0023	−0.0057
5.2	−0.0023	0.0075	0.0026	−0.0049
5.3	−0.0014	0.0069	0.0028	−0.0042
5.4	−0.0006	0.0064	0.0029	−0.0035
5.5	0.0000	0.0058	0.0029	−0.0029
5.6	0.0005	0.0052	0.0029	−0.0023
5.7	0.0010	0.0046	0.0028	−0.0018
5.8	0.0013	0.0041	0.0027	−0.0014
5.9	0.0015	0.0036	0.0026	−0.0010
6.0	0.0017	0.0031	0.0024	−0.0007
6.1	0.0018	0.0026	0.0022	−0.0004
6.2	0.0019	0.0022	0.0020	−0.0002
6.3	0.0019	0.0018	0.0018	+0.0001
6.4	0.0018	0.0015	0.0017	0.0003
6.5	0.0018	0.0012	0.0015	0.0004
6.6	0.0017	0.0009	0.0013	0.0005
6.7	0.0016	0.0006	0.0011	0.0006
6.8	0.0015	0.0004	0.0010	0.0006
6.9	0.0014	0.0002	0.0008	0.0006
7.0	0.0013	0.0001	0.0007	0.0006

The numerical values of the functions $\varphi(\beta x)$, $\psi(\beta x)$, $\theta(\beta x)$ and $\zeta(\beta x)$ are given in Table 45.[1] The functions $\varphi(\beta x)$ and $\psi(\beta x)$ are represented graphically in Fig. 157. It is seen from these curves and from Table 45 that the functions defining the bending of the shell approach zero as the quantity βx becomes large. This indicates that the bending produced in the shell is actually of a

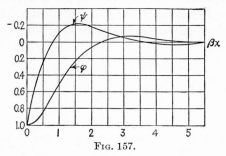

Fig. 157.

local character, as was assumed at the beginning when the constants of integration were calculated.

If the moment M_x and the deflection w are found from expressions (236), the bending moment M_φ is obtained from the first of the equations (*f*), and the value of the force N_φ from Eqs. (*e*). Thus all necessary information for calculating stresses in the shell can be found.

82. Particular Cases of Symmetrical Deformation of Circular Cylindrical Shells. *Bending of a Long Cylindrical Shell by a Load*

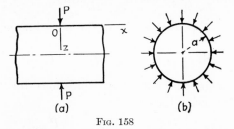

Fig. 158

Uniformly Distributed along a Circular Section (Fig. 158).—If the load is far enough from the ends of the cylinder, solution (232) can be used for each half of the shell. From considerations of symmetry we conclude that the value of Q_0 in this case is $-P/2$.

---

[1] The figures in this table are taken from the book by H. Zimmermann, "Die Berechnung des Eisenbahnoberbaues," Berlin, 1888.

We thus obtain for the right-hand portion

$$w = \frac{e^{-\beta x}}{2\beta^3 D}\left[\beta M_0(\sin \beta x - \cos \beta x) + \frac{P}{2} \cos \beta x\right], \qquad (a)$$

where x is measured from the cross section at which the load is applied.   To calculate the moment M_0 which appears in expression (a) we use expression (234) which gives the slope at $x = 0$. In our case this slope vanishes because of symmetry.   Hence,

$$2\beta M_0 - \frac{P}{2} = 0,$$

and we obtain

$$M_0 = \frac{P}{4\beta}. \qquad (b)$$

Substituting this value in expression (a), the deflection of the shell becomes

$$w = \frac{Pe^{-\beta x}}{8\beta^3 D}(\sin \beta x + \cos \beta x) = \frac{P}{8\beta^3 D}\varphi(\beta x), \qquad (237)$$

and by differentiation we find

$$\left.\begin{aligned}
\frac{dw}{dx} &= -2\beta\frac{P}{8\beta^3 D}e^{-\beta x}\sin \beta x = -\frac{P}{4\beta^2 D}\zeta(\beta x),\\
\frac{d^2w}{dx^2} &= 2\beta^2\frac{P}{8\beta^3 D}e^{-\beta x}(\sin \beta x - \cos \beta x) = -\frac{P}{4\beta D}\psi(\beta x),\\
\frac{d^3w}{dx^3} &= 4\beta^3\frac{P}{8\beta^3 D}e^{-\beta x}\cos \beta x = \frac{P}{2D}\theta(\beta x).
\end{aligned}\right\} \qquad (c)$$

Observing from Eqs. (b) and (f) of the preceding article that

$$M_x = -D\frac{d^2w}{dx^2}, \qquad Q_x = -D\frac{d^3w}{dx^3},$$

we finally obtain the following expressions for the bending moment and shearing force:

$$M_x = \frac{P}{4\beta}\psi(\beta x), \qquad Q_x = -\frac{P}{2}\theta(\beta x). \qquad (238)$$

The results obtained are all graphically represented in Fig. 159. It is seen that the maximum deflection is under the load P and that its value as given by Eq. (237) is

$$w_{\text{max.}} = \frac{P}{8\beta^3 D} = \frac{Pa^2\beta}{2Eh}. \qquad (239)$$

The maximum bending moment is also under the load and is determined from Eq. (238) as

$$M_{\text{max.}} = \frac{P}{4\beta}.$$ (240)

The maximum of the absolute value of the shearing force is

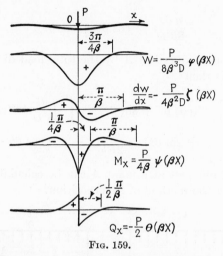

$$W = -\frac{P}{8\beta^3 D}\,\varphi(\beta x)$$

$$\frac{dw}{dx} = -\frac{P}{4\beta^2 D}\,\zeta\,(\beta x)$$

$$M_x = \frac{P}{4\beta}\,\psi\,(\beta x)$$

$$Q_x = -\frac{P}{2}\,\theta(\beta x)$$

Fig. 159.

evidently equal to $P/2$. The values of all these quantities at a certain distance from the load can be readily obtained by using Table 45. We see from this table and from Fig. 159 that all the quantities that determine the bending of the shell are small for $x > \pi/\beta$. This fact indicates that the bending is of a local character and that a shell of length $l = 2\pi/\beta$ loaded at the middle will have practically the same maximum deflection and the same maximum stress as a very long shell.

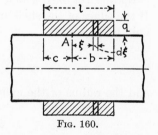

Fig. 160.

Having the solution of the problem for the case in which a load is concentrated at a circular cross section, we can readily solve the problem of a load distributed along a certain length of the cylinder by applying the principle of superposition. As an example let us consider the case of a uniform load of intensity q uniformly distributed along a length l of a cylinder (Fig. 160).

Assuming that the load is at a considerable distance from the ends of the cylinder, we can use solution (237) to calculate the deflections. The deflection at a point A produced by an elementary ring load of an intensity[1] $q \, d\xi$ at a distance ξ from A is obtained from expression (237) by substituting $q \, d\xi$ for P and ξ for x and is

$$\frac{q \, d\xi}{8\beta^3 D} e^{-\beta\xi}(\cos \beta\xi + \sin \beta\xi).$$

The deflection produced at A by the total load distributed over the length l is then

$$w = \int_0^b \frac{q \, d\xi}{8\beta^3 D} e^{-\beta\xi}(\cos \beta\xi + \sin \beta\xi) + \int_0^c \frac{q \, d\xi}{8\beta^3 D} e^{-\beta\xi}(\cos \beta\xi + \sin \beta\xi) = \frac{qa^2}{2Eh}(2 - e^{-\beta b} \cos \beta b - e^{-\beta c} \cos \beta c).$$

The bending moment at a point A can be calculated by similar application of the method of superposition.

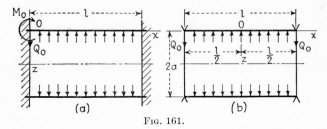

Fig. 161.

Cylindrical Shell with a Uniform Internal Pressure (Fig. 161).— If the edges of the shell are free, the internal pressure p produces only a hoop stress

$$\sigma_t = \frac{pa}{h}$$

and the radius of the cylinder increases by the amount

$$\delta = \frac{a\sigma_t}{E} = \frac{pa^2}{Eh}. \qquad (d)$$

If the ends of the shell are built in, as shown in Fig. 161a, they cannot move out, and local bending occurs at the edges. If the

---

[1] $q \, d\xi$ is the load per unit length of circumference.

length l of the shell is sufficiently large, we can use solution (232) to investigate this bending, the moment M_0 and the shearing force Q_0 being determined from the conditions that the deflection and the slope along the built-in edge $x = 0$ (Fig. 161a) vanish. According to these conditions, Eqs. (233) and (234) of the preceding article become

$$-\frac{1}{2\beta^3 D}(\beta M_0 + Q_0) = \delta,$$

$$\frac{1}{2\beta^2 D}(2\beta M_0 + Q_0) = 0,$$

where δ is given by Eq. (d).

Solving for M_0 and Q_0, we obtain

$$M_0 = 2\beta^2 \, D\delta = \frac{p}{2\beta^2}, \qquad Q_0 = -4\beta^3 \, D\delta = -\frac{p}{\beta}. \qquad (241)$$

We thus obtain a positive bending moment and a negative shearing force acting as shown in Fig. 161a. Substituting these values in expressions (236), the deflection and the bending moment at any distance from the end can be readily calculated by the use of Table 45.

If, instead of built-in edges, we have simply supported edges as shown in Fig. 161b, the deflection and the bending moment M_x vanish along the edge, $M_0 = 0$, and we obtain, by using Eqs. (233),

$$Q_0 = -2\beta^3 \, D\delta.$$

By substituting these values in solution (232) the deflection at any distance from the end can be calculated.

It was assumed in the preceding discussion that the length of the shell is large. If this is not the case, the bending at one end cannot be considered as independent of the conditions at the other end, and recourse must be had to the general solution (231) which contains four constants of integration. The particular solution of Eq. (230) for the case of uniform load ($Z = -p$) is $-p/4\beta^4 D = -pa^2/Eh$. The general solution (231) can then be put in the following form by the introduction of hyperbolic functions in place of the exponential functions:

$$w = -\frac{pa^2}{Eh} + C_1 \sin \beta x \sinh \beta x + C_2 \sin \beta x \cosh \beta x$$
$$+ C_3 \cos \beta x \sinh \beta x + C_4 \cos \beta x \cosh \beta x. \qquad (e)$$

If the origin of coordinates is taken at the middle of the cylinder, as shown in Fig. 161b, expression (e) must be an even function of x. Hence,

$$C_2 = C_3 = 0. \tag{f}$$

The constants C_1 and C_4 must now be selected so as to satisfy the conditions at the ends. If the ends are simply supported, the deflection and the bending moment M_x must vanish at the ends, and we obtain

$$(w)_{x=\frac{l}{2}} = 0, \qquad \left(\frac{d^2w}{dx^2}\right)_{x=\frac{l}{2}} = 0. \tag{g}$$

Substituting expression (e) in these relations and remembering that $C_2 = C_3 = 0$, we find

$$\left.\begin{aligned} -\frac{pa^2}{Eh} + C_1 \sin \alpha \sinh \alpha + C_4 \cos \alpha \cosh \alpha &= 0, \\ C_1 \cos \alpha \cosh \alpha - C_4 \sin \alpha \sinh \alpha &= 0, \end{aligned}\right\} \tag{h}$$

where, for the sake of simplicity,

$$\frac{\beta l}{2} = \alpha. \tag{i}$$

From these equations we obtain

$$\left.\begin{aligned} C_1 &= \frac{pa^2}{Eh} \frac{\sin \alpha \sinh \alpha}{\sin^2 \alpha \sinh^2 \alpha + \cos^2 \alpha \cosh^2 \alpha} \\ &\qquad\qquad = \frac{pa^2}{Eh} \frac{2 \sin \alpha \sinh \alpha}{\cos 2\alpha + \cosh 2\alpha}, \\ C_4 &= \frac{pa^2}{Eh} \frac{\cos \alpha \cosh \alpha}{\sin^2 \alpha \sinh^2 \alpha + \cos^2 \alpha \cosh^2 \alpha} \\ &\qquad\qquad = \frac{pa^2}{Eh} \frac{2 \cos \alpha \cosh \alpha}{\cos 2\alpha + \cosh 2\alpha}. \end{aligned}\right\} \tag{j}$$

Substituting the values (j) and (f) of the constants in expression (e) and observing from expression (229) that

$$\frac{Eh}{a^2} = 4 D\beta^4 = \frac{64\alpha^4 D}{l^4}, \tag{k}$$

we obtain

$$w = -\frac{pl^4}{64D\alpha^4}\left(1 - \frac{2 \sin \alpha \sinh \alpha}{\cos 2\alpha + \cosh 2\alpha} \sin \beta x \sinh \beta x \right.$$
$$\left. - \frac{2 \cos \alpha \cosh \alpha}{\cos 2\alpha + \cosh 2\alpha} \cos \beta x \cosh \beta x\right). \tag{l}$$

In each particular case, if the dimensions of the shell are known, the quantity α, which is dimensionless, can be calculated by means of the notation (i) and (229).   By substituting this value in expression (l) the deflection of the shell at any point can be found.

For the middle of the shell, substituting $x = 0$ in expression (l), we obtain

$$(w)_{x=0} = -\frac{pl^4}{64D\alpha^4}\left(1 - \frac{2\cos\alpha\cosh\alpha}{\cos 2\alpha + \cosh 2\alpha}\right). \qquad (m)$$

When the shell is long, α becomes large, the second term in the parenthesis of expression (m) becomes small and the deflection approaches the value (d) calculated for the case of free ends. This indicates that in the case of long shells the effect of the end supports upon the deflection at the middle is negligible.   Taking another extreme case, $viz.$, the case when α is very small, we can show by expanding the trigonometric and hyperbolic functions in power series that the expression in parenthesis in Eq. (m) approaches the value $5\alpha^4/6$ and that the deflection (l) approaches that for a uniformly loaded and simply supported beam of length l and flexural rigidity D.

Differentiating expression (l) twice and multiplying it by D, the bending moment is found as

$$M_x = -D\frac{d^2w}{dx^2} = -\frac{pl^2}{4\alpha^2}\left(\frac{\sin\alpha\sinh\alpha}{\cos 2\alpha + \cosh 2\alpha}\cosh\beta x\cos\beta x\right.$$
$$\left. - \frac{\cos\alpha\cosh\alpha}{\cos 2\alpha + \cosh 2\alpha}\sin\beta x\sinh\beta x\right). \qquad (n)$$

At the middle of the shell this moment is

$$(M_x)_{x=0} = -\frac{pl^2}{4\alpha^2}\frac{\sin\alpha\sinh\alpha}{\cos 2\alpha + \cosh 2\alpha}. \qquad (o)$$

It is seen that for large values of α, $i.e.$, for long shells, this moment becomes negligibly small and the middle portion is, for all practical purposes, under the action of merely the hoop stresses pa/h.

The case of a cylinder with built-in edges (Fig. 161a) can be treated in a similar manner.   Going directly to the final result,[1]

---

[1] Both cases are discussed in detail by I. G. Boobnov in his "Theory of Structure of Ships," vol. 2, p. 368, St. Petersburg, 1913.   Also included are numerical tables which simplify the calculations of moments and deflections.

we see that the bending moment M_0 acting along the built-in edge is

$$M_0 = \frac{p}{2\beta^2} \cdot \frac{\sinh 2\alpha - \sin 2\alpha}{\sinh 2\alpha + \sin 2\alpha} = \frac{p}{2\beta^2}\chi_2(2\alpha), \qquad (242)$$

where

$$\chi_2(2\alpha) = \frac{\sinh 2\alpha - \sin 2\alpha}{\sinh 2\alpha + \sin 2\alpha}.$$

In the case of long shells, α is large, the factor $\chi_2(2\alpha)$ in expression (242) approaches unity and the value of the moment approaches that given by the first of the expressions (241). For shorter shells the value of the factor $\chi_2(2\alpha)$ in (242) can be taken from Table 46.

TABLE 46

2α	$\chi_1(2\alpha)$	$\chi_2(2\alpha)$	$\chi_3(2\alpha)$
0.2	5.000	0.0068	0.100
0.4	2.502	0.0268	0.200
0.6	1.674	0.0601	0.300
0.8	1.267	0.1065	0.400
1.0	1.033	0.1670	0.500
1.2	0.890	0.2370	0.596
1.4	0.803	0.3170	0.689
1.6	0.755	0.4080	0.775
1.8	0.735	0.5050	0.855
2.0	0.738	0.6000	0.925
2.5	0.802	0.8220	1.045
3.0	0.893	0.9770	1.090
3.5	0.966	1.0500	1.085
4.0	1.005	1.0580	1.050
4.5	1.017	1.0400	1.027
5.0	1.017	1.0300	1.008

Cylindrical Shell Bent by Forces and Moments Distributed along the Edges.—In the preceding section this problem was discussed assuming that the shell is long and that each end can be treated independently. In the case of shorter shells both ends must be considered simultaneously by using solution (e) with four constants of integration. Proceeding as in the previous cases, the following results can be obtained: For the case of bending by uniformly distributed shearing forces Q_0 (Fig. 162a) the deflection and the slope at the ends are

$$(w)_{x=0,x=l} = -\frac{2Q_0\beta a^2}{Eh} \cdot \frac{\cosh 2\alpha + \cos 2\alpha}{\sinh 2\alpha + \sin 2\alpha}$$

$$= -\frac{2Q_0\beta a^2}{Eh}\chi_1(2\alpha),$$

$$\left(\frac{dw}{dx}\right)_{x=0,x=l} = \pm\frac{2Q_0\beta^2 a^2}{Eh} \cdot \frac{\sinh 2\alpha - \sin 2\alpha}{\sinh 2\alpha + \sin 2\alpha}$$

$$= \pm\frac{2Q_0\beta^2 a^2}{Eh}\chi_2(2\alpha). \tag{243}$$

In the case of bending by the moments M_0 (Fig. 162b) we obtain

$$(w)_{x=0,x=l} = -\frac{2M_0\beta^2 a^2}{Eh} \cdot \frac{\sinh 2\alpha - \sin 2\alpha}{\sinh 2\alpha + \sin 2\alpha}$$

$$= -\frac{2M_0\beta^2 a^2}{Eh}\chi_2(2\alpha),$$

$$\left(\frac{dw}{dx}\right)_{x=0,x=l} = \pm\frac{4M_0\beta^3 a^2}{Eh} \cdot \frac{\cosh 2\alpha - \cos 2\alpha}{\sinh 2\alpha + \sin 2\alpha}$$

$$= \pm\frac{4M_0\beta^3 a^2}{Eh}\chi_3(2\alpha). \tag{244}$$

In the case of long shells the factors χ_1, χ_2 and χ_3 in expressions (243) and (244) are close to unity, and the results coincide

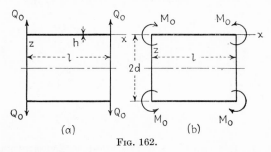

Fig. 162.

with those given by expressions (233) and (234). To simplify the calculations for shorter shells, the values of functions χ_1, χ_2 and χ_3 are given in Table 46.

Using solutions (243) and (244), the stresses in a long pipe reinforced by equidistant rings (Fig. 163) and submitted to the action of uniform internal pressure p can be readily discussed.

Assume first that there are no rings. Then, under the action of internal pressure, hoop stresses $\sigma_t = pa/h$ will be produced, and the radius of the pipe will increase by the amount

$$\delta = \frac{pa^2}{Eh}.$$

Now, taking the rings into consideration and assuming that they are absolutely rigid, we conclude that reactive forces will be produced between each ring and the pipe.   The magnitude of the forces per unit length of the circumference of the tube will be denoted by P.   The magnitude of P will now be determined

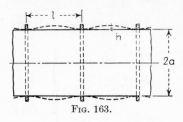

FIG. 163.

from the condition that the forces P produce a deflection of the pipe under the ring equal to the expansion δ created by the internal pressure p.   In calculating this deflection we observe that a portion of the tube between two adjacent rings may be considered as the shell shown in Figs. 162a and 162b.   In this case $Q_0 = -\frac{1}{2}P$, and the magnitude of the bending moment M_0 under a ring is determined from the condition that $dw/dx = 0$ at that point.   Hence from Eqs. (243) and (244) we find

$$-\frac{P\beta^2 a^2}{Eh}\chi_2(2\alpha) + \frac{4M_0\beta^3 a^2}{Eh}\chi_3(2\alpha) = 0,$$

from which

$$M_0 = \frac{P\chi_2(2\alpha)}{4\beta\chi_3(2\alpha)}. \qquad (p)$$

If the distance l between the rings is large,[1] the quantity

$$2\alpha = \beta l = \frac{l}{\sqrt{ah}}\sqrt[4]{3(1 - \nu^2)}$$

is also large, the functions $\chi_2(2\alpha)$ and $\chi_3(2\alpha)$ approach unity and the moment M_0 approaches the value (240).   For calculating the force P entering in Eq. (p) the expressions for deflections as given in Eqs. (243) and (244) must be used.   These expressions give

$$\frac{P\beta a^2}{Eh}\chi_1(2\alpha) - \frac{P\beta a^2}{2Eh}\frac{\chi_2^2(2\alpha)}{\chi_3(2\alpha)} = \delta = \frac{pa^2}{Eh},$$

[1] For $\nu = 0.3$, $2\alpha = 1.285l/\sqrt{ah}$.

or

$$P\beta\left[\chi_1(2\alpha) - \frac{1}{2}\frac{\chi_2^2(2\alpha)}{\chi_3(2\alpha)}\right] = \frac{\delta Eh}{a^2} = p. \qquad (245)$$

For large values of 2α this reduces to

$$\frac{P\beta a^2}{2Eh} = \delta,$$

which coincides with Eq. (239). When 2α is not large, the value of the reactive forces P is calculated from Eq. (245) by using Table 46. Solving Eq. (245) for P and substituting its expression in expression (p), we find

$$M_0 = \frac{p}{2\beta^2}\chi_2(2\alpha). \qquad (246)$$

This coincides with expression (242) previously obtained for a shell with built-in edges.

To take into account the extension of rings we observe that the reactive forces P produce in the ring a tensile force Pa and that the corresponding increase of the inner radius of the ring is[1]

$$\delta_1 = \frac{Pa^2}{AE},$$

where A is the cross-sectional area of the ring. To take this extension into account we substitute $\delta - \delta_1$, instead of δ, in Eq. (245) and obtain

$$P\beta\left[\chi_1(2\alpha) - \frac{1}{2}\frac{\chi_2^2(2\alpha)}{\chi_3(2\alpha)}\right] = p - \frac{Ph}{A}. \qquad (247)$$

From this equation, P can be readily obtained by using Table 46, and the moment found by substituting $p - (Ph/A)$, instead of p, in Eq. (246).

If the pressure p acts not only on the cylindrical shell but also on the ends, longitudinal forces

$$N_x = \frac{pa}{2}$$

---

[1] It is assumed that the cross-sectional dimensions of the ring are small in comparison with the radius a.

are produced in the shell. The extension of the radius of the cylinder is then

$$\delta' = \frac{pa^2}{Eh}\left(1 - \frac{1}{2}\nu\right),$$

and the quantity $p(1 - \frac{1}{2}\nu)$ instead of p must be substituted in Eqs. (246) and (247).

Equations (247) and (245) can be also used in the case of external uniform pressure provided the compressive stresses in the ring and in the shell are far enough from the critical stresses at which buckling may occur.[1] This case is of practical importance in the design of submarines and has been discussed by several authors.[2]

83. Pressure Vessels.—The method illustrated by the examples of the preceding article can also be applied in the

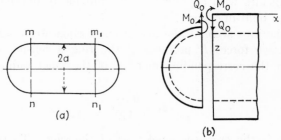

Fig. 164.

analysis of stresses in cylindrical vessels submitted to the action of internal pressure. In discussing the "membrane theory" it was repeatedly indicated that this theory fails to represent the true stresses in those portions of a shell close to the edges, since the edge conditions usually cannot be completely satisfied by considering only membrane stresses. A similar condition in which the membrane theory is inadequate is found in cylindrical pressure vessels at the joints between the cylindrical portion and the ends of the vessel. At these joints the membrane stresses are usually accompanied by local bending stresses which are

[1] Buckling of rings and cylindrical shells is discussed in the author's book "Theory of Elastic Stability."

[2] See paper by K. von Sanden and K. Günther, "Werft und Reederei," vol. 1, 1920, pp. 163–168, 189–198, 216–221, and vol. 2, 1921, pp. 505–510.

distri$\mathfrak{t}$ uted symmetrically with respect to the axis of the cylinder. These local stresses can be calculated by using solution (232) of Art. 81.

Let us begin with the simple case of a cylindrical vessel with hemispherical ends (Fig. 164).[1] At a sufficient distance from the joints mn and m_1n_1 the membrane theory is accurate enough and gives for the cylindrical portion of radius a

$$N_x = \frac{pa}{2}, \qquad N_t = pa. \qquad (a)$$

where p denotes the internal pressure.

For the spherical ends this theory gives a uniform tensile force

$$N = \frac{pa}{2}. \qquad (b)$$

The extension of the radius of the cylindrical shell under the action of the forces (a) is

$$\delta_1 = \frac{pa^2}{Eh}\left(1 - \frac{\nu}{2}\right), \qquad (c)$$

and the extension of the radius of the spherical ends is

$$\delta_2 = \frac{pa^2}{2Eh}(1 - \nu). \qquad (d)$$

Comparing expressions (c) and (d), it can be concluded that if we consider only membrane stresses we obtain a discontinuity at the joints as represented in Fig. 164b. This indicates that at the joint there must act shearing forces Q_0 and bending moments M_0 uniformly distributed along the circumference and of such magnitudes as to eliminate this discontinuity. The stresses produced by these forces are sometimes called *discontinuity stresses*.

In calculating the quantities Q_0 and M_0 we assume that the bending is of a local character so that solution (232) can be applied with sufficient accuracy in discussing the bending of the cylindrical portion. The investigation of the bending of the spherical ends represents a more complicated problem which will be fully discussed in Chap. XII. Here we obtain an approxi-

---

[1] This case was discussed by E. Meissner, *Schweiz. Bauzeitung*, vol. 86, p. 1, 1925.

mate solution of the problem by assuming that the bending is of importance only in the zone of the spherical shell close to the joint and that this zone can be treated as a portion of a long cylindrical shell[1] of radius a. If the thickness of the spherical and the cylindrical portion of the vessel is the same, the forces Q_0 produce equal rotations of the edges of both portions at the joint (Fig. 164b). This indicates that M_0 vanishes and that Q_0 alone is sufficient to eliminate the discontinuity. The magnitude of Q_0 is now determined from the condition that the sum of the numerical values of the deflections of the edges of the two parts must be equal to the difference $\delta_1 - \delta_2$ of the radial expansions furnished by the membrane theory. Using Eq. (233) for the deflections, we obtain

$$\frac{Q_0}{\beta^3 D} = \delta_1 - \delta_2 = \frac{pa^2}{2Eh},$$

from which, by using notation (229),

$$Q_0 = \frac{pa^2\beta^3 D}{2Eh} = \frac{p}{8\beta}. \tag{e}$$

Having obtained this value of the force Q_0, the deflection and the bending moment M_x can be calculated at any point by using formulas (236) which give[2]

$$w = \frac{Q_0}{2\beta^3 D}\theta(\beta x),$$

$$M_x = -D\frac{d^2 w}{dx^2} = -\frac{Q_0}{\beta}\zeta(\beta x).$$

Substituting expression (e) for Q_0 and expression (229) for β in the formula for M_x, we obtain

$$M_x = -\frac{ahp}{8\sqrt{3(1 - \nu^2)}}\zeta(\beta x). \tag{f}$$

This moment attains its numerical maximum at the distance

[1] E. Meissner, in the above-mentioned paper, showed that the error in the magnitude of the bending stresses as calculated from such an approximate solution is small for thin hemispherical shells and is smaller than 1 per cent if $a/h > 30$.

[2] Note that the direction of Q_0 in Fig. 164 is opposite to the direction in Fig. 156.

$x = \pi/4\beta$, at which point the derivative of the moment is zero, as can be seen from the fourth of the equations (236).

Combining the maximum bending stress produced by M_x with the membrane stress, we find

$$(\sigma_x)_{\text{max.}} = \frac{ap}{2h} + \frac{3}{4}\frac{ap}{h\sqrt{3(1-\nu^2)}}\varsigma\left(\frac{\pi}{4}\right) = 1.293\frac{ap}{2h}. \qquad (g)$$

This stress which acts at the outer surface of the cylindrical shell is about 30 per cent larger than the membrane stress acting in the axial direction. In calculating stresses in the circumferential direction in addition to the membrane stress pa/h, the hoop stress caused by the deflection w as well as the bending stress produced by the moment $M_\varphi = \nu M_x$ must be considered. In this way we obtain at the outer surface of the cylindrical shell

$$\sigma_t = \frac{ap}{h} - \frac{Ew}{a} - \frac{6\nu}{h^2}M_x = \frac{ap}{h}\left(1 - \frac{1}{4}\theta(\beta x) + \frac{3\nu}{4\sqrt{3(1-\nu^2)}}\varsigma(\beta x)\right).$$

Taking $\nu = 0.3$ and using Table 45, we find

$$(\sigma_t)_{\text{max.}} = 1.032\frac{ap}{h} \qquad \text{at} \qquad \beta x = 1.85. \qquad (h)$$

Since the membrane stress is smaller in the ends than in the cylinder sides, the maximum stress in the spherical ends is always smaller than the calculated stress (h). Thus the latter stress is the determining factor in the design of the vessel.

The same method of calculating discontinuity stresses can be applied in the case of ends having the form of an ellipsoid of revolution. The membrane stresses in this case are obtained from expressions (217) and (218) (see page 365). At the joint mn which represents the equator

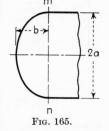

FIG. 165.

of the ellipsoid, Fig. 165, the stresses in the direction of the meridian and in the equatorial direction are, respectively,

$$\sigma_\varphi = \frac{pa}{2h}, \qquad \sigma_\theta = \frac{pa}{h}\left(1 - \frac{a^2}{2b^2}\right). \qquad (i)$$

The extension of the radius of the equator is

$$\delta_2' = \frac{a}{E}(\sigma_\theta - \nu\sigma_\varphi) = \frac{pa^2}{Eh}\left(1 - \frac{a^2}{2b^2} - \frac{\nu}{2}\right).$$

Substituting this quantity instead of δ_2 in the previous calculation of the shearing force Q_0, we find

$$\delta_1 - \delta_2' = \frac{pa^2}{Eh}\frac{a^2}{2b^2};$$

and instead of Eq. (e), we obtain

$$Q_0 = \frac{p}{8\beta} \cdot \frac{a^2}{b^2}.$$

It is seen that the shearing force Q_0 in the case of ellipsoidal ends is larger than in the case of hemispherical ends in the ratio a^2/b^2. The discontinuity stresses will evidently increase in the same proportion. For example, taking $a/b = 2$, we obtain, from expressions (g) and (h),

$$(\sigma_x)_{\text{max.}} = \frac{ap}{2h} + \frac{3ap}{h\sqrt{3(1-\nu^2)}}\zeta\left(\frac{\pi}{4}\right) = 2.172\frac{ap}{2h},$$

$$(\sigma_t)_{\text{max.}} = 1.128\frac{ap}{h}.$$

Again, $(\sigma_t)_{\text{max.}}$ is the largest stress and is consequently the determining factor in design.[1]

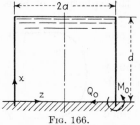

Fig. 166.

84. Cylindrical Tanks with Uniform Wall Thickness.—If a tank is submitted to the action of a liquid pressure, as shown in Fig. 166, the stresses in the wall can be analyzed by using Eq. (230). Substituting in this equation

$$Z = -\gamma(d - x), \qquad (a)$$

where γ is the weight per unit volume of the liquid, we obtain

$$\frac{d^4w}{dx^4} + 4\beta^4w = -\frac{\gamma(d - x)}{D}. \qquad (b)$$

[1] More detail regarding stresses in boilers with ellipsoidal ends can be found in the book by Höhn, "Über die Festigkeit der gewölbten Böden und der Zylinderschale," Zürich, 1927. Also included are the results of experimental investigations of discontinuity stresses which are in a good agreement with the approximate solution. See also F. Schulz-Grunow, *Ingenieur-Archiv*, vol. 4, p. 545, 1933.

A particular solution of this equation is

$$w_1 = -\frac{\gamma(d-x)}{4\beta^4 D} = -\frac{\gamma(d-x)a^2}{Eh}. \tag{c}$$

This expression represents the radial expansion of a cylindrical shell with free edges under the action of hoop stresses. Substituting expression (c) in place of $f(x)$ in expression (231), we obtain for the complete solution of Eq. (b)

$$w = e^{\beta x}(C_1 \cos \beta x + C_2 \sin \beta x) + e^{-\beta x}(C_3 \cos \beta x + C_4 \sin \beta x)$$
$$- \frac{\gamma(d-x)a^2}{Eh}.$$

In most practical cases the wall thickness h is small in comparison with both the radius a and the depth d of the tank, and we may consider the shell as infinitely long. The constants C_1 and C_2 are then equal to zero, and we obtain

$$w = e^{-\beta x}(C_3 \cos \beta x + C_4 \sin \beta x) - \frac{\gamma(d-x)a^2}{Eh}. \tag{d}$$

The constants C_3 and C_4 can now be obtained from the conditions at the bottom of the tank. Assuming that the lower edge of the wall is built into an absolutely rigid foundation, the boundary conditions are

$$(w)_{x=0} = C_3 - \frac{\gamma a^2 d}{Eh} = 0,$$

$$\left(\frac{dw}{dx}\right)_{x=0} = \left[-\beta C_3 e^{-\beta x}(\cos \beta x + \sin \beta x) \right.$$
$$+ \beta C_4 e^{-\beta x}(\cos \beta x - \sin \beta x) + \frac{\gamma a^2}{Eh}\bigg]_{x=0} = \beta(C_4 - C_3) + \frac{\gamma a^2}{Eh} = 0.$$

From these equations we obtain

$$C_3 = \frac{\gamma a^2 d}{Eh}, \qquad C_4 = \frac{\gamma a^2}{Eh}\left(d - \frac{1}{\beta}\right).$$

Expression (d) then becomes

$$w = -\frac{\gamma a^2}{Eh}\left\{ d - x - e^{-\beta x}\left[d \cos \beta x + \left(d - \frac{1}{\beta}\right)\sin \beta x\right]\right\},$$

from which, by using the notation of (235), we obtain

$$w = -\frac{\gamma a^2 d}{Eh}\left[1 - \frac{x}{d} - \theta(\beta x) - \left(1 - \frac{1}{\beta d}\right)\zeta(\beta x)\right]. \tag{e}$$

From this expression the deflection at any point can be readily calculated by the use of Table 45. The force N_φ in the circumferential direction is then

$$N_\varphi = -\frac{Ehw}{a} = \gamma ad\left[1 - \frac{x}{d} - \theta(\beta x) - \left(1 - \frac{1}{\beta d}\right)\zeta(\beta x)\right]. \quad (f)$$

From the second derivative of expression (e) we obtain the bending moment

$$M_x = -D\frac{d^2w}{dx^2} = \frac{2\beta^2\gamma a^2\,Dd}{Eh}\left[-\zeta(\beta x) + \left(1 - \frac{1}{\beta d}\right)\theta(\beta x)\right]$$

$$= \frac{\gamma adh}{\sqrt{12(1 - \nu^2)}}\left[-\zeta(\beta x) + \left(1 - \frac{1}{\beta d}\right)\theta(\beta x)\right]. \quad (g)$$

Having expressions (f) and (g), the maximum stress at any point can readily be calculated in each particular case. The bending moment has its maximum value at the bottom, where it is equal to

$$(M_x)_{x=0} = M_0 = \left(1 - \frac{1}{\beta d}\right)\frac{\gamma adh}{\sqrt{12(1 - \nu^2)}}. \quad (h)$$

The same result can be obtained by using previous solutions (233) and (234) (page 393). Assuming that the lower edge of the shell is entirely free, we obtain from expression (c)

$$(w_1)_{x=0} = -\frac{\gamma a^2 d}{Eh}, \qquad \left(\frac{dw_1}{dx}\right)_{x=0} = \frac{\gamma a^2}{Eh}. \quad (i)$$

To eliminate this displacement and rotation of the edge and thus satisfy the edge conditions at the bottom of the tank, a shearing force Q_0 and bending moment M_0 must be applied as indicated in Fig. 166. The magnitude of each of these quantities is obtained by equating expressions (233) and (234) to expressions (i) taken with reversed signs. This gives

$$-\frac{1}{2\beta^3 D}(\beta M_0 + Q_0) = +\frac{\gamma a^2 d}{Eh},$$

$$\frac{1}{2\beta^2 D}(2\beta M_0 + Q_0) = -\frac{\gamma a^2}{Eh}.$$

From these equations we again obtain expression (h) for M_0, whereas for the shearing force we find[1]

---

[1] The negative sign indicates that Q_0 has the direction shown in Fig. 166, which is opposite to the direction used in Fig. 156 when deriving expressions (233) and (234).

$$Q_0 = -\frac{\gamma a d h}{\sqrt{12(1 - \nu^2)}}\left(2\beta - \frac{1}{d}\right).$$ (j)

Taking, as an example, $a = 30$ ft., $d = 26$ ft., $h = 14$ in., $\gamma = 0.03613$ lb. per cubic inch and $\nu = 0.25$, we find $\beta = 0.01824$ in.$^{-1}$ and $\beta d = 5.691$. For such a value of the quantity βd our assumption that the shell is infinitely long will result in a very accurate value for the moment and the shearing force, and we obtain from expressions (h) and (j)

$$M_0 = 13960 \text{ in. lb. per inch}, \qquad Q_0 = -563.6 \text{ lb. per inch}.$$

In the construction of steel tanks, metallic sheets of several different thicknesses are very often used as shown in Fig. 167. Applying the particular solution (c) to each portion of uniform thickness, we find that the differences in thickness give rise to discontinuities in the displacement w_1 along the joints mn and $m_1 n_1$. These discontinuities together with the displacements at the bottom ab can be removed by applying moments and shearing forces. Assuming that the vertical dimension of each portion is sufficiently large to justify the application of the formulas for an infinitely large shell, we calculate the discontinuity moments and shearing forces as before by using Eqs. (233) and (234) and applying at each joint the two conditions that the adjacent portions of the shell have equal deflections and a common tangent. If the

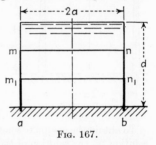

Fig. 167.

use of formulas (233) and (234) derived for an infinitely long shell cannot be justified, the general solution containing four constants of integration must be applied to each portion of the tank. The determination of the constants under such conditions becomes much more complicated, since the fact that each joint cannot be treated independently necessitates the solution of a system of simultaneous equations. This problem can be solved by approximate methods.[1]

85. Cylindrical Tanks with Non-uniform Wall Thickness.—In the case of tanks of non-uniform wall thickness the solution of the problem requires the integration of Eq. (227), considering the flexural rigidity D and the thickness h as no longer constant but as functions of x. We have thus to deal with a linear differential equation of fourth order with variable coefficients. As an example, let us consider the case when the thickness of the wall is a linear function of the coordinate x.[2] Taking the origin of the coordinates as shown in Fig. 168, we have for the thickness of the wall and for the flexural rigidity the expressions

[1] An approximate method of solving this problem was given by C. Runge, *Z. Math. Physik*, vol. 51, p. 254, 1904. This method was applied by Karl Girkmann in a design of a large welded tank, *Der Stahlbau*, vol. 4, p. 25, 1931.

[2] REISSNER, H., "Beton und Eisen," vol. 7, p. 150, 1908; see also W. Flügge, "Statik und Dynamik der Schalen," p. 132, Berlin, 1934.

$$h = \alpha x; \qquad D = \frac{E\alpha^3}{12(1 - \nu^2)}x^3; \qquad (a)$$

and Eq. (227) becomes

$$\frac{d^2}{dx^2}\left(x^3\frac{d^2w}{dx^2}\right) + \frac{12(1 - \nu^2)}{\alpha^2a^2}xw = -\frac{12(1 - \nu^2)\gamma(x - x_0)}{E\alpha^3}. \qquad (b)$$

The particular solution of this equation is

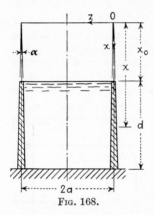

$$w_1 = -\frac{\gamma a^2}{E\alpha}\frac{x - x_0}{x}. \qquad (c)$$

This solution represents the radial expansion of a shell with free edges under the internal pressure $\gamma(x - x_0)$. As a result of the displacement (c) a certain amount of bending of the generatrices of the cylinder occurs. The corresponding bending moment is

$$M_x = -D\frac{d^2w_1}{dx^2} = -\frac{\gamma\alpha^2a^2x_0}{6(1 - \nu^2)}. \qquad (d)$$

← 2a →

Fig. 168.

This moment is independent of x and is in all practical cases of such small magnitude that its action can usually be neglected.

To obtain the complete solution of Eq. (b) we have to add to the particular solution (c) the solution of the homogeneous equation

$$\frac{d^2}{dx^2}\left(x^3\frac{d^2w}{dx^2}\right) + \frac{12(1 - \nu^2)}{\alpha^2a^2}xw = 0,$$

which, upon division by x, can be also written

$$\frac{1}{x}\frac{d^2}{dx^2}\left(x^3\frac{d^2w}{dx^2}\right) + \frac{12(1 - \nu^2)}{\alpha^2a^2}w = 0. \qquad (e)$$

The solution of this equation of the fourth order can be reduced to that of two equations of the second order[1] if we observe that

$$\frac{1}{x}\frac{d^2}{dx^2}\left(x^3\frac{d^2w}{dx^2}\right) = \frac{1}{x}\frac{d}{dx}\left\{x^2\frac{d}{dx}\left[\frac{1}{x}\frac{d}{dx}\left(x^2\frac{dw}{dx}\right)\right]\right\}.$$

To simplify the writing we introduce the following symbols

$$L(w) = \frac{1}{x}\frac{d}{dx}\left(x^2\frac{dw}{dx}\right), \qquad (f)$$

[1] This reduction was shown by G. Kirchhoff, "Berliner Monatsberichte," p. 815, 1879; see also I. Todhunter and K. Pearson, "A History of the Theory of Elasticity," vol. 2, part 2, p. 92.

$$\rho^4 = \frac{12(1 - \nu^2)}{\alpha^2 a^2}. \tag{g}$$

Equation (e) then becomes

$$L[L(w)] + \rho^4 w = 0 \tag{h}$$

and can be rewritten in one of the two following forms:

$$L[L(w) + i\rho^2 w] - i\rho^2[L(w) + i\rho^2 w] = 0, \tag{i}$$
$$L[L(w) - i\rho^2 w] + i\rho^2[L(w) - i\rho^2 w] = 0,$$

where $i = \sqrt{-1}$.

We see that Eq. (h) is satisfied by the solutions of the second-order equations

$$L(w) + i\rho^2 w = 0, \tag{j}$$
$$L(w) - i\rho^2 w = 0. \tag{k}$$

Assuming that

$$w_1 = \varphi_1 + i\varphi_2, \qquad w_2 = \varphi_3 + i\varphi_4 \tag{l}$$

are the two linearly independent solutions of Eq. (j), it can be seen that

$$w_3 = \varphi_1 - i\varphi_2 \quad \text{and} \quad w_4 = \varphi_3 - i\varphi_4 \tag{m}$$

are the solutions of Eq. (k). All four solutions (l) and (m) together then represent the complete system of independent solutions of Eq. (h). By using the sums and the differences of solutions (l) and (m), the general solution of Eq. (h) can be represented in the following form:

$$w = C_1\varphi_1 + C_2\varphi_2 + C_3\varphi_3 + C_4\varphi_4, \tag{n}$$

in which $C_1, \ldots, C_4$ are arbitrary constants. Thus the problem reduces to the determination of four functions $\varphi_1, \ldots, \varphi_4$ which can all be obtained if the complete solution of one of Eqs. (j) and (k) is known.

Taking Eq. (j) and substituting for $L(w)$ its meaning (f), we obtain

$$x\frac{d^2 w}{dx^2} + 2\frac{dw}{dx} + i\rho^2 w = 0. \tag{o}$$

By introducing new variables

$$\eta = 2\rho\sqrt{ix}, \qquad \zeta = w\sqrt{x}, \tag{p}$$

Eq. (o) becomes

$$\eta^2\frac{d^2\zeta}{d\eta^2} + \eta\frac{d\zeta}{d\eta} + (\eta^2 - 1)\zeta = 0. \tag{r}$$

We take as a solution of this equation the power series

$$\zeta_1 = a_0 + a_1\eta + a_2\eta^2 + \cdots, \tag{s}$$

Substituting this series in Eq. (r) and equating the coefficients of each power of η to zero, we obtain the following relation between the coefficients of series (s):

$$(n^2 - 1)a_n + a_{n-2} = 0. \tag{t}$$

Applying this equation to the first two coefficients and taking $a_{-1} = a_{-2} = 0$, we find that $a_0 = 0$ and that a_1 can be taken equal to any arbitrary constant. Calculating the further coefficients by means of Eq. (t), we find that series (s) is

$$\zeta = C'\frac{\eta}{2}\left(1 - \frac{\eta^2}{2\cdot 4} + \frac{\eta^4}{2\cdot 4\cdot 6} - \frac{\eta^6}{2\cdot(4\cdot 6)^2\cdot 8} + \cdots\right) = C'J_1(\eta), \tag{u}$$

where $J_1(\eta)$ is the Bessel function of the first kind and of the first order. For our further discussion it is advantageous to use the relation

$$J_1(\eta) = -\frac{d}{d\eta}\left[1 - \frac{\eta^2}{2^2} + \frac{\eta^4}{(2\cdot 4)^2} - \frac{\eta^6}{(2\cdot 4\cdot 6)^2} + \cdots\right] = -\frac{dJ_0}{d\eta}, \tag{v}$$

in which the series in the parenthesis, denoted by J_0, is the Bessel function of the first kind and of zero order. Substituting the expression $2\rho\sqrt{ix}$ for η [see notation (p)] in the series representing $J_0(\eta)$ and collecting the real and the imaginary terms, we obtain

$$J_0(\eta) = \psi_1(2\rho\sqrt{x}) + i\psi_2(2\rho\sqrt{x}), \tag{w}$$

where

$$\left.\begin{aligned}
\psi_1(2\rho\sqrt{x}) &= 1 - \frac{(2\rho\sqrt{x})^4}{(2\cdot 4)^2} + \frac{(2\rho\sqrt{x})^8}{(2\cdot 4\cdot 6\cdot 8)^2} - \cdots, \\
\psi_2(2\rho\sqrt{x}) &= -\frac{(2\rho\sqrt{x})^2}{2^2} + \frac{(2\rho\sqrt{x})^6}{(2\cdot 4\cdot 6)^2} - \frac{(2\rho\sqrt{x})^{10}}{(2\cdot 4\cdot 6\cdot 8\cdot 10)^2} + \cdots
\end{aligned}\right\} \tag{248}$$

The solution (u) then gives

$$\zeta_1 = -C'[\psi_1'(2\rho\sqrt{x}) + i\psi_2'(2\rho\sqrt{x})], \tag{a'}$$

where ψ_1' and ψ_2' denote the derivatives of the functions (248) with respect to the argument $2\rho\sqrt{x}$.

The second integral of Eq. (r) is of a more complicated form. Without derivation we shall state that it can be represented in the form

$$\zeta_2 = C''[\psi_3'(2\rho\sqrt{x}) + i\psi_4'(2\rho\sqrt{x})], \tag{b'}$$

in which ψ_3' and ψ_4' are the derivatives with respect to the argument $2\rho\sqrt{x}$ of the following functions:

$$\left.\begin{aligned}
\psi_3(2\rho\sqrt{x}) &= \frac{1}{2}\psi_1(2\rho\sqrt{x}) - \frac{2}{\pi}\left[R_1 + \log_n\frac{\beta 2\rho\sqrt{x}}{2}\psi_2(2\rho\sqrt{x})\right], \\
\psi_4(2\rho\sqrt{x}) &= \frac{1}{2}\psi_2(2\rho\sqrt{x}) + \frac{2}{\pi}\left[R_2 + \log_n\frac{\beta 2\rho\sqrt{x}}{2}\psi_1(2\rho\sqrt{x})\right],
\end{aligned}\right\} \tag{249}$$

where

$$R_1 = \left(\frac{2\rho\sqrt{x}}{2}\right)^2 - \frac{S(3)}{(3\cdot 2)^2}\left(\frac{2\rho\sqrt{x}}{2}\right)^6 + \frac{S(5)}{(5\cdot 4\cdot 3\cdot 2)^2}\left(\frac{2\rho\sqrt{x}}{2}\right)^{10} - \cdots,$$

$$R_2 = \frac{S(2)}{2^2}\left(\frac{2\rho\sqrt{x}}{2}\right)^4 - \frac{S(4)}{(4\cdot 3\cdot 2)^2}\left(\frac{2\rho\sqrt{x}}{2}\right)^8 + \frac{S(6)}{(6\cdot 5\cdot 4\cdot 3\cdot 2)^2}\left(\frac{2\rho\sqrt{x}}{2}\right)^{12} - \cdots,$$

$$S(n) = 1 + \frac{1}{2} + \frac{1}{3} + \cdots + \frac{1}{n},$$

$$\log_n \beta = 0.57722.$$

Having solutions (a') and (b') of Eq. (r), we conclude that the general solution (n) of Eq. (e) is

$$w = \frac{\zeta}{\sqrt{x}} = \frac{1}{\sqrt{x}}[C_1\psi_1'(2\rho\sqrt{x}) + C_2\psi_2'(2\rho\sqrt{x}) + C_3\psi_3'(2\rho\sqrt{x})$$

$$+ C_4\psi_4'(2\rho\sqrt{x})]. \quad (c')$$

Numerical values of the functions $\psi_1, \ldots, \psi_4$ and their first derivatives are given in Table 47.[1] A graphical representation of the functions ψ_1',

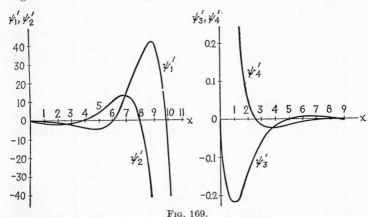

Fig. 169.

$\ldots$, ψ_4' is given in Fig. 169. It is seen that the values of these functions increase or decrease rapidly as the distance from the end increases. This indicates that in calculating the constants of integration in solution (c') we can very often proceed as we did with functions (235), *i.e.*, by considering the cylinder as an infinitely long one and using at each edge only two of the four constants in solution (c').

[1] This table was calculated by F. Schleicher; see "Kreisplatten auf Elastischer Unterlage," Berlin, 1926.   More complete tables for the same functions are given in the book by Jahnke-Emde, "Tables of Functions," Berlin, 1933.

THEORY OF PLATES AND SHELLS

TABLE 47.—TABLE OF THE $\psi(x)$ FUNCTIONS

x	$\psi_1(x)$	$\psi_2(x)$	$\dfrac{d\psi_1(x)}{dx}$	$\dfrac{d\psi_2(x)}{dx}$
0.00	+1.0000	0.0000	0.0000	0.0000
0.20	+1.0000	−0.0100	−0.0005	−0.1000
0.40	+0.9996	−0.0399	−0.0040	−0.2000
0.60	+0.9980	−0.0900	−0.0135	−0.3000
0.80	+0.9936	−0.1599	−0.0320	−0.3991
1.00	+0.9844	−0.2500	−0.0624	−0.4974
1.20	+0.9676	−0.3587	−0.1078	−0.5935
1.40	+0.9401	−0.4867	−0.1709	−0.6860
1.60	+0.8979	−0.6327	−0.2545	−0.7727
1.80	+0.8367	−0.7953	−0.3612	−0.8509
2.00	+0.7517	−0.9723	−0.4931	−0.9170
2.20	+0.6377	−1.1610	−0.6520	−0.9661
2.40	+0.4890	−1.3575	−0.8392	−0.9944
2.60	+0.3001	−1.5569	−1.0552	−0.9943
2.80	+0.0651	−1.7529	−1.2993	−0.9589
3.00	−0.2214	−2.0228	−1.7141	−0.8223
3.20	−0.5644	−2.1016	−1.8636	−0.7499
3.40	−0.9680	−2.2334	−2.1755	−0.5577
3.60	−1.4353	−2.3199	−2.4983	−0.2936
3.80	−1.9674	−2.3454	−2.8221	+0.0526
4.00	−2.5634	−2.2927	−3.1346	+0.4912
4.20	−3.2195	−2.1422	−3.4199	+1.0318
4.40	−3.9283	−1.8726	−3.6587	+1.6833
4.60	−4.6784	−1.4610	−3.8280	+2.4520
4.80	−5.4531	−0.8837	−3.9006	+3.3422
5.00	−6.2301	−0.1160	−3.8454	+4.3542
5.20	−6.9803	+0.8658	−3.6270	+6.4835
5.40	−7.6674	+2.0845	−3.2063	+6.7198
5.60	−8.2466	+3.5597	−2.5409	+8.0453
5.80	−8.7937	+5.3068	−1.5856	+9.4332
6.00	−8.8583	+7.3347	−0.2931	+10.3462

x	$\psi_3(x)$	$\psi_4(x)$	$\dfrac{d\psi_3(x)}{dx}$	$\dfrac{d\psi_4(x)}{dx}$
0.00	+0.5000		0.0000	
0.20	+0.4826	−1.1034	−0.1419	+3.1340
0.40	+0.4480	−0.6765	−0.1970	+1.4974
0.60	+0.4058	−0.4412	−0.2216	+0.9273
0.80	+0.3606	−0.2883	−0.2286	+0.6286

TABLE 47.—TABLE OF THE $\psi(x)$ FUNCTIONS.—(Continued)

x	$\psi_3(x)$	$\psi_4(x)$	$\dfrac{d\psi_3(x)}{dx}$	$\dfrac{d\psi_4(x)}{dx}$
1.00	+0.3151	−0.1825	−0.2243	+0.4422
1.20	+0.2713	−0.1076	−0.2129	+0.3149
1.40	+0.2302	−0.0542	−0.1971	+0.2235
1.60	+0.1926	−0.0166	−0.1788	+0.1560
1.80	+0.1588	+0.0094	−0.1594	+0.1056
2.00	+0.1289	+0.0265	−0.1399	+0.0679
2.20	+0.1026	+0.0371	−0.1210	+0.0397
2.40	+0.0804	+0.0429	−0.1032	+0.0189
2.60	+0.0614	+0.0446	−0.0868	+0.0039
2.80	+0.0455	+0.0447	−0.0719	−0.0066
3.00	+0.0326	+0.0427	−0.0586	−0.0137
3.20	+0.0220	+0.0394	−0.0469	−0.0180
3.40	+0.0137	+0.0356	−0.0369	−0.0204
3.60	+0.0072	+0.0314	−0.0284	−0.0213
3.80	+0.0022	+0.0260	−0.0212	−0.0210
4.00	−0.0014	+0.0230	−0.0152	−0.0200
4.20	−0.0039	+0.0192	−0.0104	−0.0185
4.40	−0.0056	+0.0156	−0.0065	−0.0168
4.60	−0.0066	+0.0125	−0.0035	−0.0148
4.80	−0.0071	+0.0097	−0.0012	−0.0129
5.00	−0.0071	+0.0073	+0.0005	−0.0109
5.20	−0.0069	+0.0053	+0.0017	−0.0091
5.40	−0.0065	+0.0037	+0.0025	−0.0075
5.60	−0.0059	+0.0023	+0.0030	−0.0060
5.80	−0.0053	+0.0012	+0.0033	−0.0047
6.00	−0.0046	+0.0004	+0.0033	−0.0036

In applying the general theory to particular cases, the calculation of the consecutive derivatives of w is simplified if we use the following relations:

$$
\left.
\begin{aligned}
\psi_1''(\xi) &= \psi_2(\xi) - \frac{1}{\xi}\psi_1'(\xi), \\[6pt]
\psi_2''(\xi) &= -\psi_1(\xi) - \frac{1}{\xi}\psi_2'(\xi), \\[6pt]
\psi_3''(\xi) &= \psi_4(\xi) - \frac{1}{\xi}\psi_3'(\xi), \\[6pt]
\psi_4''(\xi) &= -\psi_3(\xi) - \frac{1}{\xi}\psi_4'(\xi),
\end{aligned}
\right\}
\qquad (d')
$$

where the symbol ξ is used in place of $2\rho\sqrt{x}$. From expression (c') we then obtain

$$N_\varphi = -\frac{Eh}{a}w = -\frac{E\alpha}{a}\sqrt{x}[C_1\psi_1'(\xi) + C_2\psi_2'(\xi) + C_3\psi_3'(\xi) + C_4\psi_4'(\xi)], \quad (e')$$

$$\frac{dw}{dx} = \frac{1}{2x\sqrt{x}}\{C_1[\xi\psi_2(\xi) - 2\psi_1'(\xi)] - C_2[\xi\psi_1(\xi) + 2\psi_2'(\xi)]$$
$$+ C_3[\xi\psi_4(\xi) - 2\psi_3'(\xi)] - C_4[\xi\psi_3(\xi) + 2\psi_4'(\xi)]\}, \quad (f')$$

$$M_x = -D\frac{d^2w}{dx^2} = -\frac{E\alpha^3}{48(1-\nu^2)}\sqrt{x}\{C_1[(\xi)^2\psi_2'(\xi) - 4(\xi)\psi_2(\xi) + 8\psi_1'(\xi)]$$
$$- C_2[(\xi)^2\psi_1'(\xi) - 4(\xi)\psi_1(\xi) - 8\psi_2'(\xi)]$$
$$+ C_3[(\xi)^2\psi_4'(\xi) - 4(\xi)\psi_4(\xi) + 8\psi_3'(\xi)]$$
$$- C_4[(\xi)^2\psi_3'(\xi) - 4(\xi)\psi_3(\xi) - 8\psi_4'(\xi)]\}, \quad (g')$$

$$Q_x = \frac{dM_x}{dx} = \frac{E\alpha^3\rho^2}{24(1-\nu^2)}\sqrt{x}\{C_1[\xi\psi_1(\xi) + 2\psi_2'(\xi)]$$
$$+ C_2[\xi\psi_2(\xi) - 2\psi_1'(\xi)] + C_3[\xi\psi_3(\xi) + 2\psi_4'(\xi)] + C_4[\xi\psi_4(\xi) - 2\psi_3'(\xi)]\}. \quad (h')$$

By means of these formulas the deflections and the stresses can be calculated at any point, provided the constants $C_1, \ldots, C_4$ are determined from the edge conditions. The values of the functions $\psi_1, \ldots, \psi_4$ and their derivatives are to be taken from Table 47 if $2\rho\sqrt{x} \leqq 6$. For larger values of the argument, the following asymptotic expressions are sufficiently accurate:

$$\psi_1(\xi) \approx \frac{1}{\sqrt{2\pi\xi}}e^{\frac{\xi}{\sqrt{2}}}\cos\left(\frac{\xi}{\sqrt{2}} - \frac{\pi}{8}\right),$$

$$\psi_2(\xi) \approx -\frac{1}{\sqrt{2\pi\xi}}e^{\frac{\xi}{\sqrt{2}}}\sin\left(\frac{\xi}{\sqrt{2}} - \frac{\pi}{8}\right),$$

$$\psi_1'(\xi) \approx \frac{1}{\sqrt{2\pi\xi}}e^{\frac{\xi}{\sqrt{2}}}\cos\left(\frac{\xi}{\sqrt{2}} + \frac{\pi}{8}\right),$$

$$\psi_2'(\xi) \approx -\frac{1}{\sqrt{2\pi\xi}}e^{\frac{\xi}{\sqrt{2}}}\sin\left(\frac{\xi}{\sqrt{2}} + \frac{\pi}{8}\right),$$

$$\psi_3(\xi) \approx \sqrt{\frac{2}{\pi\xi}}e^{-\frac{\xi}{\sqrt{2}}}\sin\left(\frac{\xi}{\sqrt{2}} + \frac{\pi}{8}\right),$$

$$\psi_4(\xi) \approx -\sqrt{\frac{2}{\pi\xi}}e^{-\frac{\xi}{\sqrt{2}}}\cos\left(\frac{\xi}{\sqrt{2}} + \frac{\pi}{8}\right),$$

$$\psi_3'(\xi) \approx -\sqrt{\frac{2}{\pi\xi}}e^{-\frac{\xi}{\sqrt{2}}}\sin\left(\frac{\xi}{\sqrt{2}} - \frac{\pi}{8}\right),$$

$$\psi_4'(\xi) \approx \sqrt{\frac{2}{\pi\xi}}e^{-\frac{\xi}{\sqrt{2}}}\cos\left(\frac{\xi}{\sqrt{2}} - \frac{\pi}{8}\right).$$

$$(250)$$

As an example, consider a cylindrical tank of the same general dimensions as that used in the previous article (page 413), and assume that the thickness of the wall varies from 14 in. at the bottom to $3\frac{1}{2}$ in. at the top.   In such a case the distance of the origin of the coordinates (Fig. 168), from the bottom of the tank is $d + x_0 = \frac{4}{3}d = 416$ in.; hence, $(2\rho\sqrt{x})_{x=x_0+d} = 21.45$.   For such a large value of the argument, the functions $\psi_1, \ldots, \psi_4$ and their first derivatives can be replaced by their asymptotic expressions (250).   The deflection and the slope at the bottom of the tank corresponding to the particular solution (c) are

$$(w_1)_{x=x_0+d} = -\frac{\gamma a^2}{E\alpha} \cdot \frac{d}{d + x_0}, \qquad \left(\frac{dw_1}{dx}\right)_{x=x_0+d} = -\frac{\gamma a^2}{E\alpha} \cdot \frac{x_0}{(x_0 + d)^2}. \quad (i')$$

Considering the length of the cylindrical shell in the axial direction as very large, we take the constants C_3 and C_4 in solution (c') as equal to zero and determine the constants C_1 and C_2 so as to make the deflection and the slope at the bottom of the shell equal to zero.   These requirements give us the two following equations:

$$\left.\begin{array}{l}
\dfrac{1}{\sqrt{x}}[C_1\psi_1'(2\rho\sqrt{x}) + C_2\psi_2'(2\rho\sqrt{x})]_{x=x_0+d} = \dfrac{\gamma a^2}{E\alpha}\dfrac{d}{d + x_0}, \\[1.5em]
\dfrac{1}{2x\sqrt{x}}\{C_1[2\rho\sqrt{x}\psi_2(2\rho\sqrt{x}) - 2\psi_1'(2\rho\sqrt{x})] - C_2[2\rho\sqrt{x}\psi_1(2\rho\sqrt{x}) \\[1.5em]
\qquad\qquad + 2\psi_2'(2\rho\sqrt{x})]\}_{x=x_0+d} = \dfrac{\gamma a^2}{Ea}\dfrac{x_0}{(d + x_0)^2}
\end{array}\right\} \quad (j')$$

Calculating the values of functions ψ_1, ψ_2 and their derivatives from the asymptotic formulas (250) and substituting the resulting values in Eqs. (j'), we obtain

$$C_1 = -269\frac{\gamma a^2}{E\alpha}\frac{1}{\sqrt{d + x_0}} \cdot N,$$

$$C_2 = -299\frac{\gamma a^2}{E\alpha}\frac{1}{\sqrt{d + x_0}} \cdot N,$$

where

$$N = (e^{-\frac{\xi}{\sqrt{2}}}\sqrt{2\pi\xi})_{\xi=21.45}.$$

Substituting these values of the constants in expression (g'). we find for the bending moment at the bottom

$$M_0 = 13,900 \text{ lb. in. per inch.}$$

In the same manner, by using expression (h'), we find the magnitude of the shearing force at the bottom of the tank

$$Q_0 = 527 \text{ lb. per inch.}$$

These results do not differ much from the values obtained before for a tank with uniform wall thickness (page 413).

86. Thermal Stresses in Cylindrical Shells. *Uniform Temperature Distribution.*—If a cylindrical shell with free edges undergoes a uniform temperature change, no thermal stresses will be produced. But if the edges are supported or clamped, free expansion of the shell is prevented, and local bending stresses are set up at the edges. Knowing the thermal expansion of a shell when the edges are free, the values of the reactive moments and forces at the edges for any kind of symmetrical support can be readily obtained by using Eqs. (233) and (234), as was done in the cases shown in Fig. 161.

Temperature Gradient in the Radial Direction.—Assume that t_1 and t_2 are the uniform temperatures of the cylindrical wall at the inside and the outside surfaces, respectively, and that the variation of the temperature through the thickness is linear. In such a case, at points at a large distance from the ends of the shell, there will be no bending, and the stresses can be calculated by using Eq. (51) which was derived for clamped plates (see

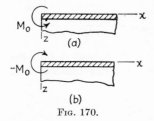

(a)

(b)

Fig. 170.

page 54). Thus the stresses at the outer and the inner surfaces are

$$\sigma_x = \sigma_\varphi = \pm \frac{E\alpha(t_1 - t_2)}{2(1 - \nu)}, \qquad (a)$$

where the upper sign refers to the outer surface, indicating that a tensile stress will act on this surface if $t_1 > t_2$.

Near the ends there will usually be some bending of the shell, and the total thermal stresses will be obtained by superposing upon (a) such stresses as are necessary to satisfy the boundary conditions. Let us consider, as an example, the condition of free edges, in which case the stresses σ_x must vanish at the ends. In calculating the stresses and deformations in this case we observe that at the edge the stresses (a) result in uniformly distributed moments M_0 (Fig. 170a) of the amount

$$M_0 = -\frac{E\alpha(t_1 - t_2)h^2}{12(1 - \nu)}. \qquad (b)$$

To obtain a free edge, moments of the same magnitude but opposite in direction must be superposed (Fig. 170b). Hence the stresses at a free edge are obtained by superposing upon the stresses (a) the stresses produced by the moments $-M_0$ (Fig. 170b). These latter stresses can be readily calculated by using solution (232). From this solution it follows that

$$(M_x)_{x=0} = \frac{E\alpha(t_1 - t_2)h^2}{12(1 - \nu)}, \qquad (M_\varphi)_{x=0} = \nu(M_x)_{x=0}$$

$$= \frac{\nu E\alpha(t_1 - t_2)h^2}{12(1 - \nu)}, \quad (c)$$

$$(N_\varphi)_{x=0} = -\frac{Eh}{a}(w)_{x=0} = \frac{Eh}{a}\frac{M_0}{2\beta^2 D} = \frac{Eh\alpha(t_1 - t_2)}{2\sqrt{3}(1 - \nu)}\sqrt{1 - \nu^2}. \quad (d)$$

It is seen that at the free edge the maximum thermal stress acts in the circumferential direction and is obtained by adding to the stress (a) the stresses produced by the moment M_φ and the force N_φ. Assuming that $t_1 > t_2$, we thus obtain

$$(\sigma_\varphi)_{\text{max.}} = \frac{E\alpha(t_1 - t_2)}{2(1 - \nu)}\left(1 - \nu + \frac{\sqrt{1 - \nu^2}}{\sqrt{3}}\right). \quad (e)$$

For $\nu = 0.3$ this stress is about 25 per cent greater than the stress (a) calculated at points at a large distance from the ends. We can therefore conclude that if a crack will occur in a brittle material such as glass due to a temperature difference $t_1 - t_2$, it will start at the edge and will proceed in the axial direction. In a similar manner the stresses can also be calculated in cases in which the edges are clamped or supported.[1]

Temperature Gradient in the Axial Direction.—If the temperature is constant through the thickness of the wall but varies along the length of the cylinder, the problem can be easily reduced to the solution of Eq. (228).[2] Let $t = F(x)$ be the increase of the temperature of the shell from a certain uniform initial temperature. Assuming that the shell is divided into infinitely thin rings by planes perpendicular to the x-axis and denoting the radius of the shell by a, the radial expansion of the rings due to the temperature change is $\alpha a F(x)$. This expansion can be eliminated and the shell can be brought to its initial diameter by applying an external pressure of an intensity Z such that

[1] Several examples of this kind are discussed in the paper by C. H. Kent, *Trans. Am. Soc. Mech. Eng.*, vol. 53, p. 167, 1931.
[2] See "Applied Elasticity," p. 146, 1925.

$$\frac{a^2 Z}{Eh} = \alpha a F(x),$$

which gives

$$Z = \frac{Eh\alpha}{a} F(x). \tag{f}$$

A load of this intensity entirely arrests the thermal expansion of the shell and produces in it only circumferential stresses having a magnitude

$$\sigma_\varphi = -\frac{aZ}{h} = -E\alpha F(x). \tag{g}$$

To obtain the total thermal stresses, we must superpose on the

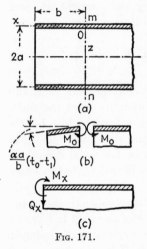

(a)

(b)

(c)

FIG. 171.

stresses (g) the stresses that will be produced in the shell by a load of the intensity $-Z$. This latter load must be applied in order to make the lateral surface of the shell free from the external load given by Eq. (f). The stresses produced in the shell by the load $-Z$ are obtained by the integration of the differential equation (230) which in this case becomes

$$\frac{d^4 w}{dx^4} + 4\beta^4 w = -\frac{Eh\alpha}{Da} F(x). \tag{h}$$

As an example of the application of this equation let us consider a long cylinder, as shown in Fig. 171a, and assume that the part of the cylinder to the right of the cross section mn has a constant temperature t_0, whereas that to the left side has a temperature that decreases linearly to a temperature t_1 at the end $x = b$ according to the relation

$$t = t_0 - \frac{(t_0 - t_1)x}{b}.$$

The temperature change at a point in this portion is thus

$$F(x) = t - t_0 = -\frac{(t_0 - t_1)x}{b}. \tag{i}$$

Substituting this expression for the temperature change in Eq. (h), we find that the particular solution of that equation is

$$w_1 = \frac{\alpha a}{b}(t_0 - t_1)x. \qquad (j)$$

The displacement corresponding to this particular solution is shown in Fig. 171b which indicates that there is at the section mn an angle of discontinuity of the magnitude

$$\frac{w_1}{x} = \frac{\alpha a}{b}(t_0 - t_1). \qquad (k)$$

To remove this discontinuity the moments M_0 must be applied. Since the stress σ_φ corresponding to the particular solution (j) cancels the stresses (g), we conclude that the stresses produced by the moments M_0 are the total thermal stresses resulting from the above-described decrease in temperature. If the distances of the cross section mn from the ends of the cylinder are large, the magnitude of the moment M_0 can be obtained at once from Eq. (234) by substituting

$$Q_0 = 0, \qquad \left(\frac{dw_1}{dx}\right)_{x=0} = -\frac{\alpha a}{2b}(t_0 - t_1)$$

to obtain[1]

$$M_0 = -\beta D\frac{\alpha a}{2b}(t_0 - t_1). \qquad (l)$$

Substituting for β its value from expression (229) and taking $\nu = 0.3$, we find that the maximum thermal stress is

$$(\sigma_x)_{\text{max.}} = \frac{6M_0}{h^2} = 0.353\frac{E\alpha}{b}\sqrt{ah}(t_0 - t_1). \qquad (m)$$

It was assumed in this calculation that the length b to the end of the cylinder is large. If this is not the case, a correction to the moment (l) must be calculated as follows. In an infinitely long shell the moment M_0 produces at the distance $x = b$ a moment and a shearing force (Fig. 171c)[2] that are given by the

---

[1] If $t_0 - t_1$ is positive, as was assumed in the derivation, M_0 is negative and thus has the direction shown in Fig. 171b.

[2] The directions M_x and Q_x shown in Fig. 171c are the positive directions if the x-axis has the direction shown in Fig. 171a.

general solution (236) as

$$
\left.
\begin{aligned}
M_x &= -D\frac{d^2w}{dx^2} = M_0\varphi(\beta b), \\
Q_x &= -D\frac{d^3w}{dx^3} = -2\beta M_0\zeta(\beta b).
\end{aligned}
\right\} \qquad (n)
$$

Since at the distance $x = b$ we have a free edge, it is necessary to apply there a moment and a force of the magnitude

$$
-M_x = -M_0\varphi(\beta b), \qquad -Q_x = 2\beta M_0\zeta(\beta b) \qquad (o)
$$

in order to eliminate the forces (n) (Fig. 171c).

The moment produced by the forces (o) at the cross section mn gives the desired correction ΔM_0 which is to be applied to the moment (l). Its value can be obtained from the third of the equations (236) if we substitute in it $-M_0\varphi(\beta b)$ instead of M_0 and $-2\beta M_0\zeta(\beta b)$* instead of Q_0. These substitutions give

$$
\Delta M = -D\frac{d^2w}{dx^2} = -M_0[\varphi(\beta b)]^2 - 2M_0[\zeta(\beta b)]^2. \qquad (p)
$$

As a numerical example, consider a cast-iron cylinder having the following dimensions: $a = 9\frac{11}{16}$ in., $h = 1\frac{3}{8}$ in., $b = 4\frac{1}{4}$ in., $\alpha = 101 \cdot 10^{-7}$, $E = 14 \cdot 10^6$ lb. per square inch, $t_0 - t_1 = 180°C$. The formula (m) then gives

$$
\sigma_{\text{max.}} = 7{,}720 \text{ lb. per square inch.} \qquad (q)
$$

In calculating the correction (p), we have

$$
\beta = \sqrt[4]{\frac{3(1 - \nu^2)}{a^2h^2}} = \frac{1}{2.84} \text{ (in.)}^{-1}, \qquad \beta b = 1.50,
$$

and, from Table 45,

$$
\psi(\beta b) = 0.234, \qquad \zeta(\beta b) = 0.223.
$$

Hence, from Eq. (p),

$$
\Delta M = -M_0(0.238^2 + 2 \cdot 0.223^2) = -0.156M_0.
$$

This indicates that the above-calculated maximum stress (q) must be diminished by 15.6 per cent to obtain the correct maximum value of the thermal stress

* The opposite sign to that in expression (o) is used here, since Eqs. (236) are derived for the direction of the x-axis opposite to that shown in Fig. 171a.

The method shown here for the calculation of thermal stresses in the case of a linear temperature gradient (*i*) can also be easily applied in cases in which $F(x)$ has other than a linear form.

87. Inextensional Deformation of a Circular Cylindrical Shell.[1] If the ends of a thin circular cylindrical shell are free, and the loading is not symmetrical with respect to the axis of the cylinder, the deformation consists principally of bending. In such cases the magnitude of deflection can be obtained with sufficient accuracy by neglecting entirely the strain in the middle surface of the shell. An example of such a loading condition is shown in Fig. 172. The shortening of the vertical diameter along which the forces P act can be found with good accuracy

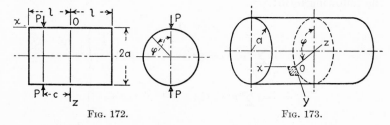

FIG. 172.   FIG. 173.

by considering only the bending of the shell and assuming that the middle surface is inextensible.

Let us first consider the limitations to which the components of displacement are subject if the deformation of a cylindrical shell is to be inextensional. Taking an element in the middle surface of the shell at a point O and directing the coordinate axes, as shown in Fig. 173, we shall denote by u, v and w the components in the x-, y- and z-directions of the displacement of the point O. The strain in the x-direction is then

$$\epsilon_x = \frac{\partial u}{\partial x}. \tag{a}$$

In calculating the strain in the circumferential direction we use Eq. (*a*) (Art. 76, page 371). Thus,

$$\epsilon_\varphi = \frac{1}{a}\frac{\partial v}{\partial \varphi} - \frac{w}{a}. \tag{b}$$

[1] The theory of inextensional deformations of shells is due to Lord Rayleigh, *Proc. London Math. Soc.*, vol. 13, 1881, and *Proc. Roy. Soc. London*, vol. 45, 1889.

The shearing strain in the middle surface can be expressed by

$$\gamma_{x\varphi} = \frac{\partial u}{a \, \partial \varphi} + \frac{\partial v}{\partial x}, \qquad (c)$$

which is the same as in the case of small deflections of plates except that $a \, d\varphi$ takes the place of dy. The condition that the deformation is inextensional then requires that the three strain components in the middle surface must vanish; *i.e.*,

$$\frac{\partial u}{\partial x} = 0, \qquad \frac{1}{a}\frac{\partial v}{\partial \varphi} - \frac{w}{a} = 0, \qquad \frac{\partial u}{a\partial \varphi} + \frac{\partial v}{\partial x} = 0. \qquad (d)$$

These requirements are satisfied if we take the displacements in the following form:

$$\left. \begin{aligned} u_1 &= 0, \\ v_1 &= a \sum_{n=1}^{\infty} (a_n \cos n\varphi - a_n' \sin n\varphi), \\ w_1 &= -a \sum_{n=1}^{\infty} n(a_n \sin n\varphi + a_n' \cos n\varphi), \end{aligned} \right\} \qquad (e)$$

where a is the radius of the middle surface of the shell, φ the central angle and a_n and a_n' constants that must be calculated for each particular case of loading. The displacements (e) represent the case in which all cross sections of the shell deform identically. On these displacements we can superpose displacements two of which vary along the length of the cylinder and which are given by the following series:

$$\left. \begin{aligned} u_2 &= -a \sum_{n=1}^{\infty} \frac{1}{n}(b_n \sin n\varphi + b_n' \cos n\varphi), \\ v_2 &= x \sum_{n=1}^{\infty} (b_n \cos n\varphi - b_n' \sin n\varphi), \\ w_2 &= -x \sum_{n=1}^{\infty} n(b_n \sin n\varphi + b_n' \cos n\varphi). \end{aligned} \right\} \qquad (f)$$

It can be readily proved by substitution in Eqs. (d) that these expressions also satisfy the conditions of inextensibility. Thus the general expressions for displacements in inextensional deformation of a cylindrical shell are

$$u = u_1 + u_2, \qquad v = v_1 + v_2, \qquad w = w_1 + w_2. \qquad (g)$$

In calculating the inextensional deformations of a cylindrical shell under the action of a given system of forces, it is advantageous to use the energy method. To establish the required expression for the strain energy of bending of the shell, we begin with the calculation of the changes of curvature of the middle surface of the shell. The change of curvature in the direction of the generatrix is equal to zero, since, as can be seen from expressions (e) and (f), the generatrices remain straight. The change of curvature of the circumference is obtained by comparing the curvature of an element mn of the

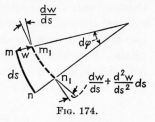

Fig. 174.

circumference (Fig. 174) before deformation with that of the corresponding element m_1n_1 after deformation. Before deformation the curvature in the circumferential direction is

$$\frac{\partial \varphi}{\partial s} = \frac{\partial \varphi}{a\, \partial \varphi} = \frac{1}{a}.$$

The curvature of the element m_1n_1 after deformation is

$$\frac{\partial \varphi_1}{\partial s_1} \approx \frac{d\varphi + \dfrac{\partial^2 w}{\partial s^2}ds}{(a - w)d\varphi}.$$

Hence the change in curvature is

$$\chi_\varphi = \frac{d\varphi + \dfrac{\partial^2 w}{\partial s^2}ds}{(a - w)d\varphi} - \frac{d\varphi}{a\, \partial \varphi} \approx \frac{1}{a^2}\left(w + \frac{\partial^2 w}{\partial \varphi^2}\right).$$

By using the second of the equations (d) we can also write

$$\chi_\varphi = \frac{1}{a^2}\left(\frac{\partial v}{\partial \varphi} + \frac{\partial^2 w}{\partial \varphi^2}\right). \qquad (h)$$

The bending moment producing this change in curvature is

$$M_\varphi = -\frac{D}{a^2}\left(\frac{\partial v}{\partial \varphi} + \frac{\partial^2 w}{\partial \varphi^2}\right),$$

and the corresponding strain energy of bending per unit area can be calculated as in the discussion of plates (see page 49) and is equal to

$$\frac{D}{2a^4}\left(\frac{\partial v}{\partial \varphi} + \frac{\partial^2 w}{\partial \varphi^2}\right)^2 = \frac{D}{2a^4}\left(w + \frac{\partial^2 w}{\partial \varphi^2}\right)^2. \tag{i}$$

In addition to bending, there will be a twist of each element such as that shown at point O in Fig. 173. In calculating this twist we note that during deformation an element of a generatrix rotates[1] through an angle equal to $-\partial w/\partial x$ with respect to the y-axis and through an angle equal to $\partial v/\partial x$ with respect to the z-axis. Considering a similar element of a generatrix at a circumferential distance $a\,d\varphi$ from the first one, we see that its rotation about the y-axis, as a result of the displacement w, is

$$-\frac{\partial w}{\partial x} - \frac{\partial^2 w}{\partial \varphi\,\partial x}d\varphi. \tag{j}$$

The rotation of the same element in the plane tangent to the shell is

$$\frac{\partial v}{\partial x} + \frac{\partial\left(\dfrac{\partial v}{\partial x}\right)}{\partial \varphi}d\varphi.$$

Because of the central angle $d\varphi$ between the two elements, the latter rotation has a component with respect to the y-axis equal to[2]

$$-\frac{\partial v}{\partial x}d\varphi. \tag{k}$$

From results (j) and (k) we conclude that the total angle of twist between the two elements under consideration is

$$-\chi_{x\varphi}a\,d\varphi = -\left(\frac{\partial^2 w}{\partial \varphi\,\partial x} + \frac{\partial v}{\partial x}\right)d\varphi$$

and that the amount of strain energy per unit area due to twist is (see page 50)

$$\frac{D(1-\nu)}{a^2}\left(\frac{\partial^2 w}{\partial \varphi\,\partial x} + \frac{\partial v}{\partial x}\right)^2. \tag{l}$$

---

[1] In determining the sign of rotation the right-hand screw rule is used.
[2] A small quantity of second order is neglected in this expression.

Adding together expressions (*i*) and (*l*) and integrating over the surface of the shell, the total strain energy of a cylindrical shell undergoing an inextensional deformation is found to be

$$V = \frac{D}{2a^4} \int \int \left[\left(\frac{\partial v}{\partial \varphi} + \frac{\partial^2 w}{\partial \varphi^2} \right)^2 + 2(1 - \nu)a^2 \left(\frac{\partial^2 w}{\partial \varphi \, \partial x} + \frac{\partial v}{\partial x} \right)^2 \right] a \, d\varphi \, dx.$$

Substituting for *w* and *v* their expressions (*g*) and integrating, we find for a cylinder of a length 2*l* (Fig. 172) the following expression for strain energy:

$$V = \pi \, Dl \sum_{n=2}^{\infty} \frac{(n^2 - 1)^2}{a^3} \left\{ n^2 \left[a^2(a_n^2 + a_n'^2) + \frac{1}{3} l^2(b_n^2 + b_n'^2) \right] + 2(1 - \nu)a^2(b_n^2 + b_n'^2) \right\}. \quad (251)$$

This expression does not contain a term with $n = 1$, since the corresponding displacements

$$\left. \begin{array}{l} v_1 = a(a_1 \cos \varphi - a_1' \sin \varphi), \\ w_1 = -a(a_1 \sin \varphi + a_1' \cos \varphi) \end{array} \right\} \quad (m)$$

represent the displacement of the circle in its plane as a rigid body. The vertical and horizontal components of this displacement are found by substituting $\varphi = \pi/2$ in expressions (*m*) to obtain

$$(v_1)_{\varphi = \frac{\pi}{2}} = -aa_1', \qquad (w_1)_{\varphi = \frac{\pi}{2}} = -aa_1.$$

Such a displacement does not contribute to the strain energy.

The same conclusion can also be made regarding the displacements represented by the terms with $n = 1$ in expressions (*f*).

Let us now apply expression (251) for the strain energy to the calculation of the deformation produced in a cylindrical shell by two equal and opposite forces *P* acting along a diameter at a distance *c* from the middle (Fig. 172). These forces produce work only during radial displacements *w* of their points of application, *i.e.*, at the points $x = c$, $\varphi = 0$ and $\varphi = \pi$. Also, since the terms with coefficients a_n and b_n in the expressions for w_1 and w_2 [see Eqs. (*e*) and (*f*)] vanish at these points, only terms with coefficients a_n' and b_n' will enter in the expression for deformation. By using the principle of virtual displacements, the equations for calculating the coefficients a_n' and b_n' are found to be

$$\frac{\partial V}{\partial a'_n} \delta a'_n = -na \, \delta a'_n (1 + \cos n\pi)P,$$

$$\frac{\partial V}{\partial b'_n} \delta b'_n = -nc \, \delta b'_n (1 + \cos n\pi)P.$$

Substituting expression (251) for V, we obtain, for the case where n is an even number,

$$\left.\begin{aligned} a'_n &= -\frac{a^2 P}{n(n^2 - 1)^2 \pi Dl}, \\ b'_n &= -\frac{ncPa^3}{(n^2 - 1)^2 \pi Dl[\frac{1}{3}n^2 l^2 + 2(1 - \nu)a^2]}. \end{aligned}\right\} \tag{n}$$

If n is an odd number, we obtain

$$a'_n = b'_n = 0. \tag{o}$$

Hence in this case, from expressions (e) and (f),

$$\left.\begin{aligned} u &= \frac{Pa^3}{\pi Dl} \sum_{n=2,4,6,\cdots} \frac{ac \cos n\varphi}{(n^2 - 1)^2[\frac{1}{3}n^2 l^2 + 2(1 - \nu)a^2]}, \\ v &= \frac{Pa^3}{\pi Dl} \sum_{n=2,4,6,\cdots} \left\{\frac{1}{n(n^2 - 1)^2} + \frac{ncx}{(n^2 - 1)^2[\frac{1}{3}n^2 l^2 + 2(1 - \nu)a^2]}\right\} \sin n\varphi, \\ w &= \frac{Pa^3}{\pi Dl} \sum_{n=2,4,6,\cdots} \left\{\frac{1}{(n^2 - 1)^2} + \frac{n^2 cx}{(n^2 - 1)^2[\frac{1}{3}n^2 l^2 + 2(1 - \nu)a^2]}\right\} \cos n\varphi. \end{aligned}\right\} \tag{p}$$

If the forces P are applied at the middle, $c = 0$ and the shortening of the vertical diameter of the shell is

$$\delta = (w)_{\varphi=0} + (w)_{\varphi=\pi} = \frac{2Pa^3}{\pi Dl} \sum_{n=2,4,6,\cdots} \frac{1}{(n^2 - 1)^2} = 0.149\frac{Pa^3}{2Dl}. \tag{q}$$

The increase in the horizontal diameter is

$$\delta_1 = -\left[(w)_{\varphi=\frac{\pi}{2}} + (w)_{\varphi=\frac{3\pi}{2}}\right] = \frac{2Pa^3}{\pi Dl} \sum_{n=2,4,6,\cdots} \frac{(-1)^{\frac{n}{2}+1}}{(n^2 - 1)^2} = 0.137\frac{Pa^3}{2Dl}. \tag{r}$$

The change in length of any other diameter can also be readily calculated. The same calculations can also be made if c is different from zero, and the deflections vary with the distance x from the middle.

Solution (p) does not satisfy the conditions at the free edges of the shell, since it requires the distribution of moments $M_x = \nu M_\varphi$ to prevent any bending in meridional planes. This bending is, however, of a local character and does not substantially affect the deflections (q) and (r) which are in satisfactory agreement with experiments.

The method just described for analyzing the inextensional deformation of cylindrical shells can also be used in calculating the deformation of a portion of a cylindrical shell which is cut from a complete cylinder of radius

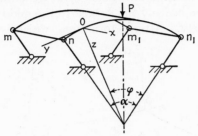

Fig. 175.

a by two axial sections making an angle α with one another (Fig. 175). For example, taking for the displacements the series

$$u = -\frac{\alpha a}{\pi} \sum \frac{b_n}{n} \sin \frac{n\pi\varphi}{\alpha},$$

$$v = a \sum a_n \cos \frac{n\pi\varphi}{\alpha} + x \sum b_n \cos \frac{n\pi\varphi}{\alpha},$$

$$w = -\frac{\pi a}{\alpha} \sum n a_n \sin \frac{n\pi\varphi}{\alpha} - \frac{x\pi}{\alpha} \sum n b_n \sin \frac{n\pi\varphi}{\alpha},$$

we obtain an inextensional deformation of the shell such that the displacements u and w and also the bending moments M_φ vanish along the edges mn and $m_1 n_1$. Such conditions are obtained if the shell is supported at points m, n, m_1, n_1 by bars directed radially and is loaded by a load P in the plane of symmetry. The deflection produced by this load can be found by applying the principle of virtual displacements.

88. General Case of Deformation of a Cylindrical Shell.[1]—To establish the differential equations for the displacements u, v and w which define the deformation of a shell, we proceed as in the case of plates. We begin with the equations of equilibrium of an element cut out from the cylindrical shell by two adjacent axial sections and by two adjacent sections perpendicular to the axis of the cylinder (Fig. 173). The corresponding element of

[1] A general theory of bending of thin shells has been developed by A. E. H. Love, see *Phil. Trans. Roy. Soc.*, *London*, Ser. A, p. 491, 1888; and his book "Elasticity," 4th ed., Chap. 24, p. 515, 1927; see also H. Lamb, *Proc. London Math. Soc.*, vol. 21.

the middle surface of the shell after deformation is shown in Figs.
176a and 176b.   In Fig. 176a the resultant forces and in Fig.
176b the resultant moments, discussed in Art. 72, are shown.
Before deformation, the axes x, y and z at any point O of the
middle surface had the directions of the generatrix, the tangent
to the circumference and the normal to the middle surface of the
shell, respectively.   After deformation, which is assumed to be

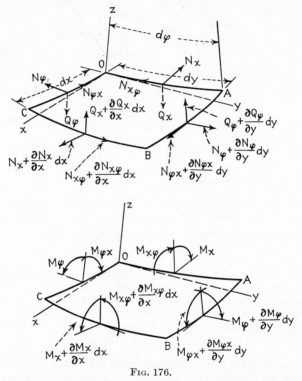

Fig. 176.

very small, these directions are slightly changed.   We then take
the z-axis normal to the deformed middle surface, the x-axis in
the direction of a tangent to the generatrix, which may have
become curved, and the y-axis perpendicular to the xz-plane.
The directions of the resultant forces will also have been slightly
changed accordingly, and these changes must be considered in
writing the equations of equilibrium of the element $OABC$.

Let us begin by establishing formulas for the angular displacements of the sides BC and AB with reference to the sides OA

and OC of the element, respectively. In these calculations we consider the displacements u, v and w as very small, calculate the angular motions produced by each of these displacements and obtain the resultant angular displacement by superposition. We begin with the rotation of the side BC with respect to the side OA. This rotation can be resolved into three component rotations with respect to the x-, y- and z-axes. The rotations of the sides OA and BC with respect to the x-axis are caused by the displacements v and w. Since the displacements v represent motion of the sides OA and BC in the circumferential direction (Fig. 173), if a is the radius of the middle surface of the cylinder, the corresponding rotation of side OA with respect to the x-axis is v/a, and that of side BC is

$$\frac{1}{a}\left(v + \frac{\partial v}{\partial x}dx\right).$$

Thus, owing to the displacements v, the relative angular motion of BC with respect to AO about the x-axis is

$$\frac{1}{a} \cdot \frac{\partial v}{\partial x}dx. \tag{a}$$

Because of the displacements w, the side OA rotates with respect to the x-axis through the angle $\partial w/a\, d\varphi$, and the side BC through the angle

$$\frac{\partial w}{a\, \partial \varphi} + \frac{\partial}{\partial x}\left(\frac{\partial w}{a\, \partial \varphi}\right)dx.$$

Thus, because of the displacements w, the relative angular displacement is

$$\frac{\partial}{\partial x}\left(\frac{\partial w}{a\, \partial \varphi}\right)dx. \tag{b}$$

Summing up (a) and (b), the relative angular displacement about the x-axis of side BC with respect to side OA is

$$\frac{1}{a}\left(\frac{\partial v}{\partial x} + \frac{\partial^2 w}{\partial x\, \partial \varphi}\right)dx. \tag{c}$$

The rotation about the y-axis of side BC with respect to side OA is caused by bending of the generatrices in axial planes and is equal to

$$-\frac{\partial^2 w}{\partial x^2}dx. \tag{d}$$

The rotation about the z-axis of side BC with respect to side OA is due to bending of the generatrices in tangential planes and is equal to

$$\frac{\partial^2 v}{\partial x^2} dx. \tag{e}$$

The formulas (c), (d) and (e) thus give the three components of rotation of the side BC with respect to the side OA.

Let us now establish the corresponding formulas for the angular displacement of side AB with respect to side OC. Because of the curvature of the cylindrical shell, the initial angle between these lateral sides of the element $OABC$ is $d\varphi$. However, because of the displacements v and w this angle will be changed. The rotation of the lateral side OC with respect to the x-axis is

$$\frac{v}{a} + \frac{\partial w}{a\, d\varphi}. \tag{f}$$

The corresponding rotation for the lateral side AB is

$$\frac{v}{a} + \frac{\partial w}{a\, d\varphi} + \frac{d}{d\varphi}\left(\frac{v}{a} + \frac{\partial w}{a\, d\varphi}\right) d\varphi.$$

Hence, instead of the initial angle $d\varphi$, we must now use the expression

$$d\varphi + d\varphi\left(\frac{\partial v}{a\, \partial\varphi} + \frac{\partial^2 w}{a\, \partial\varphi^2}\right). \tag{g}$$

In calculating the angle of rotation about the y-axis of side AB with respect to the side OC we use the expression for twist from the previous article (see page 430); this gives the required angular displacement as

$$-\left(\frac{\partial^2 w}{\partial\varphi\, \partial x} + \frac{\partial v}{\partial x}\right) d\varphi. \tag{h}$$

Rotation about the z-axis of the side AB with respect to OC is caused by the displacements v and w. Because of the displacement v, the angle of rotation of side OC is $\partial v/\partial x$, and that of side AB is

$$\frac{\partial v}{\partial x} + \frac{\partial}{a\, \partial\varphi}\left(\frac{\partial v}{\partial x}\right) a\, d\varphi;$$

so that the relative angular displacement is

$$\frac{\partial}{a\, \partial\varphi}\left(\frac{\partial v}{\partial x}\right) a\, d\varphi. \tag{i}$$

Because of the displacement w, the side AB rotates in the axial plane by the angle $\partial w/\partial x$. The component of this rotation with respect to the z-axis is

$$-\frac{\partial w}{\partial x}d\varphi. \qquad (j)$$

Summing up (i) and (j), the relative angular displacement about the z-axis of side AB with respect to side OC is

$$\left(\frac{\partial^2 v}{\partial\varphi\,\partial x} - \frac{\partial w}{\partial x}\right)d\varphi. \qquad (k)$$

Having the foregoing formulas[1] for the angles, we may now obtain three equations of equilibrium of the element $OABC$ (Fig. 176) by projecting all forces on the x-, y-, and z-axes. Beginning with those forces parallel to the resultant forces N_x and $N_{\varphi x}$ and projecting them on the x-axis, we obtain

$$\frac{\partial N_x}{\partial x}dx\,ad\varphi, \qquad \frac{\partial N_{\varphi x}}{d\varphi}d\varphi\,dx.$$

Because of the angle of rotation represented by expression (k), the forces parallel to N_y give a component in the x-direction equal to

$$-N_\varphi\left(\frac{\partial^2 v}{\partial\varphi\,\partial x} - \frac{\partial w}{\partial x}\right)d\varphi\,dx.$$

Because of the rotation represented by expression (e), the forces parallel to $N_{x\varphi}$ give a component in the x-direction equal to

$$-N_{x\varphi}\frac{\partial^2 v}{\partial x^2}dx\,ad\varphi.$$

Finally, because of angles represented by expressions (d) and (h), the forces parallel to Q_x and Q_φ give components in the x-direction equal to

$$-Q_x\frac{\partial^2 w}{\partial x^2}dx\,ad\varphi - Q_\varphi\left(\frac{\partial^2 w}{\partial\varphi\,\partial x} + \frac{\partial v}{\partial x}\right)d\varphi\,dx.$$

Regarding the external forces acting on the element, we assume that there is only a normal pressure of intensity q, the projection of which on the x-axis is zero.

---

[1] These formulas can be readily obtained for a cylindrical shell from the general formulas given by A. E. H. Love in his book "Elasticity," 4th ed., p. 523, 1927.

Summing up all the projections calculated above, we obtain

$$\frac{\partial N_x}{\partial x}dx\,ad\varphi + \frac{\partial N_{\varphi x}}{\partial \varphi}d\varphi\,dx - N_\varphi\left(\frac{\partial^2 v}{\partial\varphi\,\partial x} - \frac{\partial w}{\partial x}\right)d\varphi\,dx$$

$$- N_{x\varphi}\frac{\partial^2 v}{\partial x^2}dx\,ad\varphi - Q_x\frac{\partial^2 w}{\partial x^2}dx\,ad\varphi - Q_\varphi\left(\frac{\partial^2 w}{\partial\varphi\,\partial x} + \frac{\partial v}{\partial x}\right)d\varphi\,dx = 0.$$

In the same manner two other equations of equilibrium can be written. After simplification, all three equations can be put in the following form:

$$\left.\begin{aligned}
&a\frac{\partial N_x}{\partial x} + \frac{\partial N_{\varphi x}}{\partial \varphi} - aQ_x\frac{\partial^2 w}{\partial x^2} - aN_{x\varphi}\frac{\partial^2 v}{\partial x^2}\\
&\qquad - Q_\varphi\left(\frac{\partial v}{\partial x} + \frac{\partial^2 w}{\partial x\,\partial\varphi}\right) - N_\varphi\left(\frac{\partial^2 v}{\partial x\,\partial\varphi} - \frac{\partial w}{\partial x}\right) = 0,\\
&\frac{\partial N_\varphi}{\partial \varphi} + a\frac{\partial N_{x\varphi}}{\partial x} + aN_x\frac{\partial^2 v}{\partial x^2} - Q_x\left(\frac{\partial v}{\partial x} + \frac{\partial^2 w}{\partial x\,\partial\varphi}\right)\\
&\qquad + N_{\varphi x}\left(\frac{\partial^2 v}{\partial x\,\partial\varphi} - \frac{\partial w}{\partial x}\right) - Q_\varphi\left(1 + \frac{\partial v}{a\,\partial\varphi} + \frac{\partial^2 w}{a\,\partial\varphi^2}\right) = 0,\\
&a\frac{\partial Q_x}{\partial x} + \frac{\partial Q_\varphi}{\partial \varphi} + N_{x\varphi}\left(\frac{\partial v}{\partial x} + \frac{\partial^2 w}{\partial x\,\partial\varphi}\right) + aN_x\frac{\partial^2 w}{\partial x^2}\\
&\qquad + N_\varphi\left(1 + \frac{\partial v}{a\,\partial\varphi} + \frac{\partial^2 w}{a\,\partial\varphi^2}\right) + N_{\varphi x}\left(\frac{\partial v}{\partial x} + \frac{\partial^2 w}{\partial x\,\partial\varphi}\right) + qa = 0.
\end{aligned}\right\}\quad(252)$$

Going now to the three equations of moments with respect to the x-, y-, and z-axes (Fig. 176b) and again taking into consideration the small angular displacements of the sides BC and AB with respect to OA and OC, respectively, we obtain the following equations:

$$\left.\begin{aligned}
&a\frac{\partial M_{x\varphi}}{\partial x} - \frac{\partial M_\varphi}{\partial \varphi} - aM_x\frac{\partial^2 v}{\partial x^2} - M_{\varphi x}\left(\frac{\partial^2 v}{\partial x\,\partial\varphi} - \frac{\partial w}{\partial x}\right)\\
&\qquad\qquad\qquad\qquad\qquad\qquad\qquad + aQ_\varphi = 0,\\
&\frac{\partial M_{\varphi x}}{\partial \varphi} + a\frac{\partial M_x}{\partial x} + aM_{x\varphi}\frac{\partial^2 v}{\partial x^2} - M_\varphi\left(\frac{\partial^2 v}{\partial x\,\partial\varphi} - \frac{\partial w}{\partial x}\right)\\
&\qquad\qquad\qquad\qquad\qquad\qquad\qquad - aQ_x = 0,\\
&M_x\left(\frac{\partial v}{\partial x} + \frac{\partial^2 w}{\partial x\,\partial\varphi}\right) + aM_{x\varphi}\frac{\partial^2 w}{\partial x^2} + M_{\varphi x}\left(1 + \frac{\partial v}{a\,\partial\varphi}\right.\\
&\qquad\left. + \frac{\partial^2 w}{a\,\partial\varphi^2}\right) - M_\varphi\left(\frac{\partial v}{\partial x} + \frac{\partial^2 w}{\partial x\,\partial\varphi}\right) + a(N_{x\varphi} - N_{\varphi x}) = 0.
\end{aligned}\right\}\quad(253)$$

By using the first two of these equations[1] we can eliminate Q_x and Q_y from Eqs. (252) and obtain in this way three equations containing the resultant forces N_x, N_φ and $N_{x\varphi}$ and the moments M_x, M_φ and $M_{x\varphi}$. By using formulas (207) and (208) of Art. 72, all these quantities can be expressed in terms of the three strain components ϵ_x, ϵ_φ and $\gamma_{x\varphi}$ of the middle surface and the three curvature changes χ_x, χ_φ and $\chi_{x\varphi}$. By using the results of the previous article, these later quantities can be represented in terms of the displacements u, v and w as follows[2]:

$$\left.\begin{aligned}
\epsilon_x &= \frac{\partial u}{\partial x}, \qquad \epsilon_\varphi = \frac{\partial v}{a\,\partial\varphi} - \frac{w}{a}, \qquad \gamma_{x\varphi} = \frac{\partial u}{a\,\partial\varphi} + \frac{\partial v}{\partial x}, \\
\chi_x &= \frac{\partial^2 w}{\partial x^2}, \qquad \chi_\varphi = \frac{1}{a^2}\left(\frac{\partial v}{\partial\varphi} + \frac{\partial^2 w}{\partial\varphi^2}\right), \\
&\qquad\qquad \chi_{x\varphi} = \frac{1}{a}\left(\frac{\partial v}{\partial x} + \frac{\partial^2 w}{\partial x\,\partial\varphi}\right).
\end{aligned}\right\} \quad (254)$$

Thus we finally obtain the three differential equations for the determination of the displacements u, v and w.

In the derivation equations (252) and (253) the change of curvature of the element $OABC$ was taken into consideration. This procedure is necessary if the forces N_x, N_y and N_{xy} are not small in comparison with their *critical* values at which lateral buckling of the shell may occur.[3] If these forces are small, their effect on bending is negligible, and we can omit from Eqs. (252) and (253) all terms containing the products of the resultant forces or resultant moments with the derivatives of the small displacements u, v and w. In such a case the three Eqs. (252) and the first two equations of system (253) can be rewritten in the following simplified form:

---

[1] To satisfy the third of these equations the trapezoidal form of the sides of the element $OABC$ must be considered as mentioned in Art. 72. This question is discussed in the book by Flügge, *loc. cit.*, p. 368.

[2] The same expressions for the change of curvature as in the previous article are used, since the effect of strain in the middle surface on curvature is neglected.

[3] The problems of buckling of cylindrical shells are discussed in the author's "Theory of Elastic Stability" and will not be considered here.

$$
\left.\begin{aligned}
a\frac{\partial N_x}{\partial x} + \frac{\partial N_{\varphi x}}{\partial \varphi} &= 0, \\
\frac{\partial N_\varphi}{\partial \varphi} + a\frac{\partial N_{x\varphi}}{\partial x} - Q_\varphi &= 0, \\
a\frac{\partial Q_x}{\partial x} + \frac{\partial Q_\varphi}{\partial \varphi} + N_\varphi + qa &= 0, \\
a\frac{\partial M_{x\varphi}}{\partial x} - \frac{\partial M_\varphi}{\partial \varphi} + aQ_\varphi &= 0, \\
\frac{\partial M_{\varphi x}}{\partial \varphi} + a\frac{\partial M_x}{\partial x} - aQ_x &= 0.
\end{aligned}\right\}
\quad (255)
$$

Eliminating the shearing forces Q_x and Q_y, we finally obtain the three following equations:

$$
\left.\begin{aligned}
a\frac{\partial N_x}{\partial x} + \frac{\partial N_{\varphi x}}{\partial \varphi} &= 0, \\
\frac{\partial N_\varphi}{\partial \varphi} + a\frac{\partial N_{x\varphi}}{\partial x} + \frac{\partial M_{x\varphi}}{\partial x} - \frac{1}{a}\frac{\partial M_\varphi}{\partial \varphi} &= 0, \\
N_\varphi + \frac{\partial^2 M_{\varphi x}}{\partial x\,\partial \varphi} + a\frac{\partial^2 M_x}{\partial x^2} - \frac{\partial^2 M_{x\varphi}}{\partial x\,\partial \varphi} + \frac{1}{a}\frac{\partial^2 M_\varphi}{\partial \varphi^2} + qa &= 0.
\end{aligned}\right\}
\quad (256)
$$

By using Eqs. (207), (208) and (254), all the quantities entering in these equations can be expressed by the displacements u, v, and w, and we obtain

$$
\left.\begin{aligned}
&\frac{\partial^2 u}{\partial x^2} + \frac{1-\nu}{2a^2}\frac{\partial^2 u}{\partial \varphi^2} + \frac{1+\nu}{2a}\frac{\partial^2 v}{\partial x\,\partial \varphi} - \frac{\nu}{a}\frac{\partial w}{\partial x} = 0, \\
&\frac{1+\nu}{2}\frac{\partial^2 u}{\partial x\,\partial \varphi} + a\frac{1-\nu}{2}\frac{\partial^2 v}{\partial x^2} + \frac{1}{a}\frac{\partial^2 v}{\partial \varphi^2} - \frac{1}{a}\frac{\partial w}{\partial \varphi} \\
&\quad + \frac{h^2}{12a}\left(\frac{\partial^3 w}{\partial x^2\,\partial \varphi} + \frac{\partial^3 w}{a^2\,\partial \varphi^3}\right) + \frac{h^2}{12a}\left[(1-\nu)\frac{\partial^2 v}{\partial x^2} + \frac{\partial^2 v}{a^2\,\partial \varphi^2}\right] = 0, \\
&\nu\frac{\partial u}{\partial x} + \frac{\partial v}{a\,\partial \varphi} - \frac{w}{a} - \frac{h^2}{12}\left(a\frac{\partial^4 w}{\partial x^4} + \frac{2}{a}\cdot\frac{\partial^4 w}{\partial x^2\,\partial \varphi^2} + \frac{\partial^4 w}{a^3\,\partial \varphi^4}\right) \\
&\quad - \frac{h^2}{12}\left(\frac{2-\nu}{a}\,\frac{\partial^3 v}{\partial x^2\,\partial \varphi} + \frac{\partial^3 v}{a^3\,\partial \varphi^3}\right) = -\frac{aq(1-\nu^2)}{Eh}.
\end{aligned}\right\}
\quad (257)
$$

The problem of a laterally loaded cylindrical shell reduces in each particular case to the solution of this system of differential equations. Several applications of these equations will be shown in the next two articles.

89. Cylindrical Shells with Supported Edges.—Let us consider the case of a cylindrical shell supported at the ends and submitted to the pressure of an enclosed liquid as shown in Fig. 177.[1]   The conditions at the supports and the conditions of symmetry of

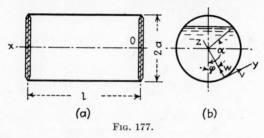

$$(a) \qquad\qquad\qquad (b)$$

Fig. 177.

deformation will be satisfied if we take the components of displacement in the form of the following series:

$$
\left.
\begin{aligned}
u &= \sum\sum A_{mn} \cos n\varphi \cos \frac{m\pi x}{l}, \\
v &= \sum\sum B_{mn} \sin n\varphi \sin \frac{m\pi x}{l}, \\
w &= \sum\sum C_{mn} \cos n\varphi \sin \frac{m\pi x}{l},
\end{aligned}
\right\} \qquad (a)
$$

in which l is the length of the cylinder and φ is the angle measured as shown in Fig. 177.[2]

The intensity of the load q is represented by the following expressions:

$$
\left.
\begin{aligned}
q &= -\gamma a(\cos \varphi - \cos \alpha), && \text{when} && \varphi < \alpha, \\
q &= 0, && \text{when} && \varphi > \alpha,
\end{aligned}
\right\} \qquad (b)
$$

in which γ is the specific weight of the liquid and the angle α defines the level of the liquid, as shown in Fig. 177b.   The load q can be represented by the series

$$
q = \sum\sum D_{mn} \cos n\varphi \sin \frac{m\pi x}{l}, \qquad (c)
$$

the coefficients D_{mn} of which can be readily calculated in the

---

[1] See the author's book "Theory of Elasticity," vol. 2, p. 385, St. Petersburg, 1916 (Russian).

[2] By substituting expressions (a) in Eqs. (254) it can be shown that the tensile forces N_x and the moments M_x vanish at the ends; the shearing forces do not vanish, however, since $\gamma_{x\varphi}$ and $M_{x\varphi}$ are not zero at the ends.

usual way from expressions (*b*). These coefficients are represented by the expression

$$D_{mn} = -\frac{8\gamma a}{mn\pi^2(n^2-1)}(\cos\alpha\sin n\alpha - n\cos n\alpha\sin\alpha), \quad (d)$$

where

$$m = 1, 3, 5, \cdots \quad \text{and} \quad n = 2, 3, 4, \cdots,$$

whereas

$$D_{m0} = -\frac{4\gamma a}{m\pi^2}(\sin\alpha - \alpha\cos\alpha), \quad (e)$$

and

$$D_{m1} = -\frac{2\gamma a}{m\pi^2}(2\alpha - \sin 2\alpha). \quad (f)$$

In the case of a cylindrical shell completely filled with liquid, we denote the pressure at the axis of the cylinder[1] by γd; then

$$q = -\gamma(d + a\cos\varphi), \quad (g)$$

and we obtain, instead of expressions (*d*), (*e*) and (*f*),

$$D_{mn} = 0, \qquad D_{m0} = -\frac{4\gamma d}{m\pi}, \qquad D_{m1} = -\frac{4\gamma a}{m\pi}. \quad (h)$$

To obtain the deformation of the shell we substitute expressions (*a*) and (*c*) in Eqs. (257). In this way we obtain for each pair of values of m and n a system of three linear equations from which the corresponding values of the coefficients A_{mn}, B_{mn} and C_{mn} can be calculated.[2] Taking a particular case in which $d = a$, we find that for $n = 0$ and $m = 1, 3, 5, \cdots$ these equations are especially simple, and we obtain

$$B_{m0} = 0, \qquad C_{m0} = -\frac{m\pi}{\lambda\nu}A_{m0} = -\frac{\pi N}{3m\left[\lambda^2(1-\nu^2) + \dfrac{\eta^2}{3}m^4\pi^4\right]},$$

where

$$N = \frac{2\gamma a l^2 h}{\pi^2 D}, \qquad \lambda = \frac{l}{a}, \qquad \eta = \frac{h}{2l}.$$

For $n = 1$ the expressions for the coefficients are more complicated. To show how rapidly the coefficients diminish as m

---

[1] In a closed cylindrical vessel this pressure can be larger than $a\gamma$.

[2] Such calculations have been made for several particular cases by I. A. Wojtaszak, *Phil. Mag.*, ser. 7, vol. 18, p. 1099, 1934; see also a paper by H. Reissner, *Z. angew. Math. Mech.*, vol. 13, p. 133, 1933.

increases, we include in Table 48 the numerical values of the coefficients for a particular case in which $a = 50$ cm., $l = 25$ cm., $h = 7$ cm., $\nu = 0.3$ and $\alpha = \pi$.

TABLE 48.—THE VALUES OF THE COEFFICIENTS IN EXPRESSIONS (a)

m	$A_{m0} \cdot \dfrac{2 \cdot 10^3}{Nh}$	$C_{m0} \cdot \dfrac{2 \cdot 10^3}{Nh}$	$A_{m1} \cdot \dfrac{2m \cdot 10^3}{Nh}$	$B_{m1} \cdot \dfrac{2 \cdot 10^3}{Nh}$	$C_{m1} \cdot \dfrac{2 \cdot 10^3}{Nh}$
1	57.88	−1,212	48.76	−71.90	−1,186
3	0.1073	− 6.742	0.3121	− 0.0744	− 6.705
5	0.00503	− 0.526	0.0247	− 0.00367	− 0.525

It is seen that the coefficients rapidly diminish as m increases. Hence, by limiting the number of coefficients to those given in the table, we shall obtain the deformation of the shell with satisfactory accuracy.

90. Deflection of a Portion of a Cylindrical Shell.—The method used in the previous article can also be applied to a por-

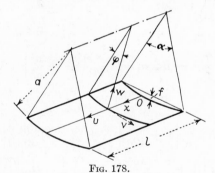

FIG. 178.

tion of a cylindrical shell which is supported along the edges and submitted to the action of a uniformly distributed load q normal to the surface (Fig. 178).[1]   We take the components of displacement in the form of the series

$$u = \sum \sum A_{mn} \sin \frac{n\pi\varphi}{\alpha} \cos \frac{m\pi x}{l},$$
$$v = \sum \sum B_{mn} \cos \frac{n\pi\varphi}{\alpha} \sin \frac{m\pi x}{l}, \qquad (a)$$
$$w = \sum \sum C_{mn} \sin \frac{n\pi\varphi}{\alpha} \sin \frac{m\pi x}{l},$$

[1] See author's book, *loc. cit.*, p. 441.

in which α is the central angle subtended by the shell and l is the length of the shell. It can be shown by substitution of expression (a) in Eq. (254) that in this way we shall satisfy the conditions at the boundary, which require that along the edges $\varphi = 0$ and $\varphi = \alpha$ the deflection w, the force N_φ and the moment M_φ vanish and that along the edges $x = 0$ and $x = l$ the deflection w, the force N_x and the moment M_x vanish. The intensity of the normal load q can be represented by the series

$$q = \sum\sum D_{mn} \sin\frac{n\pi\varphi}{\alpha} \sin\frac{m\pi x}{l}. \tag{b}$$

Substituting series (a) and (b) in Eqs. (257) and neglecting in these equations the term $h^2/12a^2$ as being small in comparison with unity, we obtain the following system of linear algebraic equations for calculating the coefficients A_{mn}, B_{mn} and C_{mn}:

$$\left.\begin{aligned}
&A_{mn}\pi\left[\left(\frac{am}{l}\right)^2 + \frac{(1-\nu)n^2}{2\alpha^2}\right] + B_{mn}\pi\frac{(1+\nu)amn}{2\alpha l} \\
&\qquad\qquad\qquad\qquad\qquad\qquad + C_{mn}\frac{\nu am}{l} = 0, \\
&A_{mn}\pi\frac{(1+\nu)amn}{2\alpha l} + B_{mn}\pi\left[\frac{(1-\nu)a^2m^2}{2l^2} + \frac{n^2}{\alpha^2}\right] \\
&\qquad\qquad + C_{mn}\frac{n}{\alpha}\left[1 + \frac{\pi^2h^2}{12a^2}\left(\frac{a^2m^2}{l^2} + \frac{n^2}{\alpha^2}\right)\right] = 0, \\
&A_{mn}\nu\pi\frac{am}{l} + B_{mn}\frac{n\pi}{\alpha}\left\{1 + \frac{\pi^2h^2}{12a^2}\left[\frac{n^2}{\alpha^2} + (2-\nu)\frac{a^2m^2}{l^2}\right]\right\} \\
&\qquad + C_{mn}\left[1 + \frac{\pi^4h^2}{12a^2}\left(\frac{a^2m^2}{l^2} + \frac{n^2}{\alpha^2}\right)^2\right] = D_{mn}\frac{a^2(1-\nu^2)}{Eh}.
\end{aligned}\right\} \tag{c}$$

To illustrate the application of these equations let us consider the case of a uniformly distributed load[1] acting on a portion of a cylindrical shell having a small angle α and a small sag $f = a[1 - \cos(\alpha/2)]$. In this particular case expression (b) becomes

$$q = \sum_{1,3,5,\cdots}\sum_{1,3,5,\cdots} \frac{16q}{\pi^2 mn} \sin\frac{m\pi x}{l} \sin\frac{n\pi\varphi}{\alpha}, \tag{d}$$

[1] The load is assumed to act toward the axis of the cylinder.

and the coefficients D_{mn} are given by the expression

$$D_{mn} = \frac{16q}{mn\pi^2}.$$

Substituting these values in Eqs. (c), we can calculate the coefficients A_{mn}, B_{mn} and C_{mn}. The calculations made for a particular case in which $\alpha a = l$ and for several values of the ratio f/h show that for small values of this ratio, series (a) are rapidly convergent and the first few terms give the displacements with satisfactory accuracy. The maximum deflection, which occurs at the center of the shell, can be represented in the form

$$w_{\text{max.}} = \beta \frac{ql^4}{D}, \qquad (e)$$

in which β is a numerical factor the magnitude of which depends upon the value of the ratio f/h. Several values of this factor are given in Table 49[1] in which the deflection of a uniformly loaded and simply supported square plate $(f/h = 0)$ is given for comparison. It is seen that the deflection rapidly diminishes as the ratio f/h increases.

TABLE 49.—THE VALUES OF THE FACTOR β IN EQ. (e)

$f/h =$	0	0.25	0.5	1.0	2.0	3.5	6.0
$\beta \times 10^5 =$	406	395	364	278	140	57	18

The calculations also show that the maximum values of the bending stresses produced by the moments M_x and M_φ diminish rapidly as f/h increases. The calculation of these stresses is very tedious in the case of larger values of f/h, since the series representing the moments become less rapidly convergent and a larger number of terms must be taken.

The method used in this article is similar to Navier's method of calculating bending of rectangular plates with simply supported edges. If only the rectilinear edges $\varphi = 0$ and $\varphi = \alpha$ of the shell in Fig. 178 are simply supported and the other two edges are built in or free, a solution similar to that of M. Lévy's method for the case of rectangular plates (see page 125) can be applied. We assume the following series for the components of displacement:

[1] This table was calculated by Woitaszak, *loc. cit.*, p. 442.

$$u = \sum U_m \sin \frac{m\pi\varphi}{\alpha},$$

$$v = \sum V_m \cos \frac{m\pi\varphi}{\alpha}, \qquad (f)$$

$$w = \sum W_m \sin \frac{m\pi\varphi}{\alpha},$$

in which U_m, V_m and W_m are functions of x only. Substituting these series in Eqs. (257), we obtain for U_m, V_m and W_m three ordinary differential equations with constant coefficients. These equations can be integrated by using exponential functions. An analysis of this kind made for a closed cylindrical shell[1] shows that the solution is very involved and that results suitable for practical application can be obtained only by introducing simplifying assumptions.

91. An Approximate Investigation of the Bending of Cylindrical Shells.—From the discussion of the previous article it may be concluded that the

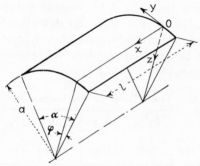

Fig. 179.

application of the general theory of bending of cylindrical shells in even the simplest cases results in very complicated calculations. To make the theory applicable to the solution of practical problems some further simplifications in this theory are necessary. In considering the membrane theory of cylindrical shells it was stated that that theory gives satisfactory results for portions of a shell at a considerable distance from the edges but that it is insufficient to satisfy all the conditions at the boundary. It is logical therefore to take the solution furnished by the membrane theory as a first approximation and use the more elaborate bending theory only to satisfy the conditions at the edges. In applying this latter theory, it must be assumed that no external load is distributed over the shell and that only forces and moments such as are necessary to satisfy the boundary conditions are

[1] See paper by K. Miesel, *Ingenieur-Archiv*, vol. 1, p. 29, 1929. An application of the theory to the calculation of stress in the hull of a submarine is shown in this paper.

applied along the edges. The bending produced by such forces can be investigated by using Eqs. (257) after placing the load q equal to zero in these equations.

In applications such as are encountered in structural engineering[1] the ends $x = 0$ and $x = l$ of the shell (Fig. 179) are usually supported in such a manner that the displacements v and w at the ends vanish. Experiments show that in such shells the bending in the axial planes is negligible, and we can assume $M_x = 0$ and $Q_x = 0$ in the equations of equilibrium (255). We can also neglect the twisting moment $M_{x\varphi}$. With these assumptions the system of Eqs. (255) can be considerably simplified, and the resultant forces and components of displacement can be all expressed in terms[2] of moment M_φ. From the fourth of the equations (255) we obtain

$$Q_\varphi = \frac{1}{a} \frac{\partial M_\varphi}{\partial \varphi}. \qquad (a)$$

Substituting this in the third equation of the same system, we obtain, for $q = 0$,

$$N_\varphi = -\frac{\partial Q_\varphi}{\partial \varphi} = -\frac{1}{a} \frac{\partial^2 M_\varphi}{\partial \varphi^2}. \qquad (b)$$

The second and the first of the equations (255) then give

$$\frac{\partial N_{x\varphi}}{\partial x} = \frac{1}{a}\left(Q_\varphi - \frac{\partial N_\varphi}{\partial \varphi}\right) = \frac{1}{a^2}\left(\frac{\partial M_\varphi}{\partial \varphi} + \frac{\partial^3 M_\varphi}{\partial \varphi^3}\right), \qquad (c)$$

$$\frac{\partial^2 N_x}{\partial x^2} = -\frac{1}{a} \frac{\partial^2 N_{x\varphi}}{\partial \varphi\, \partial x} = -\frac{1}{a^3}\left(\frac{\partial^2 M_\varphi}{\partial \varphi^2} + \frac{\partial^4 M_\varphi}{\partial \varphi^4}\right). \qquad (d)$$

The components of displacement can also be expressed in terms of M_φ and its derivatives. We begin with the known relations [see Eqs. (207) and (208)]

$$\left. \begin{aligned} \epsilon_x &= \frac{\partial u}{\partial x} = \frac{1}{Eh}(N_x - \nu N_\varphi), \\ \gamma_{x\varphi} &= \frac{\partial u}{a\, \partial \varphi} + \frac{\partial v}{\partial x} = \frac{2(1 + \nu)}{Eh} N_{x\varphi}, \\ \epsilon_\varphi &= \frac{\partial v}{a\, \partial \varphi} - \frac{w}{a} = \frac{1}{Eh}(N_\varphi - \nu N_x). \end{aligned} \right\} \qquad (e)$$

---

[1] In recent times thin reinforced cylindrical shells of concrete have been successfully applied in structures as coverings for large halls. Descriptions of some of these structures can be found in the article by F. Dischinger, "Handbuch f. Eisenbetonbau," vol. 12, 3d ed., Berlin, 1928; see also the paper by F. Dischinger and U. Finsterwalder in *Bauingenieur*, vol. 9, 1928.

[2] This approximate theory of bending of cylindrical shells was developed by U. Finsterwalder; see *Ingenieur-Archiv*, vol. 4, p. 43, 1933.

From these equations we obtain

$$\left.\begin{array}{l}
\dfrac{\partial u}{\partial x} = \dfrac{1}{Eh}(N_x - \nu N_\varphi), \\[2mm]
\dfrac{\partial^2 v}{\partial x^2} = \dfrac{1}{Eh}\left[2(1+\nu)\dfrac{\partial N_{x\varphi}}{\partial x} - \dfrac{1}{a}\left(\dfrac{\partial N_x}{\partial \varphi} - \nu\dfrac{\partial N_\varphi}{\partial \varphi}\right)\right], \\[2mm]
\dfrac{\partial^2 w}{\partial x^2} = \dfrac{1}{Eh}\left[a\left(\nu\dfrac{\partial^2 N_x}{\partial x^2} - \dfrac{\partial^2 N_\varphi}{\partial x^2}\right) + 2(1+\nu)\dfrac{\partial^2 N_{x\varphi}}{\partial x\,\partial\varphi}\right. \\[4mm]
\left.\qquad\qquad\qquad\qquad\qquad - \dfrac{1}{a}\left(\dfrac{\partial^2 N_x}{\partial\varphi^2} - \nu\dfrac{\partial^2 N_\varphi}{\partial\varphi^2}\right)\right].
\end{array}\right\} \quad (f)$$

Using these expressions together with Eqs. (b), (c) and (d) and with the expression for the bending moment

$$M_\varphi = -\frac{D}{a^2}\left(\frac{\partial v}{\partial \varphi} + \frac{\partial^2 w}{\partial \varphi^2}\right), \tag{g}$$

we finally obtain for the determination of M_φ the following differential equation of the eighth order:

$$\frac{\partial^8 M_\varphi}{\partial\varphi^8} + (2+\nu)a^2\frac{\partial^8 M_\varphi}{\partial x^2\,\partial\varphi^6} + 2\frac{\partial^6 M_\varphi}{\partial\varphi^6} + (1+2\nu)a^4\frac{\partial^8 M_\varphi}{\partial x^4\,\partial\varphi^4}$$

$$+ 2(2+\nu)a^2\frac{\partial^6 M_\varphi}{\partial x^2\,\partial\varphi^4} + \frac{\partial^4 M_\varphi}{\partial\varphi^4} + \nu a^6\frac{\partial^8 M_\varphi}{\partial x^6\,\partial\varphi^2} + (1+\nu)^2 a^4\frac{\partial^6 M_\varphi}{\partial x^4\,\partial\varphi^2}$$

$$+ (2+\nu)a^2\frac{\partial^4 M_\varphi}{\partial x^2\,\partial\varphi^2} + 12(1-\nu^2)\frac{a^6}{h^2}\frac{\partial^4 M_\varphi}{\partial x^4} = 0. \tag{h}$$

A particular solution of this equation is afforded by the expression

$$M_\varphi = A e^{\alpha\varphi} \sin\frac{m\pi x}{l}. \tag{i}$$

Substituting it in Eq. (h) and using the notation

$$\frac{m\pi a}{l} = \lambda, \tag{j}$$

the following algebraic equation for calculating α is obtained:

$$\alpha^8 + [2 - (2+\nu)\lambda^2]\alpha^6 + [(1+2\nu)\lambda^4 - 2(2+\nu)\lambda^2 + 1]\alpha^4$$

$$+ [-\nu\lambda^6 + (1+\nu)^2\lambda^4 - (2+\nu)\lambda^2]\alpha^2 + 12(1-\nu^2)\frac{a^2}{h^2}\lambda^4 = 0. \tag{k}$$

The eight roots of this equation can be put in the form

$$\alpha_{1,2,3,4} = \pm(\gamma_1 \pm i\beta_1), \qquad \alpha_{5,6,7,8} = \pm(\gamma_2 \pm i\beta_2). \tag{l}$$

Beginning with the edge $\varphi = 0$ and assuming that the moment M_φ rapidly diminishes as φ increases, we use only those four of the roots (l) which satisfy this requirement.   Then combining the four corresponding solutions (i), we obtain

$$M_\varphi = [e^{-\gamma_1 \varphi}(C_1 \cos \beta_1 \varphi + C_2 \sin \beta_1 \varphi) + e^{-\gamma_2 \varphi}(C_3 \cos \beta_2 \varphi$$
$$+ C_4 \sin \beta_2 \varphi)] \sin \frac{m\pi x}{l}, \quad (m)$$

which gives for $\varphi = 0$

$$M_\varphi = (C_1 + C_3) \sin \frac{m\pi x}{l}.$$

If instead of a single term (i) we take the trigonometric series

$$M_\varphi = \sum A_m e^{\alpha_m \varphi} \sin \frac{m\pi x}{l} \qquad (n)$$

any distribution of the bending moment M_φ along the edge $\varphi = 0$ can be obtained.   Having an expression for M_φ, the resultant forces Q_φ, N_φ and $N_{x\varphi}$ are obtained from Eqs. (a), (b) and (c).

If in some particular case the distributions of the moments M_φ and the resultant forces Q_φ, N_φ and $N_{x\varphi}$ along the edge $\varphi = 0$ are given, we can represent these distributions by sine series.   The values of the four coefficients in the terms containing $\sin (m\pi x/l)$ in these four series can then be used for the calculation of the four constants $C_1, \ldots, C_4$ in solution (m); and in this way the complete solution of the problem for the given force distribution can be obtained.

If the expressions for u, v and w in terms of M_φ are obtained by using Eqs. (f), we can use the resulting expressions to solve the problem if the displacements, instead of the forces, are given along the edge $\varphi = 0$.   Examples of such problems can be found in the previously mentioned paper by Finsterwalder,[1] who shows that the approximate method just described can be successfully applied in solving important structural problems.

[1] *Loc. cit.*, p. 447.

CHAPTER XII

SHELLS HAVING THE FORM OF A SURFACE OF REVOLUTION AND LOADED SYMMETRICALLY WITH RESPECT TO THEIR AXIS

92. Equations of Equilibrium.—Let us consider the conditions of equilibrium of an element cut from a shell by two adjacent meridian planes and two sections perpendicular to the meridians (Fig. 180).[1] It can be concluded from the condition of symmetry

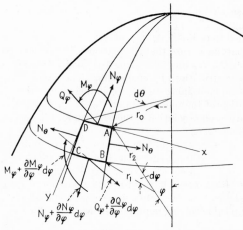

Fig. 180.

that only normal stresses will act on the sides of the element lying in the meridian planes. The stresses can be reduced to the resultant force $N_\theta \, r_1 d\varphi$ and the resultant moment $M_\theta \, r_1 d\varphi$, N_θ and M_θ being independent of the angle θ which defines the position of the meridians. The side of the element perpendicular to the meridians which is defined by the angle φ (Fig. 180) is acted upon by normal stresses which result in the force $N_\varphi \, r_2 \sin \varphi \, d\theta$ and the moment $M_\varphi \, r_2 \sin \varphi \, d\theta$ and by shearing

[1] We use for radii of curvature and for angles the same notation as in Fig. 138.

450

forces which reduce the force $Q_\varphi \, r_2 \sin \varphi \, d\theta$ normal to the shell. The external load acting upon the element can be resolved, as before, into two components $Y r_1 r_2 \sin \varphi \, d\varphi \, d\theta$ and $Z r_1 r_2 \sin \varphi \, d\varphi \, d\theta$ tangent to the meridians and normal to the shell, respectively. Assuming that the membrane forces N_θ and N_φ do not approach their critical values,[1] we neglect the change of curvature in deriving the equations of equilibrium and proceed as was shown in Art. 73. In Eq. (*f*) of that article, which was obtained by projecting the forces on the tangent to the meridian, the term $-Q_\varphi r_0$ must now be added to the left side. Also, in Eq. (*j*), which was obtained by projecting the forces on the normal to the shell, an additional term $d(Q_\varphi r_0)/d\varphi$ must be added to the left side. The third equation is obtained by considering the equilibrium of the moments with respect to the tangent to the parallel circle of all the forces acting on the element. This gives[2]

$$\left(M_\varphi + \frac{dM_\varphi}{d\varphi}d\varphi\right)\left(r_0 + \frac{dr_0}{d\varphi}d\varphi\right)d\theta - M_\varphi r_0 \, d\theta - M_\theta r_1 \cos \varphi \, d\varphi \, d\theta$$
$$- Q_\varphi r_2 \sin \varphi \, r_1 \, d\varphi \, d\theta = 0.$$

After simplification this equation, together with the two equations of Art. 73, modified as explained above, give us the following system of three equations of equilibrium:

$$\left.\begin{array}{c} \dfrac{d}{d\varphi}(N_\varphi r_0) - N_\theta r_1 \cos \varphi - r_0 Q_\varphi + r_0 r_1 Y = 0, \\[2mm] N_\varphi r_0 + N_\theta r_1 \sin \varphi + \dfrac{d(Q_\varphi r_0)}{d\varphi} + Z r_1 r_0 = 0, \\[2mm] \dfrac{d}{d\varphi}(M_\varphi r_0) - M_\theta r_1 \cos \varphi - Q_\varphi r_1 r_0 = 0. \end{array}\right\} \quad (258)$$

In these three equations of equilibrium are five unknown quantities, three resultant forces N_φ, N_θ and Q_φ and two resultant moments M_θ and M_φ. The number of unknowns can be reduced to three if we express the membrane forces N_φ and N_θ and the moments M_φ and M_θ in terms of the components v and w of the displacement. In the discussion in Art. 76 of the deformation produced by membrane stresses, we obtained for the strain

[1] The question of buckling of spherical shells is discussed in the author's "Theory of Elastic Stability," p. 491, 1936.

[2] In this derivation we observe that the angle between the planes in which the moments M_θ act is equal to $\cos \varphi \, d\theta$.

components of the middle surface the expressions

$$\epsilon_\varphi = \frac{1}{r_1}\frac{dv}{d\varphi} - \frac{w}{r_1}, \qquad \epsilon_\theta = \frac{v}{r_2}\cot\varphi - \frac{w}{r_2},$$

from which, by using Hooke's law, we obtain

$$\left.\begin{aligned} N_\varphi &= \frac{Eh}{1-\nu^2}\left[\frac{1}{r_1}\left(\frac{dv}{d\varphi}-w\right) + \frac{\nu}{r_2}(v\cot\varphi - w)\right], \\ N_\theta &= \frac{Eh}{1-\nu^2}\left[\frac{1}{r_2}(v\cot\varphi - w) + \frac{\nu}{r_1}\left(\frac{dv}{d\varphi}-w\right)\right]. \end{aligned}\right\} \quad (259)$$

To get similar expressions for the moments M_φ and M_θ let us consider the changes of curvature of the element $DABC$ shown in Fig. 180. Considering the upper and the lower sides of that element, we see that the initial angle between these two sides is $d\varphi$. Because of the displacement v along the meridian, the upper side of the element rotates with respect to the perpendicular to the meridian plane by the amount v/r_1. As a result of the displacement w, the same side further rotates with respect to the same axis by the amount $dw/r_1\, d\varphi$. Hence the total rotation of the upper side of the element is

$$\frac{v}{r_1} + \frac{dw}{r_1\,d\varphi}. \tag{a}$$

For the lower side of the element the rotation is

$$\frac{v}{r_1} + \frac{dw}{r_1\,d\varphi} + \frac{d}{d\varphi}\left(\frac{v}{r_1} + \frac{dw}{r_1\,d\varphi}\right)d\varphi.$$

Hence the change of curvature of the meridian is[1]

$$\chi_\varphi = \frac{1}{r_1}\frac{d}{d\varphi}\left(\frac{v}{r_1} + \frac{dw}{r_1\,d\varphi}\right). \tag{b}$$

To find the change of curvature in the plane perpendicular to the meridian, we observe that because of symmetry of deformation the lateral sides of the element $DABC$ each rotate in its meridian plane by an angle given by expression (a). Since the normal to the lateral side AB of the element makes an angle $(\pi/2) - \cos\varphi\,d\theta$ with the tangent to the meridian DC (y-axis),

[1] The strain of the middle surface is neglected, and the change in curvature is obtained by dividing the angular change by the length $r_1\,d\varphi$ of the arc.

the rotation of the side AB in its own plane has a component with respect to the y-axis equal to

$$-\left(\frac{v}{r_1} + \frac{dw}{r_1\,d\varphi}\right)\cos\varphi\,d\theta.$$

This results in a change of curvature

$$\chi_\theta = \left(\frac{v}{r_1} + \frac{dw}{r_1\,d\varphi}\right)\frac{\cos\varphi}{r_0} = \left(\frac{v}{r_1} + \frac{dw}{r_1\,d\varphi}\right)\frac{\cot\varphi}{r_2}. \tag{c}$$

Using expressions (b) and (c), we then obtain

$$\left. \begin{aligned} M_\varphi &= -D\left[\frac{1}{r_1}\frac{d}{d\varphi}\left(\frac{v}{r_1} + \frac{dw}{r_1\,d\varphi}\right) + \frac{\nu}{r_2}\left(\frac{v}{r_1} + \frac{dw}{r_1\,d\varphi}\right)\cot\varphi\right], \\ M_\theta &= -D\left[\left(\frac{v}{r_1} + \frac{dw}{r_1\,d\varphi}\right)\frac{\cot\varphi}{r_2} + \frac{\nu}{r_1}\frac{d}{d\varphi}\left(\frac{v}{r_1} + \frac{dw}{r_1\,d\varphi}\right)\right]. \end{aligned} \right\} \tag{260}$$

Substituting expressions (259) and (260) into Eqs. (258), we obtain three equations with three unknown quantities v, w and Q_φ. Discussion of these equations will be left to the next article.

We can also use expressions (260) to establish an important conclusion regarding the accuracy of the membrane theory discussed in Chap. X. In Art. 76 the equations for calculating the displacements v and w were established. By substituting the displacements given by these equations in expressions (260), the bending moments and bending stresses can be calculated. These stresses were neglected in the membrane theory. By comparing their magnitudes with those of the membrane stresses, a conclusion can be drawn regarding the accuracy of the membrane theory.

We take as a particular example a spherical shell under the action of its own weight (page 359). If the supports are as shown in Fig. 140a, the displacements as given by the membrane theory from Eqs. (f) and (b) (Art. 76) are

$$\left. \begin{aligned} v &= \frac{a^2 q(1+\nu)}{Eh}\left(\frac{1}{1+\cos\alpha} - \frac{1}{1+\cos\varphi}\right.\\ &\qquad\qquad\left. + \log\frac{1+\cos\varphi}{1+\cos\alpha}\right)\sin\varphi, \\ w &= v\cot\varphi - \frac{a^2 q}{Eh}\left(\frac{1+\nu}{1+\cos\varphi} - \cos\varphi\right). \end{aligned} \right\} \tag{d}$$

Substituting these expressions into formulas (260) for the bending moments, we obtain

$$M_\theta = M_\varphi = \frac{qh^2}{12} \frac{2 + \nu}{1 - \nu} \cos \varphi. \qquad (e)$$

The corresponding bending stress at the surface of the shell is numerically equal to

$$\frac{q}{2} \cdot \frac{2 + \nu}{1 - \nu} \cos \varphi.$$

Taking the ratio of this stress to the compressive stress σ given by the membrane theory [see Eqs. (211)], we find

$$\frac{q}{2} \cdot \frac{2 + \nu}{1 - \nu} \cos \varphi : \frac{aq}{h(1 + \cos \varphi)} = \frac{2 + \nu}{2(1 - \nu)} \cdot \frac{h}{a}(1 + \cos \varphi) \cos \varphi.$$

The maximum value of this ratio is found at the top of the shell where $\varphi = 0$ and has a magnitude, for $\nu = 0.3$, of

$$3.29 \frac{h}{a}. \qquad (f)$$

It is seen that in the case of a thin shell the ratio (f) of bending stresses to membrane stresses is small, and the membrane theory gives satisfactory results provided that the conditions at the supports are such that the shell can freely expand, as shown in Fig. 140a. Substituting expression (e) for the bending moments in Eqs. (258), closer approximations for the membrane forces N_φ and N_θ can be obtained. These results will differ from solutions (211) only by small quantities having the ratio h^2/a^2 as a factor.

From this discussion it follows that in the calculation of the stresses in symmetrically loaded shells we can take as a first approximation the solution given by the membrane theory and calculate the corrections by means of Eqs. (258). Such corrected values of the stresses will be accurate enough if the edges of the shell are free to expand. If the edges are not free, such forces must be so applied along the edge as to satisfy the boundary conditions. The calculation of the stresses produced by these latter forces will be discussed in the next article.

93. Reduction of the Equations of Equilibrium to Two Differential Equations of the Second Order.—From the discussion of the previous article, it is seen that by using expressions (259) and

(260) we can obtain from Eqs. (258) three equations with the three unknowns v, w and Q_φ. By using the third of these equations the shearing force Q_φ can be readily eliminated, and the three equations reduced to two equations with the unknowns v and w. The resulting equations were used by the first investigators of the bending of shells.[1] Considerable simplification of the equations can be obtained by introducing new variables.[2] As the first of the new variables we shall take the angle of rotation of a tangent to a meridian. Denoting this angle by V, we obtain from Eq. (a) of the previous article

$$V = \frac{1}{r_1}\left(v + \frac{dw}{d\varphi}\right). \tag{a}$$

As the second variable we take the quantity

$$U = r_2 Q_\varphi. \tag{b}$$

To simplify the transformation of the equations to the new variables we replace the first of the equations (258) by one similar to Eq. (209) (see page 358), which can be obtained by considering the equilibrium of the portion of the shell above the parallel circle defined by the angle φ (Fig. 180). Assuming that there is no load applied to the shell, this equation gives

$$2\pi r_0 N_\varphi \sin \varphi + 2\pi r_0 Q_\varphi \cos \varphi = 0,$$

from which

$$N_\varphi = -Q_\varphi \cot \varphi = -\frac{1}{r_2}U \cot \varphi. \tag{c}$$

Substituting in the second of the equations (258), we find, for $Z = 0$,

$$r_1 N_\theta \sin \varphi = -N_\varphi r_0 - \frac{d(Q_\varphi r_0)}{d\varphi};$$

[1] See A. Stodola, "Die Dampfturbinen," 4th ed., p. 597, 1910; H. Keller, *Mitt. Forschungsarbeiten*, vol. 124, 1912; E. Fankhauser, Dissertation, Zürich, 1913, and *V.D.I.*, vol. 58, p. 840, 1914.

[2] This method of analyzing stresses in shells was developed for the case of a spherical shell by H. Reissner, "Müller-Breslau-Festschrift," p. 181, Leipzig, 1912; it was generalized and applied to particular cases by E. Meissner, *Physik. Zeitschr.*, vol. 14, p. 343, 1913; and *Vierteljahrsschr. d. Naturforsch. Ges. Zürich*, vol. 60, p. 23, 1915.

and, observing that $r_0 = r_2 \sin \varphi$, we obtain

$$N_\theta = -\frac{1}{r_1}\frac{d}{d\varphi}(Q_\varphi r_2) = -\frac{1}{r_1}\frac{dU}{d\varphi}. \tag{d}$$

Thus both of the membrane forces N_φ and N_θ are represented in terms of the quantity U which is, as we see from notation (b), dependent on the shearing force Q_φ.

To establish the first equation connecting V and U we use Eqs. (259), from which we readily obtain

$$\frac{dv}{d\varphi} - w = \frac{r_1}{Eh}(N_\varphi - \nu N_\theta), \tag{e}$$

$$v \cot \varphi - w = \frac{r_2}{Eh}(N_\theta - \nu N_\varphi). \tag{f}$$

Eliminating w from these equations, we find

$$\frac{dv}{d\varphi} - v \cot \varphi = \frac{1}{Eh}[(r_1 + \nu r_2)N_\varphi - (r_2 + \nu r_1)N_\theta]. \tag{g}$$

Differentiation of Eq. (f) gives[1]

$$\frac{dv}{d\varphi} \cot \varphi - \frac{v}{\sin^2 \varphi} - \frac{dw}{d\varphi} = \frac{d}{d\varphi}\left[\frac{r_2}{Eh}(N_\theta - \nu N_\varphi)\right] \tag{h}$$

The derivative $dv/d\varphi$ can be readily eliminated from Eqs. (g) and (h) to obtain

$$v + \frac{dw}{d\varphi} = r_1 V = \frac{\cot \varphi}{Eh}[(r_1 + \nu r_2)N_\varphi - (r_2 + \nu r_1)N_\theta]$$
$$- \frac{d}{d\varphi}\left[\frac{r_2}{Eh}(N_\theta - \nu N_\varphi)\right].$$

Substituting expressions (c) and (d) for N_φ and N_θ, we finally obtain the following equation relating to U and V:

$$\frac{r_2}{r_1^2}\frac{d^2U}{d\varphi^2} + \frac{1}{r_1}\left[\frac{d}{d\varphi}\left(\frac{r_2}{r_1}\right) + \frac{r_2}{r_1}\cot \varphi - \frac{r_2}{r_1 h}\frac{dh}{d\varphi}\right]\frac{dU}{d\varphi}$$
$$- \frac{1}{r_1}\left[\frac{r_1}{r_2}\cot^2 \varphi - \nu - \frac{\nu}{h}\frac{dh}{d\varphi}\cot \varphi\right]U = EhV. \tag{261}$$

The second equation for U and V is obtained by substituting expressions (260) for M_φ and M_θ in the third of the equations

[1] We consider a general case by assuming in this derivation that the thickness h of the shell is variable.

(258) and using notations (*a*) and (*b*). In this way we find

$$\frac{r_2}{r_1^2}\frac{d^2V}{d\varphi^2} + \frac{1}{r_1}\left[\frac{d}{d\varphi}\left(\frac{r_2}{r_1}\right) + \frac{r_2}{r_1}\cot\varphi + 3\frac{r_2}{r_1 h}\frac{dh}{d\varphi}\right]\frac{dV}{d\varphi}$$

$$-\frac{1}{r_1}\left[\nu - \frac{3\nu\cot\varphi}{h}\frac{dh}{d\varphi} + \frac{r_1}{r_2}\cot^2\varphi\right]V = -\frac{U}{D}. \quad (262)$$

Thus the problem of bending of a shell having the form of a surface of revolution by forces and moments uniformly distributed along the parallel circle representing the edge is reduced to the integration of the two Eqs. (261) and (262) of the second order.

If the thickness of the shell is constant, the terms containing $dh/d\varphi$ as a factor vanish, and the derivatives of the unknowns U and V in both equations have the same coefficients. By introducing the notation

$$L(\ \cdots\ ) = \frac{r_2}{r_1^2}\frac{d^2(\ \ldots\ )}{d\varphi^2} + \frac{1}{r_1}\left[\frac{d}{d\varphi}\left(\frac{r_2}{r_1}\right)\right.$$

$$\left. + \frac{r_2}{r_1}\cot\varphi\right]\frac{d(\ \ldots\ )}{d\varphi} - \frac{r_1\cot^2\varphi}{r_2\cdot r_1}(\ \cdots\ ), \quad (i)$$

the equations can be represented in the following simplified form:

$$\left.\begin{array}{l} L(U) + \dfrac{\nu}{r_1}U = EhV, \\[2mm] L(V) - \dfrac{\nu}{r_1}V = -\dfrac{U}{D}. \end{array}\right\} \quad (263)$$

From this system of two simultaneous differential equations of the second order we readily obtain for each unknown an equation of the fourth order. To accomplish this we perform on the first of the equations (263) the operation indicated by the symbol $L(\ \ldots\ )$, which gives

$$LL(U) + \nu L\left(\frac{U}{r_1}\right) = EhL(V).$$

Substituting from the second of the equations (263)

$$L(V) = \frac{\nu}{r_1}V - \frac{U}{D} = \frac{\nu}{r_1 Eh}\left[L(U) + \frac{\nu}{r_1}U\right] - \frac{U}{D},$$

we obtain

$$LL(U) + \nu L\left(\frac{U}{r_1}\right) - \frac{\nu}{r_1}L(U) - \frac{\nu^2}{r_1^2}U = -\frac{Eh}{D}U. \qquad (264)$$

In the same manner we also find the second equation

$$LL(V) - \nu L\left(\frac{V}{r_1}\right) + \frac{\nu}{r_1}L(V) - \frac{\nu^2}{r_1^2}V = -\frac{Eh}{D}V. \qquad (265)$$

If the radius of curvature r_1 is constant, as is the case of a spherical or a conical shell or in a ring shell such as is shown in Fig. 145, a further simplification of Eqs. (264) and (265) is possible. Since in this case

$$L\left(\frac{U}{r_1}\right) = \frac{1}{r_1}L(U),$$

by using the notation

$$\mu^4 = \frac{Eh}{D} - \frac{\nu^2}{r_1^2} \qquad (j)$$

both equations can be reduced to the form

$$LL(U) + \mu^4 U = 0, \qquad (266)$$

which can be written in one of the two following forms:

$$L[L(U) + i\mu^2 U] - i\mu^2[L(U) + i\mu^2 U] = 0$$

or

$$L[L(U) - i\mu^2 U] + i\mu^2[L(U) - i\mu^2 U] = 0.$$

These equations indicate that the solutions of the second-order equations

$$L(U) \pm i\mu^2 U = 0 \qquad (267)$$

are also the solutions of Eq. (266). By proceeding as was explained in Art. 85, it can be shown that the complete solution of Eq. (266) can be obtained from the solution of one of Eqs. (267). The application of Eqs. (267) to particular cases will be discussed in the two following articles.

94. Spherical Shell of Constant Thickness.—In the case of a spherical shell of constant thickness $r_1 = r_2 = a$, and the symbol (*i*) of the preceding article is

$L(\ \cdots\ )$

$$= \frac{1}{a}\left[\frac{d^2}{d\varphi^2}(\ \cdots\ ) + \cot\ \varphi\frac{d}{d\varphi}(\ \cdots\ ) - \cot^2\ \varphi(\ \cdots\ )\right]. \quad (a)$$

Considering the quantity aQ_φ, instead of U, as one of the unknowns in the further discussion and introducing, instead of the constant μ, a new constant ρ defined by the equation

$$\rho^2 = \frac{a\mu^2}{2} = \sqrt{\frac{3a^2(1 - \nu^2)}{h^2} - \frac{\nu^2}{4}}, \quad (b)$$

we can represent the first of the equations (267) in the following form:

$$\frac{d^2Q_\varphi}{d\varphi^2} + \cot\ \varphi\frac{dQ_\varphi}{d\varphi} - \cot^2\ \varphi Q_\varphi + 2i\rho^2Q_\varphi = 0. \quad (268)$$

A further simplification is obtained by introducing the new variables[1]

$$\left.\begin{array}{l} x = \sin^2\ \varphi, \\ z = \dfrac{Q_\varphi}{\sin\ \varphi}. \end{array}\right\} \quad (c)$$

With these variables Eq. (268) becomes

$$x(x - 1)\frac{d^2z}{dx^2} + \left(\frac{5}{2}x - 2\right)\frac{dz}{dx} + \frac{1 - 2i\rho^2}{4}z = 0. \quad (d)$$

This equation belongs to a known type of differential equation of the second order which has the form

$$x(1 - x)y'' + [\gamma - (\alpha + \beta + 1)x]y' - \alpha\beta y = 0. \quad (e)$$

Equations (d) and (e) coincide if we put

$$\gamma = 2, \qquad \alpha = \frac{3 \pm \sqrt{5 + 8i\rho^2}}{4}, \qquad \beta = \frac{3 \mp \sqrt{5 + 8i\rho^2}}{4}. \quad (f)$$

A solution of Eq. (e) can be taken in the form of a power series

$$y = A_0 + A_1x + A_2x^2 + A_3x^3 + \cdots. \quad (g)$$

Substituting this series in Eq. (e) and equating the coefficients for each power of x to zero, we obtain the following relations

---

[1] This solution of the equation was given by E. Meissner, *loc. cit.*, p. 455.

between the coefficients:

$$A_1 = \frac{\alpha\beta}{1\cdot\gamma}A_0, \qquad A_2 = \frac{(\alpha+1)(\beta+1)}{2(\gamma+1)}A_1,$$

. . . .

$$A_n = A_{n-1}\frac{(\alpha+n-1)(\beta+n-1)}{n(\gamma+n-1)},$$

. . . .

With these relations series (g) becomes

$$y = A_0\left[1 + \frac{\alpha\beta}{1\cdot\gamma}x + \frac{\alpha(\alpha+1)\beta(\beta+1)}{1\cdot2\cdot\gamma(\gamma+1)}x^2 \right.$$
$$\left. + \frac{\alpha(\alpha+1)(\alpha+2)\beta(\beta+1)(\beta+2)}{1\cdot2\cdot3\cdot\gamma(\gamma+1)(\gamma+2)}x^3 + \cdots \right]. \quad (h)$$

This is the so-called hypergeometrical series. It is convergent for all values of x less than unity and can be used to represent one of the integrals of Eq. (d). Substituting for α, β and γ their values (f) and using the notation

$$\delta^2 = 5 + 8i\rho^2 = 5 + 4i\sqrt{\frac{12a^2(1-\nu^2)}{h^2} - \nu^2}, \qquad (i)$$

we obtain as the solution of Eq. (d):

$$z_1 = A_0\left[1 + \frac{3^2-\delta^2}{16\cdot1\cdot2}x + \frac{(3^2-\delta^2)(7^2-\delta^2)}{16^2\cdot1\cdot2\cdot2\cdot3}x^2 + \cdots\right], \quad (j)$$

which contains one arbitrary constant A_0.

The derivation of the second integral of Eq. (d) is more complicated.[1] This integral can be written in the form

$$z_2 = z_1\log x + \frac{1}{x}\varphi(x), \qquad (k)$$

where $\varphi(x)$ is a power series that is convergent for $|x| < 1$. This second solution becomes infinite for $x = 0$, i.e., at the top of the sphere (Fig. 170), and should not be considered in those cases in which there is no hole at the top of the sphere.

If we limit our investigation to these latter cases, we need consider only solution (j). Substituting for δ^2 its value (i) and

[1] Differential equations that are solved by hypergeometrical series are discussed in the book "Riemann-Weber, die partiellen Differential-Gleich-ungen," vol. 2, pp. 1–29, 1901.

dividing series (j) into its real and imaginary parts, we obtain

$$z_1 = S_1 + iS_2, \qquad\qquad (l)$$

where S_1 and S_2 are power series that are convergent when $|x| < 1$. The corresponding solution of the first of the equations (267) is then

$$U_1 = a \sin \varphi z_1 = I_1 + iI_2, \qquad\qquad (m)$$

where I_1 and I_2 are two series readily obtained from the series S_1 and S_2.

The necessary integral of the second of the equations (267) can be represented by the same series I_1 and I_2 (see page 415). Thus, for the case of a spherical shell without a hole at the top, the general solution of the differential equation (266), which is of the fourth order, can be represented in the form

$$U = aQ_\varphi = AI_1 + BI_2, \qquad\qquad (n)$$

where A and B are constants to be determined from the two conditions along the edge of the spherical shell.

Having expression (n) for U, we can readily find the second unknown V. We begin by substituting expression (m) in the first of the equations (267) which gives

$$L(I_1 + iI_2) = -i\mu^2(I_1 + iI_2).$$

Hence,

$$L(I_1) = \mu^2 I_2, \qquad L(I_2) = -\mu^2 I_1. \qquad\qquad (o)$$

Substituting expression (n) in the first of the equations (263) and applying expressions (o), we then obtain

$$\begin{aligned} EhaV &= aL(U) + \nu U \\ &= (A\nu - Ba\mu^2)I_1 + (Aa\mu^2 + B\nu)I_2 \cdots . \qquad (p) \end{aligned}$$

It is seen that the second unknown V is also represented by the series I_1 and I_2.

Having the expressions for U and V, we can obtain all the forces, moments and displacements. The forces N_φ and N_θ are found from Eqs. (c) and (d) of the previous article. The bending moments M_φ and M_θ are obtained from Eqs. (260). Observing that in the case of a spherical shell $r_1 = r_2 = a$ and using notation (a), we obtain

$$M_\varphi = -\frac{D}{a}\left(\frac{dV}{d\varphi} + \nu \cot \varphi\, V\right),$$
$$M_\theta = -\frac{D}{a}\left(\nu\frac{dV}{d\varphi} + \cot \varphi\, V\right). \tag{q}$$

In calculating the components v and w of displacement we use the expressions for the strain in the middle surface:

$$\epsilon_\varphi = \frac{1}{Eh}(N_\varphi - \nu N_\theta), \qquad \epsilon_\theta = \frac{1}{Eh}(N_\theta - \nu N_\varphi).$$

Substituting for N_φ and N_θ their expressions in U and V, we obtain expressions for ϵ_φ and ϵ_θ which can be used for calculating v and w as was explained in Art. 76.

In practical applications the displacement δ in the planes of the parallel circles is usually important. It can be obtained by projecting the components v and w on that plane. This gives (Fig. 180)

$$\delta = v \cos \varphi - w \sin \varphi.$$

The expression for this displacement in terms of the functions U and V is readily obtained if we observe that δ represents the increase in the radius r_0 of the parallel circle. Thus

$$\delta = a \sin \varphi\, \epsilon_\theta = \frac{a \sin \varphi}{Eh}(N_\theta - \nu N_\varphi) = -\frac{\sin \varphi}{Eh}\left(\frac{dU}{d\varphi} - \nu U \cot \varphi\right). \tag{r}$$

Thus all the quantities that define the bending of a spherical shell by forces and couples uniformly distributed along the edge can be represented in terms of the two series I_1 and I_2.

The ease with which practical application of this analysis can be made depends on the rapidity of convergence of the series I_1 and I_2. This convergence depends principally upon the magnitude of the quantity

$$\rho = \sqrt[4]{\frac{3a^2}{h^2}(1 - \nu^2) - \frac{\nu^2}{4}}, \tag{s}$$

which, if ν^2 is neglected in comparison with unity, becomes

$$\rho \approx \sqrt[4]{3}\sqrt{\frac{a}{h}}.$$

Calculations show[1] that for $\rho < 10$ the convergence of the series is satisfactory, and all necessary quantities can be found without much difficulty for various edge conditions.

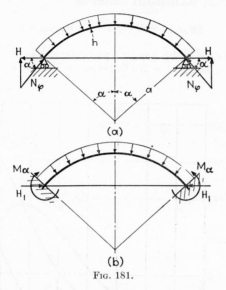

F<small>IG</small>. 181.

As an example we shall take the case of a spherical shell submitted to the action of uniform normal pressure p (Fig. 181). The membrane stresses in this case are

$$\sigma_\varphi = \sigma_\theta = -\frac{pa}{2h}, \qquad (t)$$

and the corresponding membrane forces that keep the shell in equilibrium are

$$(N_\varphi)_{\varphi=\alpha} = -\frac{pa}{2}. \qquad (u)$$

By superposing on the membrane forces horizontal forces

$$H = \frac{pa}{2}\cos\alpha$$

uniformly distributed along the edge of the shell, we obtain the case, represented in Fig. 181a, in which the loaded shell is supported by vertical reactions of a horizontal plane. The stresses in this case are obtained by

[1] Such calculations were made by L. Bolle, *Schweiz. Bauzeitung*, vol. **66**, p. 105, 1915.

superposing on the membrane stresses (t) the stresses produced by the horizontal forces H. These latter stresses can be obtained by using the general solutions (n) and (p) and determining the constants A and B in these solutions so as to satisfy the boundary conditions

$$(N_\varphi)_{\varphi=\alpha} = H \cos \alpha, \qquad (M_\varphi)_{\varphi=\alpha} = 0.$$

The stresses obtained in this way for a particular case in which $a = 56.3$ in., $h = 2.36$ in., $\alpha = 39$ deg., $p = 284$ lb. per square inch and $\nu = 0.2$ are shown in Fig. 182.

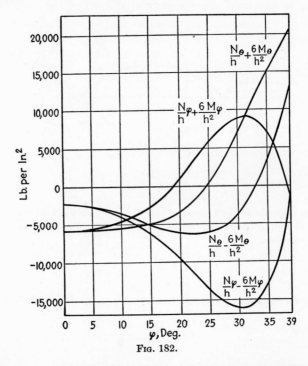

Fig. 182.

By superposing on the membrane forces (u) the horizontal forces H_1 and bending moments M_α uniformly distributed along the edge, we can also obtain the case of a shell with built-in edges (Fig. 181b). The stresses in this case are obtained by superposing on the membrane stresses (t) the stresses produced in the shell by the forces H_1 and the moments M_α. These latter stresses are obtained as before from the general solutions (n) and (p), the constants A and B being so determined as to satisfy the boundary conditions

$$(\epsilon_\theta)_{\varphi=\alpha} = 0, \qquad (V)_{\varphi=\alpha} = 0.$$

The total stresses obtained in this way for the previously cited numerical example are shown in Fig. 183.

From the calculation of the maximum compressive and maximum tensile stresses for various proportions of shells submitted to the action of a uniform normal pressure p, it was found[1] that the magnitude of these stresses depends principally on the magnitude of the quantity

$$\frac{a}{h} \sin^2 \alpha$$

and can be represented by comparatively simple formulas. For the case

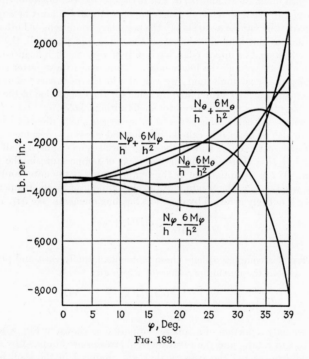

FIG. 183.

represented in Fig. 181a these formulas for the numerically greatest stress are as follows:

For $\quad \dfrac{a}{h} \sin^2 \alpha < 1.2, \qquad \sigma = -1.24 p \left(\dfrac{a \sin \alpha}{h} \right)^2 \cos \alpha;$

for $\quad 1.2 < \dfrac{a}{h} \sin^2 \alpha < 12, \qquad \sigma = \dfrac{ap}{2h} \left[\left(1.6 + 2.44 \sin \alpha \sqrt{\dfrac{a}{h}} \right) \cos \alpha - 1 \right].$

[1] See paper by Bolle, *loc. cit.*, p. 463.

For the case represented in Fig. 181*b* the formulas are:

For $\dfrac{a \sin^2 \alpha}{h} < 3,$ $\sigma = -p \left(\dfrac{a \sin \alpha}{h}\right)^2 \left[0.75 - 0.038 \left(\dfrac{a \sin \alpha}{h}\right)^2 \sin^2 \alpha \right];$

for $3 < \dfrac{a \sin^2 \alpha}{h} < 12,$ $\sigma = -1.2 \dfrac{ap}{h}.$

It was assumed in the foregoing discussion that the shell has no hole at the top. If there is such a hole, we must satisfy the boundary conditions on both the lower and the upper edges of the shell. This requires a consideration of both integrals (j) and (k) of Eq. (d) see p. 460 and finally results in a solution of Eq. (266) which contains four constants which must be adjusted in each particular case so as to satisfy the boundary conditions on both edges. Calculations of this kind show[1] that, if the angle α is not small, the forces distributed along the upper edge have only a very small influence on the magnitude of stresses at the lower edge. Thus, since these latter stresses are usually the most important, we can obtain the necessary information for the design of a shell with a hole by using for the calculation of the maximum stresses the formulas derived for shells without holes.

The method of calculating stresses in spherical shells discussed in this article can also be applied in calculating thermal stresses. Assume that the temperatures at the outer and at the inner surfaces of a spherical shell are constant but that there is a linear variation of temperature in the radial direction. If t is the difference in the temperatures at the outer and inner surfaces, respectively, the bending of the shell produced by the temperature difference is entirely arrested by constant bending moments (see Art. 14)

$$M_\varphi = M_\theta = \frac{\alpha t D (1 + \nu)}{h}. \tag{v}$$

In the case of a complete sphere these moments actually exist and produce bending stresses the maximum values of which are

$$(\sigma_\varphi)_{\text{max.}} = (\sigma_\theta)_{\text{max.}} = \frac{6 \alpha t D (1 + \nu)}{h^3} = \frac{\alpha t E}{2 (1 - \nu)}. \tag{w}$$

If we have only a portion of a sphere, supported as shown in Fig. 181*a*, the edge is free to rotate, and the total thermal stresses are obtained by superposing on stresses (w) the stresses that are produced in the shell by the moments

$$M_a = -\frac{\alpha t D (1 + \nu)}{h}$$

uniformly distributed along the edge. These latter stresses are obtained by using the method discussed in this article.[2] In the case shown in Fig.

---

[1] See paper by Bolle, *loc. cit.*, p. 463.

[2] Thermal stresses in shells have been discussed by G. Eichelberg, *Forschungsarbeiten*, no. 263, 1923.

181*b* the thermal stresses are given by formula (*w*), if the temperature of the middle surface always remains the same. Otherwise on the stresses (*w*) must be superposed stresses produced by forces *H* and moments M_α which must be determined in each particular case so as to satisfy the boundary conditions.

95. Approximate Methods of Analyzing Stresses in Spherical Shells.—In the previous article it has already been indicated that the application of the rigorous solution for the stresses in spherical shells depends on the rapidity of convergence of the series entering into the solution. The convergence becomes slower, and more and more terms of the series must be calculated, as the ratio a/h increases, *i.e.*, as the thickness of the shell becomes smaller and smaller in comparison with its radius.[1] For such shells approximate methods of solution have been developed which give very good accuracy for large values of a/h.

One of the approximate methods for the solution of the problem is the method of asymptotic integration.[2] Starting with Eq. (266) and introducing, instead of the shearing force Q_φ, the quantity

$$z = Q_\varphi \sqrt{\sin \varphi}, \qquad (a)$$

we obtain the equation

$$z^{\mathrm{IV}} + a_2 z^{\mathrm{II}} + a_1 z^{\mathrm{I}} + (\beta^4 + a_0)z = 0, \qquad (b)$$

in which

$$\left.\begin{array}{ll} a_0 = -\dfrac{63}{16 \sin^4 \varphi} + \dfrac{9}{8 \sin^2 \varphi} + \dfrac{9}{16}, & a_1 = \dfrac{3 \cos \varphi}{\sin^3 \varphi}, \\[3mm] a_2 = -\dfrac{3}{2 \sin^2 \varphi} + \dfrac{5}{2}, & 4\beta^4 = (1 - \nu^2)\left(1 + \dfrac{12a^2}{h^2}\right). \end{array}\right\} \qquad (c)$$

It can be seen that for thin shells, in which a/h is a large number, the quantity $4\beta^4$ is very large in comparison with the coefficients a_0, a_1 and a_2 provided the angle φ is not small. Since in our further discussion we shall be interested in stresses near the edge where $\varphi = \alpha$ (Fig. 181) and α is not small, we can neglect the terms with the coefficients a_0, a_1 and a_2 in Eq. (*b*). In this way

---

[1] Calculations by J. E. Ekström in *Ing. Vetensk. Akad.*, vol. 121, Stockholm, 1933, show that for $a/h = 62.5$ it is necessary to consider not less than 18 terms of the series.

[2] See O. Blumenthal's paper in *Repts. 5th Intern. Cong. Math.*, Cambridge, 1912; see also his paper in *Z. Math. Physik*, vol. 62, p. 343, 1914.

we obtain the equation

$$z^{IV} + 4\beta^4 z = 0. \qquad (d)$$

This equation is similar to Eq. (230) which we used in the investigation of the symmetrical deformation of circular cylindrical shells. Using the general solution of Eq. (d) together with notation (a), we obtain

$$Q_\varphi = \frac{1}{\sqrt{\sin \varphi}}[e^{\beta\varphi}(C_1 \cos \beta\varphi + C_2 \sin \beta\varphi) + e^{-\beta\varphi}(C_3 \cos \beta\varphi$$
$$+ C_4 \sin \beta\varphi)]. \quad (e)$$

From the previous investigation of the bending of cylindrical shells we know that the bending stresses produced by forces uniformly distributed along the edge decrease rapidly as the distance from the edge increases. A similar condition also exists in the case of thin spherical shells. Observing that the first two terms in solution (e) decrease while the second two increase as the angle φ decreases, we conclude that in the case of a sphere without a hole at the top it is permissible to take only the first two terms in solution (e) and assume

$$Q_\varphi = \frac{e^{\beta\varphi}}{\sqrt{\sin \varphi}}(C_1 \cos \beta\varphi + C_2 \sin \beta\varphi). \qquad (f)$$

Having this expression for Q_φ and using the relations (b), (c) and (d) of Art. 93 and the relations (p), (q) and (r) of Art. 94, all the quantities defining the bending of the shell can be calculated, and the constants C_1 and C_2 can be determined from the conditions at the edge. This method can be applied without any difficulty to particular cases and gives good accuracy for thin shells.[1]

Instead of working with the differential equation (266) of the fourth order, we can take, as a basis for an approximate investigation of the bending of a spherical shell, the two Eqs. (263).[2] In our case these equations can be written as follows:

---

[1] An example of application of the method of asymptotic integration is given in the author's paper; see *Bull. Soc. Eng. Tech.*, St. Petersburg, 1913. In the papers by Blumenthal, previously mentioned, means are given for the improvement of the approximate solution by the calculation of a further approximation.

[2] This method was proposed by J. W. Geckeler, *Forschungsarbeiten*, no. 276, Berlin, 1926.

$$\left.\begin{aligned}
\frac{d^2Q_\varphi}{d\varphi^2} + \cot\varphi\,\frac{dQ_\varphi}{d\varphi} - (\cot^2\varphi - \nu)Q_\varphi &= EhV, \\
\frac{d^2V}{d\varphi^2} + \cot\varphi\,\frac{dV}{d\varphi} - (\cot^2\varphi + \nu)V &= -\frac{a^2Q_\varphi}{D},
\end{aligned}\right\} \qquad (g)$$

where Q_φ is the shearing force, and V is the rotation of a tangent to a meridian as defined by Eq. (a) of Art. 93. In the case of very thin shells, if the angle φ is not small, the quantities Q_φ and V are damped out rapidly as the distance from the edge increases and have the same oscillatory character as has the function (f). Since β is large in the case of thin shells, the derivative of the function (f) is large in comparison with the function itself, and the second derivative is large in comparison with the first. This indicates that a satisfactory approximation can be obtained by neglecting the terms containing the functions Q_φ and V and their first derivatives in the left side of Eqs. (g). In this way Eqs. (g) can be replaced by the following simplified system of equations[1]:

$$\left.\begin{aligned}
\frac{d^2Q_\varphi}{d\varphi^2} &= EhV, \\
\frac{d^2V}{d\varphi^2} &= -\frac{a^2}{D}Q_\varphi.
\end{aligned}\right\} \qquad (h)$$

By eliminating V from these equations, we obtain

$$\frac{d^4Q_\varphi}{d\varphi^4} + 4\lambda^4 Q_\varphi = 0, \qquad (i)$$

where

$$\lambda^4 = 3(1 - \nu^2)\left(\frac{a}{h}\right)^2. \qquad (j)$$

The general solution of this equation is

$$Q_\varphi = C_1 e^{\lambda\varphi}\cos\lambda\varphi + C_2 e^{\lambda\varphi}\sin\lambda\varphi + C_3 e^{-\lambda\varphi}\cos\lambda\varphi \\ + C_4 e^{-\lambda\varphi}\sin\lambda\varphi. \qquad (k)$$

Considering the case in which there is no hole at the top (Fig. 184a) and the shell is bent by forces and moments uniformly

---

[1] This simplification of the problem is equivalent to the replacement of the portion of the shell near the edge by a tangent conical shell and application to this conical shell of the equation that was developed for a circular cylinder (Art. 81); see E. Meissner, "A. Stodola Festschrift," p. 406, Zürich, 1929.

distributed along the edge, we need consider from the general solution (k) only the first two terms, which decrease as the angle φ decreases. Thus

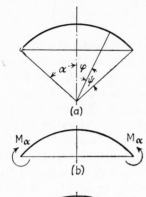

(a)

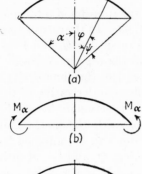

(b)

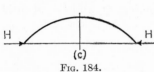

(c)

Fig. 184.

$$Q_\varphi = C_1 e^{\lambda\varphi} \cos \lambda\varphi + C_2 e^{\lambda\varphi} \sin \lambda\varphi. \quad (l)$$

The two constants C_1 and C_2 are to be determined in each particular case from the conditions at the edge $(\varphi = \alpha)$. In discussing the edge conditions it is advantageous to introduce the angle $\psi = \alpha - \varphi$ (Fig. 184). Substituting $\alpha - \psi$ for φ in expression (l) and using the new constants C and γ, we can represent solution (l) in the form

$$Q_\varphi = Ce^{-\lambda\psi} \sin (\lambda\psi + \gamma). \quad (m)$$

Now, employing Eqs. (b), (c) and (d) of Art. 93, we find

$$\left. \begin{array}{l} N_\varphi = -Q_\varphi \cot \varphi = -\cot (\alpha - \psi)Ce^{-\lambda\psi} \sin (\lambda\psi + \gamma), \\[2mm] N_\theta = -\dfrac{dQ_\varphi}{d\varphi} = -\lambda\sqrt{2}Ce^{-\lambda\psi} \sin \left(\lambda\psi + \gamma - \dfrac{\pi}{4}\right). \end{array} \right\} \quad (269)$$

From the first of the equations (h) we obtain the expression for the angle of rotation

$$V = \frac{1}{Eh} \frac{d^2Q_\varphi}{d\varphi^2} = -\frac{2\lambda^2}{Eh}Ce^{-\lambda\psi} \cos (\lambda\psi + \gamma). \quad (270)$$

The bending moments can be determined from Eqs. (q) of the preceding article. Neglecting the terms containing V in these equations, we find

$$\left. \begin{array}{l} M_\varphi = -\dfrac{D}{a} \dfrac{dV}{d\varphi} = \dfrac{a}{\lambda\sqrt{2}}Ce^{-\lambda\psi} \sin \left(\lambda\psi + \gamma + \dfrac{\pi}{4}\right), \\[3mm] M_\theta = \nu M_\varphi = \dfrac{a\nu}{\lambda\sqrt{2}}Ce^{-\lambda\psi} \sin \left(\lambda\psi + \gamma + \dfrac{\pi}{4}\right). \end{array} \right\} \quad (271)$$

Finally, from Eq. (r) of the previous article we find the horizontal component of displacement to be

$$\delta \approx -\frac{\sin \varphi}{Eh} \frac{dU}{d\varphi} = -\frac{a}{Eh} \sin (\alpha - \psi)\lambda\sqrt{2}Ce^{-\lambda\psi} \sin \left(\lambda\psi + \gamma - \frac{\pi}{4}\right). \quad (272)$$

With the aid of formulas (269) to (272) various particular cases can readily be treated.

Take as an example the case shown in Fig. 184b.   The boundary conditions are

$$(M_\varphi)_{\varphi=\alpha} = M_\alpha, \qquad (N_\varphi)_{\varphi=\alpha} = 0. \qquad (n)$$

By substituting $\psi = 0$ in the first of the equations (269), it can be concluded that the second of the boundary conditions (n) is satisfied by taking the constant γ equal to zero.   Substituting $\gamma = 0$ and $\psi = 0$ in the first of the equations (271), we find that to satisfy the first of the conditions (n) we must have

$$M_\alpha = \frac{a}{2\lambda}C,$$

which gives

$$C = \frac{M_\alpha 2\lambda}{a}.$$

Substituting values thus determined for the constants γ and C in expressions (270) and (272) and taking $\psi = 0$, we obtain the rotation and the horizontal displacement of the edge as follows:

$$(V)_{\psi=0} = -\frac{4\lambda^3 M_\alpha}{Eah}, \qquad (\delta)_{\psi=0} = \frac{2\lambda^2 \sin \alpha}{Eh}M_\alpha. \qquad (273)$$

In the case represented in Fig. 184c, the boundary conditions are

$$(M_\varphi)_{\varphi=\alpha} = 0, \qquad (N_\varphi)_{\varphi=\alpha} = -H \cos \alpha. \qquad (o)$$

To satisfy the first of these conditions, we must take $\gamma = -\pi/4$. To satisfy the second boundary condition, we use the first of the equations (269) which gives

$$-H \cos \alpha = C \cot \alpha \sin \frac{\pi}{4},$$

from which we determine

$$C = -\frac{2H \sin \alpha}{\sqrt{2}}.$$

Substituting the values of the constants γ and C in (270) and (272), we find

$$(V)_{\psi=0} = \frac{2\lambda^2 \sin \alpha}{Eh}H, \qquad (\delta)_{\psi=0} = -\frac{2a\lambda \sin^2 \alpha}{Eh}H. \qquad (274)$$

It can be seen that the coefficient of M_α in the second of the formulas (273) is the same as the coefficient of H in the first of the formulas (274). This should follow at once from the reciprocity theorem.

Formulas (273) and (274) can readily be applied in solving particular problems. Take as an example the case of a spherical shell with a built-in edge and submitted to the action of a uniform normal pressure p (Fig. 185a). Considering first the corresponding membrane problem (Fig. 185b), we find a uniform compression of the shell

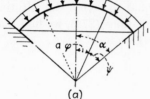

(a)

$$N_\varphi = N_\theta = -\frac{pa}{2}.$$

The edge of this shell experiences no rotation and undergoes a horizontal displacement

$$\delta = \frac{a \sin \alpha}{Eh}(N_\theta - \nu N_\varphi)$$

$$= -\frac{pa^2(1 - \nu)}{2Eh} \sin \alpha. \quad (p)$$

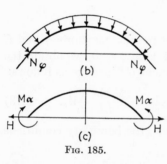

Fig. 185.

To obtain the solution of the given problem we superpose on the membrane forces of Fig. 185b forces and moments uniformly distributed along the edge as in Fig. 185c. These forces and moments are of such magnitude that the corresponding horizontal displacement is equal and opposite to the displacement (p), and the corresponding rotation of the edge is equal to zero. In this way, by using formulas (273) and (274), we obtain the following equations for the determination of M_α and H:

$$-\frac{4\lambda^3}{Eah}M_\alpha + \frac{2\lambda^2 \sin \alpha}{Eh}H = 0,$$

$$\frac{2\lambda^2 \sin \alpha}{Eh}M_\alpha - \frac{2a\lambda \sin^2 \alpha}{Eh}H = \frac{pa^2(1 - \nu)}{2Eh} \sin \alpha,$$

from which

$$\left.\begin{array}{l} M_\alpha = -\dfrac{pa^2(1 - \nu)}{4\lambda^2} = -\dfrac{pah}{4}\sqrt{\dfrac{1 - \nu}{3(1 + \nu)}}, \\[3mm] H = \dfrac{2\lambda}{a \sin \alpha}M_\alpha = -\dfrac{pa(1 - \nu)}{2\lambda \sin \alpha}. \end{array}\right\} \quad (r)$$

The negative signs indicate that M_α and H have directions opposite to those shown in Fig. 184.

The approximate equations (h) were obtained by neglecting the unknown functions Q_φ and V and their first derivatives in the exact equations (g).

A better approximation is obtained if we introduce the new variables[1]

$$Q_1 = Q_\varphi \sqrt{\sin \varphi}, \qquad V_1 = V \sqrt{\sin \varphi}.$$

Substituting

$$Q_\varphi = \frac{Q_1}{\sqrt{\sin \varphi}}, \qquad V = \frac{V_1}{\sqrt{\sin \varphi}}$$

in Eqs. (g), we find that the terms containing the first derivatives of Q_1 and V_1 vanish. Hence, to obtain a simplified system of equations similar to Eqs. (h), we have to neglect only the terms containing the quantities Q_1 and V_1 in comparison with the terms containing the second derivatives of the same quantities. This gives

$$\frac{d^2Q_1}{d\varphi^2} = EhV_1,$$

$$\frac{d^2V_1}{d\varphi^2} = -\frac{a^2}{D}Q_1.$$

The solution of these equations can be obtained in the same manner as in the case of Eqs. (h). Returning to the original variables Q_φ and V, we then obtain, instead of expressions (m) and (270), the following solutions:[2]

$$\left.\begin{aligned}
Q_\varphi &= C\frac{e^{-\lambda\psi}}{\sqrt{\sin (\alpha - \psi)}} \sin (\lambda\psi + \gamma), \\
V &= -\frac{2\lambda^2}{Eh}C\frac{e^{-\lambda\psi}}{\sqrt{\sin (\alpha - \psi)}} \cos (\lambda\psi + \gamma).
\end{aligned}\right\} \tag{275}$$

Proceeding now in exactly the same way as in our previous discussion, we obtain the following expressions in place of formulas (269), (271) and (272):

$$\left.\begin{aligned}
N_\varphi &= -\cot (\alpha - \psi)C\frac{e^{-\lambda\psi}}{\sqrt{\sin (\alpha - \psi)}} \sin (\lambda\psi + \gamma), \\
N_\theta &= C\frac{\lambda e^{-\lambda\psi}}{2\sqrt{\sin (\alpha - \psi)}} [2 \cos (\lambda\psi + \gamma) - (k_1 + k_2) \sin (\lambda\psi + \gamma)], \\
M_\varphi &= \frac{a}{2\lambda}C\frac{e^{-\lambda\psi}}{\sqrt{\sin (\alpha - \psi)}} [k_1 \cos (\lambda\psi + \gamma) + \sin (\lambda\psi + \gamma)], \\
M_\theta &= \frac{a}{4\nu\lambda}C\frac{e^{-\lambda\psi}}{\sqrt{\sin (\alpha - \psi)}} \{[(1 + \nu^2)(k_1 + k_2) - 2k_2] \cos (\lambda\psi + \gamma) \\
&\qquad\qquad + 2\nu^2 \sin (\lambda\psi + \gamma)\}, \\
\delta &= \frac{a \sin (\alpha - \psi)}{Eh}C\frac{\lambda e^{-\lambda\psi}}{\sqrt{\sin (\alpha - \psi)}} [\cos (\lambda\psi + \gamma) - k_2 \sin (\lambda\psi + \gamma)],
\end{aligned}\right\} \tag{276}$$

[1] This is the same transformation as was used by O. Blumenthal; see Eq. (a), p. 467.

[2] This closer approximation was obtained by M. Hetényi, *Pub. Intern. Assoc. Bridge Struct. Eng.*, vol. 5, p. 173, 1938; the numerical example used in the further discussion is taken from this paper.

where

$$k_1 = 1 - \frac{1 - 2\nu}{2\lambda} \cot (\alpha - \psi),$$

$$k_2 = 1 - \frac{1 + 2\nu}{2\lambda} \cot (\alpha - \psi).$$

Applying formulas (276) to the particular cases previously discussed and represented in Fig. 184b and 184c, we obtain, instead of formulas (273) and (274), the following better approximations:

$$(V)_{\psi=0} = -\frac{4\lambda^3 M_\alpha}{Eahk_1}, \qquad (\delta)_{\psi=0} = \frac{2\lambda^2 \sin \alpha}{Ehk_1} M_\alpha, \qquad (277)$$

$$(V)_{\psi=0} = \frac{2\lambda^2 \sin \alpha}{Ehk_1} H, \qquad (\delta)_{\psi=0} = -\frac{\lambda a \sin^2 \alpha}{Eh}\left(k_2 + \frac{1}{k_1}\right) H. \quad (278)$$

By applying these formulas to the particular case shown in Fig. 185a, second approximations for the reactive moments M_α and reactive forces H are readily obtained.

To compare the first and second approximations with the exact solution, we shall consider a numerical example in which $a = 90$ in., $h = 3$ in., $\alpha = 35$ deg., $p = 1$ lb. per square inch and $\nu = \frac{1}{6}$. The first and second approximations for M_φ have been calculated by using the first of the equations (271) and the third of the equations (276) and are represented by the dotted lines in Fig. 186. For comparison the exact solution[1] has also been calculated by using the series of the previous article. This exact solution is represented by the full line in Fig. 186. In Fig. 187 the force N_θ as calculated for the same numerical example is shown. From these two figures it can be concluded that the second approximation has very satisfactory accuracy. Observing that in our example the ratio a/h is only 30 and the angle $\alpha = 35$ deg. is comparatively small, it can be concluded that the second approximation can be applied with sufficient accuracy in most cases encountered in present structural practice.[2]

---

[1] It was necessary to take 10 terms in the series to obtain sufficient accuracy in this case.

[2] The case in which the angle α is small and the solution (275) is not sufficiently accurate is discussed by J. W. Geckeler, *Ingenieur-Archiv*, vol. 1, p. 255, 1930. Application of the equations of finite differences to the same problem has been made by P. Pasternak, *Z. angew. Math. Mech.*, vol. 6, p. 1, 1926. The case of non-isotropic shells is considered by E. Steuermann, *Z. angew. Math. Mech.*, vol. 5, p. 1, 1925. One particular case of a spherical shell of variable thickness is discussed by M. F. Spotts, *J. App. Mech., Trans. A.S.M.E.*, vol. 61, 1939. The problem of non-symmetrical deformation of spherical shells is considered by A. Havers, *Ingenieur-Archiv*, vol. 6, p. 282, 1935. Further discussion of the same problem in connection with the stress analysis of a spherical dome supported by columns is given by A. Aas Jakobsen, *Ingenieur-Archiv*, vol. 8, p. 275, 1937.

96. Conical Shells.—To apply the general equations of Art. 93 to the particular case of a conical shell (Fig. 188a), we introduce in place of the

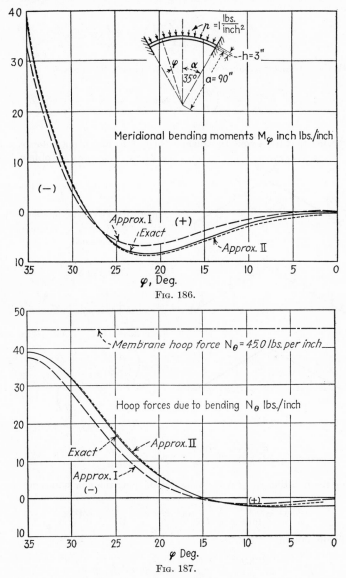

Fig. 186.

Fig. 187.

variable φ a new variable y which defines the distance from the apex of the cone. The length of an infinitesimal element of a meridian is now dy, instead of $r_1\,d\varphi$ as was previously used. As a result of such changes in the variables, the following transformations of the derivatives with respect to φ are necessary:

$$\frac{d}{d\varphi} = r_1\frac{d}{dy}, \qquad \frac{d^2}{d\varphi^2} = \frac{d}{d\varphi}\left(r_1\frac{d}{dy}\right) = r_1^2\frac{d^2}{dy^2} + \frac{dr_1}{d\varphi}\frac{d}{dy}.$$

With these transformations, the symbol (i) in Art. 93 becomes

$$L(\,\cdots\,) = r_2\frac{d^2(\,\cdots\,)}{dy^2} + \left(\frac{dr_2}{dy} + \frac{r_2}{r_1}\cot\varphi\right)\frac{d(\,\cdots\,)}{dy} - \frac{1}{r_2}\cot^2\varphi(\,\cdots\,).$$
$$(a)$$

Observing that for a cone the angle φ is constant and using notation α for $\pi/2 - \varphi$ (Fig. 188), we obtain

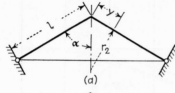

(a)

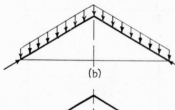

(b)

(c)

Fig. 188.

$$r_2 = y\tan\alpha, \qquad \frac{dr_2}{dy} = \tan\alpha$$

Substituting the expressions into (a) and putting $r_1 = \infty$, the symbol $L(\,\cdots\,)$ becomes

$$L(\,\cdots\,) = \tan\alpha\left[y\frac{d^2(\,\cdots\,)}{dy^2}\right.$$
$$\left. + \frac{d(\,\cdots\,)}{dy} - \frac{1}{y}(\,\cdots\,)\right].$$

Equations (267) of Art. 93 are then

$$\tan\alpha\left(y\frac{d^2U}{dy^2}\right.$$
$$\left. + \frac{dU}{dy} - \frac{U}{y}\right) \pm i\mu^2 U = 0,$$

or, with $U = r_2 Q_\varphi = y\tan\alpha\,Q_y$,[*]

$$y\frac{d^2(yQ_y)}{dy^2} + \frac{d(yQ_y)}{dy} - Q_y \pm \frac{i\mu^2 yQ_y}{\tan\alpha} = 0.$$

Using the notation (j) of Art. 93 and introducing the new notation

$$\lambda^4 = \frac{\mu^4}{\tan^2\alpha} = \frac{Eh}{D}\cot^2\alpha = \frac{12(1-\nu^2)}{h^2}\cot^2\alpha, \qquad (b)$$

we finally obtain

$$y\frac{d^2(yQ_y)}{dy^2} + \frac{d(yQ_y)}{dy} - Q_y \pm i\lambda^2 yQ_y = 0. \qquad (c)$$

[*] The subscript y is used instead of φ in the further discussion of conical shells.

Considering the first of these equations, we transform it to the known Bessel equation by introducing, instead of y, a new variable

$$\eta = 2\lambda\sqrt{i}\sqrt{y}, \tag{d}$$

which gives

$$\frac{d^2(yQ_y)}{d\eta^2} + \frac{1}{\eta}\frac{d(yQ_y)}{d\eta} + \left(1 - \frac{4}{\eta^2}\right)(yQ_y) = 0. \tag{e}$$

A similar equation has already been discussed in the treatment of a cylindrical shell of non-uniform thickness (Art. 85). The functions $\psi_1, \ldots, \psi_4$ which were introduced at that time and whose numerical values are given in Table 47 can also be applied in this case. The general solution for yQ_y which satisfies both of Eqs. (c) can then be represented in the following form:[1]

$$yQ_y = C_1\left[\psi_1(\xi) + \frac{2}{\xi}\psi_2'(\xi)\right] + C_2\left[\psi_2(\xi) - \frac{2}{\xi}\psi_1'(\xi)\right]$$
$$+ C_3\left[\psi_3(\xi) + \frac{2}{\xi}\psi_4'(\xi)\right] + C_4\left[\psi_4(\xi) - \frac{2}{\xi}\psi_3'(\xi)\right], \tag{f}$$

where $\xi = 2\lambda\sqrt{y}$, and the primes denote derivatives with respect to ξ. From our previous discussion and from the values of Table 47 we know that the functions ψ_1 and ψ_2 and their derivatives ψ_1' and ψ_2' have an oscillatory character such that the oscillations are damped out rapidly as the distance y decreases. These functions should be used in investigating the bending of a conical shell produced by forces and moments distributed uniformly along the edge $y = l$. The functions ψ_3 and ψ_4 with their derivatives also have an oscillatory character, but their oscillations increase as the distance y decreases. Hence the third and fourth terms in solution (f), which contain these functions and their derivatives, should be omitted if we are dealing with a complete cone. The two constants C_1 and C_2, which then remain, will be determined in each particular case from the boundary conditions along the edge $y = l$.

In the case of a truncated conical shell there will be an upper and a lower edge, and all four constants $C_1, \ldots, C_4$ in the general solution (f) must be considered to satisfy all the conditions at the two edges. Calculations show that for thin shells such as are commonly used in engineering and for angles α which are not close to $\pi/2$, the forces and moments applied at one edge have only a small effect on the stresses and displacements at the other edge.[2] This fact simplifies the problem, since we can use a solution with

---

[1] A very complete discussion of conical shells is given in F. Dubois' doctorate dissertation "Über die Festigkeit der Kegelschale," Zürich, 1917; this paper also contains a series of numerical examples with curves illustrating the stress distribution in conical shells having various angles at the apex.

[2] For $\alpha \approx 84$ deg., F. Dubois found that the stress distribution in a truncated conical shell has the same character as that in a circular plate with a

only two constants.   We use the terms of the integral (f) with the constants C_1 and C_2 when dealing with the lower edge of the shell and the terms with constants C_3 and C_4 when considering the conditions at the upper edge.

To calculate these constants in each particular case we need the expressions for the angle of rotation V, for the forces N_y and N_θ and for the moments M_y and M_θ.   From Eqs. (c) and (d) of Art. 93 we have

$$N_y = -Q_y \tan \alpha,$$
$$N_\theta = -\frac{dU}{dy} = -\frac{d(r_2 Q_y)}{dy} = -\frac{d(y Q_y)}{dy} \tan \alpha. \right\} \tag{g}$$

From the first of the equations (263) we obtain the rotation

$$V = \frac{1}{Eh} L(U) = \frac{\tan^2 \alpha}{Eh} \left[y \frac{d^2(y Q_y)}{dy^2} + \frac{d(y Q_y)}{dy} - Q_y \right]. \tag{h}$$

The bending moments as found from Eqs. (260) are

$$M_y = -D\left(\frac{dV}{dy} + \frac{\nu}{y} V \right), \right\}$$
$$M_\theta = -D\left(\frac{V}{y} + \nu \frac{dV}{dy} \right). \tag{i}$$

By substituting $y \tan \alpha$ for a in Eq. (r) of Art. 94 we find

$$\delta = \frac{y \sin \alpha \tan \alpha}{Eh} \left[-\frac{d(y Q_y)}{dy} + \nu Q_y \right]. \tag{j}$$

Thus all the quantities that define the bending of a conical shell are expressed in terms of the shearing force Q_y which is given by the general solution (f). The functions $\psi_1, \ldots, \psi_4$ and their first derivatives are given in Table 47 for $\xi < 6$.   For larger values of ξ the asymptotic expressions (250) (page 420) of these functions can be used with sufficient accuracy.

As an example we take the case represented in Fig. 188a.   We assume that the shell is loaded only by its weight and that the edge $(y = l)$ of the shell can rotate freely but cannot move laterally.   Considering first the corresponding membrane problem (Fig. 188b), we find

$$N_\theta = -qy \sin \alpha \tan \alpha, \right\}$$
$$N_y = -\frac{qy}{2 \cos \alpha}, \tag{k}$$

where q is the weight per unit area of the shell.   As a result of these forces

---

hole at the center.   This indicates that for such angles the forces and the moments applied at both edges must be considered simultaneously.

there will be a circumferential compression of the shell along the edge of the amount

$$\epsilon_\theta = \frac{1}{Eh}(N_\theta - \nu N_y) = -\frac{ql}{2 \cos \alpha \, Eh}(2 \sin^2 \alpha - \nu). \qquad (l)$$

To satisfy the boundary conditions of the actual problem (Fig. 188a) we must superpose on the membrane stresses given by Eqs. (k) the stresses produced in the shell by horizontal forces H (Fig. 188c) the magnitude of which is determined so as to eliminate the compression (l). To solve this latter problem we use the first two terms of solution (f) and take

$$yQ_y = C_1\left[\psi_1(\xi) + \frac{2}{\xi}\psi_2'(\xi)\right] + C_2\left[\psi_2(\xi) - \frac{2}{\xi}\psi_1'(\xi)\right]. \qquad (m)$$

The constants C_1 and C_2 will now be determined from the boundary conditions

$$(M_y)_{\xi=2\lambda\sqrt{l}} = 0, \quad (\delta)_{\xi=2\lambda\sqrt{l}} = -\epsilon_\theta l \sin \alpha = \frac{ql^2 \tan \alpha}{2Eh}(2 \sin^2 \alpha - \nu), \quad (n)$$

in which expressions (i) and (j) must be substituted for M_y and δ. After the introduction of expression (m) for yQ_y, expressions (i) and (j) become

$$M_y = \frac{2}{\xi^2}\left\{C_1\left[-\xi\psi_2'(\xi) + 2(1-\nu)\psi_2(\xi) - \frac{4(1-\nu)}{\xi}\psi_1'(\xi)\right]\right.$$
$$\left. + C_2\left[\xi\psi_1'(\xi) - 2(1-\nu)\psi_1(\xi) - \frac{4(1-\nu)}{\xi}\psi_2'(\xi)\right]\right\}, \quad (o)$$

$$\delta = \frac{y \sin \alpha}{Eh}(N_\theta - \nu N_y) = -\frac{\sin \alpha \tan \alpha}{2Eh}\left\{C_1\left[\xi\psi_1'(\xi) - 2\psi_1(\xi) - \frac{4}{\xi}\psi_2'(\xi)\right]\right.$$
$$\left. + C_2\left[\xi\psi_2'(\xi) - 2\psi_2(\xi) + \frac{4}{\xi}\psi_1'(\xi)\right]\right\} \quad (p)$$
$$+ \frac{\nu \sin \alpha \tan \alpha}{Eh}\left\{C_1\left[\psi_1(\xi) + \frac{2}{\xi}\psi_2'(\xi)\right] + C_2\left[\psi_2(\xi) - \frac{2}{\xi}\psi_1'(\xi)\right]\right\}.$$

Substituting $2\lambda\sqrt{l}$ for ξ in expressions (o) and (p) and using Table 47 or expressions (250), we obtain the left-hand sides of Eqs. (n). We can then calculate C_1 and C_2 from these equations if the load q and the dimensions of the shell are given. Calculations show that for shells of the proportions usually applied in engineering practice the quantity ξ is larger than 6, and the asymptotical expressions (250) for the functions entering in Eqs. (o) and (p) must be used. An approximate solution for conical shells, similar to that given in the previous article for spherical shells, can also readily be developed.

The case of a conical shell the thickness of which is proportional to the distance y from the apex can also be rigorously treated. The solution is simpler than that for the case of uniform thickness.[1]

97. General Case of Shells Having the Form of a Surface of Revolution.—The general method of solution of thin shell problems as developed in Art. 93 can also be applied to ring shells such as shown in Fig. 145. In this way the deformation of a ring such as shown in Fig. 189a can be discussed.[2] Combining several rings of this kind, the problem of compression of corrugated pipes such as shown in Fig. 189b can be treated.[3] Combining several conical

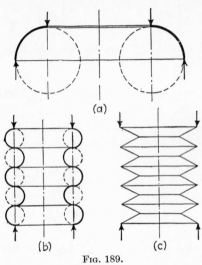

(a)

(b)   (c)

Fig. 189.

shells, we obtain a corrugated pipe shown in Fig. 189c. The compression of such a pipe can be investigated by using the solution developed for conical shells in the previous article. The method of Art. 93 is also applicable to more general surfaces of revolution provided the thickness of the wall varies in a specific

[1] MEISSNER, E., *Vierteljahrsschr. Naturforsch. Ges.* Zürich, vol. 60, p. 23, 1915; see also E. Honegger, "Festigkeitsberechnung von Kegelschalen mit linear veränderlicher Wandstärke," doctoral thesis, Zürich, 1919.

[2] Problems of this kind are rigorously treated in the paper by H. Wissler, "Festigkeitsberechnung von Ringflächenschalen," doctoral thesis, Zürich, 1916.

[3] Such corrugated pipes were considered by K. Stange, *Ingenieur-Archiv*, vol. 2, p. 47, 1931.

manner, that the general equations (261) and (262) obtain the form (263).[1]   The solution of these equations, provided it can be obtained, is usually of a complicated nature and cannot readily be applied in solving practical problems.

At the same time, all the existing solutions indicate that for thin shells for which the angle φ is not small, the stresses produced by forces and moments uniformly distributed along the edge are of a local character and die out rapidly as the distance from the edge increases.   This fact suggests the use in more general cases of the same kind of approximate solutions as were discussed in the case of spherical shells.   Starting with the general equations (261) and (262) (page 457), we neglect on the left sides of these equations the functions U and V and their first derivatives in comparison with the second derivatives.[2]   This results in the following simplified system of equations:

$$\left. \begin{aligned} \frac{r_2}{r_1^2}\frac{d^2U}{d\varphi^2} &= EhV, \\ \frac{r_2}{r_1^2}\frac{d^2V}{d\varphi^2} &= -\frac{U}{D}. \end{aligned} \right\} \qquad (a)$$

Differentiating the first of these equations twice, we obtain

$$\frac{d^2}{d\varphi^2}\left(\frac{r_2}{r_1^2}\frac{d^2U}{d\varphi^2}\right) = \frac{d^2}{d\varphi^2}(EhV). \qquad (b)$$

If after differentiation we again retain on each side only one term containing the derivative of the highest order of the functions U and V, we obtain

$$\frac{r_2}{r_1^2}\frac{d^4U}{d\varphi^4} = Eh\frac{d^2V}{d\varphi^2} = -\frac{Ehr_1^2}{r_2}\frac{U}{D}. \qquad (c)$$

After the introduction of the notation

$$\lambda^4 = \frac{1}{4}\frac{Ehr_1^2}{r_2D} = 3(1 - \nu^2)\frac{r_1^4}{r_2^2h^2} \qquad (d)$$

---

[1] See Meissner paper, *loc. cit.*, p. 455.

[2] This method of obtaining an approximate solution in a general case is due to J. W. Geckeler, *Forschungsarbeiten*, no. 276, p. 21, Berlin, 1926. An extension of Blumenthal's method of asymptotic integration on the general case of shells in form of a surface of revolution was given by E. Steuermann, *Proc. 3d Intern. Cong. Appl. Mech.*, vol. 2, p. 60, 1930.

Eq. (*c*) becomes

$$\frac{d^4U}{d\varphi^4} + 4\lambda^4 U = 0. \qquad (e)$$

This is of the same form as Eq. (*i*) in Art. 95, which was obtained for spherical shells. The difference between the two equations consists only in the fact that the factor λ, given by expression (*d*), is no longer constant in the general case but varies with the angle φ. Since the function U dies out rapidly as the distance from the edge increases, we can obtain a satisfactory approximate solution of Eq. (*e*) by replacing λ by a certain constant average value. The approximate solution previously obtained for a sphere can then be directly applied here.

To obtain a more satisfactory result the shell can be divided by parallel circles into several zones for each of which a certain constant average value of λ is used. Beginning with the first zone at the edge of the shell, the two constants of the general solution (275) are obtained from the conditions at the edge in the same manner as was illustrated for a spherical shell. Then all quantities defining the deformations and stresses in this zone are obtained from Eqs. (276). The values of these quantities at the end of the first zone give the initial values of the same quantities for the second zone. Thus, after changing the numerical value of λ for the second zone, we can continue the calculations by again using the general solution (275).[1]

If the factor λ can be represented by the expression

$$\lambda = \frac{a}{b + \varphi},$$

in which a and b are constants, a rigorous solution of Eq. (*e*) can be obtained.[2] However, since Eq. (*e*) is only an approximate relation, such a rigorous solution apparently has little advantage over the previously described approximate calculation.

---

[1] An application of this method to the calculation of stresses in full heads of pressure vessels is given in the paper by W. M. Coates, *Trans. Am. Soc. Mech. Eng.*, vol. 52, p. 117, 1930.

[2] See Geckeler's paper, *loc. cit.*, p. 481; an application of this solution to the calculation of stresses in a steep-sided dome is given in Flügge's book, "Statik und Dynamik der Schalen," p. 172, Berlin, 1934.

AUTHOR INDEX

SUBJECT INDEX

A

Anisotropic plates, 188
Anticlastic surface, 39
Approximate calculation, of critical loads, 313
Approximate investigation of bending, of cylindrical shells, 446
of shells having form of surface of revolution, 481
of spherical shells, 467
Asymptotic integration, of equation for bending of spherical shells, 467
Average curvature, 37

B

Bending moment, relation to curvature, 41
Bending moments, in plates, 41
Mohr's circle for determination of, 42
in shells, 354
Bending of plates, under combined action of lateral loads and forces in middle plane of plate, 299
to cylindrical surface, 1
by lateral load, 85
by moments distributed along the edges, 39, 199
rigorous theory of, 105
to spherical surface, 46
Boundary conditions, for built-in edges, 89
for curvilinear boundary, 93
for elastically supported edges, 92
for free edges, 89
Kirchhoff's derivation of, 95
for simply supported edges, 89

Buckling, approximate calculation of forces producing, 313
of circular plates, 322
of compressed angle sections, 317
of elliptical plates, 325
of rectangular plates with built-in edges, 320
of rectangular plates with two opposite edges simply supported, 314
Buckling load (*see* Critical load)
Built-in edge, boundary conditions for, 89
(*See also* Clamped edges)

C

Circular hole, in circular plate, 63
Circular membrane, corrugated, 337
deflection of, 337
Circular plates, central hole in, 63
concentrically loaded, 68
corrections to theory of bending of, 78
differential equation for, 58
eccentrically loaded, 266
on elastic foundation, 275
large deflections of, 333, 338
under linearly varying load, 260
loaded at center, 73
supported at several points, 270
symmetrical bending of, 55
symmetrically loaded, 57
table for deflections of, 68
uniformly loaded, 58
of variable thickness, 282
Clamped edges, boundary conditions for, 89
rectangular plates with, 222
Columns, bending of plates supported by rows of equidistant, 239

487